THE LIBRARY OF POETRY AND SONG

O man of silent mood,
A stranger among strangers then,
How art thou since renowned the Great, the Good,
Familiar as the day in all the homes of men!

UTOPIAN EDITION

THE LIBRARY
of
POETRY AND SONG

ORIGINALLY EDITED BY

WILLIAM CULLEN BRYANT

REVISED AND ENLARGED WITH RECENT
AUTHORS AND A DICTIONARY OF
POETICAL QUOTATIONS

ILLUSTRATED

VOLUME III

GARDEN CITY   NEW YORK
DOUBLEDAY, PAGE & COMPANY
1925

PRINTED IN THE UNITED STATES
AT
THE COUNTRY LIFE PRESS, GARDEN CITY, N. Y.

POEMS OF SENTIMENT
AND REFLECTION

To Thee, I fondly hoped to clasp,
A friend whom Death alone could sever,
But envy with malignant grasp,
Has torn thee from my Breast forever

POEMS OF SENTIMENT AND REFLECTION.

GOOD LIFE, LONG LIFE.

It is not growing like a tree
  In bulk, doth make man better be ;
Or standing long an oak, three hundred year,
To fall a log at last, dry, bald, and sear :
    A lily of a day
    Is fairer far in May,
  Although it fall and die that night, —
  It was the plant and flower of Light.
In small proportions we just beauties see,
And in sho.t measures life may perfect be.

BEN JONSON.

MY MINDE TO ME A KINGDOM IS.

My minde to me a kingdom is ;
  Such perfect joy therein I finde
As farre exceeds all earthly blisse
  That God or nature hath assignde ;
Though much I want that most would have,
Yet still my minde forbids to crave.

Content I live ; this is my stay, —
  I seek no more than may suffice.
I presse to beare no haughtie sway ;
  Look, what I lack my mind supplies.
Loe, thus I triumph like a king,
Content with that my mind doth bring.

I see how plentie surfets oft,
  And hastie clymbers soonest fall ;
I see that such as sit aloft
  Mishap doth threaten most of all.
These get with toile, and keepe with feare ;
Such cares my mind could never beare.

No princely pompe nor welthie store,
  No force to win the victorie,
No wylie wit to salve a sore,
  No shape to winne a lover's eye, —
To none of these I yeeld as thrall ;
For why, my mind despiseth all.

Some have too much, yet still they crave ;
  I little have, yet seek no more.
They are but poore, though much they have,
  And I am rich with little store.
They poor, I rich ; they beg, I give ;
They lacke, I lend ; they pine, I live.

I laugh not at another's losse,
  I grudge not at another's gaine ;
No worldly wave my mind can tosse ;
  I brooke that is another's bane.
I feare no foe, I fawne no friend ;
I lothe not life, nor dread mine end.

I joy not in no earthly blisse ;
  I weigh not Cresus' wealth a straw ;
For care, I care not what it is ;
  I feare not fortune's fatal law ;
My mind is such as may not move
For beautie bright, or force of love.

I wish but what I have at will ;
  I wander not to seeke for more ;
I like the plaine, I clime no hill ;
  In greatest stormes I sitte on shore,
And laugh at them that toile in vaine
To get what must be lost againe.

I kisse not where I wish to kill ;
  I feigne not love where most I hate ;
I breake no sleepe to winne my will ;
  I wayte not at the mightie's gate.
I scorne no poore, I feare no rich ;
I feele no want, nor have too much.

The court ne cart I like ne loath, —
  Extreames are counted worst of all ;
The golden meane betwixt them both
  Doth surest sit, and feares no fall ;
This is my choyce ; for why, I finde
No wealth is like a quiet minde.

My wealth is health and perfect ease ;
  My conscience clere my chiefe defence

I neither seeke by bribes to please,
 Nor by desert to breed offence.
Thus do I live ; thus will I die ;
 Would all did so as well as I !
                              SIR EDWARD DYER.*

TO THE HON. CHARLES MONTAGUE.

OUR hopes, like towering falcons, aim
 At objects in an airy height ;
But all the pleasure of the game
 Is afar off to view the flight.

The worthless prey but only shows
 The joy consisted in the strife ;
Whate'er we take, as soon we lose
 In Homer's riddle and in life.

So, whilst in feverish sleeps we think
 We taste what waking we desire,
The dream is better than the drink,
 Which only feeds the sickly fire.

To the mind's eye things well appear,
 At distance through an artful glass ;
Bring but the flattering objects near,
 They 're all a senseless gloomy mass.

Seeing aright, we see our woes :
 Then what avails it to have eyes ?
From ignorance our comfort flows,
 The only wretched are the wise.
                              MATTHEW PRIOR.

OF MYSELF.

THIS only grant me, that my means may lie
Too low for envy, for contempt too high.
 Some honor I would have,
Not from great deeds, but good alone ;
The unknown are better than ill known :
 Rumor can ope the grave.
Acquaintance I would have, but when 't depends
Not on the number, but the choice, of friends.

Books should, not business, entertain the light,
And sleep, as undisturbed as death, the night.
 My house a cottage more
Than palace ; and should fitting be
For all my use, no luxury.
 My garden painted o'er
With Nature's hand, not Art's ; and pleasures
  yield,
Horace might envy in his Sabine field.

---

* This is frequently attributed to William Byrd. Bartlett, however, gives it to Sir Edward Dyer, referring to Hannah's *Courtly
Poets* as authority ; so, also, Ward, in his *English Poets*, Vol. I., 1880.

Thus would I double my life's fading space ;
For he that runs it well twice runs his race.
 And in this true delight,
These unbought sports, this happy state,
I would not fear, nor wish, my fate ;
 But boldly say each night,
To-morrow let my sun his beams display,
Or in clouds hide them ; I have lived to-day.
                              ABRAHAM COWLEY.

BEAUTY.

'T IS much immortal beauty to admire,
But more immortal beauty to withstand ;
The perfect soul can overcome desire,
If beauty with divine delight be scanned.
For what is beauty but the blooming child
Of fair Olympus, that in night must end,
And be forever from that bliss exiled,
If admiration stand too much its friend ?
The wind may be enamored of a flower,
The ocean of the green and laughing shore,
The silver lightning of a lofty tower, —
But must not with too near a love adore ;
Or flower and margin and cloud-capped tower
Love and delight shall with delight devour !
                              LORD EDWARD THURLOW.

BEAUTY.

FROM "HYMN IN HONOR OF BEAUTY."

So every spirit, as it is most pure,
 And hath in it the more of heavenly light,
So it the fairer body doth procure
 To habit in, and it more fairly dight
With cheerful grace and amiable sight ;
 For of the soul the body form doth take ;
For soul is form, and doth the body make.

Therefore wherever that thou dost behold
 A comely corpse, with beauty fair endued,
Know this for certain, that the same doth hold
 A beauteous soul, with fair conditions thewed,
Fit to receive the seed of virtue strewed ;
 For all that fair is, is by nature good ;
That is a sign to know the gentle blood.

Yet oft it falls that many a gentle mind
 Dwells in deformèd tabernacle drowned,
Either by chance, against the course of kind,
 Or through unaptnesse in the substance found,
Which it assumèd of some stubborne ground,
 That will not yield unto her form's direction,
But is performed with some foul imperfection

A FANCY FROM FONTENELLE.

"De mémoires de Roses on n'a point vu mourir le Jardinier."

THE Rose in the garden slipped her bud,
And she laughed in the pride of her youthful blood,
As she thought of the Gardener standing by —
"He is old — so old! And he soon must die!"

The full Rose waxed in the warm June air,
And she spread and spread till her heart lay bare :
And she laughed once more as she heard his tread —
"He is older now! He will soon be dead!"

But the breeze of the morning blew, and found
That the leaves of the blown Rose strewed the ground
And he came at noon, that Gardener old,
And he raked them gently under the mould.

And I wove the thing to a random rhyme:
For the Rose is Beauty ; the Gardener, Time.

AUSTIN DOBSON.

THE WILD RIDE.

I hear in my heart, I hear in its ominous pulses,
All day, the commotion of sinewy, mane-tossing horses;
All night, from their cells, the importunate tramping and neighing.

Drawn by Edwin Forbes.

Cowards and laggards fall back; but alert to the saddle,
Straight, grim, and abreast, vault our weather-worn, galloping legion,
With stirrup-cup each to the one gracious woman that loves him.

The road is through dolor and dread, over crags and morasses;
There are shapes by the way, there are things that appal or entice us:
What odds? We are knights, and our souls are but bent on the riding

Thought's self is a vanishing wing, and joy is a cobweb,
And friendship a flower in the dust, and glory a sunbeam:
Not here is our prize, nor, alas! after these our pursuing.

A dipping of plumes, a tear, a shake of the bridle,
A passing salute to this world, and her pitiful beauty!
We hurry with never a word in the track of our fathers.

I hear in my heart, I hear in its ominous pulses,
All day, the commotion of sinewy mane-tossing horses,
All night, from their cells, the importunate tramping and neighing.

We spur to a land of no name, outracing the storm-wind;
We leap to the infinite dark, like the sparks from the anvil.
Thou leadest, O God! All 's well with Thy troopers that follow!

LOUISE IMOGEN GUINEY.

And oft it falls (aye me, the more to rue !)
That goodly beauty, albeit heavenly born,
Is foul abused, and that celestial hue,
Which doth the world with her delight adorn,
Made but the bait of sin, and sinners' scorn,
Whilst every one doth seek and sue to have it,
But every one doth seek but to deprave it.

Yet nathèmore is that faire beauty's blame,
But theirs that do abuse it unto ill :
Nothing so good, but that through guilty shame
May be corrupt, and wrested unto will :
Natheless the soule is fair and beauteous still,
However fleshe's fault it filthy make ;
For things immortal no corruption take.

EDWARD SPENSER.

THOUGHT.

THOUGHT is deeper than all speech,
    Feeling deeper than all thought ;
Souls to souls can never teach
    What unto themselves was taught.

We are spirits clad in veils ;
    Man by man was never seen ;
All our deep communing fails
    To remove the shadowy screen.

Heart to heart was never known ;
    Mind with mind did never meet ;
We are columns left alone
    Of a temple once complete.

Like the stars that gem the sky,
    Far apart, though seeming near,
In our light we scattered lie ;
    All is thus but starlight here.

What is social company
    But a babbling summer stream ?
What our wise philosophy
    But the glancing of a dream ?

Only when the sun of love
    Melts the scattered stars of thought,
Only when we live above
    What the dim-eyed world hath taught,

Only when our souls are fed
    By the fount which gave them birth,
And by inspiration led
    Which they never drew from earth,

We, like parted drops of rain,
    Swelling till they meet and run,
Shall be all absorbed again,
    Melting, flowing into one.

CHRISTOPHER PEARSE CRANCH.

CONTENTMENT.

I WEIGH not fortune's frown or smile ;
    I joy not much in earthly joys ;
I seek not state, I reck not style ;
    I am not fond of fancy's toys :
I rest so pleased with what I have,
I wish no more, no more I crave.

I quake not at the thunder's crack ;
    I tremble not at news of war ;
I swound not at the news of wrack ;
    I shrink not at a blazing star ;
I fear not loss, I hope not gain,
I envy none, I none disdain.

I see ambition never pleased ;
    I see some Tantals starved in store ;
I see gold's dropsy seldom eased ;
    I see even Midas gape for more ;
I neither want nor yet abound, —
Enough 's a feast, content is crowned.

I feign not friendship where I hate ;
    I fawn not on the great (in show) ;
I prize, I praise a mean estate, —
    Neither too lofty nor too low :
This, this is all my choice, my cheer, —
A mind content, a conscience clear.

JOSHUA SYLVESTER.

CONTENT.

FROM "FAREWELL TO FOLLIE," 1617.

SWEET are the thoughts that savor of content ;
    The quiet mind is richer than a crown ;
Sweet are the nights in careless slumber spent, —
    The poor estate scorns Fortune's angry frown :
Such sweet content, such minds, such sleep, such
        bliss,
Beggars enjoy, when princes oft do miss.

The homely house that harbors quiet rest,
    The cottage that affords no pride or care,
The mean, that 'grees with country music best,
    The sweet consort of mirth's and music's fare
Obscurèd life sets down a type of bliss ;
A mind content both crown and kingdom is.

ROBERT GREENE.

IN PRISON.

BEAT on, proud billows ; Boreas, blow ;
    Swell, curlèd waves, high as Jove's roof :
Your incivility doth show
    That innocence is tempest proof ;
Though surly Nereus frown, my thoughts are calm ;
Then strike, Affliction, for thy wounds are balm.

That which the world miscalls a jail
  A private closet is to me ;
Whilst a good conscience is my bail,
  And innocence my liberty :
Locks, bars, and solitude together met,
Make me no prisoner, but an anchoret.

I, whilst I wisht to be retired,
  Into this private room was turned ;
As if their wisdoms had conspired
  The salamander should be burned ;
Or like those sophists, that would drown a fish,
I am constrained to suffer what I wish.

The cynic loves his poverty ;
  The pelican her wilderness ;
And 't is the Indian's pride to be
  Naked on frozen Caucasus :
Contentment cannot smart ; stoics we see
Make torments easier to their apathy.

These manacles upon my arm
  I as my mistress' favors wear ;
And for to keep my ankles warm
  I have some iron shackles there :
These walls are but my garrison ; this cell,
Which men call jail, doth prove my citadel.

I 'm in the cabinet lockt up,
  Like some high-prizèd margarite,
Or, like the Great Mogul or Pope,
  Am cloistered up from public sight :
Retiredness is a piece of majesty,
And thus, proud Sultan, I 'm as great as thee.
               SIR ROGER L'ESTRANGE.

CLEON AND I.

CLEON hath a million acres, ne'er a one have I ;
Cleon dwelleth in a palace, in a cottage I ;
Cleon hath a dozen fortunes, not a penny I ;
Yet the poorer of the twain is Cleon, and not I.

Cleon, true, possesseth acres, but the landscape I ;
Half the charms to me it yieldeth money can-
    not buy.
Cleon harbors sloth and dulness, freshening
    vigor I ;
He in velvet, I in fustian, richer man am I.

Cleon is a slave to grandeur, free as thought am I ;
Cleon fees a score of doctors, need of none have I ;
Wealth-surrounded, care-environed, Cleon fears
    to die ;
Death may come, he 'll find me ready, — happier
    man am I.

Cleon sees no charms in nature, in a daisy I ;
Cleon hears no anthems ringing in the sea and
    sky ;
Nature sings to me forever, earnest listener I ;
State for state, with all attendants, who would
    change ? Not I.
               CHARLES MACKAY.

THE WANTS OF MAN.

"MAN wants but little here below,
  Nor wants that little long."
'T is not with *me* exactly so ;
  But 't is so in the song.
My wants are many and, if told,
  Would muster many a score ;
And were each wish a mint of gold,
  I still should long for more.

What first I want is daily bread —
  And canvas-backs — and wine —
And all the realms of nature spread
  Before me, when I dine.
Four courses scarcely can provide
  My appetite to quell ;
With four choice cooks from France beside,
  To dress my dinner well.

What next I want, at princely cost,
  Is elegant attire :
Black sable furs for winter's frost,
  And silks for summer's fire,
And Cashmere shawls, and Brussels lace
  My bosom's front to deck, —
And diamond rings my hands to grace,
  And rubies for my neck.

I want (who does not want ?) a wife, —
  Affectionate and fair ;
To solace all the woes of life,
  And all its joys to share.
Of temper sweet, of yielding will,
  Of firm, yet placid mind, —
With all my faults to love me still
  With sentiment refined.

And as Time's car incessant runs,
  And Fortune fills my store,
I want of daughters and of sons
  From eight to half a score.
I want (alas ! can mortal dare
  Such bliss on earth to crave ?)
That all the girls be chaste and fair,
  The boys all wise and brave.

I want a warm and faithful friend,
  To cheer the adverse hour ;

Who ne'er to flatter will descend,
  Nor bend the knee to power, —
A friend to chide me when I 'm wrong,
  My inmost soul to see ;
And that my friendship prove as strong
  For him as his for me.

I want the seals of power and place,
  The ensigns of command ;
Charged by the People's unbought grace
  To rule my native land.
Nor crown nor sceptre would I ask
  But from my country's will,
By day, by night, to ply the task
  Her cup of bliss to fill.

I want the voice of honest praise
  To follow me behind,
And to be thought in future days
  The friend of human kind,
That after ages, as they rise,
  Exulting may proclaim
In choral union to the skies
  Their blessings on my name.

These are the Wants of mortal Man, —
  I cannot want them long,
For life itself is but a span,
  And earthly bliss — a song.
My last great Want — absorbing all —
  Is, when beneath the sod,
And summoned to my final call,
  The *Mercy of my God.*
                    JOHN QUINCY ADAMS.

———◆———

CONTENTMENT.

" Man wants but little here below."

LITTLE I ask ; my wants are few ;
  I only wish a hut of stone,
(A *very plain* brown stone will do,)
  That I may call my own ;
And close at hand is such a one,
In yonder street that fronts the sun.

Plain food is quite enough for me ;
  Three courses are as good as ten ; —
If nature can subsist on three,
  Thank Heaven for three.   Amen !
I always thought cold victual nice ; —
My *choice* would be vanilla-ice.

I care not much for gold or land ; —
  Give me a mortgage here and there, —
Some good bank-stock, — some note of hand,
  Or trifling railroad share, —
I only ask that Fortune send
A *little* more than I shall spend.

Honors are silly toys, I know,
  And titles are but empty names ;
I would, *perhaps*, be Plenipo, —
  But only near St. James ;
I 'm very sure I should not care
To fill our Gubernator's chair.

Jewels are baubles ; 't is a sin
  To care for such unfruitful things ; —
One good-sized diamond in a pin, —
  Some, *not so large*, in rings, —
A ruby, and a pearl or so,
Will do for me ; — I laugh at show.

My dame should dress in cheap attire ;
  (Good heavy silks are never dear ;) —
I own perhaps I *might* desire .
  Some shawls of true Cashmere, —
Some marrowy crapes of China silk,
Like wrinkled skins on scalded milk.

I would not have the horse I drive
  So fast that folks must stop and stare ;
An easy gait — two, forty-five —
  Suits me ; I do not care ; —
Perhaps, for just a *single spurt*,
Some seconds less would do no hurt.

Of pictures, I should like to own
  Titians and Raphaels three or four —
I love so much their style and tone —
  One Turner, and no more,
(A landscape — foreground golden dirt —
The sunshine painted with a squirt.)

Of books but few, — some fifty score
  For daily use, and bound for wear ;
The rest upon an upper floor ; —
  Some *little* luxury *there*
Of red morocco's gilded gleam,
And vellum rich as country cream.

Busts, cameos, gems, — such things as these,
  Which others often show for pride,
I value for their power to please,
  And selfish churls deride ;
One Stradivarius, I confess,
Two meerschaums, I would fain possess.

Wealth's wasteful tricks I will not learn,
  Nor ape the glittering upstart fool ;
Shall not carved tables serve my turn,
  But *all* must be of buhl ?
Give grasping pomp its double share, —
I ask but *one* recumbent chair.

Thus humble let me live and die,
  Nor long for Midas' golden touch ;

If Heaven more generous gifts deny,
    I shall not miss them *much*, —
Too grateful for the blessing lent
Of simple tastes and mind content!
                OLIVER WENDELL HOLMES.

CONTENTATION.

DIRECTED TO MY DEAR FATHER, AND MOST WORTHY
FRIEND, MR. ISAAK WALTON.

HEAVEN, what an age is this! what race
    Of giants are sprung up, that dare
Thus fly in the Almighty's face,
    And with his providence make war!

I can go nowhere but I meet
    With malcontents and mutineers,
As if in life was nothing sweet,
    And we must blessings reap in tears.

O senseless man! that murmurs still
    For happiness, and does not know,
Even though he might enjoy his will,
    What he would have to make him so.

Is it true happiness to be
    By undiscerning Fortune placed
In the most eminent degree,
    Where few arrive, and none stand fast?

Titles and wealth are Fortune's toils,
    Wherewith the vain themselves insnare:
The great are proud of borrowed spoils,
    The miser's plenty breeds his care.

The one supinely yawns at rest,
    The other eternally doth toil;
Each of them equally a beast,
    A pampered horse, a laboring moil:

The titulado's oft disgraced
    By public hate or private frown,
And ne whose hand the creature raised
    Has yet a foot to kick him down.

The drudge who would all get, all save,
    Like a brute beast, both feeds and lies;
Prone to the earth, he digs his grave,
    And in the very labor dies.

Excess of ill-got, ill-kept pelf
    Does only death and danger breed;
Whilst one rich worldling starves himself
    With what would thousand others feed.

By which we see that wealth and power,
    Although they make men rich and great,
The sweets of life do often sour,
    And gull ambition with a cheat.

Nor is he happier than these,
    Who, in a moderate estate,
Where he might safely live at ease,
    Has lusts that are immoderate.

For he, by those desires misled,
    Quits his own vine's securing shade,
To expose his naked, empty head
    To all the storms man's peace invade.

Nor is he happy who is trim,
    Tricked up in favors of the fair,
Mirrors, with every breath made dim,
    Birds, caught in every wanton snare.

Woman, man's greatest woe or bliss,
    Does oftener far than serve, enslave,
And with the magic of a kiss
    Destroys whom she was made to save.

O fruitful grief, the world's disease!
    And vainer man, to make it so,
Who gives his miseries increase
    By cultivating his own woe!

There are no ills but what we make
    By giving shapes and names to things, —
Which is the dangerous mistake
    That causes all our sufferings.

We call that sickness which is health,
    That persecution which is grace,
That poverty which is true wealth,
    And that dishonor which is praise.

Alas! our time is here so short
    That in what state soe'er 't is spent,
Of joy or woe, does not import,
    Provided it be innocent.

But we may make it pleasant too,
    If we will take our measures right,
And not what Heaven has done undo
    By an unruly appetite.

The world is full of beaten roads,
    But yet so slippery withal,
That where one walks secure 't is odds
    A hundred and a hundred fall.

Untrodden paths are then the best,
    Where the frequented are unsure;
And he comes soonest to his rest
    Whose journey has been most secure.

It is content alone that makes
    Our pilgrimage a pleasure here;
And who buys sorrow cheapest takes
    An ill commodity too dear.
                CHARLES COTTON.

THE TOUCHSTONE.

A MAN there came, whence none could tell,
Bearing a Touchstone in his hand,
And tested all things in the land
　　By its unerring spell.

A thousand transformations rose
From fair to foul, from foul to fair :
The golden crown he did not spare,
　　Nor scorn the beggar's clothes.

Of heirloom jewels, prized so much,
Were many changed to chips and clods ;
And even statues of the Gods
　　Crumbled beneath its touch.

Then angrily the people cried,
" The loss outweighs the profit far ;
Our goods suffice us as they are :
　　We will not have them tried."

And, since they could not so avail
To check his unrelenting quest,
They seized him, saying, " Let him test
　　How real is our jail ! "

But though they slew him with the sword,
And in a fire his Touchstone burned,
Its doings could not be o'erturned,
　　Its undoings restored.

And when, to stop all future harm,
They strewed its ashes on the breeze,
They little guessed each grain of these
　　Conveyed the perfect charm.
　　　　　　　WILLIAM ALLINGHAM.

ON HIS OWN BLINDNESS.

TO CYRIACK SKINNER.

CYRIACK, this three years' day, these eyes, though
　　clear,
To outward view, of blemish or of spot,
Bereft of light, their seeing have forgot :
Nor to their idle orbs doth sight appear
Of sun, or moon, or star, throughout the year,
Or man or woman, yet I argue not
Against Heaven's hand or will, nor bate a jot
Of heart or hope ; but still bear up and steer
Right onward. What supports me, dost thou ask ?
The conscience, friend, to have lost them overplied
In Liberty's defence, my noble task,
Of which all Europe rings from side to side.
This thought might lead me through the world's
　　vain mask,
Content, though blind, had I no better guide.
　　　　　　　MILTON.

THE HAPPY MAN.

FROM "THE WINTER WALK AT NOON:" "THE TASK," BOOK VI.

HE is the happy man whose life even now
Shows somewhat of that happier life to come ;
Who, doomed to an obscure but tranquil state,
Is pleased with it, and, were he free to choose,
Would make his fate his choice ; whom peace,
　　the fruit
Of virtue, and whom virtue, fruit of faith,
Prepare for happiness ; bespeak him one
Content indeed to sojourn while he must
Below the skies, but having there his home.
The world o'erlooks him in her busy search
Of objects, more illustrious in her view ;
And, occupied as earnestly as she,
Though more sublimely, he o'erlooks the world.
She scorns his pleasures, for she knows them
　　not ;
He seeks not hers, for he has proved them vain,
He cannot skim the ground like summer birds
Pursuing gilded flies ; and such he deems
Her honors, her emoluments, her joys.
Therefore in contemplation is his bliss,
Whose power is such that whom she lifts from
　　earth
She makes familiar with a heaven unseen,
And shows him glories yet to be revealed.
Not slothful he, though seeming unemployed,
And censured oft as useless. Stillest streams
Oft water fairest meadows, and the bird
That flutters least is longest on the wing.
　　　　　　　WILLIAM COWPER.

THE PROBLEM.

I LIKE a church ; I like a cowl ;
I love a prophet of the soul ;
And on my heart monastic aisles
Fall like sweet strains or pensive smiles ;
Yet not for all his faith can see
Would I that cowlèd churchman be.
Why should the vest on him allure,
Which I could not on me endure ?

Not from a vain or shallow thought
His awful Jove young Phidias brought ;
Never from lips of cunning fell
The thrilling Delphic oracle :
Out from the heart of nature rolled
The burdens of the Bible old ;
The litanies of nations came,
Like the volcano's tongue of flame,
Up from the burning core below, —
The canticles of love and woe.

The hand that rounded Peter's dome,
And groined the aisles of Christian Rome,
Wrought in a sad sincerity ;
Himself from God he could not free ;
He builded better than he knew ; —
The conscious stone to beauty grew.

Know'st thou what wove yon woodbird's nest
Of leaves, and feathers from her breast ?
Or how the fish outbuilt her shell,
Painting with morn each annual cell ?
Or how the sacred pine-tree adds
To her old leaves new myriads ?
Such and so grew these holy piles,
Whilst love and terror laid the tiles.
Earth proudly wears the Parthenon,
As the best gem upon her zone ;
And Morning opes with haste her lids,
To gaze upon the Pyramids ;
O'er England's abbeys bends the sky,
As on its friends, with kindred eye ;
For, out of Thought's interior sphere,
These wonders rose to upper air ;
And Nature gladly gave them place,
Adopted them into her race,
And granted them an equal date
With Andes and with Ararat.

These temples grew as grows the grass ;
Art might obey, but not surpass.
The passive Master lent his hand
To the vast Soul that o'er him planned ;
And the same power that reared the shrine
Bestrode the tribes that knelt within.
Ever the fiery Pentecost
Girds with one flame the countless host,
Trances the heart through chanting choirs,
And through the priest the mind inspires.
The word unto the prophet spoken
Was writ on tables yet unbroken ;
The word by seers or sibyls told,
In groves of oak, or fanes of gold,
Still floats upon the morning wind,
Still whispers to the willing mind.
One accent of the Holy Ghost
The heedless world hath never lost.
I know what say the fathers wise, —
The Book itself before me lies,
Old *Chrysostom*, best Augustine,
And he who blent both in his line,
The younger *Golden Lips* or mines,
Taylor, the Shakespeare of divines.
His words are music in my ear,
I see his cowlèd portrait dear ;
And yet, for all his faith could see,
I would not the good bishop be.

                                RALPH WALDO EMERSON.

HAPPINESS.

FROM "AN ESSAY ON MAN," EPISTLE IV.

O HAPPINESS ! our being's end and aim !
Good, Pleasure, Ease, Content ! whate'er thy
        name :
That something still which prompts the eternal
        sigh,
For which we bear to live or dare to die,
Which still so near us, yet beyond us lies,
O'erlooked, seen double, by the fool, and wise.
Plant of celestial seed ! if dropped below,
Say, in what mortal soil thou deign'st to grow ?
Fair opening to some court's propitious shine,
Or deep with diamonds in the flaming mine ?
Twined with the wreaths Parnassian laurels yield,
Or reaped in iron harvests of the field ?
Where grows ?— where grows it not ? If vain
        our toil,
We ought to blame the culture, not the soil :
Fixed to no spot is happiness sincere ;
'T is nowhere to be found, or everywhere :
'T is never to be bought, but always free,
And, fled from monarchs, St. John ! dwells with
        thee.
    Ask of the learned the way ? The learned are
        blind ;
This bids to serve, and that to shun, mankind ;
Some place the bliss in action, some in ease,
Those call it pleasure, and contentment these ;
Some, sunk to beasts, find pleasure end in pain ;
Some, swelled to gods, confess even virtue vain ;
Or, indolent, to each extreme they fall, —
To trust in everything, or doubt of all.
    Who thus define it, say they more or less
Than this, that happiness is happiness ?
    Take Nature's path, and mad Opinion's leave ;
All states can reach it, and all heads conceive ;
Obvious her goods, in no extreme they dwell ;
There needs but thinking right, and meaning
        well ;
And, mourn our various portions as we please,
Equal is common sense and common ease.

                                ALEXANDER POPE.

———◆———

THE CHARACTER OF A HAPPY LIFE.

How happy is he born and taught
    That serveth not another's will ;
Whose armor is his honest thought,
    And simple truth his utmost skill !

Whose passions not his masters are ;
    Whose soul is still prepared for death,
Not tied unto the world with care
    Of public fame or private breath ;

Who envies none that chance doth raise,
　Or vice ; who never understood
How deepest wounds are given by praise,
　Nor rules of state, but rules of good ;

Who hath his life from rumors freed ;
　Whose conscience is his strong retreat ;
Whose state can neither flatterers feed,
　Nor ruin make accusers great ;

Who God doth late and early pray
　More of his grace than gifts to lend,
And entertains the harmless day
　With a well-chosen book or friend, —

This man is freed from servile bands
　Of hope to rise, or fear to fall ;.
Lord of himself, though not of lands ;
　And, having nothing, yet hath all.
　　　　　　　　SIR HENRY WOTTON.

THE HERMIT.

At the close of the day, when the hamlet is still,
And mortals the sweets of forgetfulness prove,
When naught but the torrent is heard on the hill,
And naught but the nightingale's song in the grove,
'T was thus, by the cave of the mountain afar,
While his harp rung symphonious, a hermit be-
　　gan ;
No more with himself or with nature at war,
He thought as a sage, though he felt as a man :

" Ah ! why, all abandoned to darkness and woe,
Why, lone Philomela, that languishing fall ?
For spring shall return, and a lover bestow,
And sorrow no longer thy bosom inthrall.
But, if pity inspire thee, renew the sad lay, —
Mourn, sweetest complainer, man calls thee to
　mourn !
O, scothe him whose pleasures like thine pass
　away ;
Full quickly they pass, — but they never return.

" Now, gliding remote on the verge of the sky,
The moon, half extinguished, her crescent dis-
　plays ;
But lately I marked when majestic on high
She shone, and the planets were lost in her blaze.
Roll on, thou fair orb, and with gladness pursue
The path that conducts thee to splendor again !
But man's faded glory what change shall renew ?
Ah, fool ! to exult in a glory so vain !

"'T is night, and the landscape is lovely no more.
I mourn, — but, ye woodlands, I mourn not for
　you ;

For morn is approaching your charms to restore,
Perfumed with fresh fragrance, and glittering
　　with dew.
Nor yet for the ravage of winter I mourn, —
Kind nature the embryo blossom will save ;
But when shall spring visit the mouldering urn ?
O, when shall day dawn on the night of the grave ?

"'T was thus, by the glare of false science betrayed,
That leads to bewilder, and dazzles to blind,
My thoughts wont to roam from shade onward to
　　shade,
Destruction before me, and sorrow behind.
' O pity, great Father of light,' then I cried,
' Thy creature, who fain would not wander from
　　thee !
Lo, humbled in dust, I relinquish my pride ;
From doubt and from darkness thou only canst
　　free.'

" And darkness and doubt are now flying away ;
No longer I roam in conjecture forlorn.
So breaks on the traveller, faint and astray,
The bright and the balmy effulgence of morn.
See truth, love, and mercy in triumph descending,
And nature all glowing in Eden's first bloom !
On the cold cheek of death smiles and roses are
　blending,
And beauty immortal awakes from the tomb."
　　　　　　　　JAMES BEATTIE.

THE RETIREMENT.

Farewell, thou busy world, and may
　　We never meet again ;
　Here I can eat and sleep and pray,
　And do more good in one short day
　Than he who his whole age outwears
Upon the most conspicuous theatres,
Where naught but vanity and vice appears.

Good God ! how sweet are all things here !
How beautiful the fields appear !
　　How cleanly do we feed and lie !
Lord ! what good hours do we keep !
How quietly we sleep !
　　What peace, what unanimity !
How innocent from the lewd fashion
Is all our business, all our recreation !

O, how happy here 's our leisure !
O, how innocent our pleasure !
O ye valleys ! O ye mountains !
O ye groves and crystal fountains !
How I love, at liberty,
By turns to come and visit ye !

Dear solitude, the soul's best friend,
That man acquainted with himself dost make,
And all his Maker's wonders to intend,
    With thee I here converse at will,
    And would be glad to do so still,
For it is thou alone that keep'st the soul awake.

How calm and quiet a delight
    Is it, alone,
To read and meditate and write,
    By none offended, and offending none !
To walk, ride, sit, or sleep at one's own ease ;
And, pleasing a man's self, none other to displease.

O my belovèd nymph, fair Dove,
Princess of rivers, how I love
    Upon thy flowery banks to lie,
And view thy silver stream,
When gilded by a summer's beam !
    And in it all thy wanton fry
        Playing at liberty,
And with my angle upon them
        The all of treachery
I ever learned, industriously to try !

Such streams Rome's yellow Tiber cannot show,
The Iberian Tagus, or Ligurian Po ;
The Maese, the Danube, and the Rhine,
Are puddle-water, all, compared with thine ;
And Loire's pure streams yet too polluted are
With thine, much purer, to compare ;
The rapid Garonne and the winding Seine
        Are both too mean,
    Belovèd Dove, with thee
        To vie priority ;
Nay, Tame and Isis, when conjoined, submit,
And lay their trophies at thy silver feet.

O my belovèd rocks, that rise
To awe the earth and brave the skies !
From some aspiring mountain's crown
    How dearly do I love,
Giddy with pleasure to look down,
And from the vales to view the noble heights
        above !
O my belovèd caves ! from dog-star's heat,
And all anxieties, my safe retreat ;
What safety, privacy, what true delight,
    In the artificial night
    Your gloomy entrails make,
    Have I taken, do I take !
How oft, when grief has made me fly,
To hide me from society
E'en of my dearest friends, have I,
    In your recesses' friendly shade,
    All my sorrows open laid,
And my most secret woes intrusted to your
        privacy !

Lord ! would men let me alone,
    What an over-happy one
        Should I think myself to be, —
Might I in this desert place
(Which most men in discourse disgrace)
        Live but undisturbed and free !
Here in this despised recess,
        Would I, maugre winter's cold
And the summer's worst excess,
        Try to live out to sixty full years old ;
        And, all the while,
            Without an envious eye
On any thriving under Fortune's smile,
Contented live, and then contented die.
                                CHARLES COTTON.

──────◆──────

VERSES

SUPPOSED TO BE WRITTEN BY ALEXANDER SELKIRK
DURING HIS SOLITARY ABODE IN THE ISLAND OF JUAN
FERNANDEZ.

I AM monarch of all I survey, —
    My right there is none to dispute ;
From the centre all round to the sea,
    I am lord of the fowl and the brute.
O Solitude ! where are the charms
    That sages have seen in thy face ?
Better dwell in the midst of alarms
    Than reign in this horrible place.

I am out of humanity's reach ;
    I must finish my journey alone,
Never hear the sweet music of speech, —
    I start at the sound of my own.
The beasts that roam over the plain
    My form with indifference see ;
They are so unacquainted with man,
    Their tameness is shocking to me.

Society, friendship, and love,
    Divinely bestowed upon man !
O, had I the wings of a dove,
    How soon would I taste you again !
My sorrows I then might assuage
    In the ways of religion and truth, —
Might learn from the wisdom of age,
    And be cheered by the sallies of youth.

Religion ! what treasure untold
    Resides in that heavenly word ! —
More precious than silver and gold,
    Or all that this earth can afford ;
But the sound of the church-going bell
    These valleys and rocks never heard,
Never sighed at the sound of a knell,
    Or smiled when a Sabbath appeared.

Ye winds that have made me your sport,
  Convey to this desolate shore
Some cordial, endearing report
  Of a land I shall visit no more !
My friends, — do they now and then send
  A wish or a thought after me ?
O, tell me I yet have a friend,
  Though a friend I am never to see.

How fleet is a glance of the mind !
  Compared with the speed of its flight,
The tempest itself lags behind,
  And the swift-wingèd arrows of light.
When I think of my own native land,
  In a moment I seem to be there ;
But, alas ! recollection at hand
  Soon hurries me back to despair.

But the sea-fowl is gone to her nest,
  The beast is laid down in his lair ;
Even here is a season of rest,
  And I to my cabin repair.
There's mercy in every place,
  And mercy — encouraging thought ! —
Gives even affliction a grace,
  And reconciles man to his lot.
                    WILLIAM COWPER.

THE GOOD GREAT MAN.

How seldom, friend, a good great man inherits
  Honor and wealth, with all his worth and pains!
It seems a story from the world of spirits
When any man obtains that which he merits,
  Or any merits that which he obtains.

For shame, my friend ! renounce this idle strain !
What wouldst thou have a good great man obtain ?
Wealth, title, dignity, a golden chain,
Or heap of corses which his sword hath slain ?
Goodness and greatness are not means, but ends.
Hath he not always treasures, always friends, —
The good great man ? Three treasures, — love,
    and light,
And calm thoughts, equable as infant's breath ;
And three fast friends, more sure than day or
    night, —
Himself, his Maker, and the angel Death.
                SAMUEL TAYLOR COLERIDGE.

EXAMPLE.

WE scatter seeds with careless hand,
  And dream we ne'er shall see them more ·
    But for a thousand years
    Their fruit appears,
  In weeds that mar the land,
    Or healthful store.

The deeds we do, the words we say, —
  Into still air they seem to fleet,
    We count them ever past ;
    But they shall last, —
  In the dread judgment they
    And we shall meet.

I charge thee by the years gone by,
  For the love's sake of brethren dear,
    Keep thou the one true way,
    In work and play,
  Lest in that world their cry
    Of woe thou hear.
                    JOHN KEBLE.

LIVING WATERS.

THERE are some hearts like wells, green-mossed
    and deep
    As ever Summer saw ;
And cool their water is, — yea, cool and sweet ;—
    But you must come to draw.
They hoard not, yet they rest in calm content,
    And not unsought will give ;
They can be quiet with their wealth unspent,
    So self-contained they live.

And there are some like springs, that bubbling
    burst
    To follow dusty ways,
And run with offered cup to quench his thirst
    Where the tired traveller strays ;
That never ask the meadows if they want
    What is their joy to give ; —
Unasked, their lives to other life they grant,
    So self-bestowed they live !

And One is like the ocean, deep and wide,
    Wherein all waters fall ;
That girdles the broad earth, and draws the tide,
    Feeding and bearing all ;
That broods the mists, that sends the clouds
    abroad,
    That takes, again to give ; —
Even the great and loving heart of God,
    Whereby all love doth live.
                    CAROLINE S. SPENCER.

THE SEASIDE WELL.

"Waters flowed over my head : then I said, I am cut off."—
Lamentations, iii. 54.

ONE day I wandered where the salt sea-tide
    Backward had drawn its wave,
And found a spring as sweet as e'er hillside
    To wild-flowers gave.

Freshly it sparkled in the sun's bright look,
    And mid its pebbles strayed,
As if it thought to join a happy brook
    In some green glade.

But soon the heavy sea's resistless swell
    Came rolling in once more,
Spreading its bitter o'er the clear sweet well
    And pebbled shore.
Like a fair star thick buried in a cloud,
    Or life in the grave's gloom,
The well, enwrapped in a deep watery shroud,
    Sunk to its tomb.

As one who by the beach roams far and wide,
    Remnant of wreck to save,
Again I wandered when the salt sea-tide
    Withdrew its wave ;
And there, unchanged, no taint in all its sweet,
    No anger in its tone,
Still as it thought some happy brook to meet,
    The spring flowed on.

While waves of bitterness rolled o'er its head,
    Its heart had folded deep
Within itself, and quiet fancies led,
    As in a sleep ;
Till, when the ocean loosed his heavy chain,
    And gave it back to day,
Calmly it turned to its own life again
    And gentle way.

Happy, I thought, that which can draw its life
    Deep from the nether springs,
Safe 'neath the pressure, tranquil mid the strife,
    Of surface things.
Safe — for the sources of the nether springs
    Up in the far hills lie ;
Calm — for the life its power and freshness brings
    Down from the sky.

So, should temptations threaten, and should sin
    Roll in its whelming flood,
Make strong the fountain of thy grace within
    My soul, O God !
If bitter scorn, and looks, once kind, grown
    strange,
    With crushing chillness fall,
From secret wells let sweetness rise, nor change
    My heart to gall !

When sore thy hand doth press, and waves of
    thine
    Afflict me like a sea, —
Deep calling deep, — infuse from source divine
    Thy peace in me !
And when death's tide, as with a brimful cup,
    Over my soul doth pour,
Let hope survive, — a well that springeth up
    Forevermore !

Above my head the waves may come and go,
    Long brood the deluge dire,
But life lies hidden in the depths below
    Till waves retire, —
Till death, that reigns with overflowing flood,
    At length withdraw its sway,
And life rise sparkling in the sight of God
    An endless day.
                      ANONYMOUS.

THE MEN OF OLD.

I KNOW not that the men of old
    Were better than men now,
Of heart more kind, of hand more bold,
    Of more ingenuous brow ;
I heed not those who pine for force
    A ghost of time to raise,
As if they thus could check the course
    Of these appointed days.

Still it is true, and over-true,
    That I delight to close
This book of life self-wise and new,
    And let my thoughts repose
On all that humble happiness
    The world has since foregone, —
The daylight of contentedness
    That on those faces shone !

With rights, though not too closely scanned,
    Enjoyed as far as known,
With will by no reverse unmanned,
    With pulse of even tone,
They from to-day, and from to-night,
    Expected nothing more
Than yesterday and yesternight
    Had proffered them before.

To them was life a simple art
    Of duties to be done,
A game where each man took his part,
    A race where all must run ;
A battle whose great scheme and scope
    They little cared to know,
Content, as men-at-arms, to cope
    Each with his fronting foe.

Man now his virtue's diadem
    Puts on, and proudly wears . —
Great thoughts, great feelings, came to them
    Like instincts unawares ;
Blending their souls' sublimest needs
    With tasks of every day
They went about their gravest deeds
    As noble boys at play.

And what if Nature's fearful wound
  They did not probe and bare,
For that their spirits never swooned
  To watch the misery there, —
For that their love but flowed more fast,
  Their charities more free,
Not conscious what mere drops they cast
  Into the evil sea.

A man's best things are nearest him,
  Lie close about his feet ;
It is the distant and the dim
  That we are sick to greet ;
For flowers that grow our hands beneath
  We struggle and aspire, —
Our hearts must die, except they breathe
  The air of fresh desire.

Yet, brothers, who up reason's hill
  Advance with hopeful cheer, —
Oh, loiter not, those heights are chill,
  As chill as they are clear ;
And still restrain your haughty gaze
  The loftier that ye go,
Remembering distance leaves a haze
  On all that lies below.

    RICHARD MONCKTON MILNES, LORD HOUGHTON.

HISTORY OF A LIFE.

DAY dawned ; — within a curtained room,
Filled to faintness with perfume,
A lady lay at point of doom.

Day closed ; — a Child had seen the light :
But, for the lady fair and bright,
She rested in undreaming night.

Spring rose ; — the lady's grave was green ;
And near it, oftentimes, was seen
A gentle Boy with thoughtful mien.

Years fled ; — he wore a manly face,
And struggled in the world's rough race,
And won at last a lofty place.

And then he died ! Behold before ye
Humanity's poor sum and story ;
Life, — Death, — and all that is of Glory.
    BRYAN WALLER PROCTER (*Barry Cornwall*).

THE ROSE-BUSH.

A CHILD sleeps under a rose-bush fair,
The buds swell out in the soft May air ;
Sweetly it rests, and on dream-wings flies
To play with the angels in Paradise.
    And the years glide by.

A Maiden stands by the rose-bush fair,
The dewy blossoms perfume the air ;
She presses her hand to her throbbing breast,
With love's first wonderful rapture blest.
    And the years glide by.

A Mother kneels by the rose-bush fair,
Soft sigh the leaves in the evening air ;
Sorrowing thoughts of the past arise,
And tears of anguish bedim her eyes.
    And the years glide by.

Naked and lone stands the rose-bush fair,
Whirled are the leaves in the autumn air,
Withered and dead they fall to the ground,
And silently cover a new-made mound.
    And the years glide by.
    From the German, by WILLIAM W. CALDWELL.

LIFE.

I MADE a posie, while the day ran by :
" Here will I smell my remnant out, and tie
    My life within this band."
But Time did beckon to the flowers, and they
By noon most cunningly did steal away,
    And withered in my hand.

My hand was next to them, and then my heart ;
I took, without more thinking, in good part
    Time's gentle admonition ;
Who did so sweetly death's sad taste convey,
Making my minde to smell my fatall day,
    Yet sug'ring the suspicion.

Farewell, dear flowers ! sweetly your time ye
    spent ;
Fit, while ye lived, for smell or ornament,
    And after death for cures.
I follow straight without complaints or grief ;
Since, if my scent be good, I care not if
    It be as short as yours.
    GEORGE HERBERT.

THE RIVER OF LIFE.

THE more we live, more brief appear
  Our life's succeeding stages ;
A day to childhood seems a year,
  And years like passing ages.

The gladsome current of our youth,
  Ere passion yet disorders,
Steals lingering like a river smooth
  Along its grassy borders.

But, as the careworn cheek grows wan,
    And sorrow's shafts fly thicker,
Ye stars, that measure life to man,
    Why seem your courses quicker ?

When joys have lost their bloom and breath,
    And life itself is vapid,
Why, as we near the Falls of Death,
    Feel we its tide more rapid ?

It may be strange, — yet who would change
    Time's course to slower speeding,
When one by one our friends have gone,
    And left our bosoms bleeding ?

Heaven gives our years of fading strength
    Indemnifying fleetness ;
And those of youth, a seeming length,
    Proportioned to their sweetness.
                          THOMAS CAMPBELL.

THE VOYAGE OF LIFE.

FROM "THE SPLEEN."

THUS, then, I steer my bark, and sail
On even keel with gentle gale ;
At helm I make my reason sit,
My crew of passions all submit.
If dark and blustering prove some nights,
Philosophy puts forth her lights ;
Experience holds the cautious glass,
To shun the breakers, as I pass,
And frequent throws the wary lead,
To see what dangers may be hid ;
And once in seven years I 'm seen
At Bath or Tunbridge to careen.
Though pleased to see the dolphins play,
I mind my compass and my way.
With store sufficient for belief,
And wisely still prepared to reef,
Nor wanting the dispersive bowl
Of cloudy weather in the soul,
I make (may Heaven propitious send
Such wind and weather to the end),
Neither becalmed nor overblown,
Life's voyage to the world unknown.
                          MATTHEW GREEN.

THE ROSARY OF MY TEARS.

SOME reckon their age by years,
    Some measure their life by art ;
But some tell their days by the flow of their tears,
    And their lives by the moans of their heart.

The dials of earth may show
    The length, not the depth of years, —

Few or many they come, few or many they go, —
    But time is best measured by tears.

Ah ! not by the silver gray
    That creeps through the sunny hair,
And not by the scenes that we pass on our way,
    And not by the furrows the fingers of care

On forehead and face have made, —
    Not so do we count our years ;
Not by the sun of the earth, but the shade
    Of our souls, and the fall of our tears.

For the young are ofttimes old,
    Though their brows be bright and fair ;
While their blood beats warm, their hearts are
        cold —
    O'er them the spring — but winter is there.

And the old are ofttimes young
    When their hair is thin and white ;
And they sing in age, as in youth they sung,
    And they laugh, for their cross was light.

But, bead by bead, I tell
    The Rosary of my years ;
From a cross — to a cross they lead ; 't is well,
    And they 're blest with a blessing of tears.

Better a day of strife
    Than a century of sleep ;
Give me instead of a long stream of life
    The tempests and tears of the deep.

A thousand joys may foam
    On the billows of all the years ;
But never the foam brings the lone back home, —
    He reaches the haven through tears.
                          ABRAM J. RYAN.

THE AIM OF LIFE.

FROM "FESTUS."

WE live in deeds, not years ; in thoughts, not
        breaths ;
In feelings, not in figures on a dial.
We should count time by heart-throbs.   He most
        lives,
Who thinks most, feels the noblest, acts the best.
And he whose heart beats quickest lives the
        longest :
Lives in one hour more than in years do some
Whose fat blood sleeps as it slips along their
        veins.
Life is but a means unto an end ; that end,
Beginning, mean, and end to all things, — God.
The dead have all the glory of the world.
                          PHILIP JAMES BAILEY.

LIFE.

My life is like the summer rose,
That opens to the morning sky,
But, ere the shades of evening close,
Is scattered on the ground — to die !
Yet on the rose's humble bed
The sweetest dews of night are shed,
As if she wept the waste to see, —
But none shall weep a tear for me !

My life is like the autumn leaf
That trembles in the moon's pale ray ;
Its hold is frail, — its date is brief,
Restless, and soon to pass away !
Yet, ere that leaf shall fall and fade,
The parent tree will mourn its shade,
The winds bewail the leafless tree, —
But none shall breathe a sigh for me !

My life is like the prints which feet
Have left on Tampa's desert strand ;
Soon as the rising tide shall beat,
All trace will vanish from the sand ;
Yet, as if grieving to efface
All vestige of the human race,
On that lone shore loud moans the sea, —
But none, alas ! shall mourn for me !

RICHARD HENRY WILDE.

BY THE SEA.

Upon the lonely shore I lie ;
    The wind is faint, the tide is low.
Someway there seems a human sigh
    In the great waves that inward flow, —

As if all love, and loss, and pain,
    That ever swept their shining track,
Had met within the caverned main,
    And, rising, moaningly come back.

Upon the lonely shore I lie,
    And gaze along its level sands.
Still from the sea steals out the cry
    I left afar in crowded lands.

Upon the sea-beach, cool and still,
    I press my cheek ; and yet I hear
The jar of earth, and catch the thrill
    Of human effort, hot and near.

Come, Peace of nature ! Lone I lie
    Within the calm Midsummer noon.
All human want I fain would fly,
    Sing, Summer sea, in silvery croon !

In Noon's great gladness hush thy moan,
    In vast possession unbereft ;
No music, haunting all thy tone,
    Can make me want the world I've left.

MARY CLEMMER.

HOPE.

FROM "THE PLEASURES OF HOPE."*

Unfading Hope ! when life's last embers burn,
When soul to soul, and dust to dust return !
Heaven to thy charge resigns the awful hour !
O, then thy kingdom comes ! Immortal Power !
What though each spark of earth-born rapture fly
The quivering lip, pale cheek, and closing eye !
Bright to the soul thy seraph hands convey
The morning dream of life's eternal day, —
Then, then, the triumph and the trance begin,
And all the phœnix spirit burns within !

            .   .   .

Daughter of Faith, awake, arise, illume
The dread unknown, the chaos of the tomb ;
Melt, and dispel, ye spectre-doubts, that roll
Cimmerian darkness o'er the parting soul !
Fly, like the moon-eyed herald of Dismay,
Chased on his night-steed by the star of day !
The strife is o'er, — the pangs of Nature close,
And life's last rapture triumphs o'er her woes.
Hark ! as the spirit eyes, with eagle gaze,
The noon of Heaven undazzled by the blaze,
On heavenly winds that waft her to the sky,
Float the sweet tones of star-born melody ;
Wild as that hallowed anthem sent to hail
Bethlehem's shepherds in the lonely vale,
When Jordan hushed his waves, and midnight still
Watched on the holy towers of Zion hill !

            .   .   .

Eternal Hope ! when yonder spheres sublime
Pealed their first notes to sound the march of Time,
Thy joyous youth began, — but not to fade.
When all the sister planets have decayed ;
When wrapt in fire the realms of ether glow,
And Heaven's last thunder shakes the world
        below ;
Thou, undismayed, shalt o'er the ruins smile,
And light thy torch at Nature's funeral pile.

THOMAS CAMPBELL.

THE VANITY OF THE WORLD.

False world, thou ly'st : thou canst not lend
        The least delight :
Thy favors cannot gain a friend,
        They are so slight :

* This poem was written when the author was but twenty-one
years of age.

Thy morning pleasures make an end
    To please at night :
Poor are the wants that thou supply'st,
And yet thou vaunt'st, and yet thou vy'st
With heaven : fond earth, thou boasts ; false
        world, thou ly'st.

Thy babbling tongue tells golden tales
    Of endless treasure ;
Thy bounty offers easy sales
    Of lasting pleasure ;
Thou ask'st the conscience what she ails,
    And swear'st to ease her ;
There 's none can want where thou supply'st ;
There 's none can give where thou deny'st.
Alas ! fond world, thou boasts ; false world, thou
    ly'st.

What well-advisèd ear regards
    What earth can say ?
Thy words are gold, but thy rewards
    Are painted clay :
Thy cunning can but pack the cards,
    Thou canst not play :
Thy game at weakest, still thou vy'st ;
If seen, and then revy'd, deny'st :
Thou art not what thou seem'st ; false world,
    thou ly'st.

Thy tinsel bosom seems a mint
    Of new-coined treasure ;
A paradise, that has no stint,
    No change, no measure ;
A painted cask, but nothing in 't,
    Nor wealth, nor pleasure :
Vain earth ! that falsely thus comply'st
With man ; vain man ! that thou rely'st
On earth ; vain man, thou dot'st ; vain earth,
    thou ly'st.

What mean dull souls, in this high measure,
    To haberdash
In earth's base wares, whose greatest treasure
    Is dross and trash ?
The height of whose enchanting pleasure
    Is but a flash ?
Are these the goods that thou supply'st
Us mortals with ? Are these the high'st ?
Can these bring cordial peace ? false world, thou
    ly'st.
               FRANCES QUARLES.

GOOD BY.

Good by, proud world, I 'm going home :
Thou art not my friend, and I 'm not thine.
Long through thy weary crowds I roam ;
A river-ark on the ocean brine,
Long I 've been tossed like the driven foam,
But now, proud world, I 'm going home.

Good by to Flattery's fawning face ;
To Grandeur with his wise grimace ;
To upstart Wealth's averted eye ;
To supple Office, low and high ;
To crowded halls, to court and street ;
To frozen hearts and hasting feet ;
To those who go, and those who come ;
Good by, proud world ! I 'm going home.

I 'm going to my own hearth-stone,
Bosomed in yon green hills alone, —
A secret nook in a pleasant land,
Whose groves the frolic fairies planned ;
Where arches green, the livelong day,
Echo the blackbird's roundelay,
And vulgar feet have never trod
A spot that is sacred to thought and God.

O, when I am safe in my sylvan home,
I tread on the pride of Greece and Rome ;
And when I am stretched beneath the pines,
Where the evening star so holy shines,
I laugh at the lore and the pride of man,
At the sophist schools, and the learnèd clan ;
For what are they all, in their high conceit,
When man in the bush with God may meet ?
               RALPH WALDO EMERSON.

THE NEVERMORE.

Look in my face ; my name is Might-have-been ;
I am also called No-more, Too-late, Farewell ;
Unto thine ear I hold the dead-sea shell
Cast up thy Life's foam-fretted feet between ;
Unto thine eyes the glass where that is seen
    Which had Life's form and Love's, but by my
        spell
Is now a shaken shadow intolerable,
Of ultimate things unuttered the frail screen.

Mark me, how still I am ! But should there dart
    One moment through my soul the soft surprise
    Of that winged Peace which lulls the breath of
        sighs, —
Then shalt thou see me smile, and turn apart
Thy visage to mine ambush at thy heart
    Sleepless with cold commemorative eyes.
              DANTE GABRIEL ROSSETTI.

THE GENIUS OF DEATH.

What is death ? 'T is to be free,
    No more to love or hope or fear,
To join the great equality ;
    All, all alike are humbled there.

The mighty grave
Wraps lord and slave ;
Nor pride nor poverty dares come
Within that refuge-house, — the tomb.

Spirit with the drooping wing
And the ever-weeping eye,
Thou of all earth's kings art king ;
Empires at thy footstool lie ;
Beneath thee strewed,
Their multitude
Sink like waves upon the shore ;
Storms shall never raise them more.

What 's the grandeur of the earth
To the grandeur round thy throne ?
Riches, glory, beauty, birth,
To thy kingdom all have gone.
Before thee stand
The wondrous band, —
Bards, heroes, sages, side by side,
Who darkened nations when they died.

Earth has hosts, but thou canst show
Many a million for her one ;
Through thy gates the mortal flow
Hath for countless years rolled on.
Back from the tomb
No step has come,
There fixed till the last thunder's sound
Shall bid thy prisoners be unbound.
GEORGE CROLY.

---◆---

LINES

WRITTEN BY ONE IN THE TOWER, BEING YOUNG AND
CONDEMNED TO DIE.

MY prime of youth is but a frost of cares ;
My feast of joy is but a dish of pain ;
My crop of corn is but a field of tares ;
And all my good is but vain hope of gain :
The day is [fled], and yet I saw no sun ;
And now I live, and now my life is done !

The spring is past, and yet it hath not sprung ;
The fruit is dead, and yet the leaves are green ;
My youth is gone, and yet I am but young ;
I saw the world, and yet I was not seen :
My thread is cut, and yet it is not spun ;
And now I live, and now my life is done !

I sought my death, and found it in my womb ;
I looked for life, and saw it was a shade ;
I trod the earth, and knew it was my tomb ;
And now I die, and now I am but made :
The glass is full, and now my glass is run ;
And now I live, and now my life is done !
CHIDIOCK TYCHBORN.

LINES

FOUND IN HIS BIBLE IN THE GATE-HOUSE AT
WESTMINSTER.

E'EN such is time ; that takes in trust
Our youth, our joys, our all we have,
And pays us but with earth and dust ;
Who in the dark and silent grave,
When we have wandered all our ways,
Shuts up the story of our days :
But from this earth, this grave, this dust,
My God shall raise me up, I trust.
SIR WALTER RALEIGH.

---◆---

THE SOUL'S ERRAND.

Go, soul, the body's guest,
Upon a thankless arrant !
Fear not to touch the best,
The truth shall be thy warrant :
Go, since I needs must die,
And give the world the lie.

Go, tell the court it glows
And shines like rotten wood ;
Go, tell the church it shows
What 's good, and doth no good .
If church and court reply,
Then give them both the lie.

Tell potentates they live
Acting by others' action,
Not loved unless they give,
Not strong but by a faction :
If potentates reply,
Give potentates the lie.

Tell men of high condition
That manage the estate,
Their purpose is ambition,
Their practice only hate :
And if they once reply,
Then give them all the lie.

Tell them that brave it most,
They beg for more by spending,
Who, in their greatest cost,
Seek nothing but commending :
And if they make reply,
Then give them all the lie.

Tell zeal it wants devotion ;
Tell love it is but lust ;
Tell time it is but motion ;
Tell flesh it is but dust :
And wish them not reply,
For thou must give the lie.

Tell age it daily wasteth ;
  Tell honor how it alters ;
Tell beauty how she blasteth ;
  Tell favor how it falters :
And as they shall reply,
Give every one the lie.

Tell wit how much it wrangles
  In tickle points of niceness ;
Tell wisdom she entangles
  Herself in over-wiseness :
And when they do reply,
Straight give them both the lie.

Tell physic of her boldness ;
  Tell skill it is pretension ;
Tell charity of coldness ;
  Tell law it is contention :
And as they do reply,
So give them still the lie.

Tell fortune of her blindness ;
  Tell nature of decay ;
Tell friendship of unkindness ;
  Tell justice of delay :
And if they will reply,
Then give them all the lie.

Tell arts they have no soundness,
  But vary by esteeming ;
Tell schools they want profoundness,
  And stand too much on seeming :
If arts and schools reply,
Give arts and schools the lie.

Tell faith it 's fled the city ;
  Tell how the country erreth ;
Tell, manhood shakes off pity ;
  Tell, virtue least preferreth :
And if they do reply,
Spare not to give the lie.

So when thou hast, as I
  Commanded thee, done blabbing, —
Although to give the lie
  Deserves no less than stabbing, —
Yet, stab at thee that will,
No stab the soul can kill.
SIR WALTER RALEIGH.

LETTERS.

EVERY day brings a ship,
Every ship brings a word ;
Well for those who have no fear,
Looking seaward well assured
That the word the vessel brings
Is the word they wish to hear.
RALPH WALDO EMERSON.

BRAHMA.

IF the red slayer think he slays,
  Or if the slain think he is slain,
They know not well the subtle ways
  I keep, and pass, and turn again.

Far or forgot to me is near ;
  Shadow and sunlight are the same ;
The vanished gods to me appear ;
  And one to me are shame and fame.

They reckon ill who leave me out ;
  When me they fly, I am the wings ;
I am the doubter and the doubt,
  And I the hymn the Brahmin sings.

The strong gods pine for my abode,
  And pine in vain the sacred Seven ;
But thou, meek lover of the good !
  Find me, and turn thy back on heaven.
RALPH WALDO EMERSON.

BRAHMA'S ANSWER.

ONCE, when the days were ages,
  And the old Earth was young,
The high gods and the sages
  From Nature's golden pages
  Her open secrets wrung.
  Each questioned each to know
Whence came the Heavens above, and whence the
    Earth below.

Indra, the endless giver
  Of every gracious thing
The gods to him deliver,
  Whose bounty is the river
  Of which they are the spring —
  Indra, with anxious heart,
Ventures with Vivochunu where Brahma is a
    part.

" Brahma ! Supremest Being !
  By whom the worlds are made,
Where we are blind, all-seeing,
  Stable, where we are fleeing,
  Of Life and Death afraid, —
  Instruct us, for mankind,
What is the body, Brahma ? O Brahma ! what
    the mind ? "

Hearing as though he heard not
  So perfect was his rest,
So vast the soul that erred not,
So wise the lips that stirred not —
  His hand upon his breast
  He laid, whereat his face
Was mirrored in the river that girt that holy
    place.

They questioned each the other
  What Brahma's answer meant.
Said Vivochunu, " Brother,
Through Brahma the great Mother
  Hath spoken her intent :
  Man ends as he began, —
The shadow on the water is all there is of man ! "

"The earth with woe is cumbered,
  And no man understands ;
They see their days are numbered
By one that never slumbered
  Nor stayed his dreadful hands.
  I see with Brahma's eyes —
The body is the shadow that on the water lies : "

Thus Indra, looking deeper,
  With Brahma's self possessed.
So dry thine eyes, thou weeper !
And rise again, thou sleeper !
  The hand on Brahma's breast
  Is his divine assent,
Covering the soul that dies not. This is what
  Brahma meant.

RICHARD HENRY STODDARD.

RETRIBUTION.

Ὀψὲ θεῶν ἀλέουσι μύλοι, ἀλέουσι δὲ λεπτά.

(" The mills of the gods grind late, but they grind fine.")
GREEK POET.

Though the mills of God grind slowly, yet they
  grind exceeding small ;
Though with patience he stands waiting, with
  exactness grinds he all.

From the German of F. VON LOGAU. Translation of H. W. LONGFELLOW.

TIME.

FROM 'NIGHT THOUGHTS," NIGHT I.

The bell strikes one : we take no note of time,
But from its loss. To give it, then, a tongue,
Is wise in man. As if an angel spoke,
I feel the solemn sound. If heard aright,
It is the knell of my departed hours :
Where are they ? With the years beyond the flood.
It is the signal that demands despatch ;
How much is to be done ! my hopes and fears
Start up alarmed, and o'er life's narrow verge
Look down — on what ? a fathomless abyss ;
A dread eternity ; how surely mine !
And can eternity belong to me,
Poor pensioner on the bounties of an hour ?

Time the supreme! — Time is eternity ;
Pregnant with all eternity can give ;
Pregnant with all that makes archangels smile.
Who murders time, he crushes in the birth
A power ethereal, only not adored.
  Ah ! how unjust to Nature and himself,
Is thoughtless, thankless, inconsistent man !
Like children babbling nonsense in their sports,
We censure Nature for a span too short :
That span too short, we tax as tedious too ;
Torture invention, all expedients tire,
To lash the lingering moments into speed,
And whirl us (happy riddance !) from ourselves.
Art, brainless Art ! our furious charioteer
(For Nature's voice, unstifled, would recall),
Drives headlong towards the precipice of death !
Death, most our dread ; death, thus more dread-
      ful made :
O, what a riddle of absurdity !
Leisure is pain ; takes off our chariot wheels :
How heavily we drag the load of life !
Blest leisure is our curse : like that of Cain,
It makes us wander ; wander earth around
To fly that tyrant, Thought. As Atlas groaned
The world beneath, we groan beneath an hour.
We cry for mercy to the next amusement :
The next amusement mortgages our fields ;
Slight inconvenience ! prisons hardly frown,
From hateful Time if prisons set us free.
Yet when Death kindly tenders us relief,
We call him cruel ; years to moments shrink,
Ages to years. The telescope is turned.
To man's false optics (from his folly false)
Time, in advance, behind him hides his wings,
And seems to creep, decrepit with his age ;
Behold him when past by ; what then is seen
But his broad pinions, swifter than the winds ?
And all mankind, in contradiction strong,
Rueful, aghast, cry out on his career.

.   .   .   .   .

  Ye well arrayed ! ye lilies of our land !
Ye lilies male ! who neither toil nor spin
(As sister-lilies might) if not so wise
As Solomon, more sumptuous to the sight !
Ye delicate ! who nothing can support,
Yourselves most insupportable ! for whom
The winter rose must blow, the sun put on
A brighter beam in Leo ; silky-soft
Favonius, breathe still softer, or be chid ;
And other worlds send odors, sauce, and song,
And robes, and notions, framed in foreign looms !
O ye Lorenzos of our age ! who deem
One moment unamused a misery
Not made for feeble man ! who call aloud
For every bawble drivelled o'er by sense ;
For rattles, and conceits of every cast,
For change of follies and relays of joy,

To drag you patient through the tedious length
Of a short winter's day, — say, sages ! say,
Wit's oracles ! say, dreamers of gay dreams !
How will you weather an eternal night,
Where such expedients fail ?

DR. EDWARD YOUNG.

PROCRASTINATION.

FROM "NIGHT THOUGHTS," NIGHT I.

BE wise to-day ; 't is madness to defer ;
Next day the fatal precedent will plead ;
Thus on, till wisdom is pushed out of life.
Procrastination is the thief of time ;.
Year after year it steals, till all are fled,
And to the mercies of a moment leaves
The vast concerns of an eternal scene.
If not so frequent, would not this be strange ?
That 't is so frequent, this is stranger still.
Of man's miraculous mistakes this bears
The palm, " That all men are about to live,"
Forever on the brink of being born.
All pay themselves the compliment to think
They one day shall not drivel : and their pride
On this reversion takes up ready praise ;
At least, their own ; their future selves applaud :
How excellent that life they ne'er will lead !
Time lodged in their own hands is folly's veils ;
That lodged in Fate's, to wisdom they consign ;
The thing they can't but purpose, they postpone :
'T is not in folly not to scorn a fool,
And scarce in human wisdom to do more.
All promise is poor dilatory man,
And that through every stage.   When young,
    indeed,
In full content we sometimes nobly rest,
Unanxious for ourselves, and only wish,
As duteous sons, our fathers were more wise.
At thirty, man suspects himself a fool ;
Knows it at forty, and reforms his plan ;
At fifty, chides his infamous delay,
Pushes his prudent purpose to resolve ;
In all the magnanimity of thought,
Resolves, and re-resolves ; then dies the same.

    And why ? Because he thinks himself immortal.
All men think all men mortal but themselves ;
Themselves, when some alarming shock of fate
Strikes through their wounded hearts the sudden
    dread ;
But their hearts wounded, like the wounded air,
Soon close ; where passed the shaft, no trace is
    found.
As from the wing no scar the sky retains,
The parted wave no furrow from the keel,
So dies in human hearts the thought of death :
Even with the tender tears which Nature sheds
O'er those we love, we drop it in their grave.

DR. EDWARD YOUNG.

WHAT IS TIME?

I ASKED an aged man, with hoary hairs,
Wrinkled and curved with worldly cares :
" Time is the warp of life," said he ; " O, tell
The young, the fair, the gay, to weave it well !'
I asked the ancient, venerable dead,
Sages who wrote, and warriors who bled :
From the cold grave a hollow murmur flowed,
" Time sowed the seed we reap in this abode ! "
I asked a dying sinner, ere the ide
Of life had left his veins : " Time ! " he replied ;
" I've lost it ! ah, the treasure ! " and he died.
I asked the golden sun and silver spheres,
Those bright chronometers of days and years :
They answered, " Time is but a meteor glare,"
And bade me for eternity prepare.
I asked the Seasons, in their annual round,
Which beautify or desolate the ground ;
And they replied (no oracle more wise),
" 'T is Folly's blank, and Wisdom's highest
    prize ! "
I asked a spirit lost, — but O the shriek
That pierced my soul ! I shudder while I speak
It cried, " A particle ! a speck ! a mite
Of endless years, duration infinite ! "
Of things inanimate my dial I
Consulted, and it made me this reply, —
" Time is the season fair of living well,
The path of glory or the path of hell."
I asked my Bible, and methinks it said,
" Time is the present hour, the past has fled ;
Live ! live to-day ! to-morrow never yet
On any human being rose or set."
I asked old Father Time himself at last ;
But in a moment he flew swiftly past ;
His chariot was a cloud, the viewless wind
His noiseless steeds, which left no trace behind.
I asked the mighty angel who shall stand
One foot on sea and one on solid land :
" Mortal ! " he cried, " the mystery now is o'er ;
Time was, Time is, but Time shall be no more ! "

WILLIAM MARSDEN.

THE JESTER'S SERMON.

THE Jester shook his hood and bells, and leaped
    upon a chair ;
The pages laughed, the women screamed, and
    tossed their scented hair ;
The falcon whistled, staghounds bayed, the lap-
    dog barked without,
The scullion dropped the pitcher brown, the cook
    railed at the lout ;
The steward, counting out his gold, let pouch
    and money fall, —
And why ? because the Jester rose to say grace
    in the hall !

The page played with the heron's plume, the
  steward with his chain ;
The butler drummed upon the board, and laughed
  with might and main ;
The grooms beat on their metal cans, and roared
  till they were red, —
But still the Jester shut his eyes and rolled his
  witty head,
And when they grew a little still, read half a
  yard of text,
And, waving hand, struck on the desk, then
  frowned like one perplexed.

" Dear sinners all," the fool began, " man's life
  is but a jest,
A dream, a shadow, bubble, air, a vapor at the
  best.
In a thousand pounds of law I find not a single
  ounce of love ;
A blind man killed the parson's cow in shooting
  at the dove ;
The fool that eats till he is sick must fast till he
  is well ;
The wooer who can flatter most will bear away
  the belle.

" Let no man halloo he is safe till he is through
  the wood ;
He who will not when he may, must tarry when
  he should ;
He who laughs at crooked men should need walk
  very straight ;
O, he who once has won a name may lie abed
  till eight ;
Make haste to purchase house and land, be very
  slow to wed ;
True coral needs no painter's brush, nor need be
  daubed with red.

" The friar, preaching, cursed the thief (the
  pudding in his sleeve) ;
To fish for sprats with golden hooks is foolish,
  by your leave ;
To travel well, — an ass's ears, hog's mouth, and
  ostrich legs ;
He does not care a pin for thieves who limps
  about and begs ;
Be always first man at a feast and last man at a
  fray ;
The short way round, in spite of all, is still the
  longest way ;
When the hungry curate licks the knife, there's
  not much for the clerk ;
When the pilot, turning pale and sick, looks up
  — the storm grows dark."

Then loud they laughed ; the fat cook's tears ran
  down into the pan ;
The steward shook, that he was forced to drop
  the brimming can ;
And then again the women screamed, and every
  staghound bayed, —
And why ? because the motley fool so wise a ser-
  mon made.
GEORGE WALTER THORNBURY.

ON AN INTAGLIO HEAD OF MINERVA.

THE cunning hand that carved this face,
  A little helmeted Minerva, —
The hand, I say, ere Phidias wrought,
  Had lost its subtile skill and fervor.

Who was he ? Was he glad or sad,
  Who knew to carve in such a fashion ?
Perchance he shaped this dainty head
  For some brown girl that scorned his passion

But he is dust : we may not know
  His happy or unhappy story :
Nameless, and dead these thousand years,
  His work outlives him, — there's his glory !

Both man and jewel lay in earth
  Beneath a lava-buried city ;
The thousand summers came and went,
  With neither haste nor hate nor pity.

The years wiped out the man, but left
  The jewel fresh as any blossom,
Till some Visconti dug it up, —
  To rise and fall on Mabel's bosom !

O Roman brother ! see how Time
  Your gracious handiwork has guarded,
See how your loving, patient art
  Has come, at last, to be rewarded !

Who would not suffer slights of men,
  And pangs of hopeless passion also,
To have his carven agate-stone
  On such a bosom rise and fall so !
THOMAS BAILEY ALDRICH

ON A FAN

THAT BELONGED TO THE MARQUISE DE POMPADOUR.

(BALLADE.)

CHICKEN-SKIN, delicate, white,
  Painted by Carlo Vanloo,
Loves in a riot of light,

Roses and vaporous blue ;
Hark to the dainty *frou-frou!*
Picture above, if you can,
Eyes that could melt as the dew, —
This was the Pompadour's fan !

See how they rise at the sight,
Thronging the *Œil de Bœuf* through,
Courtiers as butterflies bright,
Beauties that Fragonard drew,
Talon-rouge, falaba, queue,
Cardinal, duke, — to a man,
Eager to sigh or to sue, —
This was the Pompadour's fan !

Ah, but things more than polite
Hung on this toy, *voyez-vous!*
Matters of state and of might,
Things that great ministers do ;
Things that, maybe, overthrew
Those in whose brains they began ; —
Here was the sign and the cue, —
This was the Pompadour's fan !

ENVOY.

Where are the secrets it knew ?
Weavings of plot and of plan ?
— But where is the Pompadour, too ?
This was the Pompadour's *fan !*
AUSTIN DOBSON.

THE FLOOD OF YEARS.

A MIGHTY Hand, from an exhaustless urn,
Pours forth the never-ending Flood of Years
Among the nations.   How the rushing waves
Bear all before them !   On their foremost edge,
And there alone, is Life ; the Present there
Tosses and foams and fills the air with roar
Of mingled noises.   There are they who toil,
And they who strive, and they who feast, and they
Who hurry to and fro.   The sturdy hind —
Woodman and delver with the spade — are there,
And busy artisan beside his bench,
And pallid student with his written roll.
A moment on the mounting billow seen —
The flood sweeps over them and they are gone.
There groups of revellers, whose brows are twined
With roses, ride the topmost swell awhile,
And as they raise their flowing cups to touch
The clinking brim to brim, are whirled beneath
The waves and disappear.   I hear the jar
Of beaten drums, and thunders that break forth
From cannon, where the advancing billow sends
Up to the sight long files of armed men,
That hurry to the charge through flame and smoke.
The torrent bears them under, whelmed and hid,

Slayer and slain, in heaps of bloody foam.
Down go the steed and rider ; the plumed chief
Sinks with his followers ; the head that wears
The imperial diadem goes down beside
The felon's with cropped ear and branded cheek.
A funeral train — the torrent sweeps away
Bearers and bier and mourners.   By the bed
Of one who dies men gather sorrowing,
And women weep aloud ; the flood rolls on ;
The wail is stifled, and the sobbing group
Borne under.   Hark to that shrill sudden shout —
The cry of an applauding multitude
Swayed by some loud-tongued orator who wields
The living mass, as if he were its soul.
The waters choke the shout and all is still.
Lo, next, a kneeling crowd and one who spreads
The hands in prayer ; the engulfing wave o'er-
takes
And swallows them and him.   A sculptor wields
The chisel, and the stricken marble grows
To beauty ; at his easel, eager-eyed,
A painter stands, and sunshine, at his touch,
Gathers upon the canvas, and life glows ;
A poet, as he paces to and fro,
Murmurs his sounding line.   Awhile they ride
The advancing billow, till its tossing crest
Strikes them and flings them under while their
tasks
Are yet unfinished.   See a mother smile
On her young babe that smiles to her again —
The torrent wrests it from her arms ; she shrieks,
And weeps, and midst her tears is carried down.
A beam like that of moonlight turns the spray
To glistening pearls ; two lovers, hand in hand,
Rise on the billowy swell and fondly look
Into each other's eyes.   The rushing flood
Flings them apart ; the youth goes down ; the
maid,
With hands outstretched in vain and streaming
eyes,
Waits for the next high wave to follow him.
An aged man succeeds ; his bending form
Sinks slowly ; mingling with the sullen stream
Gleam the white locks and then are seen no more.
Lo, wider grows the stream ; a sea-like flood
Saps earth's walled cities ; massive palaces
Crumble before it ; fortresses and towers
Dissolve in the swift waters ; populous realms,
Swept by the torrent. see their ancient tribes
Engulfed and lost, their very languages
Stifled and never to be uttered more.
I pause and turn my eyes, and, looking back,
Where that tumultuous flood has passed, I see
The silent Ocean of the Past, a waste
Of waters weltering over graves, its shores
Strewn with the wreck of fleets, where mast and
hull

Drop away piecemeal ; battlemented walls
Frown idly, green with moss, and temples stand
Unroofed, forsaken by the worshippers.
There lie memorial stones, whence time has
   gnawed
The graven legends, thrones of kings o'erturned,
The broken altars of forgotten gods,
Foundations of old cities and long streets
Where never fall of human foot is heard
Upon the desolate pavement. I behold
Dim glimmerings of lost jewels far within
The sleeping waters, diamond, sardonyx,
Ruby and topaz, pearl and chrysolite,
Once glittering at the banquet on fair brows
That long ago were dust ; and all around,
Strewn on the waters of that silent sea,
Are withering bridal wreaths, and glossy locks
Shorn from fair brows by loving hands, and scrolls
O'erwritten — haply with fond words of love
And vows of friendship — and fair pages flung
Fresh from the printer's engine. There they lie
A moment and then sink away from sight.

I look, and the quick tears are in my eyes,
For I behold, in every one of these,
A blighted hope, a separate history
Of human sorrow, telling of dear ties
Suddenly broken, dreams of happiness
Dissolved in air, and happy days, too brief,
That sorrowfully ended, and I think
How painfully must the poor heart have beat
In bosoms without number, as the blow
Was struck that slew their hope or broke their
   peace.
Sadly I turn, and look before, where yet
The Flood must pass, and I behold a mist
Where swarm dissolving forms, the brood of Hope,
Divinely fair, that rest on banks of flowers
Or wander among rainbows, fading soon
And reappearing, haply giving place
To shapes of grisly aspect, such as Fear
Moulds from the idle air ; where serpents lift
The head to strike, and skeletons stretch forth
The bony arm in menace. Further on
A belt of darkness seems to bar the way,
Long, low and distant, where the Life that Is
Touches the Life to come. The Flood of Years
Rolls toward it, nearer and nearer. It must pass
That dismal barrier. What is there beyond ?
Hear what the wise and good have said. Beyond
That belt of darkness still the years roll on
More gently, but with not less mighty sweep.
They gather up again and softly bear
All the sweet lives that late were overwhelmed
And lost to sight — all that in them was good,
Noble, and truly great and worthy of love —
The lives of infants and ingenuous youths,
Sages and saintly women who have made

Their households happy — all are raised and borne
By that great current on its onward sweep,
Wandering and rippling with caressing waves
Around green islands, fragrant with the breath
Of flowers that never wither. So they pass,
From stage to stage, along the shining course
Of that fair river broadening like a sea.
As its smooth eddies curl along their way,
They bring old friends together ; hands are
   clasped
In joy unspeakable ; the mother's arms
Again are folded round the child she loved
And lost. Old sorrows are forgotten now,
Or but remembered to make sweet the hour
That overpays them ; wounded hearts that bled
Or broke are healed forever. In the room
Of this grief-shadowed Present there shall be
A Present in whose reign no grief shall gnaw
The heart, and never shall a tender tie
Be broken — in whose reign the eternal Change
That waits on growth and action shall proceed
With everlasting Concord hand in hand.
WILLIAM CULLEN BRYANT.

THREE DAYS.

So much to do : so little done !
Ah ! yesternight I saw the sun
Sink beamless down the vaulted gray, —
The ghastly ghost of YESTERDAY.

So little done : so much to do !
Each morning breaks on conflicts new ;
But eager, brave, I 'll join the fray,
And fight the battle of TO-DAY.

So much to do : so little done !
But when it 's o'er, — the victory won, —
Oh ! then, my soul, this strife and sorrow
Will end in that great, glad TO-MORROW.
JAMES R. GILMORE.

INSIGNIFICANT EXISTENCE.

THERE are a number of us creep
Into this world, to eat and sleep ;
And know no reason why we 're born,
But only to consume the corn,
Devour the cattle, fowl, and fish,
And leave behind an empty dish.
The crows and ravens do the same,
Unlucky birds of hateful name ;
Ravens or crows might fill their places,
And swallow corn and carcasses,

Then if their tombstone, when they die,
Be n't taught to flatter and to lie,
There's nothing better will be said
Than that "they've eat up all their bread,
Drunk up their drink, and gone to bed."

ISAAC WATTS.

NEW YEAR'S EVE.

FROM "IN MEMORIAM."

RING out, wild bells, to the wild sky,
　The flying cloud, the frosty light ;
　The year is dying in the night ;
Ring out, wild bells, and let him die.

Ring out the old, ring in the new ;
　Ring, happy bells, across the snow ;
　The year is going, let him go ;
Ring out the false, ring in the true.

Ring out the grief that saps the mind,
　For those that here we see no more ;
　Ring out the feud of rich and poor,
Ring in redress to all mankind.

Ring out a slowly dying cause
　And ancient forms of party strife ;
　Ring in the nobler modes of life,
With sweeter manners, purer laws.

Ring out false pride in place and blood,
　The civic slander and the spite ;
　Ring in the love of truth and right,
Ring in the common love of good.

Ring out old shapes of foul disease,
　Ring out the narrowing lust of gold ;
　Ring out the thousand wars of old,
Ring in the thousand years of peace.

Ring in the valiant man and free,
　The larger heart, the kindlier hand ;
　Ring out the darkness of the land,
Ring in the Christ that is to be.

ALFRED TENNYSON.

THE CLOSING YEAR.

'T IS midnight's holy hour, — and silence now
Is brooding like a gentle spirit o'er
The still and pulseless world. Hark ! on the
　winds
The bell's deep tones are swelling, —'t is the
　knell
Of the departed year.   No funeral train
Is sweeping past ; yet, on the stream and wood,
With melancholy light, the moonbeams rest

Like a pale, spotless shroud ; the air is stirred
As by a mourner's sigh ; and on yon cloud
That floats so still and placidly through heaven,
The spirits of the seasons seem to stand, —
Young Spring, bright Summer, Autumn's solemn
　form,
And Winter with its aged locks, — and breathe,
In mournful cadences that come abroad
Like the far wind-harp's wild and touching wail,
A melancholy dirge o'er the dead year,
Gone from the earth forever.

　　　　　　　　　　　　　　　'T is a time
For memory and for tears.   Within the deep,
Still chambers of the heart, a spectre dim,
Whose tones are like the wizard's voice of Time
Heard from the tomb of ages, points its cold
And solemn finger to the beautiful
And holy visions that have passed away,
And left no shadow of their loveliness
On the dead waste of life.   That spectre lifts
The coffin-lid of Hope and Joy and Love,
And bending mournfully above the pale,
Sweet forms that slumber there, scatters dead
　flowers
O'er what has passed to nothingness.

　　　　　　　　　　　　　　　　The year
Has gone, and with it, many a glorious throng
Of happy dreams.   Its mark is on each brow,
Its shadow in each heart.   In its swift course
It waved its sceptre o'er the beautiful,
And they are not.   It laid its pallid hand
Upon the strong man, and the haughty form
Is fallen, and the flashing eye is dim.
It trod the hall of revelry, where thronged
The bright and joyous, and the tearful wail
Of stricken ones is heard where erst the song
And reckless shout resounded.

　　　　　　　　　　　　　　It passed o'er
The battle-plain where sword and spear and
　shield
Flashed in the light of midday, and the strength
Of serried hosts is shivered, and the grass,
Green from the soil of carnage, waves above
The crushed and mouldering skeleton.   It came,
And faded like a wreath of mist at eve ;
Yet ere it melted in the viewless air
It heralded its millions to their home
In the dim land of dreams.

　　　　　　　　　　　　Remorseless Time !
Fierce spirit of the glass and scythe ! — what
　power
Can stay him in his silent course, or melt
His iron heart to pity ?   On, still on,
He presses, and forever.   The proud bird,
The condor of the Andes, that can soar

Through heaven's unfathomable depths, or brave
The fury of the northern hurricane,
And bathe his plumage in the thunder's home,
Furls his broad wings at nightfall, and sinks
          down
To rest upon his mountain crag, — but Time
Knows not the weight of sleep or weariness,
And night's deep darkness has no chain to bind
His rushing pinions.

            Revolutions sweep
O'er earth, like troubled visions o'er the breast
Of dreaming sorrow ; cities rise and sink
Like bubbles on the water ; fiery isles
Spring blazing from the ocean, and go back
To their mysterious caverns ; mountains rear
To heaven their bald and blackened cliffs, and
          bow
Their tall heads to the plain ; new empires rise,
Gathering the strength of hoary centuries,
And rush down like the Alpine avalanche,
Startling the nations ; and the very stars,
You bright and burning blazonry of God,
Glitter awhile in their eternal depths,
And, like the Pleiads, loveliest of their train,
Shoot from their glorious spheres, and pass away
To darkle in the trackless void, — yet Time,
Time the tomb-builder, holds his fierce career,
Dark, stern, all-pitiless, and pauses not
Amid the mighty wrecks that strew his path
To sit and muse, like other conquerors,
Upon the fearful ruin he has wrought.
                    GEORGE DENISON PRENTICE.

THE DEATH OF THE OLD YEAR.

FULL knee-deep lies the winter snow,
And the winter winds are wearily sighing :
Toll ye the church-bell sad and slow,
And tread softly and speak low,
For the old year lies a-dying.
    Old year, you must not die ;
    You came to us so readily,
    You lived with us so steadily,
    Old year, you shall not die.

He lieth still : he doth not move :
He will not see the dawn of day.
He hath no other life above.
He gave me a friend, and a true true-love,
And the New-year will take 'em away.
    Old year, you must not go ;
    So long as you have been with us,
    Such joy as you have seen with us,
    Old year, you shall not go.

He frothed his bumpers to the brim ;
A jollier year we shall not see.
But, though his eyes are waxing dim,
And though his foes speak ill of him,
He was a friend to me.
    Old year, you shall not die ;
    We did so laugh and cry with you,
    I 've half a mind to die with you,
    Old year, if you must die.

He was full of joke and jest,
But all his merry quips are o'er.
To see him die, across the waste
His son and heir doth ride post-haste,
But he 'll be dead before.
    Every one for his own.
    The night is starry and cold, my friend,
    And the New-year, blithe and bold, my friend,
    Comes up to take his own.

How hard he breathes ! over the snow
I heard just now the crowing cock.
The shadows flicker to and fro :
The cricket chirps : the light burns low :
'T is nearly twelve o'clock.
    Shake hands before you die.
    Old year, we 'll dearly rue for you :
    What is it we can do for you ?
    Speak out before you die.

His face is growing sharp and thin.
Alack ! our friend is gone.
Close up his eyes : tie up his chin :
Step from the corpse, and let him in
That standeth there alone,
    And waiteth at the door.
    There 's a new foot on the floor, my friend,
    And a new face at the door, my friend,
    A new face at the door.
                        ALFRED TENNYSON.

THE APPROACH OF AGE.

SONNET XII.

WHEN I do count the clock that tells the time,
And see the brave day sunk in hideous night ;
When I behold the violet past prime,
And sable curls all silvered o'er with white ;
When lofty trees I see barren of leaves,
Which erst from heat did canopy the herd,
And summer's green all girded up in sheaves,
Borne on the bier with white and bristly beard ;
Then of thy beauty do I question make,
That thou among the wastes of time must go,
Since sweets and beauties do themselves forsake,

And die as fast as they see others grow ;
　And nothing 'gainst Time's scythe can make
　　defence,
　Save breed, to brave him when he takes thee
　　hence.
SHAKESPEARE.

TO THE VIRGINS.

GATHER ye rosebuds while ye may,
　Old Time is still a flying ;
And this same flower that smiles to-day
　To-morrow will be dying.

The glorious lamp of Heaven, the sun,
　The higher he's a getting,
The sooner will his race be run,
　And nearer he's to setting.

The age is best which is the first,
　When youth and blood are warmer ;
But being spent, the worse and worst
　Times still succeed the former.

Then be not coy, but use your time,
　And, while ye may, go marry ;
For having lost but once your prime,
　You may forever tarry.
ROBERT HERRICK.

TO-MORROW.

FROM "IRENE."

TO-MORROW's action ! can that hoary wisdom,
Borne down with years, still doat upon to-morrow !
The fatal mistress of the young, the lazy,
The coward and the fool, condemned to lose
An useless life in waiting for to-morrow,
To gaze with longing eyes upon to-morrow,
Till interposing death destroys the prospect.
Strange that this general fraud from day to day
Should fill the world with wretches, undetected !
The soldier, laboring through a winter's march,
Still sees to-morrow drest in robes of triumph ;
Still to the lover's long-expecting arms
To-morrow brings the visionary bride.
But thou, too old to bear another cheat,
Learn that the present hour alone is man's.
SAMUEL JOHNSON.

GOING AND COMING.

GOING — the great round Sun,
　Dragging the captive Day
Over behind the frowning hill,
　Over beyond the bay, —

Dying :
Coming — the dusky Night,
　Silently stealing in,
Wrapping himself in the soft warm couch
　Where the golden-haired Day hath been
　　Lying.

Going — the bright, blithe Spring ;
　Blossoms ! how fast ye fall,
Shooting out of your starry sky
　Into the darkness all
　　Blindly !
Coming — the mellow days :
　Crimson and yellow leaves ;
Languishing purple and amber fruits
　Kissing the bearded sheaves
　　Kindly !

Going — our early friends ;
　Voices we loved are dumb ;
Footsteps grow dim in the morning dew ;
　Fainter the echoes come
　　Ringing :
Coming to join our march, —
　Shoulder to shoulder pressed, —
Gray-haired veterans strike their tents
　For the far-off purple West —
　　Singing !

Going — this old, old life ;
　Beautiful world, farewell !
Forest and meadow ! river and hill !
　Ring ye a loving knell
　　O'er us !
Coming — a nobler life ;
　Coming — a better land ;
Coming — a long, long, nightless day ;
　Coming — the grand, grand
　　Chorus !
EDWARD A. JENKS.

THE FOOLISH VIRGINS.

FROM "IDYLS OF THE KING."

THE Queen looked up, and said,
"O maiden, if indeed you list to sing,
Sing, and unbind my heart, that I may weep."
Whereat full willingly sang the little maid :

"Late, late, so late ! and dark the night and
　　chill !
Late, late, so late ! but we can enter still.
Too late, too late ! Ye cannot enter now.

"No light had we : for that we do repent ;
And learning this, the bridegroom will relent
Too late, too late ! Ye cannot enter now.

"No light ; so late ! and dark and chill the
    night !
O, let us in, that we may find the light !
Too late, too late !   Ye cannot enter now.

"Have we not heard the bridegroom is so sweet ?
O, let us in, though late, to kiss his feet !
No, no, too late !   Ye cannot enter now."

So sang the novice, while full passionately,
Her head upon her hands, wept the sad Queen.
                                ALFRED TENNYSON.

OLD AGE AND DEATH.

FROM "VERSES UPON HIS DIVINE POESY."

THE seas are quiet when the winds give o'er ;
So calm are we when passions are no more.
For then we know how vain it was to boast
Of fleeting things, too certain to be lost.
Clouds of affection from our younger eyes
Conceal that emptiness which age descries.

The soul's dark cottage, battered and decayed,
Lets in new light through chinks that time has
    made :
Stronger by weakness, wiser men become,
As they draw near to their eternal home.
Leaving the old, both worlds at once they view,
That stand upon the threshold of the new.
                                EDMUND WALLER.

THE ONE GRAY HAIR.

THE wisest of the wise
Listen to pretty lies,
    And love to hear them told ;
Doubt not that Solomon
Listened to many a one, —
Some in his youth, and more when he grew old.

I never sat among
The choir of Wisdom's song,
    But pretty lies loved I
As much as any king, —
When youth was on the wing,
And (must it then be told ?) when youth had
    quite gone by.

Alas ! and I have not
The pleasant hour forgot,
    When one pert lady said, —
"O Landor ! I am quite
Bewildered with affright ;
I see (sit quiet now !) a white hair on your head !"

Another, more benign,
Drew out that hair of mine,
    And in her own dark hair
Pretended she had found
That one, and twirled it round. —
Fair as she was, she never was so fair.
                        WALTER SAVAGE LANDOR.

GROWING GRAY.

"On a l'age de son cœur." — A. D'HOUDETOT.

A LITTLE more toward the light.
Me miserum.   Here 's one that 's white,
    And one that 's turning ;
Adieu to song and "salad days."
My Muse, let 's go at once to Jay's
    And order mourning.

We must reform our rhymes, my dear,
Renounce the gay for the severe, —
    Be grave, not witty ;
We have no more the right to find
That Pyrrha's hair is neatly twined,
    That Chloe 's pretty.

Young Love 's for us a farce that 's played ;
Light canzonet and serenade
    No more may tempt us ;
Gray hairs but ill accord with dreams ;
From aught but sour didactic themes
    Our years exempt us.

"*A la bonne heure !*"   You fancy so ?
You think for one white streak we grow
    At once satiric ?
A fiddlestick !   Each hair 's a string
To which our graybeard Muse shall sing
    A younger lyric.

Our heart 's still sound.   Shall "cakes and ale '
Grow rare to youth because we rail
    At school-boy dishes ?
Perish the thought !   'T is ours to sing,
Though neither Time nor Tide can bring
    Belief with wishes.
                                AUSTIN DOBSON.

TOO LATE.

"Ah ! si la jeunesse savait — si la vieillesse pouvait !"

THERE sat an old man on a rock,
    And unceasing bewailed him of Fate, —
That concern where we all must take stock,
    Though our vote has no hearing or weight ;
        And the old man sang him an old, old song, —
        Never sang voice so clear and strong
        That it could drown the old man's long,
            For he sang the song "Too late ! too late !'

" When we want, we have for our pains
  The promise that if we but wait
Till the want has burned out of our brains,
    Every means shall be present to sate ;
      While we send for the napkin the soup gets
        cold,
      While the bonnet is trimming the face grows
        old,
      When we 've matched our buttons the pat-
        tern is sold,
      And everything comes too late — too late !

" When strawberries seemed like red heavens,
  Terrapin stew a wild dream.
When my brain was at sixes and sevens,
  If my mother had 'folks' and ice-cream,
    Then I gazed with a lickerish hunger
    At the restaurant man and fruit-monger
    But O, how I wished I were younger
      When the goodies all came in a stream —
      in a stream !

"I 've a splendid blood-horse, and — a liver
  That it jars into torture to trot ;
My row-boat 's the gem of the river, —
  Gout makes every knuckle a knot !
    I can buy boundless credits on Paris and
      Rome,
    But no palate for *menus*, no eyes for a dome —
    Those belonged to the youth who must tarry
      at home,
      When no home but an attic he 'd got —
      he 'd got !

" How I longed, in that lonest of garrets,
  Where the tiles baked my brains all July,
For ground to grow two pecks of carrots,
  Two pigs of my own in a sty,
    A rosebush — a little thatched cottage —
    Two spoons — love — a basin of pottage ! —
    Now in freestone I sit — and my dotage —
      With a woman's chair empty close by —
      close by !

"Ah ! now, though I sit on a rock,
  I have shared one seat with the great ;
I have sat — knowing naught of the clock —
  On love's high throne of state ;
    But the lips that kissed, and the arms that
      caressed,
    To a mouth grown stern with delay were
      pressed,
    And circled a breast that their clasp had
      blessed
      Had they only not come too late — too
    late !"

              FITZ HUGH LUDLOW.

THE THREE WARNINGS.

THE tree of deepest root is found
Least willing still to quit the ground ;
'T was therefore said by ancient sages,
  That love of life increased with years
So much, that in our latter stages,
When pains grow sharp and sickness rages,
  The greatest love of life appears.
This great affection to believe,
Which all confess, but few perceive,
If old assertions can't prevail,
Be pleased to hear a modern tale.

When sports went round, and all were gay,
On neighbor Dodson's wedding-day,
Death called aside the jocund groom
With him into another room,
And, looking grave, " You must," says he,
" Quit your sweet bride, and come with me.'
" With you ! and quit my Susan's side ?
With you ! " the hapless husband cried ;
" Young as I am, 't is monstrous hard !
Besides, in truth, I 'm not prepared :
My thoughts on other matters go ;
This is my wedding-day, you know."

What more he urged I have not heard,
  His reasons could not well be stronger ;
So Death the poor delinquent spared,
  And left to live a little longer.
Yet calling up a serious look,
His hour-glass trembled while he spoke —
" Neighbor," he said, " farewell ! no more
Shall Death disturb your mirthful hour ;
And further, to avoid all blame
Of cruelty upon my name,
To give you time for preparation,
And fit you for your future station,
Three several warnings you shall have,
Before you 're summoned to the grave ;
Willing for once I 'll quit my prey,
  And grant a kind reprieve,
In hopes you 'll have no more to say,
But when I call again this way,
  Well pleased the world will leave."
To these conditions both consented,
And parted perfectly contented.

What next the hero of our tale befell,
How long he lived, how wise, how well,
How roundly he pursued his course,
And smoked his pipe, and stroked his horse,
  The willing muse shall tell :
He chaffered then, he bought and sold,
Nor once perceived his growing old,
  Nor thought of Death as near :

His friends not false, his wife no shrew,
Many his gains, his children few,
  He passed his hours in peace.
But while he viewed his wealth increase,
While thus along life's dusty road
The beaten track content he trod,
Old Time, whose haste no mortal spares,
Uncalled, unheeded, unawares,
  Brought on his eightieth year.
And now, one night, in musing mood,
  As all alone he sate,
The unwelcome messenger of Fate
  Once more before him stood.

Half killed with anger and surprise,
"So soon returned!" Old Dodson cries.
"So soon, d' ye call it!" Death replies;
"Surely, my friend, you're but in jest!
  Since I was here before
'T is six-and-thirty years at least,
  And you are now fourscore."

"So much the worse," the clown rejoined;
"To spare the aged would be kind:
However, see your search be legal;
And your authority, — is 't regal?
Else you are come on a fool's errand,
With but a secretary's warrant.
Beside, you promised me three warnings,
Which I have looked for nights and mornings;
But for that loss of time and ease
I can recover damages."

"I know," cries Death, "that at the best
I seldom am a welcome guest;
But don't be captious, friend, at least:
I little thought you 'd still be able
To stump about your farm and stable:
Your years have run to a great length;
I wish you joy, though, of your strength!"

"Hold," says the farmer, "not so fast!
I have been lame these four years past."
"And no great wonder," Death replies:
"However, you still keep your eyes;
And sure, to see one's loves and friends
For legs and arms would make amends."
"Perhaps," says Dodson, "so it might,
But latterly I 've lost my sight."
"This is a shocking tale, 't is true;
But still there 's comfort left for you:
Each strives your sadness to amuse;
I warrant you hear all the news."
"There 's none," cries he; "and if there were,
I 'm grown so deaf, I could not hear."
"Nay, then," the spectre stern rejoined,
"These are unjustifiable yearnings:
  If you are lame and deaf and blind,

You 've had your three sufficient warnings;
So come along, no more we 'll part."
He said, and touched him with his dart.
And now, Old Dodson, turning pale,
Yields to his fate, — so ends my tale.
          HESTER LYNCH THRALE

WITHOUT AND WITHIN.

If every man's internal care
  Were written on his brow,
How many would our pity share
  Who raise our envy now?

The fatal secret, when revealed,
  Of every aching breast,
Would prove that only while concealed
  Their lot appeared the best.   METASTASIO.

ODE.
INTIMATIONS OF IMMORTALITY FROM RECOLLECTIONS OF EARLY CHILDHOOD.

There was a time when meadow, grove, and
      stream,
The earth, and every common sight,
    To me did seem
  Apparelled in celestial light, —
The glory and the freshness of a dream.
It is not now as it hath been of yore:
    Turn wheresoe'er I may,
      By night or day,
The things which I have seen I now can see no
      more.

    The rainbow comes and goes,
    And lovely is the rose;
    The moon doth with delight
Look round her when the heavens are bare;
    Waters on a starry night
    Are beautiful and fair;
  The sunshine is a glorious birth;
  But yet I know, where'er I go,
That there hath passed away a glory from the
      earth.

Now, while the birds thus sing a joyous song,
  And while the young lambs bound
    As to the tabor's sound,
To me alone there came a thought of grief:
A timely utterance gave that thought relief,
  And I again am strong.
The cataracts blow their trumpets from the
      steep, —
No more shall grief of mine the season wrong.
I hear the echoes through the mountain throng;
The winds come to me from the fields of sleep.

And all the earth is gay ;
            Land and sea
Give themselves up to jollity ;
            And with the heart of May
Doth every beast keep holiday ; —
            Thou child of joy,
Shout round me, let me hear thy shouts, thou
            happy shepherd boy !

Ye blessèd creatures ! I have heard the call
      Ye to each other make ; I see
The heavens laugh with you in your jubilee ;
            My heart is at your festival,
            My head hath its coronal, —
The fulness of your bliss, I feel, I feel it all.
            O evil day ! if I were sullen
            While Earth herself is adorning,
                  This sweet May morning,
            And the children are culling,
                  On every side,
            In a thousand valleys far and wide,
            Fresh flowers ; while the sun shines warm,
And the babe leaps up on his mother's arm ; —
            I hear, I hear, with joy I hear ! —
            But there 's a tree, of many, one,
A single field which I have looked upon, —
Both of them speak of something that is gone ;
            The pansy at my feet
            Doth the same tale repeat.
Whither is fled the visionary gleam ?
Where is it now, the glory and the dream

Our birth is but a sleep and a forgetting ;
The soul that rises with us, our life's star,
            Hath had elsewhere its setting,
            And cometh from afar :
            Not in entire forgetfulness,
            And not in utter nakedness,
But trailing clouds of glory, do we come
            From God, who is our home :
Heaven lies about us in our infancy !
Shades of the prison-house begin to close
            Upon the growing Boy ;
But he beholds the light, and whence it flows, —
            He sees it in his joy ;
The Youth, who daily farther from the east
      Must travel, still is nature's priest
            And by the vision sp'endid
            Is on his way attended :
At length the Man perceives it die away,
And fade into the light of common day.

Earth fills her lap with pleasures of her own ;
Yearnings she hath in her own natural kind,
And even with something of a mother's mind,
            And no unworthy aim,
            The homely nurse doth all she can
To make her foster-child, her inmate man.

Forget the glories he hath known,
And that imperial palace whence he came.

Behold the child among his new-born blisses, —
A six years' darling of a pygmy size !
See, where mid work of his own hand he lies,
Fretted by sallies of his mother's kisses,
With light upon him from his father's eyes !
See, at his feet, some little plan or chart,
Some fragment from his dream of human life,
Shaped by himself with newly learnèd art, —
            A wedding or a festival,
            A mourning or a funeral ; —
            And this hath now his heart,
            And unto this he frames his song :
            Then will he fit his tongue
To dialogues of business, love, or strife ;
            But it will not be long
            Ere this be thrown aside,
            And with new joy and pride
The little actor cons another part, —
Filling from time to time his "humorous stage'
With all the persons, down to palsied age,
That Life brings with her in her equipage ;
            As if his whole vocation
            Were endless imitation.

Thou, whose exterior semblance doth belie
            Thy soul's immensity !
Thou best philosopher, who yet dost keep
Thy heritage ! thou eye among the blind,
That, deaf and silent, read'st the eternal deep,
Haunted forever by the eternal mind ! —
            Mighty prophet ! Seer blest !
            On whom those truths do rest
Which we are toiling all our lives to find,
In darkness lost, the darkness of the grave ;
Thou over whom thy immortality
Broods like the day, a master o'er a slave,
A presence which is not to be put by ;
Thou little child, yet glorious in the might
Of heaven-born freedom on thy being's height,
Why with such earnest pains dost thou provoke
The years to bring the inevitable yoke,
Thus blindly with thy blessedness at strife ?
Full soon thy soul shall have her earthly freight,
And custom lie upon thee with a weight
Heavy as frost, and deep almost as life !

            O joy ! that in our embers
            Is something that doth live ;
            That Nature yet remembers
            What was so fugitive !
The thought of our past years in me doth breed
Perpetual benediction : not, indeed,
For that which is most worthy to be blest, —
Delight and liberty, the simple creed
Of childhood, whether busy or at rest.

With new-fledged hope still fluttering in his
    breast : —
      Not for these I raise
      The song of thanks and praise ;
But for those obstinate questionings
Of sense and outward things,
Fallings from us, vanishings ;
Blank misgivings of a creature
Moving about in worlds not realized,
High instincts, before which our mortal nature
Did tremble like a guilty thing surprised :
      But for those first affections,
      Those shadowy recollections,
    Which, be they what they may,
Are yet the fountain-light of all our day,
Are yet a master light of all our seeing ;
    Uphold us, cherish, and have power to make
Our noisy years seem moments in the being
Of the eternal silence : truths that wake,
      To perish never ;
Which neither listlessness, nor mad endeavor,
    Nor man nor boy,
Nor all that is at enmity with joy,
Can utterly abolish or destroy !
    Hence, in a season of calm weather,
      Though inland far we be,
Our souls have sight of that immortal sea
    Which brought us hither, —
    Can in a moment travel thither,
And see the children sport upon the shore,
And hear the mighty waters rolling evermore.

Then sing, ye birds, sing, sing a joyous song !
      And let the young lambs bound
      As to the tabor's sound !
We in thought will join your throng,
    Ye that pipe and ye that play,
    Ye that through your hearts to-day
    Feel the gladness of the May !
What though the radiance which was once so
      bright
Be now forever taken from my sight,
    Though nothing can bring back the hour
Of splendor in the grass, of glory in the flower ;
    We will grieve not, rather find
    Strength in what remains behind ;
    In the primal sympathy
    Which, having been, must ever be ;
    In the soothing thoughts that spring
    Out of human suffering ;
    In the faith that looks through death,
In years that bring the philosophic mind.

And O ye fountains, meadows, hills, and groves,
Forebode not any severing of our loves !
Yet in my heart of hearts I feel your might ;
I only have relinquished one delight

To live beneath your more habitual sway.
I love the brooks which down their channels fret,
Even more than when I tripped lightly as they ;
The innocent brightness of a new-born day
    Is lovely yet ;
The clouds that gather round the setting sun
Do take a sober coloring from an eye
That hath kept watch o'er man's mortality ;
Another race hath been, and other palms are won.
Thanks to the human heart by which we live,
Thanks to its tenderness, its joys, and fears, —
To me the meanest flower that blows can give
Thoughts that do often lie too deep for tears.
          WILLIAM WORDSWORTH.

SOLILOQUY : ON IMMORTALITY.

FROM "CATO," ACT V. SC. 1.

SCENE. — CATO, *sitting in a thoughtful posture, with Plato's
book on the Immortality of the Soul in his hand, and a drawn
sword on the table by him.*

It must be so — Plato, thou reasonest well ! —
Else whence this pleasing hope, this fond desire,
This longing after immortality ?
Or whence this secret dread, and inward horror,
Of falling into naught ? Why shrinks the soul
Back on herself, and startles at destruction ?
'T is the divinity that stirs within us ;
'T is Heaven itself, that points out a hereafter,
And intimates eternity to man.
Eternity ! — thou pleasing, dreadful thought !
Through what variety of untried being,
Through what new scenes and changes, must we
    pass !
The wide, the unbounded prospect lies before me ;
But shadows, clouds, and darkness rest upon it.
Here will I hold. If there 's a Power above us
(And that there is, all Nature cries aloud
Through all her works), he must delight in
    virtue ;
And that which he delights in must be happy.
But when ? or where ? This world was made for
    Cæsar.
I 'm weary of conjectures, — this must end 'em.

    (*Laying his hand on his sword.*)

    Thus am I doubly armed : my death and life,
My bane and antidote, are both before me :
This in a moment brings me to an end ;
But this informs me I shall never die.
The soul, secured in her existence, smiles
At the drawn dagger, and defies its point.
The stars shall fade away, the sun himself
Grow dim with age, and Nature sink in years ;
But thou shalt flourish in immortal youth,
Unhurt amid the war of elements,
The wrecks of matter, and the crush of worlds !
          JOSEPH ADDISON.

O, MAY I JOIN THE CHOIR INVISIBLE!

O, MAY I join the choir invisible
Of those immortal dead who live again
In minds made better by their presence ; live
In pulses stirred to generosity,
In deeds of daring rectitude, in scorn
Of miserable aims that end with self,
In thoughts sublime that pierce the night like
    stars,
And with their mild persistence urge men's minds
To vaster issues.
        So to live is heaven :
To make undying music in the world,
Breathing a beauteous order, that controls
With growing sway the growing life of man.
So we inherit that sweet purity
For which we struggled, failed, and agonized
With widening retrospect that bred despair.
Rebellious flesh that would not be subdued,
A vicious parent shaming still its child,
Poor anxious penitence, is quick dissolved ;
Its discords quenched by meeting harmonies,
Die in the large and charitable air.
And all our rarer, better, truer self,
That sobbed religiously in yearning song,
That watched to ease the burden of the world,
Laboriously tracing what must be,
And what may yet be better, — saw within
A worthier image for the sanctuary,
And shaped it forth before the multitude,
Divinely human, raising worship so
To higher reverence more mixed with love,
That better self shall live till human Time
Shall fold its eyelids, and the human sky
Be gathered like a scroll within the tomb,
Unread forever.
        This is life to come,
Which martyred men have made more glorious
For us, who strive to follow.
           May I reach
That purest heaven, — be to other souls
The cup of strength in some great agony,
Enkindle generous ardor, feed pure love,
Beget the smiles that have no cruelty,
Be the sweet presence of a good diffused,
And in diffusion ever more intense !
So shall I join the choir invisible,
Whose music is the gladness of the world.
      MARIAN EVANS LEWES CROSS (*George Eliot*).

PRE-EXISTENCE.

WHILE sauntering through the crowded street,
Some half-remembered face I meet,

Albeit upon no mortal shore
That face, methinks, has smiled before.

Lost in a gay and festal throng,
I tremble at some tender song, —

Set to an air whose golden bars
I must have heard in other stars.

In sacred aisles I pause to share
The blessings of a priestly prayer, —

When the whole scene which greets mine eyes
In some strange mode I recognize

As one whose every mystic part
I feel prefigured in my heart.

At sunset, as I calmly stand,
A stranger on an alien strand,

Familiar as my childhood's home
Seems the long stretch of wave and foam.

One sails toward me o'er the bay,
And what he comes to do and say

I can foretell. A prescient lore
Springs from some life outlived of yore.

O swift, instinctive, startling gleams
Of deep soul-knowledge ! not as *dreams*

For aye ye vaguely dawn and die,
But oft with lightning certainty

Pierce through the dark, oblivious brain,
To make old thoughts and memories plain,

Thoughts which perchance must travel back
Across the wild, bewildering track

Of countless æons ; memories far,
High-reaching as yon pallid star,

Unknown, scarce seen, whose flickering grace
Faints on the outmost rings of space !
      PAUL HAMILTON HAYNE.

A LOST CHORD.

SEATED one day at the organ,
   I was weary and ill at ease,
And my fingers wandered idly
   Over the noisy keys.

I do not know what I was playing,
   Or what I was dreaming then,
But I struck one chord of music,
   Like the sound of a great Amen.

It flooded the crimson twilight,
   Like the close of an angel's psalm,
And it lay on my fevered spirit,
   With a touch of infinite calm.

It quieted pain and sorrow,
  Like love overcoming strife ;
It seemed the harmonious echo
  From our discordant life.

It linked all perplexed meanings
  Into one perfect peace,
And trembled away into silence,
  As if it were loath to cease.

I have sought, but I seek it vainly,
  That one lost chord divine,
That came from the soul of the organ,
  And entered into mine.

It may be that Death's bright angel
  Will speak in that chord again ;
It may be that only in heaven
  I shall hear that grand Amen.

ADELAIDE ANNE PROCTER.

TO A SKELETON.

[The MS. of this poem, which appeared during the first quarter of the present century, was said to have been found in the Museum of the Royal College of Surgeons, in London, near a perfect human skeleton, and to have been sent by the curator to the *Morning Chronicle* for publication. It excited so much attention that every effort was made to discover the author, and a responsible party went so far as to offer a reward of fifty guineas for information that would discover its origin. The author preserved his *incognito*, and, we believe, has never been discovered.]

BEHOLD this ruin ! 'T was a skull
Once of ethereal spirit full.
This narrow cell was Life's retreat ;
This space was Thought's mysterious seat.
What beauteous visions filled this spot !
What dreams of pleasure long forgot !
Nor hope, nor joy, nor love, nor fear
Has left one trace of record here.

Beneath this mouldering canopy
Once shone the bright and busy eye :
But start not at the dismal void, —
If social love that eye employed,
If with no lawless fire it gleamed,
But through the dews of kindness beamed,
That eye shall be forever bright
When stars and sun are sunk in night.

Within this hollow cavern hung
The ready, swift, and tuneful tongue :
If Falsehood's honey it disdained,
And when it could not praise was chained ;
If bold in Virtue's cause it spoke,
Yet gentle concord never broke, —
This silent tongue shall plead for thee
When Time unveils Eternity !

Say, did these fingers delve the mine,
Or with the envied rubies shine ?
To hew the rock, or wear a gem,
Can little now avail to them ;
But if the page of Truth they sought,
Or comfort to the mourner brought,
These hands a richer meed shall claim
Than all that wait on Wealth and Fame.

Avails it whether bare or shod
These feet the paths of duty trod ?
If from the bowers of Ease they fled,
To seek Affliction's humble shed ;
If Grandeur's guilty bribe they spurned,
And home to Virtue's cot returned, —
These feet with angel wings shall vie,
And tread the palace of the sky !

ANONYMOUS.

THE BROTHERS.

SLUMBER, Sleep, — they were two brothers, ser-
    vants to the gods above ;
Kind Prometheus lured them downwards, ever
    filled with earthly love ;
But what gods could bear so lightly, pressed too
    hard on men beneath ;
Slumber did his brother's duty, — Sleep was
    deepened into Death.

From the German of GOETHE.

INVOCATION TO SLEEP.

FROM "VALENTINIAN."

COME, Sleep, and with thy sweet deceiving
  Lock me in delight awhile ;
  Let some pleasing dreams beguile
  All my fancies, that from thence
  I may feel an influence,
All my powers of care bereaving !

Though but a shadow, but a sliding,
  Let me know some little joy !
  We that suffer long annoy
  Are contented with a thought,
  Through an idle fancy wrought :
O, let my joys have some abiding !

JOHN FLETCHER.

SLEEP.

COME, gentle sleep! attend thy votary's prayer,
And, though death's image, to my couch repair ;
How sweet, though lifeless, yet with life to lie,
And, without dying, O how sweet to die !

DR. JOHN WOLCOTT (*Peter Pindar*)

SLEEP.

WEEP ye no more, sad fountains !
What need you flow so fast ?
Look how the snowy mountains
Heaven's sun doth gently waste.
But my sun's heavenly eyes
View not your weeping,
That now lies sleeping
Softly, now softly lies
Sleeping.

Sleep is a reconciling, —
A rest that peace begets ;
Doth not the sun rise smiling,
When fair at even he sets ?
Rest you then, rest, sad eyes, —
Melt not in weeping,
While she lies sleeping
Softly, now softly lies
Sleeping.
JOHN DOWLAND.

——◆——

SLEEP.

FROM "ASTROPHEL AND STELLA."

COME, Sleep, O Sleep, the certain knot of peace,
The baiting-place of wit, the balm of woe,
The poor man's wealth, the prisoner's release,
The indifferent judge between the high and low,
With shield of proof shield me from out the prease*
Of those fierce darts Despair at me doth throw ;
O, make me in those civil wars to cease :
I will good tribute pay, if thou do so.
Take thou of me smooth pillows, sweetest bed,
A chamber deaf to noise, and blind to light,
A rosy garland, and a weary head :
And if these things, as being thine in right,
Move not thy heavy grace, thou shalt in me
Livelier than elsewhere Stella's image see.
SIR PHILIP SIDNEY.

——◆——

SLEEP.

"He giveth his beloved sleep." — *Psalm* cxxvi. 2.

OF all the thoughts of God that are
Borne inward unto souls afar,
Among the Psalmist's music deep,
Now tell me if that any is,
For gift or grace, surpassing this, —
"He giveth his belovèd sleep" ?

What would we give to our beloved ?
The hero's heart, to be unmoved, —
The poet's star-tuned harp, to sweep, —
The patriot's voice, to teach and rouse, —
The monarch's crown, to light the brows ?
"He giveth *his* belovèd sleep."

* Press — throng.

What do we give to our beloved ?
A little faith, all undisproved, —
A little dust to overweep,
And bitter memories, to make
The whole earth blasted for our sake,
"He giveth *his* belovèd sleep."

"Sleep soft, beloved !" we sometimes say,
But have no tune to charm away
Sad dreams that through the eyelids creep ;
But never doleful dream again
Shall break the happy slumber when
"He giveth *his* belovèd sleep."

O earth, so full of dreary noise !
O men, with wailing in your voice !
O delvèd gold the wailers heap !
O strife, O curse, that o'er it fall !
God strikes a silence through you all,
And "giveth his belovèd sleep."

His dews drop mutely on the hill,
His cloud above it saileth still,
Though on its slope men sow and reap ;
More softly than the dew is shed,
Or cloud is floated overhead,
"He giveth his belovèd sleep."

For me, my heart, that erst did go
Most like a tired child at a show,
That sees through tears the mummers leap,
Would now its wearied vision close,
Would childlike on his love repose
Who "giveth his belovèd sleep."
ELIZABETH BARRETT BROWNING.

——◆——

SLEEP.

FROM "SECOND PART OF HENRY IV.," ACT III. SC. I.

KING HENRY. How many thousand of my
poorest subjects
Are at this hour asleep ! — O sleep ! O gentle
sleep !
Nature's soft nurse, how have I frighted thee,
That thou no more wilt weigh my eyelids down,
And steep my senses in forgetfulness ?
Why rather, sleep, liest thou in smoky cribs,
Upon uneasy pallets stretching thee,
And hushed with buzzing night-flies to thy
slumber,
Than in the perfumed chambers of the great,
Under the canopies of costly state,
And lulled with sounds of sweetest melody ?
O thou dull god ! why liest thou with the vile,
In loathsome beds, and leav'st the kingly couch
A watch-case, or a common 'larum-bell ?

Wilt thou upon the high and giddy mast
Seal up the ship-boy's eyes, and rock his brains
In cradle of the rude imperious surge,
And in the visitation of the winds,
Who take the ruffian billows by the top,
Curling their monstrous heads, and hanging them
With deafening clamors in the slippery clouds,
That, with the hurly, death itself awakes?
Canst thou, O partial sleep! give thy repose
To the wet sea-boy in an hour so rude;
And in the calmest and most stillest night,
With all appliances and means to boot,
Deny it to a king? Then, happy low, lie down;
Uneasy lies the head that wears a crown.

SHAKESPEARE.

SLEEPLESSNESS.

A FLOCK of sheep that leisurely pass by
One after one; the sound of rain, and bees
Murmuring; the fall of rivers, winds and seas,
Smooth fields, white sheets of water, and pure
    sky; —
I've thought of all by turns, and still I lie
Sleepless; and soon the small birds' melodies
Must hear, first uttered from my orchard trees,
And the first cuckoo's melancholy cry.
Even thus last night, and two nights more, I lay,
And could not win thee, Sleep, by any stealth:
So do not let me wear to-night away:
Without thee what is all the morning's wealth?
Come, blessèd barrier between day and day,
Dear mother of fresh thoughts and joyous health!

WILLIAM WORDSWORTH.

HYMN TO NIGHT.

YES! bear them to their rest;
The rosy babe, tired with the glare of day,
The prattler, fallen asleep e'en in his play;
    Clasp them to thy soft breast,
        O night!
Bless them in dreams with a deep, hushed delight.

Yet must they wake again,
Wake soon to all the bitterness of life,
The pang of sorrow, the temptation strife,
    Aye to the conscience pain:
        O night!
Canst thou not take with them a longer flight?

Canst thou not bear them far
E'en now, all innocent, before they know
The taint of sin, its consequence of woe,
    The world's distracting jar,
        O night!
To some ethereal, holier, happier height?

Canst thou not bear them up
Through starlit skies, far from this planet dim
And sorrowful, e'en while they sleep, to Him
    Who drank for us the cup,
        O night!
The cup of wrath, for hearts in faith contrite?

To Him, for them who slept
A babe all holy on his mother's knee,
And from that hour to cross-crowned Calvary,
    In all our sorrow wept,
        O night!
That on our souls might dawn Heaven's cheering
    light.

Go, lay their little heads
Close to that human heart, with love divine
Deep-breathing, while his arms immortal twine
    Around them, as he sheds,
        O night!
On them a brother's grace of God's own bound-
    less might.

Let them immortal wake
Among the deathless flowers of Paradise,
Where angel songs of welcome with surprise
    This their last sleep may break,
        O night!
And to celestial joy their kindred souls invite.

There can come no sorrow;
The brow shall know no shade, the eye no tears,
Forever young, through heaven's eternal years
    In one unfading morrow,
        O night!
Nor sin nor age nor pain their cherub beauty
    blight.

Would we could sleep as they,
So stainless and so calm, — at rest with Thee, —
And only wake in immortality!
    Bear us with them away,
        O night!
To that ethereal, holier, happier height.

GEORGE WASHINGTON BETHUNE

WATCHING.

SLEEP, love, sleep!
The dusty day is done.
Lo! from afar the freshening breezes sweep
Wide over groves of balm,
Down from the towering palm,
In at the open casement cooling run,
And round thy lowly bed,
Thy bed of pain,
Bathing thy patient head,
Like grateful showers of rain.

They come ;
While the white curtains, waving to and fro,
Fan the sick air ;
And pityingly the shadows come and go,
With gentle human care,
Compassionate and dumb.

The dusty day is done,
The night begun ;
While prayerful watch I keep,
Sleep, love, sleep !
Is there no magic in the touch
Of fingers thou dost love so much ?
Fain would they scatter poppies o'er thee now ;
Or, with its mute caress,
The tremulous lip some soft nepenthe press
Upon thy weary lid and aching brow ;
While prayerful watch I keep,
Sleep, love, sleep !

On the pagoda spire
The bells are swinging,
Their little golden circlet in a flutter
With tales the wooing winds have dared to utter,
Till all are ringing,
As if a choir
Of golden-nested birds in heaven were singing ,
And with a lulling sound
The music floats around,
And drops like balm into the drowsy ear ;
Commingling with the hum
Of the Sepoy's distant drum,
And lazy beetle ever droning near.
Sounds these of deepest silence born,
Like night made visible by morn ;
So silent that I sometimes start
To hear the throbbings of my heart,
And watch, with shivering sense of pain,
To see thy pale lids lift again.

The lizard, with his mouse-like eyes,
Peeps from the mortise in surprise
At such strange quiet after day's harsh din ;
Then boldly ventures out,
And looks about,
And with his hollow feet
Treads his small evening beat,
Darting upon his prey
In such a tricky, winsome sort of way,
His delicate marauding seems no sin.
And still the curtains swing,
But noiselessly ;
The bells a melancholy murmur ring,
As tears were in the sky :
More heavily the shadows fall,
Like the black foldings of a pall,
Where juts the rough beam from the wall ;

The candles flare
With fresher gusts of air ;
The beetle's drone
Turns to a dirge-like, solitary moan ;
Night deepens, and I sit, in cheerless doubt alone

EMILY CHUBBUCK JUDSON

THE DREAM.

OUR life is twofold ; sleep hath its own world,
A boundary between the things misnamed
Death and existence : sleep hath its own world,
And a wide realm of wild reality,
And dreams in their development have breath,
And tears, and tortures, and the touch of joy ;
They leave a weight upon our waking thoughts,
They take a weight from off our waking toils,
They do divide our being ; they become
A portion of ourselves as of our time,
And look like heralds of eternity ;
They pass like spirits of the past, — they speak
Like sibyls of the future ; they have power, —
The tyranny of pleasure and of pain ;
They make us what we were not, — what they
    will,
And shake us with the vision that 's gone by,
The dread of vanished shadows. — Are they so ?
Is not the past all shadow ?   What are they ?
Creations of the mind ? — The mind can make
Substances, and people planets of its own
With beings brighter than have been, and give
A breath to forms which can outlive all flesh.
I would recall a vision which I dreamed
Perchance in sleep, — for in itself a thought,
A slumbering thought, is capable of years,
And curdles a long life into one hour.

I saw two beings in the hues of youth
Standing upon a hill, a gentle hill,
Green and of a mild declivity, the last
As 't were the cape of a long ridge of such,
Save that there was no sea to lave its base,
But a most living landscape, and the wave
Of woods and cornfields, and the abodes of men
Scattered at intervals, and wreathing smoke
Arising from such rustic roofs ; the hill
Was crowned with a peculiar diadem
Of trees, in circular array, so fixed,
Not by the sport of nature, but of man :
These two, a maiden and a youth, were there
Gazing, — the one on all that was beneath
Fair as herself, — but the boy gazed on her ;
And both were young, and one was beautiful ;
And both were young, — yet not alike in youth.
As the sweet moon on the horizon's verge,
The maid was on the eve of womanhood ;

The boy had fewer summers, but his heart
Had far outgrown his years, and to his eye
There was but one belovèd face on earth,
And that was shining on him ; he had looked
Upon it till it could not pass away ;
He had no breath, no being, but in hers ;
She was his voice ; he did not speak to her,
But trembled on her words ; she was his sight,
For his eye followed hers, and saw with hers,
Which colored all his objects ; — he had ceased
To live within himself : she was his life,
The ocean to the river of his thoughts,
Which terminated all ; upon a tone,
A touch of hers, his blood would ebb and flow,
And his cheek change tempestuously, — his heart
Unknowing of its cause of agony.
But she in these fond feelings had no share :
Her sighs were not for him ; to her he was
Even as a brother, — but no more ; 't was much,
For brotherless she was, save in the name
Her infant friendship had bestowed on him ;
Herself the solitary scion left
Of a time-honored race.   It was a name
Which pleased him, and yet pleased him not, —
    and why ?
Time taught him a deep answer — when she
    loved
Another ; even *now* she loved another,
And on the summit of that hill she stood,
Looking afar if yet her lover's steed
Kept pace with her expectancy, and flew.

A change came o'er the spirit of my dream.
There was an ancient mansion, and before
Its walls there was a steed caparisoned ;
Within an antique oratory stood
The boy of whom I spake ; — he was alone,
And pale, and pacing to and fro : anon
He sate him down, and seized a pen, and traced
Words which I could not guess of ; then he leaned
His bowed head on his hands and shook, as
    't were
With a convulsion, — then arose again,
And with his teeth and quivering hands did tear
What he had written, but he shed no tears,
And he did calm himself, and fix his brow
Into a kind of quiet ; as he paused,
The lady of his love re-entered there ;
She was serene and smiling then, and yet
She knew she was by him beloved ; she knew —
For quickly comes such knowledge — that his
    heart
Was darkened with her shadow, and she saw
That he was wretched, but she saw not all.
He rose, and with a cold and gentle grasp
He took her hand ; a moment o'er his face
A tablet of unutterable thoughts

Was traced, and then it faded, as it came ;
He dropped the hand he held, and with slow
    steps
Retired, but not as bidding her adieu,
For they did part with mutual smiles ; he passed
From out the massy gate of that old Hall,
And mounting on his steed he went his way ;
And ne'er repassed that hoary threshold more.

A change came o'er the spirit of my dream.
The boy was sprung to manhood ; in the wilds
Of fiery climes he made himself a home,
And his soul drank their sunbeams ; he was girt
With strange and dusky aspects ; he was not
Himself like what he had been : on the sea
And on the shore he was a wanderer ;
There was a mass of many images
Crowded like waves upon me, but he was
A part of all ; and in the last he lay
Reposing from the noontide sultriness,
Couched among fallen columns, in the shade
Of ruined walls that had survived the names
Of those who reared them ; by his sleeping side
Stood camels grazing, and some goodly steeds
Were fastened near a fountain ; and a man,
Clad in a flowing garb, did watch the while,
While many of his tribe slumbered around :
And they were canopied by the blue sky,
So cloudless, clear, and purely beautiful,
That God alone was to be seen in heaven.

A change came o'er the spirit of my dream.
The lady of his love was wed with one
Who did not love her better : in her home,
A thousand leagues from his, — her native home,
She dwelt, begirt with growing infancy,
Daughters and sons of beauty, — but behold !
Upon her face there was the tint of grief,
The settled shadow of an inward strife,
And an unquiet drooping of the eye,
As if its lid were charged with unshed tears.
What could her grief be ? — she had all she loved,
And he who had so loved her was not there
To trouble with bad hopes, or evil wish,
Or ill-repressed affliction, her pure thoughts.
What could her grief be ? — she had loved him
    not,
Nor given him cause to deem himself beloved,
Nor could he be a part of that which preyed
Upon her mind — a spectre of the past.

A change came o'er the spirit of my dream.
The wanderer was returned. — I saw him stand
Before an altar — with a gentle bride ;
Her face was fair, but was not that which made
The starlight of his boyhood ; — as he stood
Even at the altar, o'er his brow there came

The selfsame aspect and the quivering shock
That in the antique oratory shook
His bosom in its solitude ; and then —
As in that hour — a moment o'er his face
The tablet of unutterable thoughts
Was traced, — and then it faded as it came,
And he stood calm and quiet, and he spoke
The fitting vows, but heard not his own words,
And all things reeled around him ; he could see
Not that which was, nor that which should have
　　been, —
But the old mansion, and the accustomed hall,
And the remembered chambers, and the place,
The day, the hour, the sunshine, and the shade,
All things pertaining to that place and hour,
And her who was his destiny, came back
And thrust themselves between him and the
　　light ;
What business had they there at such a time ?

A change came o'er the spirit of my dream.
The lady of his love ; — O, she was changed,
As by the sickness of the soul ! her mind
Had wandered from its dwelling, and her eyes,
They had not their own lustre, but the look
Which is not of the earth ; she was become
The queen of a fantastic realm ; her thoughts
Were combinations of disjointed things,
And forms impalpable and unperceived
Of others' sight familiar were to hers.
And this the world calls frenzy ; but the wise
Have a far deeper madness, and the glance
Of melancholy is a fearful gift ;
What is it but the telescope of truth,
Which strips the distance of its fantasies,
And brings life near in utter nakedness,
Making the cold reality too real !

A change came o'er the spirit of my dream.
The wanderer was alone as heretofore,
The beings which surrounded him were gone,
Or were at war with him ; he was a mark
For blight and desolation, compassed round
With hatred and contention ; pain was mixed
In all which was served up to him, until,
Like to the Pontic monarch of old days,
He fed on poisons and they had no power,
But were a kind of nutriment ; he lived
Through that which had been death to many men,
And made him friends of mountains : with the
　　stars
And the quick Spirit of the universe
He held his dialogues ; and they did teach
To him the magic of their mysteries ;
To him the book of Night was opened wide,
And voices from the deep abyss revealed
A marvel and a secret. — Be it so.

My dream was past ; it had no further change.
It was of a strange order, that the doom
Of these two creatures should be thus traced out
Almost like a reality, — the one
To end in madness — both in misery.
LORD BYRON.

THE SCHOLAR.

FROM " EDWIN THE FAIR."

THIS life, and all that it contains, to him
Is but a tissue of illuminous dreams
Filled with book-wisdom, pictured thought and
　　love
That on its own creations spends itself.
All things he understands, and nothing does.
Profusely eloquent in copious praise
Of action, he will talk to you as one
Whose wisdom lay in dealings and transactions ;
Yet so much action as might tie his shoe
Cannot his will command ; himself alone
By his own wisdom not a jot the gainer.
Of silence, and the hundred thousand things
'T is better not to mention, he will speak,
And still most wisely.
HENRY TAYLOR.

UNKNOWN POETS.

FROM " THE EXCURSION," BOOK I.

O, MANY are the poets that are sown
By nature ; men endowed with highest gifts,
The vision and the faculty divine ;
Yet wanting the accomplishment of verse
(Which, in the docile season of their youth,
It was denied them to acquire, through lack
Of culture and the inspiring aid of books,
Or haply by a temper too severe,
Or a nice backwardness afraid of shame),
Nor having e'er, as life advanced, been led
By circumstance to take unto the height
The measure of themselves, these favored beings,
All but a scattered few, live out their time,
Husbanding that which they possess within,
And go to the grave, unthought of. Strongest
　　minds
Are often those of whom the noisy world
Hears least.
WILLIAM WORDSWORTH.

THE POET OF NATURE.

FROM "FESTUS."

HE had no times of study, and no place ;
All places and all times to him were one.
His soul was like the wind-harp, which he loved,
And sounded only when the spirit blew,

Drawn by W. H. Drake.

THE BOOK-STALL.

IT stands in a winding street,
 A quiet and restful nook,
Apart from the endless beat
 Of the noisy heart of Trade;
 There's never a spot more cool
 Of a hot midsummer day
 By the brink of a forest pool,
 Or the bank of a crystal brook
 In the maples' breezy shade,
 Than the book-stall old and gray.

Here are precious gems of thought
 That were quarried long ago,
Some in vellum bound, and wrought
 With letters and lines of gold;
 Here are curious rows of "calf,"
 And perchance an Elzevir;

Here are countless "mos" of chaff,
And a parchment folio,
Like leaves that are cracked with cold,
All puckered and brown and sear.

In every age and clime
 Live the monarchs of the brain:
And the lords of prose and rhyme,
 Years after the long last sleep
 Has come to the kings of earth
 And their names have passed away,
 Rule on through death and birth;
 And the thrones of their domain
 Are found where the shades are deep
 In the book-stall old and gray.

CLINTON SCOLLARD

FOR AN OLD POET.

[To Richard Henry Stoddard.]

When he is old and past all singing,
    Grant, kindly Time, that he may hear
The rhythm through joyous Nature ringing,
    Uncaught by any duller ear.

Grant that, in memory's deep still cherished,
    Once more may murmur low to him
The winds that sung in years long perished
    Lit by the suns of days grown dim.

Grant that the hours when first he listened
    To bird-songs manhood may not know,
In fields whose dew for lovers glistened,
    May come back to him ere he go.

Grant only this, O Time most kindly,
    That he may hear the song you sung
When love was new—and, hearkening blindly,
    Feign his o'erwearied spirit young.

With sounds of rivers singing round him,
    On waves that long since flowed away,
O leave him, Time, where first Love found him,
    Dreaming To-morrow is To-day.

                    Henry Cuyler Bunner.

Sometime in feasts and follies, for he went
Lifelike through all things ; and his thoughts
   then rose
Like sparkles in the bright wine, brighter still ;
Sometimes in dreams, and then the shining words
Would wake him in the dark before his face.
All things talked thoughts to him. The sea
   went mad
To show his meaning ; and the awful sun
Thundered his thoughts into him ; and at night
The stars would whisper theirs, the moon sigh
   hers.
                     PHILIP JAMES BAILEY.

THE POET'S IMPULSE.

FROM "CHILDE HAROLD'S PILGRIMAGE," CANTO III.

SKY, mountains, river, winds, lake, lightnings !
   ye !
With night, and clouds, and thunder, and a
   soul
To make these felt and feeling, well may be
Things that have made me watchful ; the far
   roll
Of your departing voices is the knoll
Of what in me is sleepless, — if I rest.
But where of ye, O tempests ! is the goal ?
Are ye like those within the human breast ?
Or do ye find, at length, like eagles, some high
   nest ?

Could I embody and unbosom now
That which is most within me, — could I wreak
My thoughts upon expression, and thus throw
Soul, heart, mind, passions, feelings, strong or
   weak,
All that I would have sought, and all I seek,
Bear, know, feel, and yet breathe – into *one*
   word,
And that one word were Lightning, I would
   speak ;
But as it is, I live and die unheard,
With a most voiceless thought, sheathing it as a
   sword.
                     LORD BYRON.

THE INNER VISION.

MOST sweet it is with unuplifted eyes
To pace the ground, if path there be or none,
While a fair region round the traveller lies
Which he forbears again to look upon ;
Pleased rather with some soft ideal scene,
The work of fancy, or some happy tone
Of meditation, slipping in between
The beauty coming and the beauty gone.

If Thought and Love desert us, from that day
Let us break off all commerce with the Muse :
With Thought and Love companions of our way,—
Whate'er the senses take or may refuse, —
The mind's internal Heaven shall shed her dews
Of inspiration on the humblest lay.
                     WILLIAM WORDSWORTH.

THE POET OF TO-DAY.

MORE than the soul of ancient song is given
   To thee, O poet of to-day ! — thy dower
Comes, from a higher than Olympian heaven,
   In holier beauty and in larger power.

To thee Humanity, her woes revealing,
   Would all her griefs and ancient wrongs re-
      hearse ;
Would make thy song the voice of her appealing,
   And sob her mighty sorrows through thy verse.

While in her season of great darkness sharing,
   Hail thou the coming of each promise-star
Which climbs the midnight of her long despair-
      ing,
   And watch for morning o'er the hills afar.

Wherever Truth her holy warfare wages,
   Or Freedom pines, there let thy voice be heard ;
Sound like a prophet-warning down the ages
   The human utterance of God's living word.

But bring not thou the battle's stormy chorus,
   The tramp of armies, and the roar of fight,
Not war's hot smoke to taint the sweet morn
      o'er us,
   Nor blaze of pillage, reddening up the night.

O, let thy lays prolong that angel-singing,
   Girdling with music the Redeemer's star,
And breathe God's peace, to earth "glad tidings'
      bringing
From the near heavens, of old so dim and far !
   SARAH JANE LIPPINCOTT (*Grace Greenwood*).

BOOKS.

FROM "THE KALÉDER OF SHEPERDES," 1528.

HE that many bokes redys,
Cunnyinge shall he be.
Wysedome is soone caught ;
In many leues it is sought :
But slouth, that no boke bought,
For reason taketh no thought ;
His thryfte cometh behynde.
                     ANONYMOUS.

BOOKS.

For why, who writes such histories as these
Doth often bring the reader's heart such ease,
As when they sit and see what he doth note,
Well fare his heart, say they, this book that
　　wrote !
JOHN HIGGINS.

THE FLOWER.

How fresh, O Lord, how sweet and clean
Are thy returns ! even as the flowers in spring ;
　To which, besides their own demean,
The late-past frosts tributes of pleasure bring.
　　　Grief melts away
　　　Like snow in May,
　As if there were no such cold thing.

Who would have thought my shrivelled heart
Could have recovered greenness ? It was gone
　Quite underground ; as flowers depart
To see their mother root, when they have blown ;
　　　Where they together
　　　All the hard weather,
　Dead to the world, keep house unknown.

These are thy wonders, Lord of power,
Killing and quickning, bringing down to hell
　And up to heaven in an houre ;
Making a chiming of a passing-bell.
　　　We say amisse,
　　　This or that is :
　Thy word is all, if we could spell.

O that I once past changing were,
Fast in thy paradise, where no flower can wither !
　Many a spring I shoot up fair,
Offring at heav'n, growing and groning thither ;
　　　Nor doth my flower
　　　Want a spring-showre,
　My sinnes and I joining together.

But, while I grow in a straight line,
Still upwards bent, as if heav'n were mine own,
　Thy anger comes, and I decline :
What frost to that ? what pole is not the zone
　　　Where all things burn,
　　　When thou dost turn,
　And the least frown of thine is shown ?

And now in age I bud again ;
After so many deaths I live and write ;
　I once more smell the dew and rain,
And relish versing : O my only light,
　　　It cannot be
　　　That I am he
　On whom thy tempests fell all night !

These are thy wonders, Lord of love,
To make us see we are but flowers that glide ;
　Which when we once can finde and prove,
Thou hast a garden for us where to bide.
　　　Who would be more,
　　　Swelling through store,
　Forfeit their paradise by their pride.
GEORGE HERBERT.

YUSSOUF.

A STRANGER came one night to Yussouf's tent,
Saying, " Behold one outcast and in dread,
Against whose life the bow of power is bent,
Who flies, and hath not where to lay his head ;
I come to thee for shelter and for food,
To Yussouf, called through all our tribes ' The
　　Good.' "

" This tent is mine," said Yussouf, " but no more
Than it is God's ; come in, and be at peace ;
Freely shalt thou partake of all my store
As I of his who buildeth over these
Our tents his glorious roof of night and day,
And at whose door none ever yet heard Nay."

So Yussouf entertained his guest that night,
And, waking him ere day, said : " Here is gold,
My swiftest horse is saddled for thy flight,
Depart before the prying day grow bold."
As one lamp lights another, nor grows less,
So nobleness enkindleth nobleness.

That inward light the stranger's face made grand,
Which shines from all self-conquest ; kneeling low,
He bowed his forehead upon Yussouf's hand,
Sobbing : " O Sheik, I cannot leave thee so ;
I will repay thee ; all this thou hast done
Unto that Ibrahim who slew thy son ! "

" Take thrice the gold," said Yussouf, " for with
　　thee
Into the desert, never to return,
My one black thought shall ride away from me ;
First-born, for whom by day and night I yearn,
Balanced and just are all of God's decrees ;
Thou art avenged, my first-born, sleep in peace ! "
JAMES RUSSELL LOWELL.

ABOU BEN ADHEM.

ABOU BEN ADHEM (may his tribe increase !)
Awoke one night from a deep dream of peace,
And saw within the moonlight in his room,
Making it rich and like a lily in bloom,
An angel writing in a book of gold :
Exceeding peace had made Ben Adhem bold,

And to the presence in the room he said,
"What writest thou?" The vision raised its head,
And, with a look made of all sweet accord,
Answered, "The names of those who love the Lord."
"And is mine one?" said Abou. "Nay, not so,"
Replied the angel. Abou spoke more low,
But cheerly still; and said, "I pray thee, then,
Write me as one that loves his fellow-men."

The angel wrote, and vanished. The next night
It came again, with a great wakening light,
And showed the names whom love of God had
    blessed, —
And, lo! Ben Adhem's name led all the rest!
LEIGH HUNT.

BEAUTY.

I HAD a dream, one glorious, summer night,
In the rich bosom of imperial June.
Languid I lay upon an odorous couch,
Golden with amber, festooned wildly o'er
With crimson roses; and the longing stars
Wept tears of light upon their clustered leaves.
Above me soared the azure vault of heaven,
Vast and majestic; cinctured with that path
Whereby, perchance, the sea-born Venus found
Her way to higher spheres; that path which seems
A coronet of silver, gemmed with stars,
And bound upon the forehead of the night.
There, as I lay, the musical south wind
Shook all the roses into murmurous life,
And poured their fragrance o'er me, in a shower
Of crimson mist; and softly, through the mist,
Came a low, sweet, enchanting melody,
A far-off echo from the land of dreams,
Which with delicious languor filled the air,
And steeped in bliss the senses and the soul.
Then rose a shape, a dim and ghostly shape,
Whereto no feature was, nor settled form,
A shadowy splendor, seeming as it came
A pearly summer cloud, shot through and through
With faintest rays of sunset; yet within
A spirit dwelt; and, floating from within,
A murmur trembled sweetly into words: —

I am the ghost of a most lovely dream,
Which haunted, in old days, a poet's mind.
And long he sought for, wept, and prayed for me;
And searched through all the chambers of his soul,
And searched the secret places of the earth,
The lonely forest and the lonely shore;
And listened to the voices of the sea,
What time the stars shone out, and midnight cold
Slept on the dark waves whispering at his feet;
And sought the mystery in a human form,
Amid the haunts of men, and found it not;
And looked in woman's fond, bewildering eyes,
And mirrored there his own, and saw no sign:

But only in his sleep I came to him,
And gave him fitful glimpses of my face,
Whereof he after sang, in sweetest words;
Then died, and came to me. But evermore,
Through lonely days, and passion-haunted nights,
A life of starlit gloom, do poets seek
To rend the mystic veil that covers me,
And evermore they grasp the empty air.
For only in their dreams I come to them,
And give them fitful glimpses of my face,
And lull them, siren-like, with words of hope —
That promise, sometime, to their ravished eyes,
Beauty, the secret of the universe,
God's thought, that gives the soul eternal peace.

Then the voice ceased, and only, through the mist,
The shaken roses murmured, and the wind.
WILLIAM WINTER.

VANITY.

THE sun comes up and the sun goes down,
And day and night are the same as one;
The year grows green, and the year grows brown,
And what is it all, when all is done?
Grains of sombre or shining sand,
Gliding into and out of the hand.

And men go down in ships to the seas,
And a hundred ships are the same as one;
And backward and forward blows the breeze,
And what is it all, when all is done?
A tide with never a shore in sight
Getting steadily on to the night.

The fisher droppeth his net in the stream,
And a hundred streams are the same as one;
And the maiden dreameth her love-lit dream,
And what is it all, when all is done?
The net of the fisher the burden breaks,
And alway the dreaming the dreamer wakes.
HARRIET PRESCOTT SPOFFORD.

A PSALM OF LIFE.

TELL me not, in mournful numbers,
    Life is but an empty dream!
For the soul is dead that slumbers,
    And things are not what they seem.

Life is real! Life is earnest!
    And the grave is not its goal;
Dust thou art, to dust returnest,
    Was not spoken of the soul.

Not enjoyment, and not sorrow,
    Is our destined end or way;
But to act, that each to-morrow
    Find us farther than to-day.

Art is long, and Time is fleeting,
  And our hearts, though stout and brave,
Still, like muffled drums, are beating
  Funeral marches to the grave.

In the world's broad field of battle,
  In the bivouac of Life,
Be not like dumb, driven cattle !
  Be a hero in the strife !

Trust no Future, howe'er pleasant !
  Let the dead Past bury its dead !
Act, — act in the living Present !
  Heart within, and God o'erhead !

Lives of great men all remind us
  We can make our lives sublime,
And, departing, leave behind us
  Footprints on the sands of time ; —

Footprints, that perhaps another,
  Sailing o'er life's solemn main,
A forlorn and shipwrecked brother,
  Seeing, shall take heart again.

Let us, then, be up and doing,
  With a heart for any fate ;
Still achieving, still pursuing,
  Learn to labor and to wait.
                HENRY WADSWORTH LONGFELLOW.

MY LEGACY.

THEY told me I was heir : I turned in haste,
And ran to seek my treasure,
And wondered, as I ran, how it was placed, —
If I should find a measure
Of gold, or if the titles of fair lands
And houses would be laid within my hands.

I journeyed many roads ; I knocked at gates ;
I spoke to each wayfarer
I met, and said, "A heritage awaits
Me.   Art not thou the bearer
Of news ? some message sent to me whereby
I learn which way my new possessions lie ?"

Some asked me in ; naught lay beyond their door ;
Some smiled, and would not tarry,
But said that men were just behind who bore
More gold than I could carry ;
And so the morn, the noon, the day, were spent,
While empty-handed up and down I went.

At last one cried, whose face I could not see,
As through the mists he hasted :
"Poor child, what evil ones have hindered thee
Till this whole day is wasted ?

Hath no man told thee that thou art joint heir
With one named Christ, who waits the goods to
    share ?"

The one named Christ I sought for many days,
In many places vainly ;
I heard men name his name in many ways ;
I saw his temples plainly ;
But they who named him most gave me no sign
To find him by, or prove the heirship mine.

And when at last I stood before his face,
I knew him by no token
Save subtle air of joy which filled the place ;
Our greeting was not spoken ;
In solemn silence I received my share,
Kneeling before my brother and "joint heir."

My share ! No deed of house or spreading lands,
As I had dreamed ; no measure
Heaped up with gold ; my elder brother's hands
Had never held such treasure.
Foxes have holes, and birds in nests are fed :
My brother had not where to lay his head.

My share ! The right like him to know all pain
Which hearts are made for knowing ;
The right to find in loss the surest gain ;
To reap my joy from sowing
In bitter tears ; the right with him to keep
A watch by day and night with all who weep.

My share ! To-day men call it grief and death ;
I see the joy and life to-morrow ;
I thank my Father with my every breath,
For this sweet legacy of sorrow ;
And through my tears I call to each "joint heir"
With Christ, "Make haste to ask him for thy
    share."
                HELEN HUNT JACKSON.

SYMPATHY.

FROM "ION," ACT I. SC. 2.

              'T IS a little thing
To give a cup of water ; yet its draught
Of cool refreshment, drained by fevered lips,
May give a shock of pleasure to the frame
More exquisite than when nectarean juice
Renews the life of joy in happier hours.
It is a little thing to speak a phrase
Of common comfort which by daily use
Has almost lost its sense, yet on the ear
Of him who thought to die unmourned 't will fall
Like choicest music, fill the glazing eye
With gentle tears, relax the knotted hand
To know the bonds of fellowship again ;
And shed on the departing soul a sense,

More precious than the benison of friends
About the honored death-bed of the rich,
To him who else were lonely, that another
Of the great family is near and feels.

SIR THOMAS NOON TALFOURD.

ALEXANDER'S FEAST ; OR, THE POWER OF MUSIC.

AN ODE.

'T WAS at the royal feast, for Persia won
  By Philip's warlike son :
  Aloft in awful state
  The godlike hero sate
  On his imperial throne :
His valiant peers were placed around,
Their brows with roses and with myrtles bound
  (So should desert in arms be crowned) ;
The lovely Thais, by his side,
Sate like a blooming Eastern bride
In flower of youth and beauty's pride.
  Happy, happy, happy pair !
    None but the brave,
    None but the brave,
None but the brave deserves the fair.

CHORUS.

Happy, happy, happy pair !
  None but the brave,
  None but the brave,
None but the brave deserves the fair.

Timotheus, placed on high
  Amid the tuneful choir,
  With flying fingers touched the lyre ;
The trembling notes ascend the sky,
  And heavenly joys inspire.
The song began from Jove,
Who left his blissful seats above
(Such is the power of mighty love).
A dragon's fiery form belied the god ;
Sublime on radiant spires he rode,
  When he to fair Olympia pressed,
  And while he sought her snowy breast ;
Then round her slender waist he curled,
And stamped an image of himself, a sovereign
  of the world.
The listening crowd admire the lofty sound,
A present deity ! they shout around ;
A present deity ! the vaulted roofs rebound.
  With ravished ears
  The monarch hears,
  Assumes the god,
  Affects to nod,
And seems to shake the spheres.

CHORUS.

With ravished ears
  The monarch hears,
  Assumes the god,
  Affects to nod,
And seems to shake the spheres.

The praise of Bacchus then the sweet musician
    sung,
  Of Bacchus — ever fair and ever young :
  The jolly god in triumph comes ;
  Sound the trumpets ; beat the drums :
    Flushed with a purple grace
    He shows his honest face :
Now give the hautboys breath. He comes ! he
    comes !
  Bacchus, ever fair and young,
    Drinking joys did first ordain ;
  Bacchus' blessings are a treasure,
  Drinking is the soldier's pleasure ;
    Rich the treasure,
    Sweet the pleasure,
  Sweet is pleasure after pain.

CHORUS.

Bacchus' blessings are a treasure,
Drinking is the soldier's pleasure ;
    Rich the treasure,
    Sweet the pleasure,
  Sweet is pleasure after pain.

Soothed with the sound the king grew vain ;
  Fought all his battles o'er again ;
And thrice he routed all his foes, and thrice he
    slew the slain.
The master saw the madness rise ;
  His glowing cheeks, his ardent eyes ;
And, while he heaven and earth defied,
Changed his hand and checked his pride.
  He chose a mournful muse,
    Soft pity to infuse :
He sung Darius, great and good,
  By too severe a fate,
Fallen, fallen, fallen, fallen,
Fallen from his high estate,
  And weltering in his blood ;
Deserted, at his utmost need,
By those his former bounty fed ;
On the bare earth exposed he lies,
With not a friend to close his eyes.
With downcast looks the joyless victor sate,
  Revolving in his altered soul
    The various turns of chance below :
  And, now and then, a sigh he stole ;
    And tears began to flow.

CHORUS.

Revolving in his altered soul
  The various turns of chance below;
  And, now and then, a sigh he stole;
  And tears began to flow.

The mighty master smiled, to see
That love was in the next degree;
'T was but a kindred sound to move,
For pity melts the mind to love.
  Softly sweet, in Lydian measures,
  Soon he soothed his soul to pleasures.
War, he sung, is toil and trouble;
Honor, but an empty bubble;
Never ending, still beginning,
Fighting still, and still destroying:
  If the world be worth thy winning,
Think, O, think it worth enjoying!
  Lovely Thais sits beside thee,
  Take the good the gods provide thee.
The many rend the skies with loud applause;
So Love was crowned, but Music won the cause.
  The prince, unable to conceal his pain,
    Gazed on the fair
    Who caused his care,
  And sighed and looked, sighed and looked,
  Sighed and looked, and sighed again:
At length, with love and wine at once oppressed,
The vanquished victor sunk upon her breast.

CHORUS.

The prince, unable to conceal his pain,
  Gazed on the fair
  Who caused his care,
And sighed and looked, sighed and looked,
Sighed and looked, and sighed again:
At length, with love and wine at once oppressed,
The vanquished victor sunk upon her breast.

Now strike the golden lyre again:
A louder yet, and yet a louder strain.
Break his bands of sleep asunder,
And rouse him, like a rattling peal of thunder.
  Hark, hark, the horrid sound
    Has raised up his head;
  As awaked from the dead,
  And amazed, he stares around.
Revenge! revenge! Timotheus cries,
  See the furies arise!
  See the snakes that they rear,
  How they hiss in their hair,
And the sparkles that flash from their eyes!
  Behold a ghastly band,
  Each a torch in his hand!
Those are Grecian ghosts, that in battle were slain,
  And unburied remain,
  Inglorious on the plain:

  Give the vengeance due
  To the valiant crew.
Behold how they toss their torches on high,
  How they point to the Persian abodes,
And glittering temples of their hostile gods!
The princes applaud with a furious joy;
And the king seized a flambeau with zeal to de-
    stroy:
  Thais led the way,
  To light him to his prey,
And, like another Helen, fired another Troy!

CHORUS.

And the king seized a flambeau with zeal to de-
  stroy:
  Thais led the way,
  To light him to his prey,
And, like another Helen, fired another Troy!

  Thus, long ago,
  Ere heaving bellows learned to blow,
    While organs yet were mute;
  Timotheus, to his breathing flute,
    And sounding lyre,
Could swell the soul to rage, or kindle soft desire.
  At last divine Cecilia came,
  Inventress of the vocal frame;
The sweet enthusiast, from her sacred store,
  Enlarged the former narrow bounds,
  And added length to solemn sounds,
With nature's mother-wit, and arts unknown
    before.
Let old Timotheus yield the prize,
  Or both divide the crown;
He raised a mortal to the skies,
  She drew an angel down.

GRAND CHORUS.

At last divine Cecilia came,
  Inventress of the vocal frame;
The sweet enthusiast, from her sacred store,
  Enlarged the former narrow bounds,
  And added length to solemn sounds,
With nature's mother-wit, and arts unknown
    before.
Let old Timotheus yield the prize,
  Or both divide the crown;
He raised a mortal to the skies,
  She drew an angel down.

JOHN DRYDEN.

INVOCATION.

FROM "THE DAVIDEIS."

Awake, awake, my Lyre!
And tell thy silent master's humble tale
  In sounds that may prevail;
Sounds that gentle thoughts inspire:

'Though so exalted she,
And I so lowly be,
Tell her, such different notes make all thy har-
        mony.

Hark ! how the strings awake :
And, though the moving hand approach not near,
Themselves with awful fear
A kind of numerous trembling make.
Now all thy forces try ;
Now all thy charms apply ;
Revenge upon her ear the conquests of her eye.

Weak Lyre ! thy virtue sure
Is useless here, since thou art only found
To cure, but not to wound,
And she to wound, but not to cure.
Too weak, too, wilt thou prove
My passion to remove ;
Physic to other ills, thou 'rt nourishment to love.

Sleep, sleep again, my Lyre !
For thou canst never tell my humble tale
In sounds that will prevail,
Nor gentle thoughts in her inspire ;
All thy vain mirth lay by,
Bid thy strings silent lie,
Sleep, sleep again, my Lyre, and let thy master
        die.
                            ABRAHAM COWLEY.

------◆------

THE PASSIONS.

AN ODE FOR MUSIC.

WHEN Music, heavenly maid, was young,
While yet in early Greece she sung,
The Passions oft, to hear her shell,
Thronged around her magic cell, —
Exulting, trembling, raging, fainting, —
Possessed beyond the muse's painting ;
By turns they felt the glowing mind
Disturbed, delighted, raised, refined ;
Till once, 't is said, when all were fired,
Filled with fury, rapt, inspired,
From the supporting myrtles round
They snatched her instruments of sound ;
And, as they oft had heard apart
Sweet lessons of her forceful art,
Each (for madness ruled the hour)
Would prove his own expressive power.

First Fear his hand, its skill to try,
    Amid the chords bewildered laid,
And back recoiled, he knew not why,
    E'en at the sound himself had made.

Next Anger rushed ; his eyes, on fire,
    In lightnings owned his secret stings :
In one rude clash he struck the lyre,
    And swept with hurried hand the strings.

With woful measures wan Despair,
    Low, sullen sounds, his grief beguiled, —
A solemn, strange, and mingled air ;
    'T was sad by fits, by starts 't was wild.

But thou, O Hope, with eyes so fair, —
    What was thy delightful measure ?
Still it whispered promised pleasure,
    And bade the lovely scenes at distance hail !
Still would her touch the strain prolong ;
    And from the rocks, the woods, the vale,
She called on Echo still, through all the song ;
    And where her sweetest theme she chose,
    A soft responsive voice was heard at every close;
And Hope, enchanted, smiled, and waved her
        golden hair.
And longer had she sung — but, with a frown,
    Revenge impatient rose ;
He threw his blood-stained sword in thunder
        down ;
    And, with a withering look,
    The war-denouncing trumpet took,
And blew a blast so loud and dread,
Were ne'er prophetic sounds so full of woe !
    And ever and anon he beat
    The doubling drum with furious heat ;
And though, sometimes, each dreary pause be-
        tween,
    Dejected Pity, at his side,
    Her soul-subduing voice applied,
Yet still he kept his wild, unaltered mien,
While each strained ball of sight seemed bursting
        from his head.

Thy numbers, Jealousy, to naught were fixed, —
    Sad proof of thy distressful state ;
Of differing themes the veering song was mixed;
    And now it courted Love, — now, raving,
        called on Hate.

With eyes upraised, as one inspired,
Pale Melancholy sate retired ;
And from her wild sequestered seat,
In notes by distance made more sweet,
    Poured through the mellow horn her pensive
        soul :
    And, dashing soft from rocks around,
    Bubbling runnels joined the sound ;
Through glades and glooms the mingled meas-
        ure stole ;
Or o'er some haunted stream, with fond delay,
    Round an holy calm diffusing,
    Love of peace, and lonely musing,
In hollow murmurs died away.

But O, how altered was its sprightlier tone
When Cheerfulness, a nymph of healthiest hue,
　Her bow across her shoulder flung,
　Her buskins gemmed with morning dew,
Blew an inspiring air, that dale and thicket
　　rung, —
　The hunter's call, to faun and dryad known !
The oak-crowned sisters, and their chaste-eyed
　　queen,
　Satyrs and sylvan boys, were seen
　Peeping from forth their alleys green :
Brown Exercise rejoiced to hear ;
　And Sport leapt up, and seized his beechen
　　spear.

Last came Joy's ecstatic trial :
He, with viny crown advancing,
　First to the lively pipe his hand addrest ;
But soon he saw the brisk-awakening viol,
　Whose sweet entrancing voice he loved the best ;
They would have thought, who heard the strain,
　They saw, in Tempe's vale, her native maids
　Amidst the festal-sounding shades,
To some unwearied minstrel dancing,
While, as his flying fingers kissed the strings,
Love framed with Mirth a gay fantastic round :
Loose were her tresses seen, her zone unbound ;
　And he, amidst his frolic play,
　As if he would the charming air repay,
Shook thousand odors from his dewy wings.

O Music ! sphere-descended maid,
Friend of pleasure, wisdom's aid !
Why, goddess, why, to us denied,
Lay'st thou thy ancient lyre aside ?
As, in that loved Athenian bower,
You learned an all-commanding power,
Thy mimic soul, O nymph endeared,
Can well recall what then it heard.

Where is thy native simple heart,
Devote to virtue, fancy, art ?
Arise, as in that elder time,
Warm, energetic. chaste, sublime !
Thy wonders, in that godlike age,
Fill thy recording sister's page ;
'T is said — and I believe the tale —
Thy humblest reed could more prevail,
Had more of strength, diviner rage,
Than all which charms this laggard age, —
E'en all at once together found, —
Cecilia's mingled world of sound.
O, bid our vain endeavors cease ;
Revive the just designs of Greece !
Return in all thy simple state, —
Confirm the tales her sons relate !

　　　　　　　　　WILLIAM COLLINS.

THE NIGHTINGALE'S SONG.

FROM "MUSIC'S DUEL."

Now westward Sol had spent the richest beams
Of noon's high glory, when, hard by the streams
Of Tiber, on the scene of a green plat,
Under protection of an oak, there sat
A sweet lute's-master, in whose gentle airs
He lost the day's heat and his own hot cares.
　Close in the covert of the leaves there stood
A nightingale, come from the neighboring wood
(The sweet inhabitant of each glad tree,
Their muse, their siren, harmless siren she) :
There stood she listening, and did entertain
The music's soft report, and mould the same
In her own murmurs ; that whatever mood
His curious fingers lent, her voice made good.
　　.　　　　.　　　.　　.
　　　　　　　　　This lesson too
She gives them back ; her supple breast thrills
　　out
Sharp airs, and staggers in a warbling doubt
Of dallying sweetness, hovers o'er her skill,
And folds in waved notes, with a trembling bill,
The pliant series of her slippery song ;
Then starts she suddenly into a throng
Of short thick sobs, whose thundering volleys
　　float,
And roll themselves over her lubric throat
In panting murmurs, stilled out of her breast ;
That ever-bubbling spring, the sugared nest
Of her delicious soul, that there does lie
Bathing in streams of liquid melody ;
Music's best seed-plot ; when in ripened airs
A golden-headed harvest fairly rears
His honey-dropping tops ploughed by her breath
Which there reciprocally laboreth.
In that sweet soil it seems a holy quire,
Sounded to the name of great Apollo's lyre ;
Whose silver roof rings with the sprightly notes
Of sweet-lipped angel-imps, that swill their
　　throats
In cream of morning Helicon, and then
Prefer soft anthems to the ears of men,
To woo them from their beds, still murmuring
That men can sleep while they their matins sing
(Most divine service), whose so early lay
Prevents the eyelids of the blushing day.
There might you hear her kindle her soft voice
In the close murmur of a sparkling noise ;
And lay the groundwork of her hopeful song.
Still keeping in the forward stream so long,
Till a sweet whirlwind (striving to get out)
Heaves her soft bosom, wanders round about,
And makes a pretty earthquake in her breast,
Till the fledged notes at length forsake their nest,
Fluttering in wanton shoals, and to the sky,
Winged with their own wild echoes, prattling fly.

She opes the floodgate, and lets loose a tide
Of streaming sweetness, which in state doth ride
On the waved back of every swelling strain,
Rising and falling in a pompous train ;
And while she thus discharges a shrill peal
Of flashing airs, she qualifies their zeal
With the cool epode of a graver note ;
Thus high, thus low, as if her silver throat
Would reach the brazen voice of war's hoarse bird;
Her little soul is ravished, and so poured
Into loose ecstasies, that she is placed
Above herself, music's enthusiast.

RICHARD CRASHAW.

A SONG FOR ST. CECILIA'S DAY, 1687.

FROM harmony, from heavenly harmony,
    This universal frame began ;
    When Nature underneath a heap
        Of jarring atoms lay,
        And could not heave her head,
The tuneful voice was heard from high,
        Arise, ye more than dead !
Then cold and hot, and moist and dry,
    In order to their stations leap,
        And Music's power obey.
From harmony, from heavenly harmony,
    This universal frame began :
        From harmony to harmony,
Through all the compass of the notes it ran,
    The diapason closing full in man.

What passion cannot Music raise and quell ?
        When Jubal struck the chorded shell,
        His listening brethren stood around,
        And, wondering, on their faces fell,
        To worship that celestial sound.
Less than a God they thought there could not dwell
        Within the hollow of that shell,
        That spoke so sweetly and so well.
What passion cannot Music raise and quell ?

    The trumpet's loud clangor
        Excites us to arms,
    With shrill notes of anger,
        And mortal alarms.
    The double double double beat
        Of the thundering drum
        Cries, Hark ! the foes come ;
Charge, charge, 't is too late to retreat !

    The soft complaining flute
        In dying notes discovers
    The woes of hopeless lovers,
Whose dirge is whispered by the warbling lute.

    Sharp violins proclaim
Their jealous pangs, and desperation,
Fury, frantic indignation,
Depth of pains, and height of passion
    For the fair, disdainful dame.
    But O, what art can teach,
    What human voice can reach,
        The sacred organ's praise ?
    Notes inspiring holy love,
    Notes that wing their heavenly ways
        To mend the choirs above.

Orpheus could lead the savage race ;
And trees uprooted left their place,
        Sequacious of the lyre ;
But bright Cecilia raised the wonder higher ;
When to her organ vocal breath was given,
An angel heard, and straight appeared
        Mistaking earth for heaven.

GRAND CHORUS.

As from the power of sacred lays
    The spheres began to move,
And sung the great Creator's praise
    To all the blessed above ;
So, when the last and dreadful hour
This crumbling pageant shall devour,
The trumpet shall be heard on high,
The dead shall live, the living die,
And Music shall untune the sky.

JOHN DRYDEN.

MUSIC.

FROM "THE MERCHANT OF VENICE," ACT V. SC. I.

LORENZO. How sweet the moonlight sleeps
        upon this bank !
Here will we sit, and let the sounds of music
Creep in our ears : soft stillness, and the night,
Become the touches of sweet harmony.
Sit, Jessica : look, how the floor of heaven
Is thick inlaid with patines of bright gold :
There 's not the smallest orb which thou be-
        hold'st,
But in his motion like an angel sings,
Still quiring to the young-eyed cherubins ;
Such harmony is in immortal souls :
But whilst this muddy vesture of decay
Doth grossly close it in, we cannot hear it.

    JESSICA. I am never merry when I hear sweet
        music.
    LOR. The reason is your spirits are attentive.
    .   .   .   .   .
                Therefore the poet
Did feign that Orpheus drew trees, stones, and
    floods ;

Since naught so stockish, hard, and full of rage,
But music for the time doth change his nature.
The man that hath no music in himself,
Nor is not moved with concord of sweet sounds,
Is fit for treasons, stratagems, and spoils ;
The motions of his spirit are dull as night,
And his affections dark as Erebus :
Let no such man be trusted.

SHAKESPEARE.

TO ———.

Music, when soft voices die,
Vibrates in the memory, —
Odors, when sweet violets sicken,
Live within the sense they quicken.

Rose-leaves, when the rose is dead,
Are heaped for the belovèd's bed ;
And so thy thoughts, when thou art gone,
Love itself shall slumber on.

PERCY BYSSHE SHELLEY.

MAN.

FROM "NIGHT THOUGHTS," NIGHT I.

How poor, how rich, how abject, how august,
How complicate, how wonderful, is man !
How passing wonder He who made him such !
Who centred in our make such strange extremes,
From different natures marvellously mixed,
Connection exquisite of distant worlds !
Distinguished link in being's endless chain !
Midway from nothing to the Deity !
A beam ethereal, sullied, and absorpt !
Though sullied and dishonored, still divine !
Dim miniature of greatness absolute !
An heir of glory ! a frail child of dust !
Helpless immortal ! insect infinite !
A worm ! a god ! — I tremble at myself,
And in myself am lost.   At home a stranger,
Thought wanders up and down, surprised, aghast,
And wondering at her own.   How reason reels !
O, what a miracle to man is man !
Triumphantly distressed ! What joy ! what dread !
Alternately transported and alarmed !
What can preserve my life ? or what destroy ?
An angel's arm can't snatch me from the grave ;
Legions of angels can't confine me there.

DR. EDWARD YOUNG.

MAN — WOMAN.

Man's home is everywhere.   On ocean's flood,
Where the strong ship with storm-defying tether
Doth link in stormy brotherhood
Earth's utmost zones together,

Where'er the red gold glows, the spice-trees wave,
Where the rich diamond ripens, mid the flame
Of vertic suns that ope the stranger's grave,
He with bronzed cheek and daring step doth
rove ;
He, with short pang and slight,
Doth turn him from the checkered light
Of the fair moon through his own forests
dancing,
Where music, joy, and love
Were his young hours entrancing ;
And where ambition's thunder-claim
Points out his lot,
Or fitful wealth allures to roam,
There doth he make his home,
Repining not.

It is not thus with Woman.   The far halls,
Though ruinous and lone,
Where first her pleased ear drank a nursing-
mother's tone ;
The home with humble walls,
Where breathed a parent's prayer around her
bed ;
The valley where, with playmates true,
She culled the strawberry, bright with dew ;
The bower where Love her timid footsteps led ;
The hearthstone where her children grew ;
The damp soil where she cast
The flower-seeds of her hope, and saw them bide
the blast, —
Affection with unfading tint recalls,
Lingering round the ivied walls,
Where every rose hath in its cup a bee,
Making fresh honey of remembered things, —
Each rose without a thorn, each bee bereft of
stings.

LYDIA HUNTLEY SIGOURNEY.

WOMAN.

There in the fane a beauteous creature stands,
The first best work of the Creator's hands,
Whose slender limbs inadequately bear
A full-orbed bosom and a weight of care ;
Whose teeth like pearls, whose lips like cherries,
show,
And fawn-like eyes still tremble as they glow.

From the Sanskrit of CALIDASA.
Translation of WILSON.

APRÈS.

Down, down, Ellen, my little one,
Climbing so tenderly up to my knee ;
Why should you add to the thoughts that are
taunting me,
Dreams of your mother's arms clinging to me ?

Cease, cease, Ellen, my little one,
Warbling so fairily close to my ear;
Why should you choose, of all songs that are
haunting me,
This that I made for your mother to hear?

Hush, hush, Ellen, my little one,
Wailing so wearily under the stars;
Why should I think of her tears, that might
light to me
Love that had made life, and sorrow that mars?

Sleep, sleep, Ellen, my little one!
Is she not like her whenever she stirs?
Has she not eyes that will soon be as bright to me,
Lips that will some day be honeyed like hers?

Yes, yes, Ellen, my little one,
Though her white bosom is stilled in the grave,
Something more white than her bosom is spared
to me, —
Something to cling to and something to crave.

Love, love, Ellen, my little one!
Love indestructible, love undefiled,
Love through all deeps of her spirit lies bared
to me,
Oft as I look on the face of her child.

ARTHUR J. MUNBY.

FORTUNE.

FROM "FANNY."

BUT Fortune, like some others of her sex,
Delights in tantalizing and tormenting.
One day we feed upon their smiles, — the next
Is spent in swearing, sorrowing, and repenting.

Eve never walked in Paradise more pure
Than on that morn when Satan played the devil
With her and all her race. A lovesick wooer
Ne'er asked a kinder maiden, or more civil,
Than Cleopatra was to Antony
The day she left him on the Ionian sea.

The serpent — loveliest in his coiled ring,
With eye that charms, and beauty that outvies
The tints of the rainbow — bears upon his sting
The deadliest venom. Ere the dolphin dies
Its hues are brightest. Like an infant's breath
Are tropic winds before the voice of death

Is heard upon the waters, summoning
The midnight earthquake from its sleep of years
To do its task of woe. The clouds that fling
The lightning brighten ere the bolt appears;

The pantings of the warrior's heart are proud
Upon that battle-morn whose night-dews wet his
shroud;
The sun is loveliest as he sinks to rest;
The leaves of autumn smile when fading fast;
The swan's last song is sweetest.

FITZ-GREENE HALLECK.

ENID'S SONG.

FROM "IDYLS OF THE KING."

TURN, Fortune, turn thy wheel and lower the
proud;
Turn thy wild wheel through sunshine, storm,
and cloud;
Thy wheel and thee we neither love nor hate.

Turn, Fortune, turn thy wheel with smile or
frown;
With that wild wheel we go not up or down;
Our hoard is little, but our hearts are great.

Smile and we smile, the lords of many lands;
Frown and we smile, the lords of our own hands;
For man is man and master of his fate.

Turn, turn thy wheel above the staring crowd
Thy wheel and thou are shadows in the cloud;
Thy wheel and thee we neither love nor hate.

ALFRED TENNYSON

EXCELSIOR.

THE shades of night were falling fast,
As through an Alpine village passed
A youth, who bore, 'mid snow and ice,
A banner with the strange device —
Excelsior!

His brow was sad; his eye beneath
Flashed like a falchion from its sheath;
And like a silver clarion rung
The accents of that unknown tongue —
Excelsior!

In happy homes he saw the light
Of household fires gleam warm and bright
Above, the spectral glaciers shone,
And from his lips escaped a groan —
Excelsior!

"Try not the pass," the old man said:
"Dark lowers the tempest overhead;
The roaring torrent is deep and wide!"
And loud that clarion voice replied,
Excelsior!

"O stay," the maiden said, "and rest
Thy weary head upon this breast!"
A tear stood in his bright blue eye,
But still he answered, with a sigh,
　　　　Excelsior!

"Beware the pine-tree's withered branch!
Beware the awful avalanche!"
This was the peasant's last good-night:
A voice replied, far up the height,
　　　　Excelsior!

At break of day, as heavenward
The pious monks of Saint Bernard
Uttered the oft-repeated prayer,
A voice cried, through the startled air,
　　　　Excelsior!

A traveller, by the faithful hound,
Half buried in the snow was found,
Still grasping in his hand of ice
That banner with the strange device —
　　　　Excelsior!

There in the twilight cold and gray,
Lifeless, but beautiful, he lay,
And from the sky, serene and far,
A voice fell, like a falling star —
　　　　Excelsior!
　　　　　　HENRY WADSWORTH LONGFELLOW.

THE GIFTS OF GOD.

WHEN God at first made man,
Having a glass of blessings standing by,
Let us (said he) pour on him all we can:
Let the world's riches, which dispersèd lie,
　　　　Contract into a span.

So strength first made a way;
Then beauty flowed, then wisdom, honor, pleasure:
When almost all was out, God made a stay,
Perceiving that, alone, of all his treasure,
　　　　Rest in the bottom lay.

For if I should (said he)
Bestow this jewel also on my creature,
He would adore my gifts instead of me,
And rest in Nature, not the God of Nature:
　　　　So both should losers be.

Yet let him keep the rest,
But keep them with repining restlessness:
Let him be rich and weary, that, at least,
If goodness lead him not, yet weariness
　　　　May toss him to my breast.
　　　　　　GEORGE HERBERT.

A RIDDLE.*

THE LETTER "H."

'T WAS in heaven pronounced, and 't was mut-
　　tered in hell,
And echo caught faintly the sound as it fell;
On the confines of earth 't was permitted to rest,
And the depths of the ocean its presence con-
　　fessed;
'T will be found in the sphere when 't is riven
　　asunder,
Be seen in the lightning and heard in the thunder.
'T was allotted to man with his earliest breath,
Attends him at birth, and awaits him in death,
Presides o'er his happiness, honor, and health,
Is the prop of his house, and the end of his wealth.
In the heaps of the miser 't is hoarded with care,
But is sure to be lost on his prodigal heir.
It begins every hope, every wish it must bound,
With the husbandman toils, and with monarchs
　　is crowned.
Without it the soldier, the seaman may roam,
But woe to the wretch who expels it from home!
In the whispers of conscience its voice will be
　　found,
Nor e'en in the whirlwind of passion be drowned.
'T will not soften the heart; but though deaf be
　　the ear,
It will make it acutely and instantly hear.
Yet in shade let it rest, like a delicate flower,
Ah, breathe on it softly, — it dies in an hour.
　　　　　　CATHARINE FANSHAWE.

FATHER LAND AND MOTHER TONGUE.

OUR Father Land! and wouldst thou know
　　Why we should call it Father Land?
It is that Adam here below
　　Was made of earth by Nature's hand;
And he, our father made of earth,
　　Hath peopled earth on every hand;
And we, in memory of his birth,
　　Do call our country Father Land.

At first, in Eden's bowers, they say,
　　No sound of speech had Adam caught,
But whistled like a bird all day, —
　　And maybe 't was for want of thought:
But Nature, with resistless laws,
　　Made Adam soon surpass the birds;
She gave him lovely Eve because
　　If he 'd a wife they must *have words*.

And so the native land, I hold,
　　By male descent is proudly mine;
The language, as the tale hath told,
　　Was given in the female line.

And thus we see on either hand
  We name our blessings whence they've sprung;
We call our country Father Land,
  We call our language Mother Tongue.
SAMUEL LOVER.

SMALL BEGINNINGS.

A TRAVELLER through a dusty road strewed
  acorns on the lea ;
And one took root and sprouted up, and grew
  into a tree.
Love sought its shade, at evening time, to breathe
  its early vows ;
And age was pleased, in heats of noon, to bask
  beneath its boughs ;
The dormouse loved its dangling twigs, the birds
  sweet music bore ;
It stood a glory in its place, a blessing evermore.

A little spring had lost its way amid the grass
  and fern,
A passing stranger scooped a well, where weary
  men might turn ;
He walled it in, and hung with care a ladle at
  the brink ;
He thought not of the deed he did, but judged
  that toil might drink.
He passed again, and lo ! the well, by summers
  never dried,
Had cooled ten thousand parching tongues, and
  saved a life beside.

A dreamer dropped a random thought ; 't was
  old, and yet 't was new ;
A simple fancy of the brain, but strong in being
  true.
't shone upon a genial mind, and lo ! its light
  became
A lamp of life, a beacon ray, a monitory flame.
The thought was small ; its issue great ; a watch-
  fire on the hill,
It sheds its radiance far adown, and cheers the
  valley still !

A nameless man, amid a crowd that thronged
  the daily mart,
Let fall a word of Hope and Love, unstudied,
  from the heart ;
A whisper on the tumult thrown, — a transitory
  breath, —
It raised a brother from the dust ; it saved a
  soul from death.
O germ ! O fount ! O word of love ! O thought
  at random cast !
Ye were but little at the first, but mighty at the
  last.
CHARLES MACKAY.

THE RULING PASSION.

FROM "MORAL ESSAYS," EPISTLE I.

SEARCH thou the ruling passion ; there, alone,
The wild are constant, and the cunning known ;
The fool consistent and the false sincere ;
Priests, princes, women, no dissemblers here.

In this the lust, in that the avarice,
Were means, not ends ; ambition was the vice.

In this one passion man can strength enjoy,
As fits give vigor just when they destroy.
Time, that on all things lays his lenient hand,
Yet tames not this ; it sticks to our last sand.
Consistent in our follies and our sins,
Here honest Nature ends as she begins.
  Old politicians chew on wisdom past,
And totter on in business to the last ;
As weak, as earnest ; and as gravely out,
As sober Lanesborough dancing in the gout.
  Behold a reverend sire, whom want of grace
Has made the father of a nameless race,
Shoved from the wall perhaps, or rudely pressed
By his own son, that passes by unblessed :
Still to his wench he crawls on knocking knees,
And envies every sparrow that he sees.
  A salmon's belly, Helluo, was thy fate.
The doctor, called, declares all help too late.
"Mercy !" cries Helluo, "mercy on my soul !
Is there no hope ? — Alas ! — then bring the jowl."
  The frugal crone, whom praying priests attend,
Still tries to save the hallowed taper's end,
Collects her breath, as ebbing life retires,
For one puff more, and in that puff expires.
  "Odious ! in woollen ! 't would a saint pro-
    voke,"
Were the last words that poor Narcissa spoke ;
"No, let a charming chintz and Brussels lace
Wrap my cold limbs, and shade my lifeless face :
One would not, sure, be frightful when one's
    dead, —
And — Betty — give this cheek a little red."
  The courtier smooth, who forty years had
    shined
An humble servant to all human-kind,
Just brought out this, when scarce his tongue
    could stir,
"If — where I'm going — I could serve you, sir ?"
"I give and I devise" (old Euclio said,
And sighed) "my lands and tenements to Ned."
Your money, sir ? "My money, sir ! what, all ?
Why — if I must" (then wept) — "I give it
    Paul."
The manor, sir ? "The manor, hold !" he cried,
"Not that, — I cannot part with that," — and
    died.

And you, brave Cobham ! to the latest breath
Shall feel your ruling passion strong in death ;
Such in those moments as in all the past,
" O, save my country, Heaven !" shall be your
     last.

ALEXANDER POPE.

CONTRADICTION.

FROM "CONVERSATION.'

YE powers who rule the tongue, if such there
     are,
And make colloquial happiness your care,
Preserve me from the thing I dread and hate,
A duel in the form of a debate.
The clash of arguments and jar of words,
Worse than the mortal brunt of rival swords,
Decide no question with their tedious length,
For opposition gives opinion strength,
Divert the champions prodigal of breath,
And put the peacefully disposed to death.
O, thwart me not, Sir Soph, at every turn,
Nor carp at every flaw you may discern !
Though syllogisms hang not on my tongue,
I am not surely always in the wrong ;
'T is hard if all is false that I advance,
A fool must now and then be right by chance.
Not that all freedom of dissent I blame ;
No, — there I grant the privilege I claim.
A disputable point is no man's ground ;
Rove where you please, 't is common all around.
Discourse may want an animated No,
To brush the surface, and to make it flow ;
But still remember, if you mean to please,
To press your point with modesty and ease.
The mark at which my juster aim I take,
Is contradiction for its own dear sake.
Set your opinion at whatever pitch,
Knots and impediments make something hitch ;
Adopt his own, 't is equally in vain,
Your thread of argument is snapped again.
The wrangler, rather than accord with you,
Will judge himself deceived, and prove it too.
Vociferated logic kills me quite ;
A noisy man is always in the right.
I twirl my thumbs, fall back into my chair,
Fix on the wainscot a distressful stare,
And, when I hope his blunders are all out,
Reply discreetly, — " To be sure — no doubt ! "

WILLIAM COWPER.

DUELLING.

FROM "CONVERSATION."

THE point of honor has been deemed of use,
To teach good manners, and to curb abuse ;
Admit it true, the consequence is clear,
Our polished manners are a mask we wear,

And, at the bottom, barbarous still and rude,
We are restrained, indeed, but not subdued.
The very remedy, however sure,
Springs from the mischief it intends to cure,
And savage in its principle appears,
Tried, as it should be, by the fruit it bears.
'T is hard, indeed, if nothing will defend
Mankind from quarrels but their fatal end ;
That now and then a hero must decease,
That the surviving world may live in peace.
Perhaps at last close scrutiny may show
The practice dastardly and mean and low ;
That men engage in it compelled by force,
And fear, not courage, is its proper source ;
The fear of tyrant custom, and the fear
Lest fops should censure us, and fools should
     sneer ;
At least, to trample on our Maker's laws,
And hazard life for any or no cause,
To rush into a fixed eternal state
Out of the very flames of rage and hate,
Or send another shivering to the bar
With all the guilt of such unnatural war,
Whatever Use may urge, or Honor plead,
On Reason's verdict is a madman's deed.
Am I to set my life upon a throw
Because a bear is rude and surly ? No, —
A moral, sensible, and well-bred man
Will not affront me ; and no other can.
Were I empowered to regulate the lists,
They should encounter with well-loaded fists ;
A Trojan combat would be something new,
Let *Dares* beat *Entellus* black and blue ;
Then each might show, to his admiring friends,
In honorable bumps his rich amends,
And carry, in contusions of his skull,
A satisfactory receipt in full.

WILLIAM COWPER.

FAME.

FROM "AN ESSAY ON MAN," EPISTLE IV.

WHAT 's fame ? — a fancied life in others'
     breath,
A thing beyond us, e'en before our death.
Just what you hear, you have ; and what 's un
     known
The same (my lord) if Tully's, or your own.
All that we feel of it begins and ends
In the small circle of our foes or friends ;
To all beside, as much an empty shade
A Eugene living as a Cæsar dead ;
Alike or when or where they shone or shine,
Or on the Rubicon, or on the Rhine.
A wit 's a feather, and a chief a rod ;
An honest man 's the noblest work of God.

Fame but from death a villain's name can save,
As justice tears his body from the grave ;
When what to oblivion better were resigned
Is hung on high, to poison half mankind.
All fame is foreign, but of true desert;
Plays round the head, but comes not to the heart :
One self-approving hour whole years outweighs
Of stupid starers and of loud huzzas ;
And more true joy Marcellus exiled feels
Than Cæsar with a senate at his heels.

ALEXANDER POPE.

FAME.

Her house is all of Echo made
 Where never dies the sound ;
And as her brows the clouds invade,
 Her feet do strike the ground.

BEN JONSON.

PERSEVERANCE.

In facile natures fancies quickly grow,
But such quick fancies have but little root.
Soon the narcissus flowers and dies, but slow
The tree whose blossoms shall mature to fruit.
Grace is a moment's happy feeling, Power
A life's slow growth ; and we for many an hour
Must strain and toil, and wait and weep, if we
The perfect fruit of all we are would see.

From the Italian of LEONARDO DA VINCI.
Translation of W. W. STORY.

GREATNESS.

FROM "AN ESSAY ON MAN," EPISTLE IV.

Honor and shame from no condition rise ;
Act well your part, there all the honor lies.
Fortune in men has some small difference made,
One flaunts in rags, one flutters in brocade ;
The cobbler aproned, and the parson gowned,
The friar hooded, and the monarch crowned.
"What differ more (you cry) than crown and
  cowl ? "
I 'll tell you, friend ; a wise man and a fool.
You 'll find, if once the monarch acts the monk
Or, cobbler-like, the parson will be drunk,
Worth makes the man, and want of it the fellow ;
The rest is all but leather or prunella.
 Stuck o'er with titles, and hung round with
  strings,
That thou mayst be by kings, or whores of kings;
Boast the pure blood of an illustrious race,
In quiet flow from Lucrece to Lucrece ;
But by your fathers' worth if yours you rate,
Count me those only who were good and great.

Go ! if your ancient but ignoble blood
Has crept through scoundrels ever since the flood,
Go ! and pretend your family is young,
Nor own your fathers have been fools so long.
What can ennoble sots, or slaves, or cowards ?
Alas ! not all the blood of all the Howards.

Who wickedly is wise, or madly brave,
Is but the more a fool, the more a knave.
Who noble ends by noble means obtains,
Or, failing, smiles in exile or in chains,
Like good Aurelius let him reign, or bleed
Like Socrates, that man is great indeed.

ALEXANDER POPE.

REASON AND INSTINCT.

FROM "AN ESSAY ON MAN," EPISTLE III.

Whether with reason or with instinct blest,
Know, all enjoy that power which suits them best.
To bliss alike by that direction tend,
And find the means proportioned to their end.
Say, where full instinct is the unerring guide,
What pope or council can they need beside ?
Reason, however able, cool at best,
Cares not for service, or but serves when prest,
Stays till we call, and then not often near ;
But honest instinct comes a volunteer,
Sure never to o'ershoot, but just to hit ;
While still too wide or short is human wit,
Sure by quick nature happiness to gain,
Which heavier reason labors at in vain.
This too serves always, reason never long ;
One must go right, the other may go wrong.
See then the acting and comparing powers
One in their nature, which are two in ours ;
And reason raise o'er instinct as you can,
In this 't is God directs, in that 't is man.
 Who taught the nations of the field and wood
To shun their poison and to choose their food ?
Prescient, the tides or tempests to withstand,
Build on the wave, or arch beneath the sand ?
Who made the spider parallels design,
Sure as De Moivre, without rule or line ?
Who bid the stork, Columbus-like, explore
Heavens not his own, and worlds unknown before?
Who calls the council, states the certain day,
Who forms the phalanx, and who points the way?

ALEXANDER POPE.

SCANDAL.

FROM "EPISTLE TO DR. ARBUTHNOT," BEING THE "PRO-
LOGUE TO THE SATIRES."

Cursed be the verse, how well soe'er it flow,
That tends to make one worthy man my foe,
Give virtue scandal, innocence a fear,
Or from the soft-eyed virgin steal a tear !

But he who hurts a harmless neighbor's peace,
Insults fallen worth, or beauty in distress,
Who loves a lie, lame slander helps about,
Who writes a libel, or who copies out ;
That fop whose pride affects a patron's name,
Yet absent wounds an author's honest fame ;
Who can your merit selfishly approve,
And show the sense of it without the love ;
Who has the vanity to call you friend,
Yet wants the honor, injured, to defend ;
Who tells whate'er you think, whate'er you
    say,
And, if he lie not, must at least betray ;
Who to the Dean and silver bell can swear,
And sees at Canons what was never there ;
Who reads but with a lust to misapply,
Make satire a lampoon, and fiction lie ;
A lash like mine no honest man shall dread,
But all such babbling blockheads in his stead.
ALEXANDER POPE.

HUMANITY.

FROM "THE WINTER WALK AT NOON :"
"THE TASK," BOOK VI.

I WOULD not enter on my list of friends
(Though graced with polished manners and fine
    sense,
Yet wanting sensibility) the man
Who needlessly sets foot upon a worm.
An inadvertent step may crush the snail
That crawls at evening in the public path ;
But he that has humanity, forewarned,
Will tread aside, and let the reptile live.
The creeping vermin, loathsome to the sight,
And charged perhaps with venom, that intrudes,
A visitor unwelcome, into scenes
Sacred to neatness and repose, the alcove,
The chamber, or refectory, may die :
A necessary act incurs no blame.
Not so when, held within their proper bounds,
And guiltless of offence, they range the air,
Or take their pastime in the spacious field :
There they are privileged ; and he that hunts
Or harms them there is guilty of a wrong,
Disturbs the economy of Nature's realm,
Who, when she formed, designed them an abode.
The sum is this : If man's convenience, health,
Or safety interfere, his rights and claims
Are paramount, and must extinguish theirs.
Else they are all — the meanest things that are —
As free to live, and to enjoy that life,
As God was free to form them at the first,
Who in his sovereign wisdom made them all.
Ye, therefore, who love mercy, teach your sons
To love it too.
WILLIAM COWPER.

OF CRUELTY TO ANIMALS.

FROM "PROVERBIAL PHILOSOPHY."

SHAME upon thee, savage monarch-man, proud
    monopolist of reason ;
Shame upon creation's lord, the fierce ensan-
    guined despot :
What, man ! are there not enough, hunger and
    diseases and fatigue, —
And yet must thy goad or thy thong add another
    sorrow to existence ?
What ! art thou not content thy sin hath dragged
    down suffering and death
On the poor dumb servants of thy comfort, and
    yet must thou rack them with thy spite ?
The prodigal heir of creation hath gambled away
    his all, —
Shall he add torment to the bondage that is
    galling his forfeit serfs ?
The leader in nature's pæan himself hath marred
    her psaltery, —
Shall he multiply the din of discord by over-
    straining all the strings ?
The rebel hath fortified his stronghold, shutting
    in his vassals with him, —
Shall he aggravate the woes of the besieged by
    oppression from within ?
Thou twice-deformed image of thy Maker, thou
    hateful representative of Love,
For very shame be merciful, be kind unto the
    creatures thou hast ruined !
Earth and her million tribes are cursed for thy
    sake,
Earth and her million tribes still writhe beneath
    thy cruelty :
Liveth there but one among the million that shall
    not bear witness against thee,
A pensioner of land or air or sea that hath not
    whereof it will accuse thee ?
From the elephant toiling at a launch, to the
    shrew-mouse in the harvest-field,
From the whale which the harpooner hath
    stricken, to the minnow caught upon a pin,
From the albatross wearied in its flight, to the
    wren in her covered nest,
From the death-moth and lace-winged dragon-fly
    to the lady-bird and the gnat,
The verdict of all things is unanimous, finding
    their master cruel :
The dog, thy humble friend, thy trusting, honest
    friend ;
The ass, thine uncomplaining slave, drudging
    from morn till even ;
The lamb, and the timorous hare, and the laboring
    ox at plough ;
The speckled trout basking in the shallow, and
    the partridge gleaming in the stubble,

And the stag at bay, and the worm in thy path,
    and the wild bird pining in captivity,
And all things that minister alike to thy life and
    thy comfort and thy pride,
Testify with one sad voice that man is a cruel
    master.

MARTIN FARQUHAR TUPPER.

PLEA FOR THE ANIMALS.

FROM "THE SEASONS: SPRING."

ENSANGUINED man
Is now become the lion of the plain,
And worse.   The wolf, who from the nightly fold
Fierce drags the bleating prey, ne'er drunk her
    milk,
Nor wore her warming fleece ; nor has the steer,
At whose strong chest the deadly tiger hangs,
E'er ploughed for him.   They too are tempered
    high,
With hunger stung and wild necessity ;
Nor lodges pity in their shaggy breast.
But man, whom nature formed of milder clay,
With every kind emotion in his heart,
And taught alone to weep, — while from her lap
She pours ten thousand delicacies, herbs,
And fruits as numerous as the drops of rain
Or beams that gave them birth, — shall he, fair
    form !
Who wears sweet smiles, and looks erect on
    heaven,
E'er stoop to mingle with the prowling herd,
And dip his tongue in gore ?   The beast of prey,
Blood-stained, deserves to bleed ; but you, ye
    flocks,
What have ye done ? ye peaceful people, what,
To merit death ? you who have given us milk
In luscious streams, and lent us your own coat
Against the winter's cold ?   And the plain ox,
That harmless, honest, guileless animal,
In what has he offended ? he whose toil,
Patient and ever-ready, clothes the land
With all the pomp of harvest, — shall he bleed,
And struggling groan beneath the cruel hand,
Even of the clown he feeds ? and that, perhaps,
To swell the riot of the autumnal feast,
Won by his labor ?

JAMES THOMSON.

QUACK MEDICINES.

FROM "THE BOROUGH."

BUT now our Quacks are gamesters, and they
    play
With craft and skill to ruin and betray ;
With monstrous promise they delude the mind,
And thrive on all that tortures human-kind.

Void of all honor, avaricious, rash,
The daring tribe compound their boasted trash, —
Tincture or syrup, lotion, drop or pill ;
All tempt the sick to trust the lying bill ;
And twenty names of cobblers turned to squires
Aid the bold language of these blushless liars.
There are among them those who cannot read,
And yet they 'll buy a patent, and succeed ;
Will dare to promise dying sufferers aid,
For who, when dead, can threaten or upbraid ?
With cruel avarice still they recommend
More draughts, more syrup, to the journey's end.
" I feel it not."   "Then take it every hour."
" It makes me worse."   " Why, then it shows
    its power."
" I fear to die."   " Let not your spirits sink,
You 're always safe while you believe and drink."

      .   .   .   .   .

Troubled with something in your bile or blood,
You think your doctor does you little good ;
And, grown impatient, you require in haste
The nervous cordial, nor dislike the taste ;
It comforts, heals, and strengthens ; nay, you
    think
It makes you better every time you drink ;
Who tipples brandy will some comfort feel,
But will he to the medicine set his seal ?

      .   .   .   .

No class escapes them — from the poor man's pay
The nostrum takes no trifling part away ;
See ! those square patent bottles from the shop
Now decoration to the cupboard's top ;
And there a favorite hoard you 'll find within,
Companions meet ! the julep and the gin.

      .   .   .

Observe what ills to nervous females flow,
When the heart flutters and the pulse is low :
If once induced these cordial sips to try,
All feel the ease, and few the danger fly ;
For, while obtained, of drams they 've all the
    force,
And when denied, then drams are the resource.
    Who would not lend a sympathizing sigh,
To hear yon infant's pity-moving cry ?
Then the good nurse (who, had she borne a brain,
Had sought the cause that made her babe com-
    plain)
Has all her efforts, loving soul ! applied
To set the cry, and not the cause, aside ;
She gave her powerful sweet without remorse,
The sleeping cordial, — she had tried its force,
Repeating oft ; the infant, freed from pain,
Rejected food, but took the dose again,
Sinking to sleep, while she her joy expressed,
That her dear charge could sweetly take his rest.
Soon may she spare her cordial ; not a doubt
Remains but quickly he will rest without.

GEORGE CRABBE.

TO THE UNCO GUID.

My son, these maxims make a rule
And lump them aye thegither :
The Rigid Righteous is a foo!,
The Rigid Wise anither :
The cleanest corn that e'er was dight
May hae some pyles o' caff in ;
Sae ne'er a fellow-creature slight
For random fits o' daffin.
      SOLOMON, *Eccles.* vii. 16.

O YE wha are sae guid yoursel',
  Sae pious and sae holy,
Ye 've nought to do but mark and tell
  Your neebor's fauts and folly : —
Whase life is like a weel-gaun mill,
  Supplied wi' store o' water,
The heapèt happer's ebbing still,
  And still the clap plays clatter.

Hear me, ye venerable core,
  As counsel for poor mortals,
That frequent pass douce Wisdom's door,
  For glaikit Folly's portals !
I, for their thoughtless, careless sakes,
  Would here propone defences,
Their donsie tricks, their black mistakes,
  Their failings and mischances.

Ye see your state wi' theirs compared,
  And shudder at the niffer ;
But cast a moment's fair regard,
  What maks the mighty differ ?
Discount what scant occasion gave
  That purity ye pride in,
And (what 's aft mair than a' the lave)
  Your better art o' hidin'.

Think, when your castigated pulse
  Gies now and then a wallop,
What ragings must his veins convulse,
  That still eternal gallop :
Wi' wind and tide fair i' your tail,
  Right on ye scud your sea-way ;
But in the teeth o' baith to sail,
  It makes an unco leeway.

See Social life and Glee sit down,
  All joyous and unthinking,
Till, quite transmugrified, they 're grown
  Debauchery and Drinking :
O, would they stay to calculate
  The eternal consequences ;
Or your more dreaded hell to state,
  Damnation of expenses !

Ye high, exalted, virtuous dames,
  Tied up in godly laces,
Before ye gie poor Frailty names,
  Suppose a change o' cases ;

A dear-loved lad, convenience snug,
  A treacherous inclination, —
But, let me whisper i' your lug,
  Ye 're aiblins nae temptation.

Then gently scan your brother man,
  Still gentler sister woman ;
Though they may gang a kennin' wrang,
  To step aside is human.
One point must still be greatly dark,
  The moving why they do it ;
And just as lamely can ye mark
  How far perhaps they rue it.

Who made the heart, 't is He alone
  Decidedly can try us ;
He knows each chord, — its various tone,
  Each spring, — its various bias :
Then at the balance let 's be mute,
  We never can adjust it ;
What 's done we partly may compute,
  But know not what 's resisted.

            ROBERT BURNS.

JUDGE NOT.

JUDGE not ; the workings of his brain
  And of his heart thou canst not see ;
What looks to thy dim eyes a stain,
  In God's pure light may only be
A scar, brought from some well-won field,
Where thou wouldst only faint and yield.

The look, the air, that frets thy sight
  May be a token that below
The soul has closed in deadly fight
  With some infernal fiery foe,
Whose glance would scorch thy smiling grace
And cast thee shuddering on thy face !

The fall thou darest to despise, —
  May be the angel's slackened hand
Has suffered it, that he may rise
  And take a firmer, surer stand ;
Or, trusting less to earthly things,
May henceforth learn to use his wings.

And judge none lost ; but wait and see,
  With hopeful pity, not disdain ;
The depth of the abyss may be
  The measure of the height of pain
And love and glory that may raise
This soul to God in after days !

            ADELAIDE ANNE PROCTER.

L' ALLEGRO.

HENCE, loathed Melancholy,
  Of Cerberus and blackest Midnight born,
  In Stygian cave forlorn,
'Mongst horrid shapes, and shrieks, and sights
      unholy !
  Find out some uncouth cell,
Where brooding Darkness spreads his jealous
      wings,
And the night-raven sings ;
There under ebon shades, and low-browed rocks,
As ragged as thy locks,
  In dark Cimmerian desert ever dwell.
But come, thou goddess fair and free,
In heaven ycleped Euphrosyne,
And, by men, heart-easing Mirth ;
Whom lovely Venus, at a birth,
With two sister Graces more,
To ivy-crownèd Bacchus bore ;
Or whether (as some sager sing)
The frolic wind that breathes the spring,
Zephyr, with Aurora playing, —
As he met her once a-Maying, —
There, on beds of violets blue
And fresh-blown roses washed in dew,
Filled her with thee, a daughter fair,
So buxom, blithe, and debonair.

Haste thee, nymph, and bring with thee
Jest, and youthful Jollity, —
Quips and cranks and wanton wiles,
Nods and becks and wreathèd smiles,
Such as hang on Hebe's cheek,
And love to live in dimple sleek, —
Sport, that wrinkled Care derides,
And Laughter, holding both his sides.
Come ! and trip it, as you go,
On the light fantastic toe ;
And in thy right hand lead with thee
The mountain nymph, sweet Liberty ;
And if I give thee honor due,
Mirth, admit me of thy crew,
To live with her, and live with thee,
In unreprovèd pleasures free, —
To hear the lark begin his flight,
And singing startle the dull Night,
From his watch-tower in the skies,
Till the dappled dawn doth rise ;
Then to come, in spite of sorrow,
And at my window bid good morrow,
Through the sweet-brier, or the vine,
Or the twisted eglantine ;
While the cock with lively din
Scatters the rear of darkness thin,
And to the stack, or the barn door,
Stoutly struts his dames before ;
Oft listening how the hounds and horn

Cheerly rouse the slumbering Morn,
From the side of some hoar hill
Through the high wood echoing shrill ;
Sometime walking, not unseen,
By hedgerow elms, on hillocks green,
Right against the eastern gate,
Where the great Sun begins his state,
Robed in flames, and amber light,
The clouds in thousand liveries dight ;
While the ploughman, near at hand,
Whistles o'er the furrowed land,
And the milkmaid singeth blithe,
And the mower whets his scythe,
And every shepherd tells his tale
Under the hawthorn in the dale.

Straight mine eye hath caught new pleasures
Whilst the landscape round it measures
Russet lawns, and fallows gray,
Where the nibbling flocks do stray, —
Mountains, on whose barren breast
The laboring clouds do often rest, —
Meadows trim with daisies pied,
Shallow brooks, and rivers wide.
Towers and battlements it sees
Bosomed high in tufted trees,
Where perhaps some beauty lies,
The cynosure of neighboring eyes.
Hard by, a cottage chimney smokes
From betwixt two aged oaks,
Where Corydon and Thyrsis, met,
Are at their savory dinner set
Of herbs, and other country messes,
Which the neat-handed Phillis dresses :
And then in haste her bower she leaves,
With Thestylis to bind the sheaves ;
Or, if the earlier season lead,
To the tanned haycock in the mead.
Sometimes with secure delight
The upland hamlets will invite,
When the merry bells ring round,
And the jocund rebecks sound
To many a youth and many a maid,
Dancing in the checkered shade ;
And young and old come forth to play
On a sunshine holiday,
Till the livelong daylight fail ;
Then to the spicy nut-brown ale
With stories told of many a feat :
How fairy Mab the junkets eat, —
She was pinched and pulled, she said,
And he, by friar's lantern led ;
Tells how the drudging goblin sweat
To earn his cream-bowl duly set,
When in one night, ere glimpse of morn
His shadowy flail had thrashed the corn
That ten day-laborers could not end ;
Then lies him down the lubber fiend,

And, stretched out all the chimney's length,
Basks at the fire his hairy strength,
And, crop-full, out of doors he flings
Ere the first cock his matin rings.
Thus done the tales, to bed they creep,
By whispering winds soon lulled asleep.

Towered cities please us then,
And the busy hum of men,
Where throngs of knights and barons bold
In weeds of peace high triumphs hold, —
With store of ladies, whose bright eyes
Rain influence, and judge the prize
Of wit or arms, while both contend
To win her grace whom all commend.
There let Hymen oft appear
In saffron robe, with taper clear,
And pomp and feast and revelry,
With masque, and antique pageantry, —
Such sights as youthful poets dream
On summer eves by haunted stream ;
Then to the well-trod stage anon,
If Jonson's learnèd sock be on,
Or sweetest Shakespeare, Fancy's child,
Warble his native wood-notes wild.

And ever, against eating cares,
Lap me in soft Lydian airs,
Married to immortal verse, —
Such as the meeting soul may pierce,
In notes with many a winding bout
Of linkèd sweetness long drawn out,
With wanton heed and giddy cunning
The melting voice through mazes running,
Untwisting all the chains that tie
The hidden soul of harmony, —
That Orpheus' self may heave his head
From golden slumber on a bed
Of heaped Elysian flowers, and hear
Such strains as would have won the ear
Of Pluto, to have quite set free
His half-regained Eurydice.

These delights if thou canst give,
Mirth, with thee I mean to live.

MILTON.

————◆————

IL PENSEROSO.

HENCE, vain deluding joys,
  The brood of Folly without father bred !
  How little you bestead,
Or fill the fixèd mind with all your toys !
  Dwell in some idle brain,
And fancies fond with gaudy shapes possess,
As thick and numberless
As the gay motes that people the sunbeams, —
  Or likest hovering dreams,
  The fickle pensioners of Morpheus' train.

But hail, thou goddess, sage and holy !
Hail, divinest Melancholy !
Whose saintly visage is too bright
To hit the sense of human sight,
And therefore, to our weaker view,
O'erlaid with black, staid Wisdom's hue, —
Black, but such as in esteem
Prince Memnon's sister might beseem,
Or that starred Ethiop queen that strove
To set her beauty's praise above
The Sea-Nymphs, and their powers offended.
Yet thou art higher far descended ;
Thee bright-haired Vesta, long of yore,
To solitary Saturn bore, —
His daughter she (in Saturn's reign
Such mixture was not held a stain).
Oft in glimmering bowers and glades
He met her, and in secret shades
Of woody Ida's inmost grove,
While yet there was no fear of Jove.

Come, pensive nun, devout and pure,
Sober, steadfast, and demure,
All in a robe of darkest grain
Flowing with majestic train,
And sable stole of cyprus-lawn
Over thy decent shoulders drawn.
Come, but keep thy wonted state,
With even step, and musing gait,
And looks commercing with the skies,
Thy rapt soul sitting in thine eyes ;
There held in holy passion still,
Forget thyself to marble, till
With a sad, leaden, downward cast
Thou fix them on the earth as fast ;
And join with thee calm Peace, and Quiet, —
Spare Fast, that oft with gods doth diet,
And hears the Muses in a ring
Aye round about Jove's altar sing ;
And add to these retirèd Leisure,
That in trim gardens takes his pleasure :
But first and chiefest, with thee bring
Him that yon soars on golden wing,
Guiding the fiery-wheelèd throne, —
The cherub Contemplation ;
And the mute Silence hist along,
'Less Philomel will deign a song
In her sweetest, saddest plight,
Smoothing the rugged brow of Night,
While Cynthia checks her dragon yoke
Gently o'er the accustomed oak.
Sweet bird, that shun'st the noise of folly, —
Most musical, most melancholy !
Thee, chantress, oft, the woods among,
I woo, to hear thy even-song.
And, missing thee, I walk unseen
On the dry, smooth-shaven green,

To behold the wandering moon
Riding near her highest noon,
Like one that had been led astray
Through the heaven's wide pathless way ;
And oft, as if her head she bowed,
Stooping through a fleecy cloud.
Oft, on a plat of rising ground,
I hear the far-off curfew sound
Over some wide-watered shore,
Swinging slow with sullen roar ;
Or if the air will not permit,
Some still removèd place will fit,
Where glowing embers through the room
Teach light to counterfeit a gloom, —
Far from all resort of mirth,
Save the cricket on the hearth,
Or the bellman's drowsy charm,
To bless the doors from nightly harm ;
Or let my lamp at midnight hour
Be seen in some high lonely tower,
Where I may oft out-watch the Bear
With thrice-great Hermes, or unsphere
The spirit of Plato, to unfold
What worlds or what vast regions hold
The immortal mind that hath forsook
Her mansion in this fleshly nook ;
And of those demons that are found
In fire, air, flood, or under ground,
Whose power hath a true consent
With planet or with element.
Sometime let gorgeous Tragedy
In sceptred pall come sweeping by,
Presenting Thebes, or Pelops' line,
Or the tale of Troy divine,
Or what (though rare) of later age
Ennobled hath the buskined stage.

But, O sad Virgin, that thy power
Might raise Musæus from his bower !
Or bid the soul of Orpheus sing
Such notes as, warbled to the string,
Drew iron tears down Pluto's cheek,
And made hell grant what love did seek !
Or call up him that left half told
The story of Cambuscan bold, —
Of Camball, and of Algarsife, —
And who had Canacé to wife,
That owned the virtuous ring and glass, —
And of the wondrous horse of brass,
On which the Tartar king did ride !
And, if aught else great bards beside
In sage and solemn tunes have sung, —
Of tourneys and of trophies hung,
Of forests, and enchantments drear,
Where more is meant than meets the ear.

Thus, Night, oft see me in thy pale career,
Till civil-suited Morn appear, —

Not tricked and frounced, as she was wont
With the Attic boy to hunt,
But kerchiefed in a comely cloud,
While rocking winds are piping loud,
Or ushered with a shower still
When the gust hath blown his fill,
Ending on the rustling leaves,
With minute drops from off the eaves.
And when the sun begins to fling
His flaring beams, me, goddess, bring
To archèd walks of twilight groves,
And shadows brown, that Sylvan loves,
Of pine, or monumental oak,
Where the rude axe with heavèd stroke
Was never heard the Nymphs to daunt,
Or fright them from their hallowed haunt.
There in close covert by some brook,
Where no profaner eye may look,
Hide me from day's garish eye,
While the bee with honeyed thigh,
That at her flowery work doth sing,
And the waters murmuring
With such consort as they keep,
Entice the dewy-feathered Sleep ;
And let some strange mysterious dream
Wave at his wings, in airy stream
Of lively portraiture displayed,
Softly on my eyelids laid ;
And, as I wake, sweet music breathe
Above, about, or underneath,
Sent by some Spirit to mortals good,
Or the unseen Genius of the wood.

But let my due feet never fail
To walk the studious cloisters pale,
And love the high embowèd roof,
With antic pillars massy proof,
And storied windows, richly dight,
Casting a dim religious light.
There let the pealing organ blow
To the full-voiced quire below,
In service high and anthems clear,
As may with sweetness, through mine ear,
Dissolve me into ecstasies,
And bring all heaven before mine eyes.

And may at last my weary age
Find out the peaceful hermitage,
The hairy gown and mossy cell,
Where I may sit and rightly spell
Of every star that heaven doth shew,
And every herb that sips the dew,
Till old experience do attain
To something like prophetic strain.

These pleasures, Melancholy, give,
And I with thee will choose to live.

MILTON.

HALLOWED GROUND.

WHAT's hallowed ground?   Has earth a clod
Its Maker meant not should be trod
By man, the image of his God,
     Erect and free,
Unscourged by Superstition's rod
     To bow the knee?

That's hallowed ground where, mourned and
     missed,
The lips repose our love has kissed; —
But where's their memory's mansion?   Is't
     Yon churchyard's bowers?
No! in ourselves their souls exist,
     A part of ours.

A kiss can consecrate the ground
Where mated hearts are mutual bound:
The spot where love's first links were wound,
     That ne'er are riven,
Is hallowed down to earth's profound,
     And up to heaven!

For time makes all but true love old;
The burning thoughts that then were told
Run molten still in memory's mould;
     And will not cool
Until the heart itself be cold
     In Lethe's pool.

What hallows ground where heroes sleep?
'T is not the sculptured piles you heap!
In dews that heavens far distant weep
     Their turf may bloom;
Or Genii twine beneath the deep
     Their coral tomb.

But strew his ashes to the wind
Whose sword or voice has served mankind, —
And is he dead, whose glorious mind
     Lifts thine on high? —
To live in hearts we leave behind
     Is not to die.

Is't death to fall for Freedom's right?
He's dead alone that lacks her light!
And murder sullies in heaven's sight
     The sword he draws: —
What can alone ennoble fight?
     A noble cause!

Give that, — and welcome War to brace
Her drums, and rend heaven's reeking space!
The colors planted face to face,
     The charging cheer,
Though Death's pale horse lead on the chase,
     Shall still be dear.

And place our trophies where men kneel
To Heaven! — but Heaven rebukes my zeal!
The cause of Truth and human weal,
     O God above!
Transfer it from the sword's appeal
     To Peace and Love.

Peace, Love! the cherubim, that join
Their spread wings o'er Devotion's shrine,
Prayers sound in vain, and temples shine,
     Where they are not, —
The heart alone can make divine
     Religion's spot.

To incantations dost thou trust,
And pompous rites in domes august?
See mouldering stones and metal's rust
     Belie the vaunt,
That man can bless one pile of dust
     With chime or chant.

The ticking wood-worm mocks thee, man!
Thy temples, — creeds themselves grow wan!
But there's a dome of nobler span,
     A temple given
Thy faith, that bigots dare not ban, —
     Its space is heaven!

Its roof, star-pictured Nature's ceiling,
Where, trancing the rapt spirit's feeling,
And God himself to man revealing,
     The harmonious spheres
Make music, though unheard their pealing
     By mortal ears.

Fair stars! are not your beings pure?
Can sin, can death, your worlds obscure?
Else why so swell the thoughts at your
     Aspect above?
Ye must be heavens that make us sure
     Of heavenly love!

And in your harmony sublime
I read the doom of distant time;
That man's regenerate soul from crime
     Shall yet be drawn,
And reason on his mortal clime
     Immortal dawn.

What's hallowed ground? 'T is what gives birth
To sacred thoughts in souls of worth! —
Peace! Independence! Truth! go forth
     Earth's compass round;
And your high-priesthood shall make earth
     All hallowed ground.

THOMAS CAMPBELL.

FLOWERS WITHOUT FRUIT.

PRUNE thou thy words ; the thoughts control
  That o'er thee swell and throng ; —
They will condense within thy soul,
  And change to purpose strong.

But he who lets his feelings run
  In soft luxurious flow,
Shrinks when hard service must be done,
  And faints at every woe.

Faith's meanest deed more favor bears,
  Where hearts and wills are weighed,
Than brightest transports, choicest prayers,
  Which bloom their hour, and fade.
                        JOHN HENRY NEWMAN.

REVENGE OF INJURIES.

FROM "MARIAM."

THE fairest action of our human life
Is scorning to revenge an injury :
For who forgives without a further strife
His adversary's heart to him doth tie :
And 't is a firmer conquest truly said
To win the heart than overthrow the head.

If we a worthy enemy do find,
  To yield to worth, it must be nobly done ;
But if of baser metal be his mind,
  In base revenge there is no honor won.
Who would a worthy courage overthrow ?
And who would wrestle with a worthless foe ?

We say our hearts are great, and cannot yield ;
  Because they cannot yield, it proves them poor :
Great hearts are tasked beyond their power but
    seld :
  The weakest lion will the loudest roar.
Truth's school for certain does this same allow,
High-heartedness doth sometimes teach to bow.
                        LADY ELIZABETH CAREW.

A TEAR.

O THAT the chemist's magic art
  Could crystallize this sacred treasure !
Long should it glitter near my heart,
  A secret source of pensive pleasure.

The little brilliant, ere it fell,
  Its lustre caught from Chloe's eye ;
Then, trembling, left its coral cell, —
  The spring of Sensibility !

Sweet drop of pure and pearly light !
  In thee the rays of Virtue shine,
More calmly clear, more mildly bright,
  Than any gem that gilds the mine.

Benign restorer of the soul !
  Who ever fliest to bring relief,
When first we feel the rude control
  Of Love or Pity, Joy or Grief.

The sage's and the poet's theme,
  In every clime, in every age,
Thou charm'st in Fancy's idle dream,
  In Reason's philosophic page.

That very law which moulds a tear,
  And bids it trickle from its source, —
That law preserves the earth a sphere,
  And guides the planets in their course.
                        SAMUEL ROGERS.

MIGNON'S SONG.

FROM "WILHELM MEISTER."

KNOW'ST thou the land where bloom the citron
    bowers,
Where the gold-orange lights the dusky grove ?
High waves the laurel there, the myrtle flowers,
And through a still blue heaven the sweet winds
    rove.
Know'st thou it well ?
                There, there with thee,
O friend, O loved one ! fain my steps would flee

Know'st thou the dwelling ? — there the pillars
    rise,
Soft shines the hall, the painted chambers glow ;
And forms of marble seem with pitying eyes
To say, " Poor child ! what thus hath wrought
    thee woe ? "
Know'st thou it well ?
                There, there with thee,
O my protector ! homewards might I flee !

Know'st thou the mountain ? — high its bridge
    is hung,
Where the mule seeks through mist and cloud
    his way ;
There lurk the dragon-race, deep caves among,
O'er beetling rocks there foams the torrent spray.
Know'st thou it well ?
                With thee, with thee,
There lies my path, O father ! let us flee !
            From the German of GOETHE. Trans-
                lation of FELICIA HEMANS.

THE OLD MAID.

WHY sits she thus in solitude ?   Her heart
  Seems melting in her eyes' delicious blue ;
And as it heaves, her ripe lips lie apart,
  As if to let its heavy throbbings through ;
In her dark eye a depth of softness swells,
  Deeper than that her careless girlhood wore ;
And her cheek crimsons with the hue that tells
  The rich, fair fruit is ripened to the core.

It is her thirtieth birthday !   With a sigh
  Her soul hath turned from youth's luxuriant
    bowers,
And her heart taken up the last sweet tie
  That measured out its links of golden hours !
She feels her inmost soul within her stir
  With thoughts too wild and passionate to
    speak ;
Yet her full heart — its own interpreter —
  Translates itself in silence on her cheek.

Joy's opening buds, affection's glowing flowers,
  Once lightly sprang within her beaming track ;
O, life was beautiful in those lost hours,
  And yet she does not wish to wander back !
No ! she but loves in loneliness to think
  On pleasures past, though nevermore to be ;
Hope links her to the future, — but the link
  That binds her to the past is memory.

                              AMELIA B. WELBY.

LOVE AGAINST LOVE.

As unto blowing roses summer dews,
  Or morning's amber to the tree-top choirs,
So to my bosom are the beams that use
  To rain on me from eyes that love inspires.
Your love, — vouchsafe it, royal-hearted Few,
  And I will set no common price thereon ;
O, I will keep, as heaven his holy blue,
  Or night her diamonds, that dear treasure won.
But aught of inward faith must I forego,
  Or miss one drop from truth's baptismal hand,
Think poorer thoughts, pray cheaper prayers,
    and grow
Less worthy trust, to meet your heart's demand, —
Farewell !   Your wish I for your sake deny :
Rebel to love, in truth to love, am I.

                              DAVID A. WASSON.

A RENUNCIATION.

IF women could be fair, and yet not fond,
  Or that their love were firm, not fickle still,
I would not marvel that they make men bond
  By service long to purchase their good-will ;

But when I see how frail those creatures are,
  I muse that men forget themselves so far.

To mark the choice they make, and how they
    change,
How oft from Phœbus they do flee to Pan ;
Unsettled still, like haggards wild they range,
  These gentle birds that fly from man to man ;
Who would not scorn and shake them from the
    fist,
And let them fly, fair fools, which way they list ?

Yet for disport we fawn and flatter both,
  To pass the time when nothing else can please,
And train them to our lure with subtle oath,
  Till, weary of their wiles, ourselves we ease ;
And then we say when we their fancy try,
To play with fools, O, what a fool was I !

                    EDWARD VERE, EARL OF OXFORD.

FAITH.

BETTER trust all and be deceived,
  And weep that trust and that deceiving,
Than doubt one heart that, if believed,
  Had blessed one's life with true believing.

O, in this mocking world too fast
  The doubting fiend o'ertakes our youth ;
Better be cheated to the last
  Than lose the blessed hope of truth.

                    FRANCES ANNE KEMBLE BUTLER.

THE SUM OF LIFE.

FROM "THE GARDEN" : "THE TASK," BOOK VI.

I WAS a stricken deer, that left the herd
Long since ; with many an arrow deep infixed
My panting side was charged, when I withdrew,
To seek a tranquil death in distant shades.
There was I found by one who had himself
Been hurt by the archers.   In his side he bore,
And in his hands and feet, the cruel scars.
With gentle force soliciting the darts,
He drew them forth, and healed, and bade me live.
Since then, with few associates, in remote
And silent woods I wander, far from those
My former partners of the peopled scene ;
With few associates, and not wishing more.
Here much I ruminate, as much I may,
With other views of men and manners now
Than once, and others of a life to come.
I see that all are wanderers, gone astray
Each in his own delusions ; they are lost
In chase of fancied happiness, still wooed
And never won.   Dream after dream ensues ;

And still they dream, that they shall still succeed ;
And still are disappointed.   Rings the world
With the vain stir.   I sum up half mankind,
And add two-thirds of the remaining half,
And find the total of their hopes and fears
Dreams, empty dreams.

WILLIAM COWPER.

THE WILL.

BEFORE I sigh my last gasp, let me breathe,
Great Love, some legacies : here I bequeathe
Mine eyes to Argus, if mine eyes can see,
If they be blind, then, Love, I give them thee ;
My tongue to Fame ; to embassadors mine ears ;
     To women, or the sea, my tears ;
   Thou, Love, hast taught me heretofore
By making me serve her who had twenty more,
That I should give to none, but such as had too
     much before.

My constancy I to the planets give ;
My truth to them who at the court do live ;
Mine ingenuity and openness
To Jesuits ; to buffoons my pensiveness ;
My silence to any who abroad have been ;
     My money to a Capuchin.
   Thou, Love, taught'st me, by appointing me
To love there, where no love received can be,
Only to give to such as have an incapacity. *

My faith I give to Roman Catholics ;
All my good works unto the schismatics
Of Amsterdam ; my best civility
And courtship to an University ;
My modesty I give to shoulders bare ;
     My patience let gamesters share.
   Thou, Love, taught'st me, by making me
Love her, that holds my love disparity,
Only to give to those that count my gifts indig-
     nity.

I give my reputation to those
Which were my friends ; mine industry to foes ;
To schoolmen I bequeathe my doubtfulness ;
My sickness to physicians, or excess ;
To Nature all that I in rhyme have writ ;
     And to my company my wit.
   Thou, Love, by making me adore
Her, who begot this love in me before,
Taught'st me to make, as though I gave, when I
     do but restore.

To him, for whom the passing-bell next tolls,
I give my physic-books ; my written rolls
Of moral counsels I to Bedlam give :
My brazen medals unto them which live

* No good capacity.

In want of bread ; to them which pass among
     All foreigners, mine English tongue.
Thou, Love, by making me love one
Who thinks her friendship a fit portion
For younger lovers, dost my gifts thus dispro-
     portion.

Therefore I 'll give no more, but I 'll undo
The world by dying ; because Love dies too.
Then all your beauties will be no more worth
Than gold in mines, where none doth draw it
     forth ;
And all your graces no more use shall have,
     Than a sun-dial in a grave.
Thou, Love, taught'st me, by making me
Love her, who doth neglect both me and thee,
To invent and practise this one way to annihilate
all three.

DR. JOHN DONNE.

FRAGMENTS.

THE COURSE OF LIFE.

TIME.

Time rolls his ceaseless course.
   Lady of the Lake, Cant. iii.   SCOTT.

The heavens on high perpetually do move ;
By minutes meal the hour doth steal away,
By hours the days, by days the months remove,
And then by months the years as fast decay ;
Yea, Virgil's verse and Tully's truth do say
That Time flieth, and never claps her wings ;
But rides on clouds, and forward still she flings.
                                   G. GASCOIGNE.

                    On our quick'st decrees
Th' inaudible and noiseless foot of Time
Steals, ere we can effect them.
   All's Well that Ends Well, Act v. *Sc.* 3.   SHAKESPEARE.

And then he drew a dial from his poke,
And, looking on it with lack-lustre eye,
Says very wisely, " It is ten o'clock :
Thus may we see," quoth he, " how the world
     wags :
'T is but an hour ago since it was nine ;
And after one hour more 't will be eleven ;
And so, from hour to hour, we ripe and ripe,
And then, from hour to hour, we rot and rot ;
And thereby hangs a tale."
   As You Like It, Act ii. *Sc.* 7.   SHAKESPEARE.

                    Come what come may,
Time and the hour runs through the roughest day.
   Macbeth, Act i. *Sc.* 3.   SHAKESPEARE.

LIFE.

Let us (since life can little more supply
Than just to look about us, and to die)
Expatiate free o'er all this scene of man ;
A mighty maze ! but not without a plan.

Together let us beat this ample field,
Try why the open, what the covert yield.

Essay on Man, Epistle I.   POPE.

The world's a theatre, the earth a stage
Which God and nature do with actors fill.

Apology for Actors.   T. HEYWOOD.

To-morrow, and to-morrow, and to-morrow,
Creeps in this petty pace from day to day,
To the last syllable of recorded time ;
And all our yesterdays have lighted fools
The way to dusty death.   Out, out, brief candle !
Life's but a walking shadow ; a poor player,
That struts and frets his hour upon the stage,
And then is heard no more : it is a tale
Told by an idiot, full of sound and fury,
Signifying nothing.

Macbeth, Act v. Sc. 5.   SHAKESPEARE.

Life is a jest, and all things show it ;
I thought so once, but now I know it.

My Own Epitaph.   J. GAY.

The web of our life is of a mingled
Yarn, good and ill together.

All's Well that Ends Well, Act iv. Sc. 3.   SHAKESPEARE.

And what's a life ? — a weary pilgrimage,
Whose glory in one day doth fill the stage
With childhood, manhood, and decrepit age.

What is Life?   F. QUARLES.

But thought's the slave of life, and life time's
    fool.

King Henry IV., Pt. I. Act v. Sc. 5.   SHAKESPEARE.

On life's vast ocean diversely we sail,
Reason the card, but passion is the gale.

Essay on Man, Epistle II.   POPE.

MANKIND.

          Man !
Thou pendulum betwixt a smile and tear.

Childe Harold, Cant. iv.   BYRON.

      More servants wait on man
Than he'll take notice of.   In ev'ry path
He treads down that which doth befriend him
When sicknesse makes him pale and wan.
O mightie love ! Man is one world, and hath
    Another to attend him.

Man.   G. HERBERT.

Like leaves on trees the race of man is found,
Now green in youth, now withering on the ground:
Another race the following spring supplies ;
They fall successive, and successive rise.

Iliad, Book vi.   Translation of POPE.   HOMER.

Know then thyself, presume not God to scan ;
The proper study of mankind is man.

Created half to rise, and half to fall ;
Great lord of all things, yet a prey to all ;
Sole judge of truth, in endless error hurled ;
The glory, jest, and riddle of the world !

Essay on Man, Epistle II.   POPE.

THE PAST.

O, call back yesterday, bid time return.

To-day, unhappy day, too late.

King Richard II., Act iii. Sc. 2.   SHAKESPEARE.

         Things without all remedy,
Should be without regard : what's done is done.

Macbeth, Act iii. Sc. 2.   SHAKESPEARE.

Gone, glimmering through the dream of things
    that were,

A school-boy's tale, the wonder of an hour !

Childe Harold, Cant. ii.   BYRON.

Not heaven itself upon the past has power ;
But what has been, has been, and I have had my
    hour.

Imitation of Horace, Book i. Ode 29.   DRYDEN.

          Applause
To that blest son of foresight ; lord of fate !
That awful independent on to-morrow
Whose work is done ; who triumphs in the past ;
Whose yesterdays look backwards with a smile.

Night Thoughts, Night ii.   DR. E. YOUNG.

ACHILLES. . . . What ! are my deeds forgot ?
ULYSSES.   Time hath, my lord, a wallet at his
    back,
Wherein he puts alms for oblivion.

For time is like a fashionable host,
That slightly shakes his parting guest by the
    hand,
And with his arms outstretched, as he would fly,
Grasps-in the comer.   Welcome ever smiles,
And farewell goes out sighing.

Troilus and Cressida, Act iii. Sc. 3.   SHAKESPEARE.

The Present.

This narrow isthmus 'twixt two boundless seas,
The past, the future, two eternities !
Lalla Rookh : The Veiled Prophet of Khorassan. T. MOORE.

Lo ! on a narrow neck of land,
'Twixt two unbounded seas I stand.
Hymn. C. WESLEY.

Heaven from all creatures hides the book of Fate,
All but the page prescribed, their present state.
Essay on Man, Epistle I. POPE.

Nothing is there to come, and nothing past,
But an eternal Now does always last.
Davideis, Vol. I. Book i. A. COWLEY.

Defer not till to-morrow to be wise,
To-morrow's sun to thee may never rise.
Letter to Cobham. W. CONGREVE.

Happy the man, and happy he alone,
He who can call to-day his own :
He who, secure within, can say,
To-morrow, do thy worst, for I have lived to-day.
Imitation of Horace, Book i. *Ode 29.* DRYDEN.

The Future.

The best of prophets of the Future is the Past.
Letter, Jan. 28, 1821. BYRON.

As though there were a tie,
And obligation to posterity.
We get them, bear them, breed and nurse.
What has posterity done for us,
That we, lest they their rights should lose,
Should trust our necks to gripe of noose.
McFingal, Cant. ii. J. TRUMBULL.

All that 's bright must fade, —
The brightest still the fleetest ;
All that 's sweet was made
But to be lost when sweetest !
National Airs : All that 's bright must fade. T. MOORE.

When I consider life, 't is all a cheat.
Yet, fooled with hope, men favor the deceit ;
Trust on, and think to-morrow will repay :
To-morrow 's falser than the former day ;
Lies worse ; and, while it says we shall be blest
With some new joys, cuts off what we possest.
Strange cozenage ! none would live past years
again,
Yet all hope pleasure in what yet remain.
Aureng-Zebe ; or, The Great Mogul, Act iv. *Sc.* i. DRYDEN.

Beware of desperate steps. The darkest day,
Live till to-morrow, will have passed away.
The Needless Alarm. COWPER.

Fate.

Men at some time are masters of their fates ;
The fault, dear Brutus, is not in our stars,
But in ourselves, that we are underlings.
Julius Cæsar, Act i. *Sc. 2.* SHAKESPEARE.

Man is his own star, and the soul that can
Render an honest and a perfect man
Commands all light, all influence, all fate.
Nothing to him falls early, or too late.
Upon an Honest Man's Fortune. J. FLETCHER.

Our remedies oft in ourselves do lie,
Which we ascribe to Heaven : the fated sky
Gives us free scope ; only, doth backward pull
Our slow designs, when we ourselves are dull.
All 's Well that Ends Well, Act i. *Sc.* i. SHAKESPEARE

There 's a divinity that shapes our ends,
Rough-hew them how we will.
Hamlet, Act v. *Sc. 2.* SHAKESPEARE.

I 'll make assurance doubly sure,
And take a bond of Fate.
Macbeth, Act iv. *Sc.* i. SHAKESPEARE

Youth.

Gay hope is theirs, by fancy fed,
Less pleasing when possessed ;
The tear forgot as soon as shed,
The sunshine of the breast.
Theirs buxom health of rosy hue,
Wild wit, invention ever new,
And lively cheer of vigor born ;
The thoughtless day, the easy night,
The spirits pure, the slumbers light.
That fly the approach of morn.
On a Distant Prospect of Eton College. T. GRAY

Long as the year's dull circle seems to run
When the brisk minor pants for twenty-one.
Imitations of Horace, Epistle I. Book i. POPE

Returning, he proclaims by many a grace,
By shrugs and strange contortions of his face,
How much a dunce that has been sent to roam
Excels a dunce that has been kept at home.
The Progress of Error. COWPER.

The nimble-footed mad-cap Prince of Wales,
And his comrades, that daffed the world aside,
And bid it pass.
King Henry IV., Part I. Act iv. *Sc.* i. SHAKESPEARE.

Manhood.

Be wise with speed :
A fool at forty is a fool indeed.
Love of Fame, Satire ii. DR. E. YOUNG.

Not two strong men the enormous weight could
    raise ;
Such men as live in these degenerate days.
    Iliad, Book v. Translation of POPE.   HOMER.

Nor love thy life, nor hate ; but what thou liv'st
Live well ; how long or short permit to heaven.
    Paradise Lost, Book xi.   MILTON.

       What tho' short thy date ?
Virtue, not rolling suns, the mind matures.
That life is long which answers life's great end.
The time that bears no fruit deserves no name.
The man of wisdom is the man of years.
In hoary youth Methusalems may die ;
O, how misdated on their flatt'ring tombs !
    Night Thoughts, Night v.   DR. E. YOUNG.

Live while you live, the epicure would say,
And seize the pleasures of the present day ;
Live while you live, the sacred preacher cries,
And give to God each moment as it flies.
Lord, in my views, let both united be ;
I live in pleasure when I live to thee.
    Epigram on his Family Arms. [Dum vivimus vivamus.]
                        P. DODDRIDGE.

OLD AGE.

            My May of life
Is fall'n into the sear, the yellow leaf ;
And that which should accompany old age,
As honour, love, obedience, troops of friends,
I must not look to have ; but, in their stead,
Curses, not loud, but deep, mouth-honor, breath,
Which the poor heart would fain deny, and dare
    not.
Macbeth, Act v. Sc. 3.   SHAKESPEARE.

And wrinkles, the d——d democrats, won't flatter.
    Don Juan, Cant. x.   BYRON.

Strange ! that a harp of thousand strings
Should keep in tune so long.
    Hymns and Spiritual Songs, Book ii. Hymn 19.   WATTS.

           In sober state,
Through the sequestered vale of rural life,
The venerable patriarch guileless held
The tenor of his way.
    Death.   B. PORTEUS.

       Time has laid his hand
Upon my heart, gently, not smiting it,
But as a harper lays his open palm
Upon his harp, to deaden its vibrations.
    The Golden Legend.   LONGFELLOW.

But grant, the virtues of a temp'rate prime
Bless with an age exempt from scorn or crime ;
An age that melts with unperceived decay,
And glides in modest innocence away.
    Vanity of Human Wishes.   DR. S. JOHNSON.

                 O Heavens,
If you do love old men, if your sweet sway
Allow obedience, if yourselves are old,
Make it your cause ; send down, and take my
    part !
    King Lear, Act ii. Sc. 4.   SHAKESPEARE.

DEATH.

Man wants but little, nor that little long.
How soon he must resign his very dust !
    Night Thoughts, Night iv.   DR. E. YOUNG.

" While there is life, there's hope," he cried ;
"Then why such haste ? " so groaned and died.
    The Sick Man and the Angel.   J. GAY.

Lovely in death the beauteous ruin lay ;
And if in death still lovely, lovelier there ;
Far lovelier ! pity swells the tide of love.
    Night Thoughts, Night iii.   DR. E. YOUNG.

Nothing is here for tears, nothing to wail
Or knock the breast, no weakness, no contempt,
Dispraise or blame, nothing but well and fair,
And what may quiet us in a death so noble.
    Samson Agonistes.   MILTON.

There is a calm for those who weep,
A rest for weary pilgrims found,
They softly lie and sweetly sleep
           Low in the ground.
    The Grave.   J. MONTGOMERY.

IMMORTALITY.

I know no evil death can show, which life
Has not already shown to those who live
Embodied longest. If there be indeed
A shore, where mind survives, 't will be as mind
All unincorporate.
    Sardanapalus.   BYRON.

To be no more — sad cure ; for who would lose,
Though full of pain, this intellectual being,
Those thoughts that wander through eternity,
To perish rather, swallowed up and lost
In the wide womb of uncreated night,
Devoid of sense and motion ?
    Paradise Lost, Book ii.   MILTON.

I have asked that dreadful question of the hills
That look eternal ; of the flowing streams
That lucid flow forever ; of the stars,
Amid whose fields of azure my raised spirit
Hath trod in glory : all were dumb ; but now,
While I thus gaze upon thy living face,
I feel the love that kindles through its beauty
Can never wholly perish : we *shall* meet
Again, Clemanthe !
    Ion.   T. N. TALFOURD.

THE SEXES.

WOMAN.

First, then, a woman will, or won't, depend on 't ;
If she will do 't, she will ; and there 's an end on 't.
But if she won't, since safe and sound your trust is,
Fear is affront, and jealousy injustice.
Epilogue to Zara. A. HILL.

Women, like princes, find few real friends.
Advice to a Lady. LORD LYTTELTON.

What mighty ills have not been done by woman ?
Who was 't betrayed the Capitol ? A woman !
Who lost Mark Antony the world ? A woman !
Who was the cause of a long ten years' war,
And laid at last old Troy in ashes ? Woman !
Destructive, damnable, deceitful woman !
The Orphan, Act iii. Sc. 1. T. OTWAY.

She and comparisons are odious.
The Comparison. DR. J. DONNE.

So doth one sound the sleeping spirit wake
To brave the danger, and to bear the harm —
A low and gentle voice — dear woman's chiefest
   charm.

An excellent thing it is ! and ever lent
   To truth and love, and meekness ; they who
      own
This gift, by the all-gracious Giver sent,
   Ever by quiet step and smile are known ;
By kind eyes that have wept, hearts that have
      sorrowed —
By patience never tired, from their own trials
      borrowed.
Woman's Voice. E. ARNOLD.

Woman's gentle brain.
As You Like It, Act iv. Sc. 3. SHAKESPEARE.

Not she with traitorous kiss her Saviour stung,
Not she denied him with unholy tongue ;
She, while apostles shrank, could danger brave,
Last at his cross and earliest at his grave.
Woman, her Character and Influence. E. S. BARRETT.

And yet believe me, good as well as ill,
Woman's at best a contradiction still.
Moral Essays, Epistle II. POPE.

A native grace
Sat fair-proportioned in her polished limbs,
Veiled in a simple robe their best attire,
Beyond the pomp of dress ; for loveliness
Needs not the foreign aid of ornament,
But is, when unadorned, adorned the most.
The Seasons : Autumn. J. THOMSON.

The maid who modestly conceals
Her beauties, while she hides, reveals ;
Give but a glimpse, and fancy draws
Whate'er the Grecian Venus was.
The Spider and the Bee. E. MOORE.

Th' adorning thee with so much art
   Is but a barb'rous skill ;
'T is like the poisoning of a dart,
   Too apt before to kill.
The Waiting-Maid. A. COWLEY.

For where is any author in the world
Teaches such beauty as a woman's eye ?
Love's Labor's Lost, Act iv. Sc. 3. SHAKESPEARE.

Woman may err, woman may give her mind
To evil thoughts, and lose her pure estate ;
But, for one woman who affronts her kind
By wicked passions and remorseless hate,
A thousand make amends in age and youth,
By heavenly pity, by sweet sympathy,
By patient kindness, by enduring truth,
By love, supremest in adversity.
Praise of Women. CH. MACKAY.

Accuse not Nature, she hath done her part ;
Do thou but thine.
Paradise Lost, Book viii. MILTON.

MAN — WOMAN.

If the heart of a man is depressed with cares,
The mist is dispelled when a woman appears.
The Beggar's Opera, Act ii. Sc. 1. J. GAY.

Without the smile from partial beauty won,
O, what were man ? — a world without a sun.
Pleasures of Hope, Part II. T. CAMPBELL

She 's beautiful, and therefore to be wooed ;
She is a woman, therefore to be won.
King Henry VI., Part I. Act v. Sc. 3. SHAKESPEARE.

He was a lover of the good old school,
Who still become more constant as they cool.
Beppo, Cant. xxxiv. BYRON.

We cannot fight for love as men may do ;
We should be wooed, and were not made to woo.
Midsummer Night's Dream, Act ii. Sc. 1. SHAKESPEARE.

I give thee all — I can no more,
   Though poor the offering be ;
My heart and lute are all the store
   That I can bring to thee.
My Heart and Lute. T. MOORE.

Since maids, in modesty, say " No " to that
Which they would have the profferer construe
      "Ay."
Two Gentlemen of Verona, Act i. Sc. 2.   SHAKESPEARE.

The woman that deliberates is lost.
      Cato, Act iv. Sc. 1.   T. ADDISON.

My friends were poor but honest ; so 's my love.
Be not offended, for it hurts not him
That he is loved of me.
      All's Well that Ends Well, Act i. Sc. 3.   SHAKESPEARE.

In her first passion, woman loves her lover :
In all the others, all she loves is love.
      Don Juan, Cant. iii.   BYRON.

True as the needle to the pole,
   Or as the dial to the sun ;
Constant as gliding waters roll,
   Whose swelling tides obey the moon ;
From every other charmer free,
My life and love shall follow thee.
      Song.   B. BOOTH.

Was ever woman in this humor wooed ?
Was ever woman in this humor won ?
      King Richard III., Act i. Sc. 2.   SHAKESPEARE.

Man's love is of man's life a thing apart ;
   'T is woman's whole existence. Man may range
The court, camp, church, the vessel, and the mart,
   Sword, gown, gain, glory, offer in exchange
Pride, fame, ambition, to fill up his heart,
   And few there are whom these cannot estrange :
Men have all these resources, we but one, —
To love again, and be again undone.
      Don Juan, Cant. i.   BYRON.

Thou wouldst be loved ? — then let thy heart
   From its present pathway part not !
Being everything which now thou art,
   Be nothing which thou art not.
So with the world thy gentle ways,
   Thy grace, thy more than beauty,
Shall be an endless theme of praise,
   And love — a simple duty.
To F. S. O.   E. A. POE.

All these good parts a perfect woman make ;
Add love to me, they make a perfect wife ;
Without her love, her beauty I should take
As that of pictures dead — *that* gives it life ;
Till then her beauty, like the sun, doth shine
Alike to all ; — *that* only makes it mine.
A Wife.   SIR T. OVERBURY.

And oft, when half induced to tread
   Such paths as unto sin decoy,
I 've felt her fond hand press my head,
   And that soft touch hath saved her boy !
The Mother's Hand.   C. SWAIN.

CHARACTER AND ACTION.

VIRTUE.

The world in all doth but two nations bear,
The good, the bad, and these mixed everywhere.
      The Loyal Scot.   A. MARVELL.

He that has light within his own clear breast
May sit in the centre and enjoy bright day ;
But he that hides a dark soul and foul thoughts
Benighted walks under the midday sun.
      Comus.   MILTON.

What nothing earthly gives or can destroy, —
The soul's calm sunshine, and the heartfelt joy,
Is Virtue's prize.
      Essay on Man, Epistle IV.   POPE.

The morning pearls
Dropt in the lily's spotless bosom
Are less chastely cold,
Ere the meridian sun
Has kissed them into heat.
      Chastity.   W. CHAMBERLAYNE.

1ST BROTHER.   What hidden strength,
Unless the strength of Heaven, if you mean that ?
   2D BROTHER. I mean that too, but yet a
      hidden strength
Which, if Heaven gave it, may be termed her arm
'T is chastity, my Brother, chastity :
She that has that is clad in complete steel.

   .   .   .   .   .

So dear to heaven is saintly chastity,
That, when a soul is found sincerely so,
A thousand liveried angels lacky her,
Driving far off each thing of sin and guilt.
      Comus.   MILTON.

Adieu, dear, amiable youth !
   Your heart can ne'er be wanting !
May prudence, fortitude, and truth
   Erect your brow undaunting !
In ploughman phrase, " God send you speed,"
   Still daily to grow wiser ;
And may you better reck the rede,
   Than ever did the adviser !
Epistle to a Young Friend.   R. BURNS.

What stronger breastplate than a heart untainted !
Thrice is he armed that has his quarrel just ;
And he but naked, though locked up in steel,
Whose conscience with injustice is corrupted.
      King Henry VI., Part II. Act iii. Sc. 2.   SHAKESPEARE.

True, conscious honor is to feel no sin ;
He 's armed without that 's innocent within.
      Imitations of Horace, Epistle I. Book 1.   POPE.

Be noble ! and the nobleness that lies
In other men, sleeping, but never dead,
Will rise in majesty to meet thine own.
Sonnet.   J. R. LOWELL.

This above all, — to thine own self be true ;
And it must follow, as the night the day,
Thou canst not then be false to any man.

Hamlet, Act i. *Sc.* 3.   SHAKESPEARE.

And thus he bore without abuse
  The grand old name of gentleman,
  Defamed by every charlatan,
And soiled with all ignoble use.

In Memoriam, cx.   TENNYSON.

NOBLE LIVING.

                    If our virtues
Did not go forth of us, 't were all alike
As if we had them not. Spirits are not finely
    touched,
But to fine issues ; nor Nature never lends
The smallest scruple of her excellence,
But, like a thrifty goddess, she determines
Herself the glory of a creditor —
Both thanks and use.

Measure for Measure, Act i. *Sc.* 1.   SHAKESPEARE.

The flighty purpose never is o'ertook,
Unless the deed go with it.

Macbeth, Act iv. *Sc.* 1.   SHAKESPEARE.

Our acts our angels are, or good or ill,
Our fatal shadows that walk by us still.

An Honest Man's Fortune.   J. FLETCHER.

That light we see is burning in my hall.
How far that little candle throws his beams !
So shines a good deed in a naughty world.

Merchant of Venice, Act v. *Sc.* 1.   SHAKESPEARE.

DUTY.

When I 'm not thanked at all, I 'm thanked
    enough.
I 've done my duty, and I 've done no more.

Tom Thumb the Great, Act i. *Sc.* 3.   H. FIELDING.

Stern Daughter of the Voice of God !
O Duty !
        .   .   .   .
Through no disturbance of my soul,
Or strong compunction in me wrought,
I supplicate for thy control ;
But in the quietness of thought.

To humbler functions, awful Power !
I call thee : I myself commend
Unto thy guidance from this hour ;
O, let my weakness have an end !
Give unto me, made lowly wise,
The spirit of self-sacrifice ;
The confidence of reason give ;
And in the light of truth thy bondman let me live !

Ode to Duty.   WORDSWORTH.

HONESTY.

                    You yourself
Are much condemned to have an itching palm.
        .   .   .   .   .
There is no terror, Cassius, in your threats ;
For I am armed so strong in honesty,
That they pass by me as the idle wind,
Which I respect not.

Julius Cæsar, Act iv. *Sc.* 3.   SHAKESPEARE.

FALSEHOOD.

Who dares think one thing, and another tell,
My heart detests him as the gates of hell.

Iliad, Book ix. *Translation of* POPE.   HOMER.

                    Like one,
Who having, unto truth, by telling of it,
Made such a sinner of his memory,
To credit his own lie.

The Tempest, Act i. *Sc.* 2.   SHAKESPEARE.

                    He was a man
Who stole the livery of the court of Heaven
To serve the Devil in.

Course of Time, Book viii.   R. POLLOK.

The Devil can cite Scripture for his purpose.
An evil soul, producing holy witness,
Is like a villain with a smiling cheek,
A goodly apple rotten at the heart.
O, what a goodly outside falsehood hath !

Merchant of Venice, Act i. *Sc.* 3.   SHAKESPEARE.

BENEVOLENCE.

That man may last, but never lives,
Who much receives but nothing gives ;
Whom none can love, whom none can thank,
Creation's blot, creation's blank.

When Jesus dwelt.   T. GIBBONS.

Do good by stealth, and blush to find it fame.

Epilogue to Satires, Dial. i.   POPE.

Who builds a church to God, and not to fame,
Will never mark the marble with his name :
Go, search it there, where to be born and die,
Of rich and poor makes all the history ;
Enough that virtue filled the space between.
Proved by the ends of being to have been.

Moral Essays, Epistle III.   POPE.

B.* O say, what sums that generous hand
    supply ?
What mines to swell that boundless charity ?
  P.† Of debts and taxes, wife and children clear,
This man possessed — five hundred pounds a year.
Blush, grandeur, blush ; proud courts, withdraw
    your blaze !
Ye little stars, hide your diminished rays !

Moral Essays, Epistle III.   POPE.

- Lord Bathurst.   † Pope.

MERCY.

Sweet mercy is nobility's true badge.

Titus Andronicus, Act i. *Sc.* 2.   SHAKESPEARE.

The quality of mercy is not strained, —
It droppeth as the gentle rain from heaven
Upon the place beneath : it is twice blessed, —
It blesseth him that gives, and him that takes :
'T is mightiest in the mightiest ; it becomes
The thronèd monarch better than his crown ;
His sceptre shows the force of temporal power,
The attribute to awe and majesty,
Wherein doth sit the dread and fear of kings :
But mercy is above this sceptred sway, —
It is enthronèd in the hearts of kings,
It is an attribute to God himself ;
And earthly power doth then show likest God's,
When mercy seasons justice.

Merchant of Venice, Act iv. *Sc.* 1.   SHAKESPEARE.

———

FOLLY AND WISDOM.

Wisdom is ofttimes nearer when we stoop
Than when we soar.

The Excursion, Book iii.   WORDSWORTH.

                    To know
That which before us lies in daily life
Is the prime wisdom.

Paradise Lost, Book viii.   MILTON.

Good sense, which only is the gift of Heaven,
And though no science, fairly worth the seven.

Moral Essays, Epistle IV.   POPE.

The weak have remedies, the wise have joys,
Superior wisdom is superior bliss.

Night Thoughts, Night viii.   DR. E. YOUNG.

Be wisely worldly, be not worldly wise.

Emblems, Book ii.   F. QUARLES.

                    With wisdom fraught,
Not such as books, but such as practice taught.

On the King's Return.   E. WALLER.

Who are a little wise the best fools be.

The Triple Fool.   DR. J. DONNE.

For fools rush in where angels fear to tread.

Essay on Criticism, Part III.   POPE.

Those that I rev'rence, those I fear — the wise ;
At fools I laugh, not fear them.

Cymbeline, Act iv. *Sc.* 2.   SHAKESPEARE.

In idle wishes fools supinely stay ;
Be there a will, and wisdom finds a way.

The Birth of Flattery.   G. CRABBE.

Some positive, persisting fools we know,
Who, if once wrong, will need be always so ;
But you with pleasure own your errors past,
And make each day a critique on the last.

POPE.

Yet proud of parts, with prudence some dispense,
And play the fool because they 're men of sense.

Epistle to Pope.   DR. E. YOUNG.

This fellow 's wise enough to play the fool ;
And to do that well craves a kind of wit.

Twelfth Night, Act iii. *Sc.* 1.   SHAKESPEARE.

———

GOOD NATURE AND RECKLESSNESS.

Care to our coffin adds a nail, no doubt,
And every grin, so merry, draws one out.

Expostulatory Odes : xv.   DR. WOLCOTT (*Peter Pindar*).

But evil is wrought by want of thought
As well as want of heart.

The Lady's Dream.   T. HOOD.

———

FORGIVENESS AND RESENTMENT.

The smallest worm will turn, being trodden on.
And doves will peck in safeguard at their brood.

King Henry VI., Part III. Act ii. *Sc.* 2.   SHAKESPEARE.

Forgiveness to the injured does belong ;
But they ne'er pardon who have done the wrong.

Conquest of Granada, Part II. Act i. *Sc.* 2.   DRYDEN.

Good nature and good sense must ever join ;
To err is human, to forgive divine.

Essay on Criticism, Part II.   POPE.

———

AMBITION.

                    I have no spur
To prick the sides of my intent ; but only
Vaulting ambition, which o'er-leaps itself,
And falls on the other.

Macbeth, Act i. *Sc.* 7.   SHAKESPEARE.

But wild ambition loves to slide, not stand,
And Fortune's ice prefers to Virtue's land.

Absalom and Achitophel, Part I.   DRYDEN

And he that stands upon a slippery place
Makes nice of no vile hold to stay him up.

King John, Act iii. *Sc.* 4.   SHAKESPEARE,

Ambition's monstrous stomach does increase
By eating, and it fears to starve unless
It still may feed, and all it sees devour.

Playhouse to Let.   SIR W. DAVENANT.

Lowliness is young ambition's ladder,
Whereto the climber-upward turns his face ;
But when he once attains the upmost round,
He then unto the ladder turns his back,
Looks in the clouds, scorning the base degrees
By which he did ascend.

Julius Cæsar, Act ii. *Sc.* 1.   SHAKESPEARE.

To reign is worth ambition, though in hell :
Better to reign in hell, than serve in heaven.

Paradise Lost, Book i.   MILTON.

THE RULING PASSION.

The ruling passion, be it what it will,
The ruling passion conquers reason still.

.   .   .   .   .

Hear then the truth : 'T is Heav'n each passion
    sends
And different men directs to different ends.
Extremes in nature equal good produce ;
Extremes in man concur to general use.

Moral Essays, Epistle III.   POPE.

And hence one master-passion in the breast,
Like Aaron's serpent, swallows up the rest.

Essay on Man, Epistle II.   POPE.

SELF-CONCEIT.

To observations which ourselves we make,
We grow more partial for the observer's sake.

Moral Essays, Epistle I.   POPE.

'T is with our judgments as our watches, none
Go just alike, yet each believes his own.

Essay on Criticism, Part I.   POPE.

PRIDE AND VANITY.

'T is pride, rank pride, and haughtiness of soul ;
I think the Romans call it stoicism.

Cato, Act i. *Sc.* 4.   J. ADDISON.

In pride, in reasoning pride, our error lies ;
All quit their sphere and rush into the skies.

Essay on Man, Epistle I.   POPE.

Pride, like an eagle, builds among the stars.

Night Thoughts, Night v.   DR. E. YOUNG.

Of all the causes which conspire to blind
Man's erring judgment, and misguide the mind,
What the weak head with strongest bias rules,
Is pride, the never failing vice of fools.

Essay on Criticism, Part II.   POPE.

As eddies draw things frivolous and light,
How is man's heart by vanity drawn in !

Night Thoughts, Night viii.   DR. E. YOUNG.

The fashion wears out more apparel than the man.

Much Ado about Nothing, Act iii. *Sc.* 3.   SHAKESPEARE.

Nothing exceeds in ridicule, no doubt,
A fool in fashion, but a fool that 's out ;
His passion for absurdity 's so strong
He cannot bear a rival in the wrong.
Though wrong the mode, comply : more sense
    is shown
In wearing others' follies than our own.

Night Thoughts.   DR. E. YOUNG.

Sir Plume (of amber snuff-box justly vain,
And the nice conduct of a clouded cane),
With earnest eyes, and round unthinking face,
He first the snuff-box opened, then the case.

Rape of the Lock.   POPE.

PHASES OF FEELING.

PAIN AND WEARINESS.

So when a raging fever burns,
We shift from side to side by turns,
And 't is a poor relief we gain
To change the place, but keep the pain.

Hymns and Spiritual Songs, Book ii. *Hymn* 146.   WATTS.

Till this heroic lesson thou hast learned :
To frown at pleasure, and to smile in pain.

Night Thoughts, Night viii.   DR. E. YOUNG.

There 's nothing in this world can make me joy
Life is as tedious as a twice-told tale,
Vexing the dull ear of a drowsy man.

King John, Act iii. *Sc.* 4.   SHAKESPEARE.

My heart is drowned with grief,
My body round engirt with misery ;
For what 's more miserable than discontent ?

King Henry VI., Part II. Act iii. *Sc.* 1.   SHAKESPEARE.

        Grief hath changed me,
And careful hours, with Time's deformèd hand,
Hath written strange defeatures in my face.

Comedy of Errors, Act v. *Sc.* i.   SHAKESPEARE.

REMORSE AND RETRIBUTION.

The mind is its own place, and in itself
Can make a heaven of hell, a hell of heaven.

Paradise Lost, Book i.   MILTON.

Amid the roses fierce Repentance rears
Her snaky crest.

The Seasons : Spring.   J. THOMSON.

The thorns which I have reaped are of the tree
I planted — they have torn me, and I bleed ;
I should have known what fruit would spring
    from such a seed.
Childe Harold, Cant. iv.   BYRON.

               We but teach
Bloody instructions, which, being taught, return
To plague the inventor.   This even-handed jus-
    tice
Commends the ingredients of our poisoned chalice
To our own lips.
    Macbeth, Act i. *Sc.* 7.   SHAKESPEARE.

So the struck eagle, stretched upon the plain,
No more through rolling clouds to soar again,
Viewed his own feather on the fatal dart,
And winged the shaft that quivered in his heart.
    English Bards and Scotch Reviewers.   BYRON.

DESPAIR.

Talk not of comfort ; 't is for lighter ills :
I will indulge my sorrows, and give way
To all the pangs and fury of despair.
    Cato.   J. ADDISON.

And, in that deep and utter agony,
Though then than ever most unfit to die,
I fell upon my knees and prayed for death.
    Bertram.   C. MATURIN.

            All hope is lost
Of my reception into grace ; what worse,
For where no hope is left, is left no fear.
    Paradise Regained.   MILTON.

Hope ! let the wretch, once conscious of the joy,
Whom now despairing agonies destroy,
Speak, for he can, and none so well as he,
What treasures centre, what delights, in thee.
    Hope.   COWPER.

It is to hope, though hope were lost.
    Come here, fond youth.   A. L. BARBAULD.

FEAR AND DOUBT.

         Our doubts are traitors,
And make us lose the good we oft might win,
By fearing to attempt.
    Measure for Measure, Act i. *Sc.* 2.   SHAKESPEARE.

LADY MACBETH. Letting *I dare not* wait
    upon *I would,*
Like the poor cat i' the adage.
    MACBETH.   Prythee, peace :
I dare do all that may become a man ;
Who dares do more, is none.
    Macbeth, Act i. *Sc.* 7.   SHAKESPEARE.

But now, I am cabined, cribbed, confined, bound in
To saucy doubts and fears.
    Macbeth, Act iii. *Sc.* 4.   SHAKESPEARE.

Attempt the end, and never stand to doubt ;
Nothing 's so hard but search will find it out.
    Seek and Find.   R. HERRICK.

Tender-handed stroke a nettle,
    And it stings you for your pains ;
Grasp it like a man of mettle,
    And it soft as silk remains.
Verses written on a Window in Scotland.   A. HILL.

Fortune her gifts may variously dispose,
And these be happy called, unhappy those ;
But Heaven's just balance equal will appear,
When those are placed in *hope,* and these in *fear.*
Not present good or ill the joy or curse,
But future views of better or of worse.
    Essay on Man, Epistle III.   POPE.

           Often do the spirits
Of great events stride on before the events,
And in to-day already walks to-morrow.
    The Death of Wallenstein.   S. T. COLERIDGE.

HOPE.

Hope ! of all ills that men endure,
The only cheap and universal cure !

Hope ! thou first-fruits of happiness !
Thou gentle dawning of a bright success !

Brother of Faith ! 'twixt whom and thee
The joys of Heaven and Earth divided be !
    For Hope.   A. COWLEY.

Hope ! thou nurse of young desire.
    Love in a Village, Act i. *Sc.* 1.   I. BICKERSTAFF.

True hope is swift, and flies with swallow's wings ;
Kings it makes gods, and meaner creatures kings.
    King Richard III., Act v. *Sc.* 2.   SHAKESPEARE.

Hope, like a cordial, innocent though strong,
Man's heart at once inspirits and serenes ;
Nor makes him pay his wisdom for his joys.
    Night Thoughts.   DR. E. YOUNG.

Hope, like the glimm'ring taper's light,
    Adorns and cheers the way ;
And still, as darker grows the night,
    Emits a brighter ray.
    The Captivity, Act ii.   GOLDSMITH.

Thy wish was father, Harry, to that thought.
    King Henry IV., Part II. Act iv. *Sc.* 4.   SHAKESPEARE.

Cease, every joy, to glimmer on my mind,
But leave — oh ! leave the light of Hope behind !
    Pleasures of Hope, Part II.   T. CAMPBELL.

Among the Redwoods

FAREWELL to such a world! Too long I press
  The crowded pavement with unwilling feet.
Pity makes pride, and hate breeds hatefulness,
  And both are poisons.   In the forest sweet
The shade, the peace!   Immensity, that seems
To drown the human life of doubts and dreams.

Far off the massive portals of the wood,
  Buttressed with shadow, misty-blue, serene,
Waited my coming.   Speedily I stood
  Where the dun wall rose roofed in plumy green.
Dare one go in?—Glance backward!   Dusk as night
Each column, fringed with sprays of amber light.

Let me, along this fallen bole, at rest,
  Turn to the cool, dim roof my glowing face.
Delicious dark on weary eyelids prest!
  Enormous solitude of silent space,
But for a low and thunderous ocean sound,
Too far to hear, felt thrilling through the ground.

No stir nor call the sacred hush profanes;
  Save when from some bare tree-top, far on high,
Fierce disputations of the clamorous cranes
  Fall muffled, as from out the upper sky.
So still, one dreads to wake the dreaming air,
Breaks a twig softly, moves the foot with care.

The hollow dome is green with empty shade,
  Struck through with slanted shafts of afternoon;
Aloft, a little rift of blue is made,
  Where slips a ghost that last night was the moon.
Beside its pearl a sea-cloud stays its wing,
Beneath, a tilted hawk is balancing.

AMONG THE REDWOODS.
Continued.

The heart feels not in every time and mood
  What is around it.   Dull as any stone
I lay; then, like a darkening dream, the wood
  Grew Karnac's temple, where I breathed alone
In the awed air strange incense, and uprose
Dim, monstrous columns in their dread repose.

The mind not always sees; but if there shine
  A bit of fern-lace bending over moss,
A silky glint that rides a spider-line,
  On a trefoil two shadow spears that cross,
Three grasses that toss up their nodding heads,
With spring and curve like clustered fountain-threads,

Suddenly, through side windows of the eye,
  Deep solitudes, where never souls have met;
Vast spaces, forest corridors that lie
  In a mysterious world, unpeopled yet.
Because the outward eye was elsewhere caught,
The awfulness and wonder come unsought.

If death be but resolving back again
  Into the world's deep soul, this is a kind
Of quiet, happy death, untouched by pain
  Or sharp reluctance.   For I feel my mind
Is interfused with all I hear and see;
As much a part of All as cloud or tree.

Listen! A deep and solemn wind on high;
  The shafts of shining dust shift to and fro;
The columned trees sway imperceptibly,
  And creak as mighty masts when trade-winds blow.
The cloudy sails are set; the earth ship swings
Along the sea of space to grander things.

EDWARD ROWLAND SILL.

Besides what hope the never-ending flight
Of future days may bring.
Paradise Lost, Book ii. MILTON.

Hope humbly then ; with trembling pinions
soar ;
Wait the great teacher Death, and God adore.
What future bliss he gives not thee to know,
But gives that hope to be thy blessing now.
Hope springs eternal in the human breast :
Man never is, but always to be, blest.
The soul, uneasy and confined from home,
Rests and expatiates in a life to come.
Essay on Man, Epistle I. POPE.

'T is expectation makes a blessing dear ;
Heaven were not heaven, if we knew what it were.
Against Fruition. SIR JOHN SUCKLING.

DISAPPOINTMENT.

We 're charmed with distant views of happiness,
But near approaches make the prospect less.
Against Enjoyment. T. YALDEN.

Oft expectation fails, and most oft there
Where most it promises ; and oft it hits
Where hope is coldest, and despair most fits.
All's Well that Ends Well, Act ii. *Sc.* 1. SHAKESPEARE.

As distant prospects please us, but when near
We find but desert rocks and fleeting air.
The Dispensatory, Cant. iii. S. GARTH.

Why wish for more ?
Wishing, of all employments, is the worst ;
Philosophy's reverse and health's decay.
Night Thoughts, Night iv. DR. E. YOUNG.

MEMORY.

While memory holds a seat
In this distracted globe. Remember thee ?
Yea, from the table of my memory
I 'll wipe away all trivial fond records,
All saws of books, all forms, all pressures past,
That youth and observation copied there ;
And thy commandment all alone shall live
Within the book and volume of my brain.
Hamlet, Act i. *Sc.* 5. SHAKESPEARE.

The leaves of memory seem to make
A mournful rustling in the dark.
The Fire of Drift-wood. LONGFELLOW.

Remembrance and reflection how allied !
What thin partitions sense from thought divide !
Essay on Man, Epistle I. POPE.

And, when the stream
Which overflowed the soul was passed away,
A consciousness remained that it had left,
Deposited upon the silent shore
Of memory, images and precious thoughts
That shall not die, and cannot be destroyed.
The Excursion, Book vii. WORDSWORTH

Joys too exquisite to last,
—And yet *more* exquisite when past.
The Little Cloud. J. MONTGOMERY.

How blessings brighten as they take their flight !
Night Thoughts, Night ii. DR. E. YOUNG.

The face recalls some face, as 't were with pain,
You once have seen, but ne'er will see again.
Beppo, Cant. xiii. BYRON.

Absent or dead, still let a friend be dear,
(A sigh the absent claims, the dead a tear.)
Epistle to Robert, Earl of Oxford, and Earl of Mortimer. POPE.

For it so falls out,
That what we have we prize not to the worth,
Whiles we enjoy it, but being lacked and lost,
Why, then we rack the value ; then we find
The virtue, that possession would not show us
Whiles it was ours. So will it fare with Claudio:
When he shall hear she died upon his words,
Th' idea of her life shall sweetly creep
Into his study of imagination,
And every lovely organ of her life
Shall come apparelled in more precious habit,
More moving-delicate, and full of life,
Into the eye and prospect of his soul,
Than when she lived indeed.
Much Ado about Nothing, Act iv. *Sc.* 1. SHAKESPEARE

PHASES OF FORTUNE.

FORTUNE.

Fortune, men say, doth give too much to many,
But yet she never gave enough to any.
Epigrams. SIR J. HARRINGTON.

Are there not, dear Michal,
Two points in the adventure of the diver,
One — when, a beggar, he prepares to plunge ?
One — when, a prince, he rises with his pearl ?
Festus, I plunge.
Paracelsus. R. BROWNING.

When Fortune means to men most good,
She looks upon them with a threatening eye.
King John, Act iii. *Sc.* 4 SHAKESPEARE

Yet true it is, as cow chews cud,
And trees, at spring, do yield forth bud,
Except wind stands, as never it stood,
It is an ill wind turns none to good.
The Winds.   T. TUSSER.

There is some soul of goodness in things evil,
Would men observingly distil it out.
King Henry V., Act iv. Sc. 1.   SHAKESPEARE.

For 't is a truth well known to most,
That whatsoever thing is lost,
We seek it, ere it come to light,
In every cranny but the right.
The Retired Cat.   COWPER.

                I have set my life upon a cast,
And I will stand the hazard of the die.
King Richard III., Act v. Sc. 4.   SHAKESPEARE.

ELEMENTS OF SUCCESS.

MACBETH. If we should fail, —
LADY MACBETH.   We fail !
But screw your courage to the sticking place,
And we 'll not fail.
Macbeth, Act i. Sc. 7.   SHAKESPEARE.

In the lexicon of youth, which fate reserves
For a bright manhood, there is no such word
As — *fail.*
Richelieu, Act ii. Sc. 2.   BULWER-LYTTON.

The star of the unconquered will.
The Light of Stars.   LONGFELLOW.

'T is not in mortals to command success,
But we 'll do more, Sempronius ; we 'll deserve it.
Cato, Act i. Sc. 2.   J. ADDISON.

To maken vertue of necessite.
The Knightes Tale.   CHAUCER.

And many strokes, though with a little axe,
Hew down and fell the hardest-timbered oak.
King Henry VI., Part III., Act ii. Sc. 1.   SHAKESPEARE.

Striving to better, oft we mar what 's well.
King Lear, Act i. Sc. 4.   SHAKESPEARE.

A wild dedication of yourselves
To unpathed waters, undreamed shores.
Winter's Tale, Act iv. Sc. 3.   SHAKESPEARE.

   There is a tide in the affairs of men,
Which, taken at the flood, leads on to fortune ;
Omitted, all the voyage of their life
Is bound in shallows and in miseries.
On such a full sea are we now afloat ;
And we must take the current when it serves,
Or lose our ventures.
Julius Cæsar, Act iv. Sc. 3.   SHAKESPEARE.

In my school-days, when I had lost one shaft,
I shot his fellow of the self-same flight
The self-same way, with more advisèd watch,
To find the other forth ; and by adventuring both,
I oft found both.
Merchant of Venice, Act i. Sc. 1.   SHAKESPEARE.

Who breaketh his credit, or cracketh it twice,
Trust such, with a süerty, if ye be wise :
Or if he be angry, for asking thy due,
Once even, to him afterward, lend not anew.
Good Husbandry Lessons.   T. TUSSER.

He is well paid that is well satisfied.
Merchant of Venice, Act iv. Sc. 1.   SHAKESPEARE.

A PROPHECY OF ENTERPRISE.
[1781.]

Soon shall thy arm, unconquered steam ! afar
Drag the slow barge, or drive the rapid car ;
Or on wide waving wings expanded bear
The flying-chariot through the field of air.
The Botanic Garden, Part I. Ch. 1.   E. DARWIN.

POVERTY.

                Take physic, pomp ;
Expose thyself to feel what wretches feel.
King Lear, Act iii. Sc. 4.   SHAKESPEARE.

Through tattered clothes small vices do appear ;
Robes and furred gowns hide all.
King Lear, Act iv. Sc. 6.   SHAKESPEARE.

Yon friendless man, at whose dejected eye
Th' unfeeling proud one looks, and passes by,
Condemned on penury's barren path to roam,
Scorned by the world, and left without a home.
Pleasures of Hope.   T. CAMPBELL.

Rest here, distrest by poverty no more.
Epitaph on C. Philips.   DR. S. JOHNSON.

RICHES.

Gold ! gold ! gold ! gold !
Bright and yellow, hard and cold,
Molten, graven, hammered and rolled ;
Heavy to get, and light to hold ;
Hoarded, bartered, bought, and sold,
Stolen, borrowed, squandered, doled :
Spurned by the young, but hugged by the old
To the very verge of the churchyard mould ;
Price of many a crime untold :
Gold ! gold ! gold ! gold !
Good or bad a thousand-fold !
   How widely its agencies vary, —
To save, to ruin, to curse, to bless, —
As even its minted coins express,
Now stamped with the image of good Queen Bess
   And now of a Bloody Mary.
Miss Kilmansegg.   T. HOOD.

Mammon, the least erected spirit that fell
From heaven ; for even in heaven his looks and
    thoughts
Were always downward bent, admiring more
The riches of heaven's pavement, trodden gold,
Than aught divine or holy else enjoyed
In vision beatific.
  Paradise Lost, Book i.   MILTON.

Religious, punctual, frugal, and so forth ;
His word would pass for more than he was worth.
One solid dish his week-day meal affords,
An added pudding solemnized the Lord's.
Constant at church and change, his gains were
    sure,
His giving rare, save farthings to the poor.
  Moral Essays, Epistle III.   POPE.

The devil was piqued such saintship to behold,
And longed to tempt him, like good Job of old ;
For Satan now is wiser than of yore,
And tempts by making rich, not making poor.
  Moral Essays, Epistle III.   POPE.

Here Wisdom calls, " Seek virtue first, be bold ;
As gold to silver, virtue is to gold."
There London's voice, " Get money, money still,
And then let Virtue follow if she will."
  Imitations of Horace, Epistle I. Book i.   POPE.

             Be but great,
With praise or infamy — leave that to fate ;
Get place and wealth ; if possible, with grace ;
If not, by any means get wealth and place.
  Imitations of Horace, Epistle I. Book i.   POPE.

For what is worth in anything,
But so much money as 't will bring ?
  Hudibras, Part II.   DR. S. BUTLER.

You have too much respect upon the world :
They lose it, that do buy it with much care.
  Merchant of Venice, Act i. *Sc.* 1.   SHAKESPEARE.

INTELLECTUAL ACTIVITY.
CONVERSATION.

Words are like leaves ; and where they most
    abound,
Much fruit of sense beneath is rarely found.
  Essay on Criticism, Part II.   POPE.

And I oft have heard defended,
Little said is soonest mended.
  The Shepherd's Hunting.   G. WITHER.

Therefore, since brevity is the soul of wit,
And tediousness the limbs and outward flour-
    ishes,
I will be brief.
  Hamlet, Act ii. *Sc.* 2.   SHAKESPEARE.

KING RICHARD. Be eloquent in my behalf to her.
QUEEN ELIZABETH. An honest tale speeds best,
    being plainly told.
  King Richard III., Act iv. *Sc.* 4.   SHAKESPEARE.

And, when you stick on conversation's burrs,
Don't strew your pathway with those dreadful
    urs.
  Urania.   O. W. HOLMES.

           In his brain —
Which is as dry as the remainder biscuit
After a voyage — he hath strange places crammed
With observation, the which he vents
In mangled forms.
  As You Like It, Act ii. *Sc.* 7.   SHAKESPEARE.

They never taste who always drink ;
They always talk who never think.
  Upon a Passage in the Scaligerana.   M. PRIOR.

O dear discretion ! how his words are suited.
  Merchant of Venice, Act iii. *Sc.* 5.   SHAKESPEARE

His wit invites you by his looks to come,
But, when you knock, it never is at home.
  Conversation.   COWPER.

Bid me discourse, I will enchant thine ear.
  Venus and Adonis.   SHAKESPEARE.

A man in all the world's new fashion planted,
That hath a mint of phrases in his brain.
  Love's Labor Lost, Act ii. *Sc.* 4.   SHAKESPEARE.

And gentle Dulness ever loves a joke.
  The Dunciad, Book ii.   POPE.

O, many a shaft, at random sent,
Finds mark the archer little meant !
And many a word, at random spoken,
May soothe, or wound, a heart that's broken !
  Lord of the Isles, Cant. v.   SCOTT.

ARGUMENT.

          And why, sir, must they so ?
The why is plain as way to parish church.
  As You Like It, Act ii. *Sc.* 7.   SHAKESPEARE

Who shall decide, when doctors disagree,
And soundest casuists doubt, like you and me ?
  Moral Essays, Epistle III.   POPE.

Much may be said on both sides.
  The Covent Garden Tragedy, Sc. 8.   H. FIELDING.

He that complies against his will
Is of his own opinion still.
  Hudibras, Part III.   DR. S. BUTLER.

Quoth she, I 've heard old cunning stagers
Say, fools for arguments use wagers.
  Hudibras, Part II.   S. BUTLER.

A second Daniel, a Daniel, Jew !
Now, infidel, I have thee on the hip.

. . . . .

A Daniel, still say I ; a second Daniel ! —
I thank thee, Jew, for teaching me that word.
Merchant of Venice, Act iv. Sc. 1.   SHAKESPEARE.

To leave this keen encounter of our wits.
King Richard III., Act i. Sc. 2.   SHAKESPEARE.

ORATORY.

For rhetoric, he could not ope
His mouth, but out there flew a trope.

. . . . .

For all a rhetorician's rules
Teach nothing but to name his tools.
Hudibras, Part I. Cant. i.   DR. S. BUTLER.

Where nature's end of language is declined,
And men talk only to conceal the mind.
Love of Fame, Satire ii.   DR. E. YOUNG.

To syllable-dissectors they appeal.
Allow them accent-cadence, — fools may feel ;
But, spite of all the criticising elves,
Those who would make us feel — must feel them-
selves.
The Rosciad.   C. CHURCHILL.

    Thence to the famous orators repair,
Those ancient, whose resistless eloquence
Wielded at will that fierce democratie,
Shook the arsenal, and fulmined over Greece,
To Macedon, and Artaxerxes' throne.
Paradise Regained, Book iv.   MILTON.

Words that weep and tears that speak.
The Prophet.   A. COWLEY.

THE STAGE.

        I have heard
That guilty creatures, sitting at a play,
Have by the very cunning of the scene
Been struck so to the soul, that presently
They have proclaimed their malefactions.

. . . . .

        The play's the thing
Wherein I'll catch the conscience of the King.
Hamlet, Act ii. Sc. 2.   SHAKESPEARE.

Lo, where the stage, the poor, degraded stage,
Holds its warped mirror to a gaping age.
Curiosity.   C. SPRAGUE.

        Nay, an thou'lt mouth,
I'll rant as well as thou.
Hamlet, Act v. Sc. 1.   SHAKESPEARE.

There still remains, to mortify a wit,
The many-headed monster of the pit.
Imitations of Horace, Epistle I. Book ii.   POPE.

New forms arise, and different views engage,
Superfluous lags the vet'ran on the stage,
Till pitying Nature signs the last release,
And bids afflicted worth retire to peace.
Vanity of Human Wishes.   DR. S. JOHNSON.

A veteran see ! whose last act on the stage
Entreats your smiles for sickness and for age ;
Their cause I plead, — plead it in heart and
    mind ;
A fellow-feeling makes one wondrous kind.
Prologue on Quitting the Stage in 1776.   D. GARRICK.

I hold the world but as the world, Gratiano ;
A stage, where every man must play a part,
And mine a sad one.
Merchant of Venice, Act i. Sc. 1   SHAKESPEARE.

LEARNING.

'Tis education forms the common mind ;
Just as the twig is bent the tree's inclined.
Moral Essays, Epistle I.   POPE.

With too much quickness ever to be taught ;
With too much thinking to have common
    thought.
Moral Essays, Epistle II.   POPE.

Glad that you thus continue your resolve
To suck the sweets of sweet philosophy ;
Only, good master, while we do admire
This virtue and this moral discipline,
Let's be no stoics, nor no stocks, I pray.

. . . . .

No profit grows where is no pleasure ta'en ;
In brief, sir, study what you most affect.
Taming of the Shrew, Act i. Sc. 1.   SHAKESPEARE.

Some, for renown, on scraps of learning dote,
And think they grow immortal as they quote.
Love of Fame, Satire i.   DR. E. YOUNG.

With just enough of learning to misquote.
English Bards and Scotch Reviewers.   BYRON.

Whence is thy learning ?   Hath thy toil
O'er books consumed the midnight oil ?
Fables : The Shepherd and the Philosopher.   J. GAY.

Small have continual plodders ever won,
    Save base authority from others' books.
These earthly godfathers of heaven's lights,
    That give a name to every fixèd star,
Have no more profit of their shining nights
    Than those that walk, and wot not what they
    are.
Love's Labor Lost, Act i. Sc. 1.   SHAKESPEARE.

Love seldom haunts the breast where learning
lies,
And Venus sets ere Mercury can rise.

The Wife of Bath: Her Prologue. POPE.

A little learning is a dangerous thing ;
Drink deep, or taste not the Pierian spring :
There shallow draughts intoxicate the brain,
And drinking largely sobers us again.

Essay on Criticism, Part II. POPE.

AUTHORS.

Shut, shut the door, good John ! fatigued I said,
Tie up the knocker, say I 'm sick, I 'm dead.
The Dog-star rages ! nay, 't is past a doubt,
All Bedlam, or Parnassus, is let out :
Fire in each eye, and papers in each hand,
They rave, recite, and madden round the land.

Epistle to Dr. Arbuthnot : Prologue to the Satires. POPE.

Why did I write ? what sin to me unknown
Dipped me in ink, — my parents', or my own ?

Epistle to Dr. Arbuthnot : Prologue to the Satires. POPE.

Whether the charmer sinner it, or saint it,
If folly grow romantic, I must paint it.

Moral Essays, Epistle II. POPE.

Beneath the rule of men entirely great
The pen is mightier than the sword.

Richelieu, Act ii. Sc. 2. E. BULWER-LYTTON.

And so I penned
It down, until at last it came to be,
For length and breadth, the bigness which you
see.

Pilgrim's Progress : Apology for his Book. J. BUNYAN.

BOOKS.

If there 's a hole in a' your coats,
I rede ye tent it ;
A chiel 's amang ye takin' notes,
And, faith, he 'll prent it.

On Captain Grose's Peregrinations through Scotland. BURNS.

'T is pleasant, sure, to see one's name in print ;
A book 's a book, although there 's nothing in 't.

English Bards and Scotch Reviewers. BYRON.

Lest men suspect your tale untrue,
Keep probability in view.
The traveller leaping o'er those bounds,
The credit of his book confounds.

The Painter who pleased Nobody and Everybody. J. GAY.

Immodest words admit of no defence,
For want of decency is want of sense.

. . . . .

But foul descriptions are offensive still,
Either for being like or being ill.

Essay on Translated Verse. EARL OF ROSCOMMON.

But words are things, and a small drop of ink,
Falling, like dew, upon a thought, produces
That which makes thousands, perhaps millions,
think.

Don Juan, Cant. iii. BYRON.

Me, poor man ! — My library
Was dukedom large enough.

Tempest, Act i. Sc. 2. SHAKESPEARE.

His study ! with what authors is it stored ?
In books, not authors, curious is my lord ;
To all their dated backs he turns you round ;
These Aldus printed, those Du Sueil has bound !
Lo, some are vellum, and the rest as good
For all his lordship knows, but they are wood.
For Locke or Milton 't is in vain to look,
These shelves admit not any modern book.

Moral Essays, Epistle IV. POPE.

'T is strange — but true ; for truth is always
strange ;
Stranger than fiction.

Don Juan, Cant. xiv. BYRON.

Oh ! rather give me commentators plain,
Who with no deep researches vex the brain ;
Who from the dark and doubtful love to run,
And hold their glimmering tapers to the sun.

The Parish Register, Part I., Introduction. G. CRABBE.

The readers and the hearers like my books,
But yet some writers cannot them digest ;
But what care I ? for when I make a feast
I would my guests should praise it, not the
cooks.

Epigrams. SIR J. HARRINGTON.

Dreams, books, are each a world ; and books, we
know,
Are a substantial world, both pure and good ;
Round these, with tendrils strong as flesh and
blood,
Our pastime and our happiness will grow.

Personal Talk. WORDSWORTH.

And choose an author as you choose a friend.

Essay on Translated Verse. EARL OF ROSCOMMON.

Then felt I like some watcher of the skies
When a new planet swims into his ken ;
Or like stout Cortez when with eagle eyes
He stared at the Pacific — and all his men
Looked at each other with a wild surmise —
Silent, upon a peak in Darien.

On first looking into Chapman's Homer. KEATS.

My days among the Dead are passed ;
  Around me I behold,
Where'er these casual eyes are cast,
  The mighty minds of old ;
My never-failing friends are they,
  With whom I converse day by day.
Occasional Pieces, xviii.   R. SOUTHEY.

      There studious let me sit,
And hold high converse with the mighty dead ;
Sages of ancient time, as gods revered,
As gods beneficent, who blest mankind
With arts, with arms, and humanized a world.
  The Seasons : Winter.   THOMSON.

CRITICISM AND SATIRE.

And finds, with keen, discriminating sight,
Black 's not so black ; — nor white so *very* white.
  New Morality.   G. CANNING.

In words, as fashions, the same rule will hold,
Alike fantastic if too new or old :
Be not the first by whom the new are tried,
Nor yet the last to lay the old aside.
  Essay on Criticism, Part II.   POPE.

Poets lose half the praise they should have got,
Could it be known what they discreetly blot.
  Upon Roscommon's Translation of Horace's De Arte Poetica.
                 E. WALLER.

Even copious Dryden wanted, or forgot,
The last and greatest art, the art to blot.
  Imitations of Horace, Epistle I. Book ii.   POPE.

True ease in writing comes from art, not chance,
As those move easiest who have learned to dance.
'T is not enough no harshness gives offence ;
The sound must seem an echo to the sense.
Soft is the strain when zephyr gently blows,
And the smooth stream in smoother numbers
  flows ;
But when loud surges lash the sounding shore,
The hoarse rough verse should like the torrent
  roar.
When Ajax strives some rock's vast weight to
  throw,
The line too labors, and the words move slow ;
Not so when swift Camilla scours the plain,
Flies o'er th' unbending corn, and skims along
  the main.
  Essay on Criticism, Part II.   POPE.

Then, at the last and only couplet fraught
With some unmeaning thing they call a thought,
A needless Alexandrine ends the song,
That, like a wounded snake, drags its slow length
  along.
  Essay on Criticism, Part II.   POPE.

           As soon
Seek roses in December, — ice in June ;
Hope constancy in wind, or corn in chaff,
Believe a woman, or an epitaph,
Or any other thing that 's false, before
You trust in critics.
  English Bards and Scotch Reviewers.   BYRON.

Vex not thou the poet's mind
  With thy shallow wit :
Vex not thou the poet's mind ;
  For thou canst not fathom it.
  The Poet's Mind.   TENNYSON.

Prepare for rhyme — I 'll publish, right or wrong :
Fools are my theme, let satire be my song.
  English Bards and Scotch Reviewers.   BYRON.

Satire 's my weapon, but I 'm too discreet
To run amuck, and tilt at all I meet.
  Imitation of Horace, Satire I. Book ii.   POPE.

Satire should, like a polished razor keen,
Wound with a touch that 's scarcely felt or seen.
  To the Imitator of the first Satire of Horace, Book ii.
            LADY M. W. MONTAGU.

POETS AND POETRY.

Of all those arts in which the wise excel,
Nature's chief masterpiece is writing well ;
No writing lifts exalted man so high
As sacred and soul-moving poesy.
  Essay on Poetry.   DUKE OF BUCKINGHAMSHIRE.

For his chaste Muse employed her heaven-taught
  lyre
None but the noblest passions to inspire,
Not one immoral, one corrupted thought,
One line which, dying, he could wish to blot.
  Prologue to Thomson's Coriolanus.   LORD LYTTELTON.

Wisdom married to immortal verse.
  The Excursion, Book vii.   WORDSWORTH.

There is a pleasure in poetic pains
Which only poets know.
  The Timepiece : The Task, Book ii.   COWPER.

        Most wretched men
Are cradled into poetry by wrong ;
They learn in suffering what they teach in song.
  Julian and Maddalo.   SHELLEY.

Lovers and madmen have such seething brains,
Such shaping fantasies, that apprehend
More than cool reason ever comprehends.
The lunatic, the lover, and the poet
Are of imagination all compact.
  Midsummer Night's Dream, Act v. *Sc.* 1.   SHAKESPEARE.

I do but sing because I must,
And pipe but as the linnets sing.
In Memoriam, xxi.   TENNYSON.

While pensive poets painful vigils keep,
Sleepless themselves to give their readers sleep.
The Dunciad, Book i.   POPE.

For wheresoe'er I turn my ravished eyes,
Gay gilded scenes and shining prospects rise,
Poetic fields encompass me around,
And still I seem to tread on classic ground.
A Letter from Italy.   ADDISON.

Eye Nature's walks, shoot folly as it flies,
And catch the manners living as they rise ;
Laugh where we must, be candid where we can,
But vindicate the ways of God to man.
Essay on Man, Epistle I.   POPE.

Poets, like painters, thus unskilled to trace
The naked nature and the living grace,
With gold and jewels cover every part,
And hide with ornaments their want of art.
True wit is nature to advantage dressed,
What oft was thought, but ne'er so well expressed.
Essay on Criticism, Part II.   POPE.

Apt alliteration's artful aid.
The Prophecy of Famine.   C. CHURCHILL.

But those that write in rhyme still make
The one verse for the other's sake ;
For one for sense, and one for rhyme,
I think 's sufficient at one time.
Hudibras, Part II.   DR. S. BUTLER.

For rhyme the rudder is of verses,
With which, like ships, they steer their courses.
Hudibras, Part I.   DR. S. BUTLER.

I had rather be a kitten, and cry, mew,
Than one of these same metre ballad-mongers ;
I had rather hear a brazen can'stick turned,
Or a dry wheel grate on the axle-tree ;
And that would set my teeth nothing on edge,
Nothing so much as mincing poetry :
'T is like the forced gait of a shuffling nag.
King Henry IV., Part I. Act iii. Sc. I.   SHAKESPEARE.

Go boldly forth, my simple lay,
Whose accents flow with artless ease,
Like orient pearls at random strung.
A Persian Song of Hafiz.   SIR W. JONES.

One simile that solitary shines
In the dry desert of a thousand lines.
Imitations of Horace, Epistle I. Book ii.   POPE.

Jewels five-words long,
That on the stretched forefinger of all time
Sparkle forever.
The Princess, Cant. ii.   TENNYSON.

Choice word and measured phrase above the reach
Of ordinary men.
Resolution and Independence.   WORDSWORTH.

A poem round and perfect as a star.
A Life Drama.   A. SMITH.

My eyes make pictures, when they are shut.
A Day-Dream.   S. T. COLERIDGE.

The poet in a golden clime was born,
    With golden stars above ;
Dowered with the hate of hate, the scorn of scorn,
    The love of love.
The Poet.   TENNYSON.

Give me that growth which some perchance deem
    sleep,
Wherewith the steadfast coral-stems arise,
Which, by the toil of gathering energies,
Their upward way into clear sunshine keep
Until, by Heaven's sweetest influences,
Slowly and slowly spreads a speck of green
Into a pleasant island in the seas,
Where, mid tall palms, the cane-roofed home is seen,
And wearied men shall sit at sunset's hour,
Hearing the leaves and loving God's dear power
Sonnet VII.   J. R. LOWELL.

Still govern thou my song,
Urania, and fit audience find, though few.
Paradise Lost, Book vii.   MILTON.

Thanks untraced to lips unknown
Shall greet me like the odors blown
From unseen meadows newly mown,
Or lilies floating in some pond,
Wood-fringed, the wayside gaze beyond ;
The traveller owns the grateful sense
Of sweetness near, he knows not whence,
And, pausing, takes with forehead bare
The benediction of the air.
Snow-Bound.   J. G. WHITTIER.

THE MIND.

How small, of all that human hearts endure,
That part which laws or kings can cause or cure !
Still to ourselves in every place consigned,
Our own felicity we make or find.
With secret course, which no loud storms annoy,
Glides the smooth current of domestic joy.
Lines added to Goldsmith's Traveller.   DR. S. JOHNSON.

Now see that noble and most sovereign reason,
Like sweet bells jangled, out of tune and harsh.
Hamlet, Act iii. Sc. 1.   SHAKESPEARE.

Measure your mind's height by the shade it
       casts !
Paracelsus.   R. BROWNING.

He that of such a height hath built his mind,
And reared the dwelling of his thoughts so strong,
As neither fear nor hope can shake the frame
Of his resolvèd powers ; nor all the wind
Of vanity or malice pierce to wrong
His settled peace, or to disturb the same ;
What a fair seat hath he, from whence he may
The boundless wastes and wilds of man survey ?
.   .   .   .
              Unless above himself he can
Erect himself, how poor a thing is man !
To the Countess of Cumberland.   S. DANIEL.

Were I so tall to reach the pole,
Or grasp the ocean with my span,
I must be measured by my soul :
The mind 's the standard of the man.
Horæ Lyricæ, Book ii. : False Greatness.   DR. I. WATTS.

PHILOSOPHY.

HORATIO. O day and night, but this is won-
       drous strange !
HAMLET. And therefore as a stranger give it
       welcome.
There are more things in heaven and earth,
       Horatio,
Than are dreamt of in your philosophy.
Hamlet, Act i. Sc. 5.   SHAKESPEARE.

Philosophy will clip an angel's wings.
Lamia, Part II.   J. KEATS.

Sure, He that made us with such large discourse,
Looking before and after, gave us not
That capability and godlike reason,
To fust in us unused.
Hamlet, Act iv. Sc. 4.   SHAKESPEARE.

Thinking is but an idle waste of thought,
And naught is everything and everything is
       naught.
Rejected Addresses : Cui Bono?   H. and J. SMITH.

When Bishop Berkeley said " there was no mat-
       ter,"
And proved it — 't was no matter what he said.
Don Juan, Cant. xi.   BYRON.

His cogitative faculties immersed
In cogibundity of cogitation.
Chronon, Act i. Sc. 1.   H. CAREY.

Hot philosophers
Stood banding factions, all so strongly propt ;
I staggered, knew not which was firmer part,
But thought, quoted, read, observed, and pried,
Stufft noting-books : and still my spaniel slept.
At length he waked, and yawned ; and by yon sky
For aught I know, he knew as much as I.
A Scholar and his Dog.   J. MARSTON.

He knew what 's what, and that 's as high
As metaphysic wit can fly.
Hudibras, Part I.   DR. S. BUTLER.

There is nothing either good or bad, but thinking makes it so.
Hamlet, Act ii. Sc. 2.   SHAKESPEARE.

Not so the son ; he marked this oversight,
And then mistook reverse of wrong for right ;
(For What to shun, will no great knowledge need,
But What to follow, is a task indeed !)
Moral Essays, Epistle III.   POPE.

The intellectual power, through words and things,
Went sounding on, a dim and perilous way !
The Excursion, Book iii.   WORDSWORTH.

                    In discourse more sweet,
(For eloquence the soul, song charms the sense,)
Others apart sat on a hill retired,
In thoughts more elevate, and reasoned high
Of providence, foreknowledge, will, and fate,
Fixed fate, free will, foreknowledge absolute ;
And found no end, in wand'ring mazes lost.
Of good and evil much they argued then,
Of happiness and final misery,
Passion and apathy, and glory and shame ;
Vain wisdom all, and false philosophy.
Paradise Lost, Book ii.   MILTON.

Slave to no sect, who takes no private road,
But looks through nature up to nature's God.
.   .   .   .
And knows where faith, law, morals, all began,
All end, in love of God and love of man.
Essay on Man, Epistle IV.   POPE.

MUSIC.

If music be the food of love, play on ;
Give me excess of it, that, surfeiting,
The appetite may sicken, and so die.
That strain again — it had a dying fall :
O, it came o'er my ear like the sweet south,
That breathes upon a bank of violets,
Stealing, and giving odor.
Twelfth Night, Act i. Sc. 1.   SHAKESPEARE

There is a charm, a power, that sways the breast ;
Bids every passion revel or be still ;
Inspires with rage, or all our cares dissolves ;
Can soothe distraction, and almost despair.
Art of Preserving Health.　　　J. ARMSTRONG.

Music hath charms to soothe a savage breast,
To soften rocks, or bend a knotted oak.
I 've read that things inanimate have moved,
And, as with living souls, have been informed
By magic numbers and persuasive sound.
The Mourning Bride, Act i. Sc. 1.　　W. CONGREVE.

　　　　　　Where music dwells
Lingering and wandering on, as loath to die,
Like thoughts whose very sweetness yieldeth proof
That they were born for immortality.
Ecclesiastical Sonnets, Part III. xliii.　　WORDSWORTH.

　　　　　——

SCULPTURE.

As when, O lady mine,
With chiselled touch
The stone unhewn and cold
Becomes a living mould,
The more the marble wastes
The more the statue grows.
Sonnet.　Tr. of Mrs. HENRY ROSCOE.　M. ANGELO.

　　　　　——

THE PROFESSIONS.

THE CLERGY AND THE PULPIT.

O for a forty parson power !
Don Juan, Cant. v.　　　　　BYRON

Wel oughte a prest ensample for to yive,
By his clennesse, how that his sheep shulde lyve.
　·　　·　　·　　·
To draw folk to heven by fairnesse
By good ensample, this was his busynesse.
Canterbury Tales : Prologue.　　CHAUCER.

What makes all doctrines plain and clear ?
About two hundred pounds a year.
And that which was proved true before,
Prove false again ?　Two hundred more.
Hudibras, Part III.　　　DR. S. BUTLER.

Do not, as some ungracious pastors do,
Show me the steep and thorny way to Heaven,
Whilst, like a puffed and reckless libertine,
Himself the primrose path of dalliance treads,
And recks not his own rede.
Hamlet, Act i. Sc. 3.　　SHAKESPEARE.

He 'stablishes the strong, restores the weak,
Reclaims the wanderer, binds the broken heart.
The Timepiece : The Task. Book ii　,　COWPER.

　　　　Of right and wrong he taught
Truths as refined as ever Athens heard ;
And (strange to tell !) he practised what he
　　preached.
Art of Preserving Health.　　　J. ARMSTRONG.

　　　　　——

MEDICINE AND DOCTORS.

I do remember an apothecary.
　·　　·　　·　　·　　·
Sharp misery had worn him to the bones :
And in his needy shop a tortoise hung,
An alligator stuffed, and other skins
Of ill-shaped fishes ; and about his shelves
A beggarly account of empty boxes.
Romeo and Juliet, Act v. Sc. 1.　　SHAKESPEARE

With us ther was a Doctour of Phisik,
In al this world ne was ther non him lyk
To speke of phisik and of surgerye.

He knew the cause of every maladye,
Were it of hoot or colde, or moyste or drye,
And wher engendered and of what humour :
He was a verrey parfight practisour.
　·　　·　　·　　·
For gold in phisik is a cordial,
Therfore he lovedè gold in special.
Canterbury Tales : Prologue.　　CHAUCER

"Is there no hope ? " the sick man said.
The silent doctor shook his head
And took his leave with signs of sorrow,
Despairing of his fee to-morrow.
The Sick Man and the Angel.　　J. GAY.

　　　　　But when ill indeed,
E'en dismissing the doctor don't always succeed
Lodgings for Single Gentlemen.　G. COLMAN, *the Younger.*

　　　　　——

LAWYERS AND THE LAW.

So wise, so grave, of so perplexed a tongue
And loud withal, that could not wag, nor scarce
Lie still, without a fee.
Valpone.　　　　　B. JONSON.

While lawyers have more sober sense
Than t' argue at their own expense,
But make their best advantages
Of others' quarrels, like the Swiss.
Hudibras.　　　　DR. S. BUTLER.

Each wanton judge new penal statutes draw,
Laws grind the poor, and rich men rule the law.
The Traveller.　　　GOLDSMITH

Laws, as we read in ancient sages,
Have been like cobwebs in all ages.
Cobwebs for little flies are spread,
And laws for little folks are made ;
But if an insect of renown,
Hornet or beetle, wasp or drone,
Be caught in quest of sport or plunder,
The flimsy fetter flies in sunder.
                                        J. BEATTIE.

Between two hawks, which flies the higher pitch,
Between two dogs, which hath the deeper mouth,
Between two horses, which doth bear him best,
Between two girls, which hath the merriest eye,
I have, perhaps, some shallow spirit of judg-
      ment ;
But in these nice sharp quillets of the law,
Good faith, I am no wiser than a daw.
      King Henry VI., Part I. Act ii. Sc. 4.   SHAKESPEARE.

Mastering the lawless science of our law,
That codeless myriad of precedent,
That wilderness of single instances.
      Aylmer's Field.   TENNYSON.

For twelve honest men have decided the cause,
Who are judges alike of the facts and the laws.
      The Honest Jury.   W. PULTENEY.

The hungry judges soon the sentence sign,
And wretches hang, that jurymen may dine.
      Rape of the Lock, Cant. iii.   POPE.

Dame Justice, weighing long the doubtful right,
Takes, opens, swallows it before their sight.
The cause of strife removed so rarely well,
There, take (says Justice), take ye each a shell ;
We thrive at Westminster on fools like you ;
'T was a fat oyster — live in peace — adieu.
      Verbatim from Boileau.   POPE.

THE PRESS.

Now stir the fire, and close the shutters fast,
Let fall the curtains, wheel the sofa round,
And while the bubbling and loud hissing urn
Throws up a steamy column, and the cups,
That cheer but not inebriate, wait on each,
So let us welcome peaceful evening in.

This folio of four pages, happy work !
Which not e'en critics criticise ; that holds
Inquisitive attention while I read,
      .   .   .   .   .
What is it but a map of busy life,
Its fluctuations and its vast concerns ?
T is pleasant, through the loop-holes of retreat,
To peep at such a world, — to see the stir
Of the great Babel, and not feel the crowd.
      .   .   .   .   .

While fancy, like the finger of a clock,
Runs the great circuit, and is still at home.
      Winter Evening : The Task, Book iv.   COWPER.

THE JESTER.

                              When I did hear
The motley fool thus moral on the time,
My lungs began to crow like chanticleer,
That fools should be so deep contemplative ;
And I did laugh, sans intermission,
An hour by his dial. — O noble fool !
A worthy fool ! — Motley 's the only wear.
      As You Like It, Act ii. *Sc.* 7.   SHAKESPEARE.

PERSONAL AND PUBLIC OPINION.

PRAISE.

The love of praise, howe'er concealed by art,
Reigns more or less, and glows in every heart.
      Love of Fame, Satire i.   DR. E. YOUNG.

To things of sale a seller's praise belongs.
      Love's Labor Lost, Act iv. *Sc.* 3.   SHAKESPEARE.

                              I have bought
Golden opinions from all sorts of people.
      Macbeth, Act i. *Sc.* 7.   SHAKESPEARE.

Who hath not owned, with rapture-smitten frame,
The power of grace, the magic of a name ?
      Pleasures of Hope, Part II.   T. CAMPBELL.

FLATTERY.

'T is an old maxim in the schools,
That flattery 's the food of fools ;
Yet now and then your men of wit
Will condescend to take a bit.
      Cadenus and Vanessa.   DEAN SWIFT.

But flattery never seems absurd ;
The flattered always takes your word :
Impossibilities seem just ;
They take the strongest praise on trust.
Hyperboles, though ne'er so great,
Will still come short of self-conceit.
      The Painter who pleased Nobody and Everybody.   J. GAY.

                              He loves to hear
That unicorns may be betrayed with trees,
And bears with glasses, elephants with holes,
Lions with toils, and men with flatterers.
But when I tell him he hates flatterers,
He says he does, being then most flattered.
      Julius Cæsar, Act ii. *Sc.* 1.   SHAKESPEARE

Ne'er
Was flattery lost on Poet's ear :
A simple race ! they waste their toil
For the vain tribute of a smile.

Lay of the Last Minstrel, Cant. iv.   SCOTT.

SCANDAL AND SLANDER.

There 's nothing blackens like the ink of fools.
If true, a woful likeness ; and, if lies,
" Praise undeserved is scandal in disguise."

Imitations of Horace, Epistle I. Book ii.   POPE.

And there 's a lust in man no charm can tame
Of loudly publishing our neighbor's shame ;
On eagles' wings immortal scandals fly,
While virtuous actions are but born and die.

Satire ix. *Trans. of* S. HARVEY.   JUVENAL.

A third interprets motions, looks and eyes ;
At every word a reputation dies.

Rape of the Lock, Cant. iii.   POPE.

                    No, 't is slander,
Whose edge is sharper than the sword ; whose
          tongue
Outvenoms all the worms of Nile ; whose breath
Rides on the posting winds, and doth belie
All comers of the world.

Cymbeline, Act iii. *Sc.* 4.   SHAKESPEARE.

REPUTATION.

Good name in man and woman, dear my lord,
Is the immediate jewel of their souls :
Who steals my purse, steals trash ; 't is something,
          nothing ;
'T was mine, 't is his, and has been slave to
          thousands ;
But he that filches from me my good name
Robs me of that which not enriches him,
And makes me poor indeed.

Othello, Act iii. *Sc.* 3.   SHAKESPEARE.

After my death I wish no other herald,
No other speaker of my living actions,
To keep mine honor from corruption,
But such an honest chronicler as Griffith.

King Henry VIII., Act v. *Sc.* 2.   SHAKESPEARE.

HAMLET.   Horatio, I am dead ;
Thou liv'st ; report me and my cause aright
To the unsatisfied.

HORATIO.   Never believe it :
          (*Taking the cup.*)
I am more an antique Roman than a Dane :
Here 's yet some liquor left.

HAM.   As thou 'rt a man,

Give me the cup : let go ; by heaven I 'll have 't.—
          (*Struggling :* HAMLET *gets the cup.*)
O God ! — Horatio, what a wounded name,
Things standing thus unknown, shall live behind
          me !
If thou didst ever hold me in thy heart,
Absent thee from felicity awhile,
And in this harsh world draw thy breath in pain,
To tell my story.

Hamlet, Act v. *Sc.* 2.   SHAKESPEARE.

FAME.

What shall I do to be forever known,
And make the age to come my own ?

The Motto.   A. COWLEY.

By Jove ! I am not covetous for gold ;

      .   .   .   .

But, if it be a sin to covet honor,
I am the most offending soul alive.

King Henry V., Act iv. *Sc.* 3.   SHAKESPEARE.

                    Your name is great
In mouths of wisest censure.

Othello, Act ii. *Sc.* 3.   SHAKESPEARE.

      It deserves with characters of brass
A forted residence 'gainst the tooth of time
And razure of oblivion.

Measure for Measure, Act v. *Sc.* 1.   SHAKESPEARE.

What is glory but the blaze of fame,
The people's praise, if always praise unmixt ?

      .   .   .   .

And what delight to be by such extolled,
To live upon their tongues and be their talk,
Of whom to be dispraised were no small praise ?

Paradise Regained, Book iii.   MILTON.

One touch of nature makes the whole world kin,—
That all with one consent praise new-born gawds,

      .   .   .   .

And give to dust, that is a little gilt,
More laud than gilt o'er-dusted.

Troilus and Cressida, Act iii. *Sc.* 3.   SHAKESPEARE.

Thrice happy he whose name has been well spelt
In the despatch : I knew a man whose loss
Was printed *Grove*, although his name was Grove.

Don Juan, Cant. viii.   BYRON.

What is the end of Fame ? 'T is but to fill
      A certain portion of uncertain paper.

Don Juan, Cant. i.   BYRON.

Nor Fame I slight, nor for her favors call :
She comes unlooked for, if she comes at all.

      .   .   .   .

Unblemished let me live, or die unknown ;
O grant an honest fame, or grant me none !

The Temple of Fame.   POPE

Ah ! who can tell how hard it is to climb
The steep where fame's proud temple shines
    afar !
Ah ! who can tell how many a soul sublime
Has felt the influence of malignant star,
And waged with Fortune an eternal war ;
Checked by the scoff of pride, by envy's frown,
And poverty's unconquerable bar,
    In life's low vale remote has pined alone,
Then dropt into the grave, unpitied and un-
    known !
The Minstrel, Book i.   J. BEATTIE.

Fame is the spur that the clear spirit doth raise
(That last infirmity of noble mind)
To scorn delights, and live laborious days ;
But the fair guerdon when we hope to find,
And think to burst out into sudden blaze,
Comes the blind Fury with the abhorred shears,
And slits the thin-spun life. But not the praise,
Phœbus replied, and touched my trembling ears ;
Fame is no plant that grows on mortal soil,

But lives and spreads aloft by those pure eyes
And perfect witness of all-judging Jove.
As he pronounces lastly in each deed,
Of so much fame in heaven expect thy meed.
Lycidas.   MILTON.

CLASS AND CASTE.

ARISTOCRACY.

Order is Heaven's first law, and, this confest,
Some are, and must be, greater than the rest.
Essay on Man, Epistle IV.   POPE.

         Whoe'er amidst the sons
Of reason, valor, liberty, and virtue,
Displays distinguished merit, is a noble
Of Nature's own creating.
Coriolanus, Act iii. *Sc.* 3.   J. THOMSON.

None but himself can be his parallel.
The Double Falsehood.   LOUIS THEOBALD.

He lives to build, not boast, a generous race ;
No tenth transmitter of a foolish face.
The Bastard.   R. SAVAGE.

         Such souls,
Whose sudden visitations daze the world,
Vanish like lightning, but they leave behind
A voice that in the distance far away
Wakens the slumbering ages.
Philip Van Artevelde, Act i. *Sc.* 7.   SIR H. TAYLOR.

SNOBBERY.

Let wealth and commerce, laws and learning die,
But leave us still our old nobility.
England's Trust, and other Poems.   LORD J. MANNERS.

In men this blunder still you find,
All think their little set mankind.
Florio, Part I.   HANNAH MORE.

     GLENDOWER. And all the courses of my life
         do show,
I am not in the roll of common men.

I can call spirits from the vasty deep.
     HOTSPUR. Why, so can I, or so can any man ;
But will they come when you do call for them ?
King Henry IV., Part I. Act iii. *Sc.* 1.   SHAKESPEARE.

Know ye not then, said Satan, filled with scorn, —
Know ye not me ?

Not to know me argues yourselves unknown,
The lowest of your throng.
Paradise Lost, Book iv.   MILTON.

And if his name be George, I'll call him Peter;
For new-made honor doth forget men's names.
King John, Act i. *Sc.* 1.   SHAKESPEARE.

What woful stuff this madrigal would be
In some starved hackney sonneteer, or me,
But let a lord once own the happy lines,
How the wit brightens ! how the style refines !
Essay on Criticism, Part II.   POPE.

'T is from high life high characters are drawn ;
A saint in crape is twice a saint in lawn.
Moral Essays, Epistle I.   POPE.

STATE-CRAFT.

For just experience tells, in every soil,
That those that think must govern those that toil.
The Traveller.   GOLDSMITH.

'T is thus the spirit of a single mind
Makes that of multitudes take one direction.
Don Juan.   BYRON.

What should it be, that thus their faith can bind ?
The power of Thought — the magic of the Mind !
Linked with success, assumed and kept with skill,
That moulds another's weakness to its will.
The Corsair.   BYRON.

Treason doth never prosper : what's the reason ?
For if it prosper, none dare call it treason.
Epigrams.   SIR J. HARRINGTON.

A cutpurse of the empire and the rule,
That from a shelf the precious diadem stole,
And put it in his pocket !

Hamlet, Act iii. *Sc.* 4.   SHAKESPEARE.

Measures, not men, have always been my mark.

The Good-Natured Man, Act ii.   GOLDSMITH.

ABUSE OF AUTHORITY.

Oh ! it is excellent
To have a giant's strength ; but it is tyrannous
To use it like a giant.

.   .   .   .   .

Could great men thunder
As Jove himself does, Jove would ne'er be quiet ;
For every pelting, petty officer
Would use his heaven for thunder, —
Nothing but thunder.   Merciful Heaven !
Thou rather, with thy sharp and sulphurous bolt,
Split'st the unwedgeable and gnarlèd oak,
Than the soft myrtle : but man, proud man !
Drest in a little brief authority, —
Most ignorant of what he's most assured,
His glassy essence, — like an angry ape,
Plays such fantastic tricks before high heaven,
As make the angels weep ; who, with our spleens,
Would all themselves laugh mortal.

Measure for Measure, Act ii. *Sc.* 2.   SHAKESPEARE.

THE PEOPLE.

Who o'er the herd would wish to reign,
Fantastic, fickle, fierce, and vain ! —
Vain as the leaf upon the stream,
And fickle as a changeful dream ;
Fantastic as a woman's mood,
And fierce as Frenzy's fevered blood.
Thou many-headed monster thing,
O, who would wish to be thy king !

Lady of the Lake, Cant. v.   SCOTT.

He that depends
Upon your favors swims with fins of lead,
And hews down oaks with rushes.   Hang ye !
    Trust ye ?
With every minute you do change a mind ;
And call him noble that was now your hate,
Him vile that was your garland.

Coriolanus, Act i. *Sc.* 1.   SHAKESPEARE.

The scum
That rises upmost when the nation boils.

Don Sebastian.   DRYDEN.

From lowest place when virtuous things proceed,
The place is dignified by the doer's deed.

All's Well that Ends Well, Act ii. *Sc.* 3.   SHAKESPEARE.

Through all disguise, form, place or name,
    Beneath the flaunting robes of sin,
Through poverty and squalid shame,
    Thou lookest on the man within.

On man, as man, retaining yet,
    Howe'er debased, and soiled, and dim,
The crown upon his forehead set —
    The immortal gift of God to him.

Democracy.   J. G. WHITTIER.

MISCELLANEOUS.

SOLITUDE.

Alone ! — that worn-out word,
So idly spoken, and so coldly heard ;
Yet all that poets sing, and grief hath known,
Of hopes laid waste, knells in that word — ALONE!

The New Timon, Part II.   E. BULWER-LYTTON.

All heaven and earth are still, — though not in
        sleep,
But breathless, as we grow when feeling most ;
And silent, as we stand in thoughts too deep ; —
All heaven and earth are still ; from the high
        host .
Of stars, to the lulled lake and mountain-coast,
All is concentred in a life intense,
Where not a beam, nor air, nor leaf is lost,
But hath a part of being, and a sense
Of that which is of all Creator and defence.

Then stirs the feeling infinite, so felt
In solitude, where we are *least* alone.

Childe Harold, Cant. iii.   BYRON.

Such was that happy garden-state,
While man there walked without a mate :
After a place so pure and sweet,
What other help could yet be meet !
But 't was beyond a mortal's share
To wander solitary there :
Two paradises are in one,
To live in paradise alone.

The Garden (Translated).   A. MARVELL.

Pacing through the forest,
Chewing the cud of sweet and bitter fancy.

As You Like It, Act iv. *Sc.* 3.   SHAKESPEARE.

A feeling of sadness and longing,
    That is not akin to pain,
And resembles sorrow only
    As the mist resembles the rain.

The Day is Done.   LONGFELLOW

Converse with men makes sharp the glittering wit.
But God to man doth speak in solitude.

Highland Solitude.   J. S. BLACKIE.

But if much converse perhaps
Thee satiate, to short absence I could yield ;
For solitude sometimes is best society,
And short retirement urges sweet return.
Paradise Lost, Book ix.   MILTON.

SOCIAL PLEASURES.

Here thou, great Anna ! whom three realms obey,
Dost sometimes counsel take — and sometimes tea.
Rape of the Lock, Cant. iii.   POPE.

    She that asks
Her dear five hundred friends, contemns them all,
And hates their coming.
The Timepiece: The Task, Book ii. COWPER.

The company is "mixed" (the phrase I quote is
As much as saying, they 're below your notice).
Beppo.   BYRON.

    Hands promiscuously applied,
Round the slight waist or down the glowing side.
The Waltz.   BYRON.

O give me the sweet shady side of Pall Mall.
Town and Country.   C. MORRIS.

We may live without poetry, music, and art ;
We may live without conscience and live without
  heart ;
We may live without friends ; we may live
  without books ;
But civilized man cannot live without cooks.
We may live without books, — what is knowledge
  but grieving ?
We may live without hope, — what is hope but
  deceiving ?
We may live without love, — what is passion
  but pining ?
But where is the man that can live without
  dining ?
Lucile, Cant. ii. R. BULWER LYTTON (*Owen Meredith*).

There my retreat the best companions grace,
Chiefs out of war, and statesmen out of place ;
There St. John mingles with my friendly bowl,
The feast of reason and the flow of soul.
Imitations of Horace, Satire i. *Book* 2. POPE.

Across the walnuts and the wine.
The Miller's Daughter.   TENNYSON.

When in the Hall of Smoke they congress hold,
And the sage berry sunburnt Mocha bears
Has cleared their inward eye : then, smoke-
  enrolled.
The Castle of Indolence, Cant. i. J. THOMSON.

Sublime tobacco ! which from east to west,
Cheers the tar's labor or the Turkman's rest,

Divine in hookahs, glorious in a pipe,
When tipped with amber, mellow, rich and ripe ;
Like other charmers, wooing the caress
More dazzlingly when daring in full dress ;
Yet thy true lovers more admire by far
Thy naked beauties — Give me a cigar !
The Island, Cant. ii.   BYRON.

Yes, social friend, I love thee well,
 In learned doctors' spite ;
Thy clouds all other clouds dispel,
 And lap me in delight.
To my Cigar.   C. SPRAGUE.

And when the smoke ascends on high,
Then thou behold'st the vanity
  Of worldly stuff,
  Gone with a puff :
   Thus think, and smoke tobacco.

And seest the ashes cast away,
Then to thyself thou mayest say,
  That to the dust
  Return thou must.
   Thus think, and smoke tobacco.
    ANONYMOUS. — Before 1689.

MANNERS AND CUSTOMS.

Such is the custom of Branksome Hall.
The Lay of the Last Minstrel, Cant. i. SCOTT.

But to my mind, — though I am native here,
And to the manner born, — it is a custom
More honored in the breach, than the observance.
Hamlet, Act i. *Sc.* 4. SHAKESPEARE.

Manners with fortunes, humors turn with climes,
Tenets with books, and principles with times.
Moral Essays, Epistle I.   POPE.

Plain living and high thinking are no more.
The homely beauty of the good old cause
Is gone ; our peace, our fearful innocence,
And pure religion breathing household laws.
Written in London, September, 1802. WORDSWORTH.

DIFFERING TASTES.

    Different minds
Incline to different objects : one pursues
The vast alone, the wonderful, the wild ;
Another sighs for harmony, and grace,
And gentlest beauty.

Such and so various are the tastes of men.
Pleasures of the Imagination Book III. M. AKENSIDE.

What's one man's poison, signor,
Is another's meat or drink.
    Love's Cure, Act iii. Sc. 2.   BEAUMONT and FLETCHER.

Variety's the very spice of life,
That gives it all its flavor.
    The Timepiece: The Task, Book ii.   COWPER.

Not chaos-like together crushed and bruised,
But, as the world, harmoniously confused,
Where order in variety we see,
And where, though all things differ, all agree.
    Windsor Forest.   POPE.

QUARRELLING.

O, shame to men! devil with devil damned
Firm concord holds, men only disagree
Of creatures rational.
    Paradise Lost, Book ii.   MILTON.

TRIFLES.

Think naught a trifle, though it small appear;
Small sands the mountain, moments make the
        year,
And trifles life.
    Love of Fame, Satire vi.   DR. E. YOUNG.

Pretty! in amber to observe the forms
Of hair, or straws, or dirt, or grubs, or worms!
The things, we know, are neither rich nor rare,
But wonder how the devil they got there!
    Epistle to Dr. Arbuthnot: Prologue to Satires.   POPE.

What dire offence from amorous causes springs,
What mighty contests rise from trivial things.
    The Rape of the Lock, Cant. i.   POPE.

A little fire is quickly trodden out,
Which, being suffered, rivers cannot quench.
    King Henry VI., Part III. Act iv. Sc. 8.   SHAKESPEARE.

CRAFT.

                    Our better part remains
To work in close design, by fraud or guile,
What force effected not; that he no less
At length from us may find, who overcomes
By force hath overcome but half his foe.
    Paradise Lost, Book i.   MILTON.

TEMPTATION.

How oft the sight of means to do ill deeds
Makes ill deeds done!
    King John, Act iv. Sc. 2.   SHAKESPEARE.

PRUDENT SPEECH.

Let it be tenable in your silence still.

Give it an understanding, but no tongue.
    Hamlet, Act i. Sc. 2.   SHAKESPEARE.

Give every man thine ear, but few thy voice;
Take each man's censure, but reserve thy judg-
        ment.
    Hamlet, Act i. Sc. 3.   SHAKESPEARE.

And oftentimes excusing of a fault
Doth make the fault the worse by the excuse,
As patches, set upon a little breach,
Discredit more in hiding of the fault
Than did the fault before it was so patched.
    King John, Act iv. Sc. 2.   SHAKESPEARE.

MODERATION.

Reason's whole pleasure, all the joys of sense,
Lie in three words, — health, peace, and compe-
        tence.
But health consists with temperance alone,
And peace, O Virtue! peace is all thine own.
    Essay on Man, Epistle IV.   POPE.

These violent delights have violent ends,
And in their triumph die; like fire and powder,
Which as they kiss consume.

Therefore love moderately; long love doth so;
Too swift arrives as tardy as too slow.
    Romeo and Juliet, Act ii. Sc. 6.   SHAKESPEARE.

They surfeited with honey; and began
To loathe the taste of sweetness, whereof a little
More than a little is by much too much.
    King Henry IV., Part I. Act iii. Sc. 2.   SHAKESPEARE.

He that holds fast the golden mean,
And lives contentedly between
        The little and the great,
Feels not the wants that pinch the poor,
Nor plagues that haunt the rich man's door.
    Translation of Horace, Book ii. Ode x.   COWPER.

If then to all men happiness was meant,
God in externals could not place content.
    Essay on Man, Epistle IV.   POPE.

IDLENESS AND ENNUI.

'T is the voice of the sluggard; I heard him
        complain,
"You have waked me too soon, I must slumber
        again."
    The Sluggard.   DR. I. WATTS.

Absence of occupation is not rest,
A mind quite vacant is a mind distressed.
    Retirement.   COWPER.

To sigh, yet feel no pain,
  To weep, yet scarce know why;
To sport an hour with Beauty's chain,
  Then throw it idly by.
The Blue Stocking.   T. MOORE.

The keenest pangs the wretched find
  Are rapture to the dreary void,
The leafless desert of the mind,
  The waste of feelings unemployed.
The Giaour.   BYRON.

    Their only labor was to kill the time
    (And labor dire it is, and weary woe);
    They sit, they loll, turn o'er some idle rhyme;
    Then, rising sudden, to the glass they go,
    Or saunter forth, with tottering step and slow:
    This soon too rude an exercise they find;
    Straight on the couch their limbs again they
      throw,
    Where hours on hours they sighing lie reclined,
  And court the vapory god, soft breathing in the
      wind.
The Castle of Indolence, Cant. I.   J. THOMSON.

HANG SORROW!

And this the burden of his song forever used
    to be,
I care for nobody, no not I, if nobody cares for
    me.
Love in a Village, Act I. Sc. 2.   I. BICKERSTAFF.

Without the door let sorrow lie;
And if for cold it hap to die,
We'll bury't in a Christmas pie,
  And evermore be merry.

        .   .   .   .

And Jack shall pipe, and Gill shall dance,
  And all the town be merry.

        .   .   .   .

For Christmas comes but once a year,
  And then they shall be merry.

        .   .   .   .

Though others' purses be more fat,
Why should we pine, or grieve at that?
Hang sorrow! care will kill a cat,
  And therefore let's be merry.
Christmas.   G. WITHER.

NIGHT AND SLEEP.

Tired nature's sweet restorer, balmy Sleep!
He, like the world, his ready visit pays
Where fortune smiles; the wretched he forsakes:
Swift on his downy pinions flies from woe,
And lights on lids unsullied with a tear.
  Night Thoughts, Night i.   DR. E. YOUNG.

Thou hast been called, O sleep! the friend of
    woe;
But 't is the happy that have called thee so.
  Curse of Kehama, Cant. xv.   R. SOUTHEY.

She bids you on the wanton rushes lay you down,
And rest your gentle head upon her lap,
And she will sing the song that pleaseth you,
And on your eyelids crown the god of sleep,
Charming your blood with pleasing heaviness;
Making such difference betwixt wake and sleep
As is the difference betwixt day and night,
The hour before the heavenly-harnessed team
Begins his golden progress in the east.
  King Henry IV., Part I. Act iii. Sc. 1.   SHAKESPEARE.

                        Weariness
Can snore upon the flint, when restive sloth
Finds the down pillow hard.
  Cymbeline, Act iii. Sc. 6.   SHAKESPEARE.

Care-charming sleep, thou easer of all woes,
Brother to Death, sweetly thyself dispose
On this afflicted prince; fall like a cloud
In gentle showers; . . . sing his pain
Like hollow murmuring wind or silver rain.
  Valentinian.   BEAUMONT and FLETCHER.

    Midnight brought on the dusky hour
Friendliest to sleep and silence.
  Paradise Lost, Book v.   MILTON.

And the night shall be filled with music,
  And the cares that infest the day
Shall fold their tents like the Arabs,
  And as silently steal away.
The Day is Done.   LONGFELLOW.

To all, to each, a fair good-night,
And pleasing dreams, and slumbers light!
  Marmion: L'Envoy, To the Reader.   SCOTT.

POEMS OF FANCY

The very tones in which we spake

Had something strange I could but mark;

The leaves of memory seemed to make

A mournful rustling in the dark.

Henry W. Longfellow

POEMS OF FANCY.

FANTASY.

FROM "THE VISION OF DELIGHT."

BREAK, Fantasy, from thy cave of cloud,
  And spread thy purple wings,
Now all thy figures are allowed,
  And various shapes of things ;
Create of airy forms a stream,
It must have blood, and naught of phlegm ;
And though it be a waking dream,
  Yet let it like an odor rise
    To all the senses here,
  And fall like sleep upon their eyes,
    Or music in their ear.

BEN JONSON.

DELIGHTS OF FANCY.

FROM " THE PLEASURES OF IMAGINATION."

As Memnon's marble harp renowned of old
By fabling Nilus, to the quivering touch
Of Titan's ray, with each repulsive string
Consenting, sounded through the warbling air
Unbidden strains ; e'en so did Nature's hand
To certain species of external things
Attune the finer organs of the mind ;
So the glad impulse of congenial powers,
Or of sweet sound, or fair-proportioned form,
The grace of motion, or the bloom of light,
Thrills through imagination's tender frame,
From nerve to nerve ; all naked and alive
They catch the spreading rays ; till now the soul
At length discloses every tuneful spring,
To that harmonious movement from without,
Responsive.   Then the inexpressive strain
Diffuses its enchantment ; Fancy dreams
Of sacred fountains and Elysian groves,
And vales of bliss ; the Intellectual Power
Bends from his awful throne a wondering ear,
And smiles ; the passions gently soothed away,
Sink to divine repose, and love and joy
Alone are waking ; love and joy serene
As airs that fan the summer.   O attend,
Whoe'er thou art whom these delights can touch,

Whose candid bosom the refining love
Of nature warms ; O, listen to my song,
And I will guide thee to her favorite walks,
And teach thy solitude her voice to hear,
And point her loveliest features to thy view.

MARK AKENSIDE.

FANCY.

EVER let the Fancy roam,
Pleasure never is at home :
At a touch sweet Pleasure melteth,
Like to bubbles when rain pelteth ;
Then let wingèd Fancy wander
Through the thought still spread beyond her :
Open wide the mind's cage-door,
She 'll dart forth, and cloudward soar.

O sweet Fancy ! let her loose ;
Summer's joys are spoilt by use,
And the enjoying of the Spring
Fades as does its blossoming :
Autumn's red-lipped fruitage too,
Blushing through the mist and dew,
Cloys with tasting.   What do then ?
Sit thee by the ingle, when
The sear fagot blazes bright,
Spirit of a winter's night ;
When the soundless earth is muffled,
And the cakèd snow is shuffled
From the ploughboy's heavy shoon ;
When the Night doth meet the Noon
In a dark conspiracy
To banish Even from her sky.
— Sit thee there, and send abroad
With a mind self-overawed
Fancy, high-commissioned : — send her !
She has vassals to attend her ;
She will bring, in spite of frost,
Beauties that the earth hath lost ;
She will bring thee, all together,
All delights of summer weather ;
All the buds and bells of May
From dewy sward or thorny spray ;

All the heapèd Autumn's wealth,
With a still, mysterious stealth ;
She will mix these pleasures up
Like three fit wines in a cup,
And thou shalt quaff it ; — thou shalt hear
Distant harvest-carols clear ;
Rustle of the reapèd corn ;
Sweet birds antheming the morn ;
And in the same moment — hark !
'T is the early April lark,
Or the rooks, with busy caw,
Foraging for sticks and straw.
Thou shalt, at one glance, behold
The daisy and the marigold ;
White-plumed lilies, and the first
Hedge-grown primrose that hath burst ;
Shaded hyacinth, alway
Sapphire queen of the mid-May ;
And every leaf, and every flower
Pearlèd with the self-same shower.
Thou shalt see the field-mouse peep
Meagre from its cellèd sleep ;
And the snake all winter-thin
Cast on sunny bank its skin ;
Freckled nest-eggs thou shalt see
Hatching in the hawthorn tree,
When the hen-bird's wing doth rest
Quiet on her mossy nest ;
Then the hurry and alarm
When the bee-hive casts its swarm ;
Acorns ripe down-pattering
While the autumn breezes sing.

O sweet Fancy ! let her loose ;
Everything is spoilt by use :
Where 's the cheek that doth not fade,
Too much gazed at ?   Where 's the maid
Whose lip mature is ever new ?
Where 's the eye, however blue,
Doth not weary ?   Where 's the face
One would meet in every place ?
Where 's the voice, however soft,
One would hear so very oft ?
At a touch sweet Pleasure melteth
Like to bubbles when rain pelteth.
Let then wingèd Fancy find
Thee a mistress to thy mind :
Dulcet-eyed as Ceres' daughter,
Ere the god of torment taught her
How to frown and how to chide ;
With a waist and with a side
White as Hebe's, when her zone
Slipt its golden clasp, and down
Fell her kirtle to her feet
While she held the goblet sweet,
And Jove grew languid. — Break the mesh
Of the Fancy's silken leash ;

Quickly break her prison-string,
And such joys as these she 'll bring :
— Let the wingèd Fancy roam,
Pleasure never is at home.

JOHN KEATS.

HALLO, MY FANCY.

[1650.]

In melancholic fancy,
  Out of myself,
In the vulcan dancy,
All the world surveying,
  Nowhere staying,
    Just like a fairy elf ;
Out o'er the tops of highest mountains skipping,
Out o'er the hills, the trees and valleys tripping,
Out o'er the ocean seas, without an oar or shipping.
  Hallo, my fancy, whither wilt thou go ?

  Amidst the misty vapors,
    Fain would I know
  What doth cause the tapers ;
  Why the clouds benight us,
  And affright us
    While we travel here below.
Fain would I know what makes the roaring
    thunder,
And what these lightnings be that rend the
    clouds asunder,
And what these comets are on which we gaze
    and wonder.
  Hallo, my fancy, whither wilt thou go ?

  Fain would I know the reason
    Why the little ant,
  All the summer season,
  Layeth up provision,
  On condition
    To know no winter's want :
And how these little fishes, that swim beneath
    salt water,
Do never blind their eye ; methinks it is a matter
An inch above the reach of old Erra Pater !
  Hallo, my fancy, whither wilt thou go ?

  Fain would I be resolved
    How things are done ;
  And where the bull was calved
  Of bloody Phalaris,
  And where the tailor is
    That works to the man i' the moon !
Fain would I know how Cupid aims so rightly ;
And how these little fairies do dance and leap
    so lightly ;
And where fair Cynthia makes her ambles
    nightly.
  Hallo, my fancy, whither wilt thou go ?

In conceit like Phaeton,
    I 'll mount Phœbus' chair,
Having ne'er a hat on,
All my hair a-burning
In my journeying,
    Hurrying through the air.
Fair would I hear his fiery horses neighing,
And see how they on foamy bits are playing ;
All the stars and planets I will be surveying !
    Hallo, my fancy, whither wilt thou go ?

O, from what ground of nature
    Doth the pelican,
That self-devouring creature,
Prove so froward
And untoward,
    Her vitals for to strain ?
And why the subtle fox, while in death's wounds
    is lying,
Doth not lament his pangs by howling and by
    crying ;
And why the milk-white swan doth sing when
    she 's a-dying.
    Hallo, my fancy, whither wilt thou go ?

Fain would I conclude this,
    At least make essay,
What similitude is ;
Why fowls of a feather
Flock and fly together,
    And lambs know beasts of prey :
How Nature's alchymists, these small laborious
    creatures,
Acknowledge still a prince in ordering their
    matters,
And suffer none to live, who slothing lose their
    features.
    Hallo, my fancy, whither wilt thou go ?

I 'm rapt with admiration,
    When I do ruminate,
Men of an occupation,
How each one calls him brother,
Yet each envieth other,
    And yet still intimate !
Yea, I admire to see some natures farther sun-
    d'red,
Than antipodes to us.   Is it not to be wond'red ?
In myriads ye 'll find, of one mind scarce a hun-
    dred ?
    Hallo, my fancy, whither wilt thou go ?

What multitude of notions
    Doth perturb my pate,
Considering the motions,
How the heavens are preserved,
And this world served
    In moisture, light, and heat !

If one spirit sits the outmost circle turning,
Or one turns another, continuing in journeying,
If rapid circles' motion be that which they call
        burning !
    Hallo, my fancy, whither wilt thou go ?

Fain also would I prove this,
    By considering
What that, which you call love, is :
Whether it be a folly
Or a melancholy,
    Or some heroic thing !
Fain I 'd have it proved, by one whom love hath
    wounded,
And fully upon one his desire hath founded,
Whom nothing else could please though the
    world were rounded.
    Hallo, my fancy, whither wilt thou go ?

To know this world's centre,
    Height, depth, breadth, and length,
Fain would I adventure
To search the hid attractions
Of magnetic actions,
    And adamantine strength.
Fain would I know, if in some lofty mountain,
Where the moon sojourns, if there be trees or
    fountain ;
If there be beasts of prey, or yet be fields to
    hunt in.
    Hallo, my fancy, whither wilt thou go ?

Fain would I have it tried
    By experiment,
By none can be denied !
If in this bulk of nature,
There be voids less or greater,
    Or all remains complete.
Fain would I know if beasts have any reason ;
If falcons killing eagles do commit a treason ;
If fear of winter's want make swallows fly the
    season.
    Hallo, my fancy, whither wilt thou go ?

Hallo, my fancy, hallo !
    Stay, stay at home with me,
I can thee no longer follow,
For thou hast betrayed me,
And bewrayed me ;
    It is too much for thee.
Stay, stay at home with me ; leave off thy lofty
    soaring ;
Stay thou at home with me, and on thy books
    be poring ;
For he that goes abroad lays little up in storing :
    Thou 'rt welcome home, my fancy, welcome
        home to me.
                                WILLIAM CLELAND.

THE CLOUD.

I BRING fresh showers for the thirsting flowers,
    From the seas and the streams ;
I bear light shade for the leaves when laid
    In their noonday dreams.
From my wings are shaken the dews that waken
    The sweet buds every one,
When rocked to rest on their mother's breast,
    As she dances about the sun.
I wield the flail of the lashing hail,
    And whiten the green plains under ;
And then again I dissolve it in rain,
    And laugh as I pass in thunder.

I sift the snow on the mountains below,
    And their great pines groan aghast ;
And all the night 't is my pillow white,
    While I sleep in the arms of the blast.
Sublime on the towers of my skyey bowers
    Lightning, my pilot, sits :
In a cavern under is fettered the thunder ;
    It struggles and howls by fits.

Over earth and ocean, with gentle motion,
    This pilot is guiding me,
Lured by the love of the genii that move
    In the depths of the purple sea ;
Over the rills and the crags and the hills,
    Over the lakes and plains,
Wherever he dream, under mountain or stream,
    The spirit he loves remains ;
And I all the while bask in heaven's blue smile,
    Whilst he is dissolving in rains.

The sanguine sunrise, with his meteor eyes,
    And his burning plumes outspread,
Leaps on the back of my sailing rack,
    When the morning star shines dead.
As, on the jag of a mountain crag
    Which an earthquake rocks and swings,
An eagle, alit, one moment may sit
    In the light of its golden wings ;
And when sunset may breathe, from the lit sea
    beneath,
    Its ardors of rest and of love,
And the crimson pall of eve may fall
    From the depth of heaven above,
With wings folded I rest on mine airy nest,
    As still as a brooding dove.

That orbèd maiden with white fire laden,
    Whom mortals call the moon,
Glides glimmering o'er my fleece-like floor
    By the midnight breezes strewn ;
And wherever the beat of her unseen feet,
    Which only the angels hear,
May have broken the woof of my tent's thin roof,
    The stars peep behind her and peer ;

And I laugh to see them whirl and flee,
    Like a swarm of golden bees,
When I widen the rent in my wind-built tent,
    Till the calm rivers, lakes, and seas,
Like strips of the sky fallen through me on high,
    Are each paved with the moon and these.

I bind the sun's throne with a burning zone,
    And the moon's with a girdle of pearl ;
The volcanoes are dim, and the stars reel and swim,
    When the whirlwinds my banner unfurl.
From cape to cape, with a bridge-like shape,
    Over a torrent sea,
Sunbeam-proof, I hang like a roof,
    The mountains its columns be.
The triumphal arch through which I march
    With hurricane, fire, and snow,
When the powers of the air are chained to my
    chair,
    Is the million-colored bow ;
The sphere-fire above its soft colors wove,
    While the moist earth was laughing below.

I am the daughter of the earth and water ;
    And the nursling of the sky ;
I pass through the pores of the ocean and shores ;
    I change, but I cannot die.
For after the rain, when, with never a stain,
    The pavilion of heaven is bare,
And the winds and sunbeams, with their convex
    gleams,
    Build up the blue dome of air, —
I silently laugh at my own cenotaph,
    And out of the caverns of rain,
Like a child from the womb, like a ghost from
    the tomb,
    I rise and upbuild it again.
                PERCY BYSSHE SHELLEY.

FANCY IN NUBIBUS.

O, IT is pleasant, with a heart at ease,
Just after sunset, or by moonlight skies,
To make the shifting clouds be what you please,
Or let the easily persuaded eyes
Own each quaint likeness issuing from the mould
Of a friend's fancy ; or, with head bent low,
And cheek aslant, see rivers flow of gold,
'Twixt crimson banks ; and then a traveller go
From mount to mount, through Cloudland, gor
    geous land !
Or, listening to the tide with closèd sight,
Be that blind Bard, who on the Chian strand,
By those deep sounds possessed with inward light,
Beheld the Iliad and the Odyssey,
Rise to the swelling of the voiceful sea.
                SAMUEL TAYLOR COLERIDGE.

THE SUNSET CITY.

THERE's a city that lies in the Kingdom of Clouds,
    In the glorious country on high,
Which an azure and silvery curtain enshrouds,
    To screen it from mortal eye ;

A city of temples and turrets of gold,
    That gleam by a sapphire sea,
Like jewels more splendid than earth may behold,
    Or are dreamed of by you and by me.

And about it are highlands of amber that reach
    Far away till they melt in the gloom ;
And waters that hem an immaculate beach
    With fringes of luminous foam.

Aerial bridges of pearl there are,
    And belfries of marvellous shapes,
And lighthouses lit by the evening star,
    That sparkle on violet capes ;

And hanging gardens that far away
    Enchantedly float aloof ;
Rainbow pavilions in avenues gay,
    And banners of glorious woof !

When the Summer sunset's crimsoning fires
    Are aglow in the western sky,
The pilgrim discovers the domes and spires
    Of this wonderful city on high ;

And gazing enrapt as the gathering shade
    Creeps over the twilight lea,
Sees palace and pinnacle totter and fade,
    And sink in the sapphire sea ;

Till the vision loses by slow degrees
    The magical splendor it wore ;
The silvery curtain is drawn, and he sees
    The beautiful city no more !
                HENRY SYLVESTER CORNWELL.

THE CASTLE IN THE AIR.

ADDRESSED TO A LADY WHO DATED HER LETTERS FROM
    "THE LITTLE CORNER OF THE WORLD."

IN the region of clouds, where the whirlwinds
        arise,
    My castle of fancy was built.
The turrets reflected the blue of the skies,
    And the windows with sunbeams were gilt.

The rainbow sometimes in its beautiful state
    Enamelled the mansion around ;
And the figures that fancy in clouds can create
    Supplied me with gardens and ground.

I had grottos and fountains and orange-tree
        groves ;
    I had all that enchantment has told ;
I had sweet shady walks for the gods and their
        loves ;
    I had mountains of coral and gold.

But a storm that I felt not had risen and rolled,
    While wrapped in a slumber I lay ;
And when I awoke in the morning, behold,
    My castle was carried away !

It passed over rivers and valleys and groves ;
    The world, it was all in my view ;
I thought of my friends, of their fates, of their
        loves,
    And often, full often, of you.

At length it came over a beautiful scene,
    Which Nature in silence had made ;
The place was but small, but 't was sweetly serene,
    And checkered with sunshine and shade.

I gazed and I envied, with painful good-will,
    And grew tired of my seat in the air,
When all of a sudden my castle stood still
    As if some attraction was there.

Like a lark in the sky it came fluttering down,
    And placed me exactly in view,
When, whom should I meet in this charming
        retreat,
    This corner of calmness, but you ?

Delighted to find you in honor and ease,
    I felt no more sorrow nor pain,
But, the wind coming fair, I ascended the breeze,
    And went back to my castle again.
                THOMAS PAINE.

IN THE MIST.

SITTING all day in a silver mist,
    In silver silence all the day,
    Save for the low, soft kiss of spray
And the lisp of sands by waters kissed,
    As the tide draws up the bay.

Little I hear and nothing I see,
    Wrapped in that veil by fairies spun ;
    The solid earth is vanished for me,
And the shining hours speed noiselessly,
    A woof of shadow and sun.

Suddenly out of the shifting veil
    A magical bark, by the sunbeams lit,
    Flits like a dream — or seems to flit --
With a golden prow and a gossamer sail
    And the waves make room for it

A fair, swift bark from some radiant realm, —
　Its diamond cordage cuts the sky
　　In glittering lines ; all silently
A seeming spirit holds the helm,
　And steers.　Will he pass me by !

Ah ! not for me is the vessel here ;
　Noiseless and swift as a sea-bird's flight
　She swerves and vanishes from the sight ;
No flap of sail, no parting cheer, —
　She has passed into the light.

Sitting some day in a deeper mist,
　Silent, alone, some other day,
　　An unknown bark, from an unknown bay,
By unknown waters lapped and kissed,
　Shall near me through the spray.

No flap of sail, no scraping of keel,
　Shadowy, dim, with a banner dark,
　It will hover, will pause, and I shall feel
A hand which grasps me, and shivering steal
　To the cold strand, and embark, —

Embark for that far, mysterious realm
　Where the fathomless, trackless waters flow.
　Shall I feel a Presence dim, and know
Thy dear hand, Lord, upon the helm,
　Nor be afraid to go ?

And through black waves and stormy blast
　And out of the fog-wreaths, dense and dun,
　Guided by thee, shall the vessel run,
Gain one fair haven, night being past,
　And anchor in the sun ?
　　　　　　　SARAH WOOLSEY (*Susan Coolidge*).

THE BLESSED DAMOZEL.

THE blessed damozel leaned out
　From the gold bar of heaven ;
Her eyes were deeper than the depth
　Of waters stilled at even ;
She had three lilies in her hand,
　And the stars in her hair were seven.

Her robe, ungirt from clasp to hem,
　No wrought flowers did adorn,
But a white rose of Mary's gift,
　For service neatly worn ;
Her hair that lay along her back
　Was yellow like ripe corn.

Her seemed she scarce had been a day
　One of God's choristers ;
The wonder was not yet quite gone
　From that still look of hers ;

Albeit, to them she left, her day
　Had counted as ten years.

It was the rampart of God's house
　That she was standing on ;
By God built over the sheer depth
　The which is space begun ;
So high, that looking downward thence
　She scarce could see the sun.

It lies in heaven, across the flood
　Of ether, as a bridge.
Beneath, the tides of day and night
　With flame and darkness ridge
The void, as low as where this earth
　Spins like a fretful midge.

Heard hardly, some of her new friends
　Amid their loving games
Spake evermore among themselves
　Their virginal chaste names ;
And the souls mounting up to God
　Went by her like thin flames.

And still she bowed herself and stopped
　Out of the circling charm ;
Until her bosom must have made
　The bar she leaned on warm,
And the lilies lay as if asleep
　Along her bended arm.

From the fixed place of heaven she saw
　Time like a pulse shake fierce
Through all the worlds.　Her gaze still strove
　Within the gulf to pierce
The path ; and now she spoke as when
　The stars sang in their spheres.

　　.　　　　.　　　　.　　　　.

"I wish that he were come to me,
　For he will come," she said.
"Have I not prayed in heaven ? — on earth,
　Lord, Lord, has he not prayed ?
Are not two prayers a perfect strength ?
　And shall I feel afraid ?"

　　.　　　　.　　　　.　　　　.

She gazed and listened, and then said,
　Less sad of speech than mild, —
"All this is when he comes." She ceased.
　The light thrilled toward her, filled
With angels in strong level flight.
　Her eyes prayed, and she smiled.

(I saw her smile.)　But soon their path
　Was vague in distant spheres ;
And then she cast her arms along
　The golden barriers,
And laid her face between her hands,
　And wept. (I heard her tears.)
　　　　　　　DANTE GABRIEL ROSSETTI.

GOETHE, AT EIGHTY.

THE SUNKEN CITY.

HARK ! the faint bells of the sunken city
    Peal once more their wonted evening chime !
From the deep abysses floats a ditty,
    Wild and wondrous, of the olden time.

Temples, towers, and domes of many stories
    There lie buried in an ocean grave, —
Undescried, save when their golden glories
    Gleam, at sunset, through the lighted wave.

And the mariner who had seen them glisten,
    In whose ears those magic bells do sound,
Night by night bides there to watch and listen,
    Though death lurks behind each dark rock
      round.

So the bells of memory's wonder-city
    Peal for me their old melodious chime ;
So my heart pours forth a changeful ditty,
    Sad and pleasant, from the bygone time.

Domes and towers and castles, fancy-builded,
    There lie lost to daylight's garish beams, —
There lie hidden till unveiled and gilded,
    Glory-gilded, by my nightly dreams !

And then hear I music sweet upknelling
    From many a well-known phantom band,
And, through tears, can see my natural dwelling
    Far off in the spirit's luminous land !
        From the German of WILHELM MUELLER. Trans-
        lation of JAMES CLARENCE MANGAN.

THE LORE–LEI.

I KNOW not whence it rises,
    This thought so full of woe ; —
But a tale of the times departed
    Haunts me — and will not go.

The air is cool, and it darkens,
    And calmly flows the Rhine ;
The mountain peaks are sparkling
    In the sunny evening-shine.

And yonder sits a maiden,
    The fairest of the fair ;
With gold is her garment glittering,
    And she combs her golden hair.

With a golden comb she combs it,
    And a wild song singeth she,
That melts the heart with a wondrous
    And powerful melody.

The boatman feels his bosom
    With a nameless longing move ;
He sees not the gulfs before him,
    His gaze is fixed above,

Till over boat and boatman
    The Rhine's deep waters run ;
And this with her magic singing
    The Lore-Lei hath done !
        From the German of HEINRICH HEINE.

THE FISHER.

THE waters purled, the waters swelled, —
    A fisher sat near by,
And earnestly his line beheld
    With tranquil heart and eye ;
And while he sits and watches there,
    He sees the waves divide,
And, lo ! a maid, with glistening hair,
    Springs from the troubled tide.

She sang to him, she spake to him, —
    " Why lur'st thou from below,
In cruel mood, my tender brood,
    To die in day's fierce glow ?
Ah ! didst thou know how sweetly there
    The little fishes dwell,
Thou wouldst come down their lot to share,
    And be forever well.

" Bathes not the smiling sun at night —
    The moon too — in the waves ?
Comes he not forth more fresh and bright
    From ocean's cooling caves ?
Canst thou unmoved that deep world see,
    That heaven of tranquil blue,
Where thine own face is beckoning thee
    Down to the eternal dew ? "

The waters purled, the waters swelled, —
    They kissed his naked feet ;
His heart a nameless transport held,
    As if his love did greet.
She spake to him, she sang to him ;
    Then all with him was o'er, —
Half drew she him, half sank he in, —
    He sank to rise no more.
        From the German of GOETHE. Trans-
        lation of CHARLES T. BROOKS.

THE SIRENS' SONG.

FROM THE " INNER TEMPLE MASQUE."

STEER hither, steer your wingèd pines,
    All beaten mariners :
Here lie undiscovered mines,
    A prey to passengers ;

Perfumes far sweeter than the best
That make the phœnix urn and nest :
    Fear not your ships,
Nor any to oppose you save our lips ;
    But come on shore,
Where no joy dies till love has gotten more.

For swelling waves our panting breasts,
    Where never storms arise,
Exchange ; and be awhile our guests :
    For stars, gaze on our eyes.
The compass, love shall hourly sing ;
And, as he goes about the ring,
    We will not miss
To tell each point he nameth with a kiss.
              WILLIAM BROWNE.

THE FORSAKEN MERMAN.

COME, dear children, let us away ;
    Down and away below.
Now my brothers call from the bay ;
Now the great winds shorewards blow ;
Now the salt tides seaward flow ;
Now the wild white horses play,
Champ and chafe and toss in the spray.
    Children dear, let us away.
        This way, this way.

Call her once before you go.
    Call once yet,
In a voice that she will know :
    " Margaret ! Margaret ! "
Children's voices should be dear
(Call once more) to a mother's ear :
Children's voices wild with pain,
    Surely she will come again.
Call her once, and come away,
    This way, this way.
" Mother dear, we cannot stay !
The wild white horses foam and fret,
    Margaret ! Margaret ! "

Come, dear children, come away down.
    Call no more.
One last look at the white-walled town,
And the little gray church on the windy shore,
    Then come down.
She will not come, though you call all day.
    Come away, come away.

Children dear, was it yesterday
We heard the sweet bells over the bay ?
    In the caverns where we lay,
    Through the surf and through the swell,
The far-off sound of a silver bell ?

Sand-strewn caverns cool and deep,
Where the winds are all asleep ;
Where the spent lights quiver and gleam ;
Where the salt weed sways in the stream ;
Where the sea-beasts, ranged all round,
Feed in the ooze of their pasture-ground ;
Where the sea-snakes coil and twine,
Dry their mail and bask in the brine ;
Where great whales come sailing by,
Sail and sail, with unshut eye,
Round the world forever and aye ?
    When did music come this way ?
    Children dear, was it yesterday ?

Children dear, was it yesterday
(Call yet once) that she went away ?
Once she sat with you and me,
    On a red gold throne in the heart of the sea.
    And the youngest sat on her knee.
She combed its bright hair, and she tended it well,
When down swung the sound of the far-off bell,
She sighed, she looked up through the clear
    green sea,
She said, "I must go, for my kinsfolk pray
In the little gray church on the shore to-day.
'T will be Easter-time in the world, — ah me !
And I lose my poor soul, Merman, here with
    thee."
I said : "Go up, dear heart, through the waves :
Say thy prayer, and come back to the kind sea-
    caves."
She smiled, she went up through the surf in the
    bay,
    Children dear, was it yesterday ?

Children dear, were we long alone ?
"The sea grows stormy, the little ones moan ;
Long prayers," I said, "in the world they say."
"Come," I said, and we rose through the surf in
    the bay.
We went up the beach in the sandy down
Where the sea-stocks bloom, to the white-walled
    town,
Through the narrow paved streets, where all was
    still,
To the little gray church on the windy hill.
From the church came a murmur of folk at
    their prayers,
But we stood without in the cold blowing airs.
We climbed on the graves, on the stones worn
    with rains,
And we gazed up the aisle through the small
    leaded panes,
She sat by the pillar ; we saw her clear ;
"Margaret, hist ! come quick, we are here.
Dear heart," I said, "we are here alone.
The sea grows stormy, the little ones moan."

But, ah, she gave me never a look,
For her eyes were sealed to the holy book.
"Loud prays the priest ; shut stands the
    door."
Come away, children, call no more,
Come away, come down, call no more.

Down, down, down,
Down to the depths of the sea.
She sits at her wheel in the humming town,
    Singing most joyfully.
Hark what she sings : " O joy, O joy,
From the humming street, and the child with
    its toy,
From the priest and the bell, and the holy well,
    From the wheel where I spun,
    And the blessed light of the sun."
    And so she sings her fill,
    Singing most joyfully,
    Till the shuttle falls from her hand,
    And the whizzing wheel stands still.
She steals to the window, and looks at the sand,
    And over the sand at the sea ;
    And her eyes are set in a stare ;
    And anon there breaks a sigh,
    And anon there drops a tear,
    From a sorrow-clouded eye,
    And a heart sorrow-laden,
        A long, long sigh,
For the cold strange eyes of a little Mermaiden,
And the gleam of her golden hair.

Come away, away, children,
Come, children, come down.
The hoarse wind blows colder,
Lights shine in the town.
She will start from her slumber
When gusts shake the door ;
She will hear the winds howling,
Will hear the waves roar.
We shall see, while above us
The waves roar and whirl,
A ceiling of amber,
A pavement of pearl, —
Singing, " Here came a mortal,
But faithless was she,
And alone dwell forever
The kings of the sea."

But, children, at midnight,
When soft the winds blow,
When clear falls the moonlight,
When spring-tides are low ;
When sweet airs come seaward
From heaths starred with broom ;
And high rocks throw mildly
On the blanched sands a gloom :

Up the still, glistening beaches,
Up the creeks we will hie ;
Over banks of bright seaweed
The ebb-tide leaves dry.
We will gaze from the sand-hills,
At the white sleeping town ;
At the church on the hillside —
And then come back, down.
Singing, " There dwells a loved one,
But cruel is she :
She left lonely forever
The kings of the sea."

MATTHEW ARNOLD.

UNA AND THE RED CROSSE KNIGHT.

FROM "THE FAERIE QUEENE," BOOK I. CANTO I.

A GENTLE Knight was pricking on the plaine,
Ycladd in mightie armes and silver shielde,
Wherein old dints of deepe woundes did re-
    maine,
The cruell markes of many a bloody fielde ;
Yet armes till that time did he never wield :
His angry steede did chide his foming bitt,
As much disdayning to the curbe to yield :
Full iolly knight he seemd, and faire did sitt,
As one for knightly giusts and fierce encounters
    . fitt.

And on his brest a bloodie crosse he bore,
The deare remembrance of his dying Lord,
For whose sweete sake that glorious badge he
    wore,
And dead, as living ever, him ador'd :
Upon his shield the like was also scor'd,
For soveraine hope, which in his helpe he had,
Right, faithfull, true he was in deede and word ;
But of his cheere,* did seeme too solemne sad ;
Yet nothing did he dread, but ever was ydrad.†

Upon a great adventure he was bond,
That greatest Gloriana to him gave,
That greatest glorious queene of Faery lond,
To winne him worshippe, and her grace to have,
Which of all earthly thinges he most did crave:
And ever, as he rode, his hart did earne
To prove his puissance in battell brave
Upon his foe, and his new force to learne ;
Upon his foe, a Dragon horrible and stearne.

A lovely Ladie rode him faire beside,
Upon a lowly asse more white then snow ;
Yet she much whiter ; but the same did hide
Under a vele, that wimpled was full low ;

* countenance.   † dreaded

And over all a blacke stole shee did throw :
As one that inly mournd, so was she sad,
And heavie sate upon her palfrey slow ;
Seemèd in heart some hidden care she had ;
And by her in a line a milke-white lambe she lad.

So pure and innocent as that same lambe
She was in life and every vertuous lore ;
And by descent from royall lynage came
Of ancient kinges and queenes, that had of yore
Their scepters stretcht from east to westerne
    shore,
And all the world in their subiection held ;
Till that infernall feend with foule uprore
Forwasted * all their land, and then expeld ;
Whom to avenge, she had this Knight from far
    compeld.

Behind her farre away a Dwarfe did lag,
That lasie seemd, in being ever last,
Or wearièd with bearing of her bag
Of needments at his backe.   Thus as they past,
The day with cloudes was suddeine overcast,
And angry Iove an hideous storme of raine
Did poure into his lemans lap so fast,
That everie wight to shrowd it did constrain ;
And this faire couple eke to shroud themselves
    were fain.

Enforst to seeke some covert nigh at hand, ·
A shadie grove not farr away they spide,
That promist ayde the tempest to withstand ;
Whose loftie trees, yclad with sommers pride,
Did spred so broad, that heavens light did hide,
Not perceable with power of any starr :
And all within were pathes and alleies wide,
With footing worne, and leading inward farr :
Faire harbour that them seemes ; so in they
    entred ar.

EDMUND SPENSER.

THE CAVE OF SLEEP.

FROM THE "FAERIE QUEENE," BOOK I. CANTO I.

HE, making speedy way through spersèd † ayre,
And through the world of waters wide and deepe,
To Morpheus house doth hastily repaire,
Amid the bowels of the earth full steepe,
And low, where dawning day doth never peepe,
His dwelling is ; there Tethys his wet bed
Doth ever wash, and Cynthia still doth steepe
In silver deaw his ever-drouping hed,
Whiles sad Night over him her mantle black doth
    spred.

* *For* is here intensive.   † dispersed.

And, more to lulle him in his slumber soft,
A trickling streame from high rock tumbling
    downe,
And ever-drizling raine upon the loft,
Mixt with a murmuring winde, much like the
    sowne *
Of swarming bees, did cast him in a swowne. †
No other noyse, nor peoples troublous cryes,
As still are wont t' annoy the wallèd towne,
Might there be heard ; but carelesse Quiet lyes
Wrapt in eternall silence, farre from enimyes.

EDMUND SPENSER.

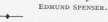

UNA AND THE LION.

FROM THE "FAERIE QUEENE," BOOK I. CANTO III.

ONE day, nigh wearie of the yrkesome way,
From her unhastie beast she did alight ;
And on the grasse her dainty limbs did lay
In secrete shadow, far from all mens sight ;
From her fayre head her fillet she undight,
And layd her stole aside.   Her angels face,
As the great eye of heaven, shyned bright,
And made a sunshine in the shady place ;
Did never mortall eye behold such heavenly grace.

It fortunèd, out of the thickest wood
A ramping lyon rushèd suddeinly,
Hunting full greedy after salvage blood : ‡
Soone as the royall virgin he did spy,
With gaping mouth at her ran greedily,
To have attonce devoured her tender corse ;
But to the pray whenas he drew more ny,
His bloody rage aswagèd with remorse, §
And, with the sight amazd, forgat his furious
    forse.

Instead thereof, he kist her wearie feet,
And lickt her lilly hands with fawning tong ;
As he her wrongèd innocence did weet. ‖
O how can beautie maister the most strong,
And simple truth subdue avenging wrong !
Whose yielded pryde and proud submission,
Still dreading death, when she had markèd long,
Her hart gan melt in great compassion ;
And drizling teares did shed for pure affection.

" The lyon, lord of everie beast in field,"
Quoth she, "his princely puissance doth abate,
And mightie proud to humble weake does yield,
Forgetfull of the hungry rage, which late
Him prickt, in pittie of my sad estate : —
But he, my lyon, and my noble lord,
How does he find in cruell hart to hate
Her, that him lovd, and ever most adord
As the god of my life ? why hath he me abhord ?"

* sound.   † swoon — deep sleep.
‡ blood of wild animals.   § pity.   ‖ understand.

Redounding tears did choke th' end of her plaint,
Which softly ecchoed from the neighbour wood ;
And, sad to see her sorrowfull constraint,
The kingly beast upon her gazing stood ;
With pittie calmd, downe fell his angry mood.
At last, in close hart shutting up her payne,
Arose the virgin borne of heavenly brood,
And to her snowy palfrey got agayne,
To seeke her strayèd champion if she might attayne.

The lyon would not leave her desolate,
But with her went along, as a strong gard
Of her chast person, and a faythfull mate
Of her sad troubles and misfortunes hard :
Still, when she slept, he kept both watch and ward ;
And, when she wakt, he wayted diligent,
With humble service to her will prepard ;
From her fayre eyes he took commandment,
And ever by her lookes conceivèd her intent.

EDMUND SPENSER.

THE BOWER OF BLISS.

FROM THE "FAERIE QUEENE," BOOK II. CANTO XII.

THERE the most daintie paradise on ground
Itselfe doth offer to his sober eye,
In which all pleasures plenteously abownd,
And none does others happinesse envye ;
The painted flowres ; the trees upshooting hye ;
The dales for shade ; the hilles for breathing space ;
The trembling groves ; the christall running by ;
And, that which all faire workes doth most aggrace, *
The art, which all that wrought, appearèd in no place.

One would have thought (so cunningly the rude
And scornèd partes were mingled with the fine)
That Nature had for wantonesse ensude †
Art, and that Art at Nature did repine ;
So striving each th' other to undermine,
Each did the others worke more beautify ;
So diff'ring both in willes agreed in fine :
So all agreed, through sweete diversity,
This gardin to adorne with all variety.

And in the midst of all a fountaine stood,
Of richest substance that on earth might bee,
So pure and shiny that the silver flood
Through every channell running one might see ;
Most goodly it with curious ymageree

Was over wrought, and shapes of naked Boyes,
Of which some seemed with lively iollitee
To fly about, playing their wanton toyes,
Whylest others did themselves embay * in liquid ioyes.

And over all, of purest gold, was spred
A trayle of yvie in his native hew ;
For the rich metall was so colourèd,
That wight, who did not well avised † it vew,
Would surely deeme it to bee yvie trew :
Low his lascivious armes adown did creepe,
That, themselves dipping in the silver dew,
Their fleecy flowres they fearefully did steepe,
Which drops of christall seemed for wantones to weep.

Infinit streames continually did well
Out of this fountaine, sweet and faire to see,
The which into an ample laver fell,
And shortly grew to so great quantitie,
That like a little lake it seemed to bee ;
Whose depth exceeded not three cubits hight,
That through the waves one might the bottom see,
All pav'd beneath with iaspar shining bright,
That seemd the fountaine in that sea did sayle upright.

Eftsoons ‡ they heard a most melodious sound,
Of all that mote delight a daintie eare,
Such as attonce might not on living ground,
Save in this paradise, be heard elsewhere.
Right hard it was for wight which did it heare,
To read what manner musicke that mote bee ;
For all that pleasing is to living eare
Was there consorted in one harmonee ;
Birdes, voices, instruments, windes, waters, all agree :

The ioyous birdes, shrouded in chearefull shade,
Their notes unto the voice attempred sweet ;
Th' angelicall soft trembling voyces made
To th' instruments divine respondence meet ;
The silver-sounding instruments did meet
With the base murmure of the waters fall ;
The waters fall, with difference discreet,
Now soft, now loud, unto the wind did call ;
The gentle warbling wind low answerèd to all.

EDMUND SPENSER.

THE LADY LOST IN THE WOOD.

FROM "COMUS."

THIS way the noise was, if mine ear be true,
My best guide now ; methought it was the sound
Of riot and ill-managed merriment,
Such as the jocund flute or gamesome pipe

---

* give grace to.   † imitated.   * bathe.   † with attention.   ‡ immediately.

Stirs up amongst the loose, unlettered hinds,
When for their teeming flocks and granges full
In wanton dance they praise the bounteous Pan,
And thank the gods amiss.   I should be loath
To meet the rudeness and swilled insolence
Of such late wassailers ; yet O, where else
Shall I inform my unacquainted feet
In the blind mazes of this tangled wood ?
My brothers, when they saw me wearied out
With this long way, resolving here to lodge
Under the spreading favor of these pines,
Stepped, as they said, to the next thicket side
To bring me berries, or such cooling fruit
As the kind, hospitable woods provide.
They left me then, when the gray-hooded even,
Like a sad votarist in palmer's weed,
Rose from the hindmost wheels of Phœbus' wain.
But where they are, and why they came not
    back,
Is now the labor of my thoughts : 't is likeliest
They had engaged their wandering steps too far,
And envious darkness, ere they could return,
Had stole them from me ; else, O thievish night,
Why shouldst thou, but for some felonious end,
In thy dark lantern thus close up the stars,
That nature hung in heaven, and filled their
    lamps
With everlasting oil, to give due light
To the misled and lonely traveller ?
This is the place, as well as I may guess,
Whence even now the tumult of loud mirth
Was rife, and perfect in my listening ear,
Yet naught but single darkness do I find.
What might this be?   A thousand fantasies
Begin to throng into my memory,
Of calling shapes, and beckoning shadows dire,
And airy tongues, that syllable men's names
On sands and shores and desert wildernesses.
These thoughts may startle well, but not astound
The virtuous mind, that ever walks attended
By a strong-siding champion, Conscience.
O welcome, pure-eyed Faith, white-handed Hope,
Thou hovering angel girt with golden wings,
And thou unblemished form of Chastity ;
I see you visibly, and now believe
That he, the Supreme Good, to whom all things ill
Are but as slavish officers of vengeance,
Would send a glistering guardian, if need were,
To keep my life and honor unassailed.
                                            MILTON.

———◆———

THE NYMPH OF THE SEVERN.

FROM "COMUS."

THERE is a gentle nymph not far from hence
That with moist curb sways the smooth Severn
    stream.
Sabrina is her name, a virgin pure ;

Whilom she was the daughter of Locrine,
That had the sceptre from his father Brute.
She, guiltless damsel, flying the mad pursuit
Of her enragèd stepdame Guendolen,
Commended her fair innocence to the flood,
That stayed her flight with his cross-flowing
    course.
The water-nymphs that in the bottom played,
Held up their pearlèd wrists, and took her in,
Bearing her straight to aged Nereus' hall,
Who, piteous of her woes, reared her lank head,
And gave her to his daughters to imbathe
In nectared lavers strewed with asphodel,
And through the porch and inlet of each sense
Dropped in ambrosial oils, till she revived,
And underwent a quick immortal change,
Made Goddess of the river : still she retains
Her maiden gentleness, and oft at eve
Visits the herds along the twilight meadows,
Helping all urchin blasts, and ill-luck signs
That the shrewd meddling elf delights to make,
Which she with precious vialed liquors heals ;
For which the shepherds at their festivals
Carol her goodness loud in rustic lays,
And throw sweet garland wreaths into her stream
Of pansies pinks, and gaudy daffodils.
                                            MILTON.

———◆———

THE HAUNT OF THE SORCERER.

FROM "COMUS."

WITHIN the navel of this hideous wood,
Immured in cypress shades a sorcerer dwells,
Of Bacchus and of Circè born, great Comus,
Deep skilled in all his mother's witcheries ;
And here to every thirsty wanderer
By sly enticement gives his baneful cup,
With many murmurs mixed, whose pleasing
    poison
The visage quite transforms of him that drinks,
And the inglorious likeness of a beast
Fixes instead, unmoulding reason's mintage
Charactered in the face : this I have learnt
Tending my flocks hard by i' the hilly crofts,
That brow this bottom-glade, whence night by
    night,
He and his monstrous rout are heard to howl,
Like stabled wolves, or tigers at their prey,
Doing abhorrèd rites to Hecatè
In their obscurèd haunts of inmost bowers.
Yet have they many baits, and guileful spells,
T' inveigle and invite the unwary sense
Of them that pass unweeting by the way.
This evening late, by them the chewing flocks
Had ta'en their supper on the savory herb
Of knot-grass dew-besprent, and were in fold,

BEETHOVEN'S THIRD SYMPHONY.

PASSION and pain, the outcry of despair,
  The pang of the unattainable desire,
  And youth's delight in pleasures that expire,
And sweet high dreamings of the good and fair
Clashing in swift soul-storm, through which no prayer
  Uplifted stays the destined death-stroke dire.
  Then through a mighty sorrowing, as through fire,
The soul burnt pure yearns forth into the air
Of the dear earth and, with the scent of flowers
  And song of birds assuaged, takes heart again,
  Made cheerier with this drinking of God's wine,
And turns with healing to the world of men,
And high above a sweet strong angel towers,
  And Love makes life triumphant and divine.

                              RICHARD HOVEY.

After a Painting by Emile Brèton.

THE VOYAGE OF SLEEP.

To sleep I give myself away,
  Unclasp the fetters of the mind,
Forget the sorrows of the day,
  The burdens of the heart unbind.

With empty sail this tired bark
  Drifts out upon the sea of rest,
While all the shore behind grows dark,
  And silence reigns from east to west.

At last awakes the hidden breeze
  That bears me to the land of dreams,
Where music sighs among the trees,
  And murmurs in the winding streams.

O weary day, O weary day,
  That dawns in fear and ends in strife,
That brings no cooling draft to allay
  The burning fever-thirst of life.

O sacred night when angel hands
  Are pressed upon the tired brow,
And when the soul on shining sands
  Descends with angels from the prow.

To sleep I give myself away,
  My heart forgets its vague unrest,
And all the clamor of the day,
  And drifts toward the quiet west.

ARTHUR W. H. EATON.

I sat me down to watch upon a bank
With ivy canopied, and interwove
With flaunting honeysuckle, and began,
Wrapt in a pleasing fit of melancholy,
To meditate my rural minstrelsy,
Till fancy had her fill, but ere a close,
The wonted roar was up amidst the woods,
And filled the air with barbarous dissonance ;
At which I ceased, and listened them awhile,
Till an unusual stop of sudden silence
Gave respite to the drowsy frighted steeds,
That draw the litter of close-curtained sleep ;
At last a soft and solemn-breathing sound
Rose like a stream of rich distilled perfumes,
And stole upon the air, that even Silence
Was took ere she was ware, and wished she might
Deny her nature, and be never more,
Still to be so displaced.   I was all ear,
And took in strains that might create a soul
Under the ribs of death : but O, ere long
Too well I did perceive it was the voice
Of my most honored Lady, your dear sister.
Amazed I stood, harrowed with grief and fear,
And O, poor hapless nightingale, thought I,
How sweet thou sing'st, how near the deadly
    snare !

MILTON.

THE CASTLE OF INDOLENCE.

FROM CANTO I.

The castle hight of Indolence,
    And its false luxury ;
Where for a little time, alas !
    We lived right jollily.

O MORTAL man, who livest here by toil,
Do not complain of this thy hard estate ;
That like an emmet thou must ever moil,
Is a sad sentence of an ancient date ;
And, certes, there is for it reason great ;
For, though sometimes it makes thee weep and
    wail,
And curse thy star, and early drudge and late ;
Withouten that would come a heavier bale,
Loose life, unruly passions, and diseases pale.

In lowly dale, fast by a river's side,
With woody hill o'er hill encompassed round
A most enchanting wizard did abide,
Than whom a fiend more fell is nowhere found.
It was, I ween, a lovely spot of ground ;
And there a season atween June and May,
Half prankt with spring, with summer half
    embrowned,
A listless climate made, where, sooth to say,
No living wight could work, ne cared even for
    play.

Was naught around but images of rest :
Sleep-soothing groves, and quiet lawns be-
    tween ;
And flowery beds that slumbrous influence kest,
From poppies breathed ; and beds of pleasant
    green,
Where never yet was creeping creature seen.
Meantime, unnumbered glittering streamlets
    played,
And hurlèd everywhere their waters sheen ;
That, as they bickered through the sunny glade,
Though restless still themselves, a lulling mur-
    mur made.

Joined to the prattle of the purling rills
Were heard the lowing herds along the vale,
And flocks loud beating from the distant hills,
And vacant shepherds piping in the dale :
And, now and then, sweet Philomel would wail,
Or stockdoves plain amid the forest deep,
That drowsy rustled to the sighing gale ;
And still a coil the grasshopper did keep ;
Yet all these sounds yblent inclinèd all to sleep.

Full in the passage of the vale, above,
A sable, silent, solemn forest stood ;
Where naught but shadowy forms was seen to
    move,
As Idless fancied in her dreaming mood :
And up the hills, on either side, a wood
Of blackening pines, aye waving to and fro,
Sent forth a sleepy horror through the blood ;
And where this valley winded out, below,
The murmuring main was heard, and scarcely
    heard, to flow.

A pleasing land of drowsyhed it was,
Of dreams that wave before the half-shut eye ;
And of gay castles in the clouds that pass,
Forever flushing round a summer sky :
There eke the soft delights, that witchingly
Instil a wanton sweetness through the breast,
And the calm pleasures always hovered nigh ;
But whate'er smacked of noyance or unrest
Was far, far off expelled from this delicious nest.

The landscape such, inspiring perfect ease,
Where Indolence (for so the wizard hight)
Close-hid his castle mid embowering trees,
That half shut out the beams of Phœbus bright,
And made a kind of checkered day and night ;
Meanwhile, unceasing at the massy gate,
Beneath a spacious palm, the wicked wight
Was placed ; and to his lute, of cruel fate
And labor harsh, complained, lamenting man's
    estate.

Thither continual pilgrims crowded still,
From all the roads of earth that pass there by :
For, as they chanced to breathe on neighbor-
    ing hill,
The freshness of this valley smote their eye,
And drew them ever and anon more nigh ;
Till clustering round the enchanter false they
    hung,
Ymolten with his siren melody ;
While o'er the enfeebling lute his hand he
    flung,
And to the trembling chords these tempting
    verses sung :

"Behold ! ye pilgrims of this earth, behold !
See all, but man, with unearned pleasure gay :
See her bright robes the butterfly unfold,
Broke from her wintry tomb in prime of May !
What youthful bride can equal her array ?
Who can with her for easy pleasure vie ?
From mead to mead with gentle wing to stray,
From flower to flower on balmy gales to fly,
Is all she has to do beneath the radiant sky.

"Behold the merry minstrels of the morn,
The swarming songsters of the careless grove,
Ten thousand throats ! that, from the flower-
    ing thorn,
Hymn their good God, and carol sweet of love,
Such grateful kindly raptures them emove :
They neither plough nor sow ; ne, fit for flail,
E'er to the barn the nodden sheaves they
    drove :
Yet theirs each harvest dancing in the gale,
Whatever crowns the hill, or smiles along the
    vale.

"Outcast of nature, man ! the wretched thrall
Of bitter dropping sweat, of sweltry pain,
Of cares that eat away the heart with gall,
And of the vices, an inhuman train,
That all proceed from savage thirst of gain :
For when hard-hearted interest first began
To poison earth, Astræa left the plain ;
Guile, violence, and murder seized on man,
And, for soft milky streams, with blood the
    rivers ran.

"Come, ye who still the cumbrous load of life
Push hard up hill ; but as the furthest steep
You trust to gain, and put an end to strife,
Down thunders back the stone with mighty
    sweep,
And hurls your labors to the valley deep,
Forever vain : come, and withouten fee,
I in oblivion will your sorrows steep,
Your cares, your toils ; will steep you in a sea
Of full delight : O, come, ye weary wights, to me !

"With me, you need not rise at early dawn,
To pass the joyless day in various stounds ;
Or, louting low, on upstart fortune fawn,
And sell fair honor for some paltry pounds ;
Or through the city take your dirty rounds,
To cheat, and dun, and lie, and visit pay,
Now flattering base, now giving secret wounds ;
Or prowl in courts of law for human prey,
In venal senate thieve, or rob on broad highway.

"No cocks, with me, to rustic labor call,
From village on to village sounding clear ;
To tardy swain no shrill-voiced matrons squall ;
No dogs, no babes, no wives, to stun your ear ;
No hammers thump ; no horrid blacksmith
    sear,
Ne noisy tradesman your sweet slumbers start,
With sounds that are a misery to hear :
But all is calm, as would delight the heart
Of Sybarite of old, all nature, and all art.

"Here naught but candor reigns, indulgent
    ease,
Good-natured lounging, sauntering up and
    down :
They who are pleased themselves must always
    please ;
On others' ways they never squint a frown,
Nor heed what haps in hamlet or in town :
Thus, from the source of tender Indolence,
With milky blood the heart is overflown,
Is soothed and sweetened by the social sense ;
For interest, envy, pride, and strife are banished
    hence.

"What, what is virtue, but repose of mind,
A pure ethereal calm, that knows no storm ;
Above the reach of wild ambition's wind,
Above those passions that this world deform,
And torture man, a proud malignant worm ?
But here, instead, soft gales of passion play,
And gently stir the heart, thereby to form
A quicker sense of joy ; as breezes stray
Across the enlivened skies, and make them still
    more gay.

"The best of men have ever loved repose :
They hate to mingle in the filthy fray ;
Where the soul sours, and gradual rancor
    grows,
Imbittered more from peevish day to day.
E'en those whom fame has lent her fairest ray,
The most renowned of worthy wights of yore,
From a base world at last have stolen away :
So Scipio, to the soft Cumæan shore
Retiring, tasted joy he never knew before.

" But if a little exercise you choose,
Some zest for ease, 't is not forbidden here :
Amid the groves you may indulge the Muse,
Or tend the blooms, and deck the vernal year ;
Or softly stealing, with your watery gear,
Along the brooks, the crimson-spotted fry
You may delude : the whilst, amused, you hear
Now the hoarse stream, and now the zephyr's
    sigh,
Attunèd to the birds, and woodland melody.

" O grievous folly ! to heap up estate,
Losing the days you see beneath the sun ;
When, sudden, comes blind unrelenting fate,
And gives the untasted portion you have won
With ruthless toil, and many a wretch undone,
To those who mock you, gone to Pluto's reign,
There with sad ghosts to pine, and shadows
    dun :
But sure it is of vanities most vain,
To toil for what you here untoiling may obtain."

He ceased.   But still their trembling ears re-
    tained
The deep vibrations of his witching song ;
That, by a kind of magic power, constrained
To enter in, pell-mell, the listening throng.
Heaps poured on heaps, and yet they slipt
    along,
In silent ease ; as when beneath the beam
Of summer moons, the distant woods among,
Or by some flood all silvered with the gleam,
The soft-embodied fays through airy portal
    stream :

By the smooth demon so it ordered was,
And here his baneful bounty first began :
Though some there were who would not fur-
    ther pass,
And his alluring baits suspected han.
The wise distrust the too fair-spoken man.
Yet through the gate they cast a wishful eye:
Not to move on, perdie, is all they can :
For do their very best they cannot fly,
But often each way look, and often sorely sigh.

When this the watchful wicked wizard saw,
With sudden spring he leaped upon them
    straight ;
And soon as touched by his unhallowed paw,
They found themselves within the cursèd gate:
Full hard to be repassed, like that of fate.
Not stronger were of old the giant crew,
Who sought to pull high Jove from regal state ;
Though feeble wretch he seemed, of sallow hue:
Certes, who bides his grasp, will that encounter
    rue.

     .   .   .

Ye gods of quiet, and of sleep profound !
Whose soft dominion o'er this castle sways,
And all the widely silent places round,
Forgive me, if my trembling pen displays
What never yet was sung in mortal lays.
But how shall I attempt such arduous string ?
I who have spent my nights and nightly days
In this soul-deadening place loose-loitering :
Ah! how shall I for this uprear my moulted wing ?

Come on, my Muse, nor stoop to low despair,
Thou imp of Jove, touched by celestial fire !
Thou yet shalt sing of war, and actions fair,
Which the bold sons of Britain will inspire :
Of ancient bards thou yet shalt sweep the lyre ;
Thou yet shalt tread in tragic pall the stage,
Paint love's enchanting woes, the hero's ire,
The sage's calm, the patriot's noble rage,
Dashing corruption down through every worth-
    less age.

The doors, that knew no shrill alarming bell
Ne cursèd knocker plied by villain's hand,
Self-opened into halls, where who can tell
What elegance and grandeur wide expand ;
The pride of Turkey and of Persia land ?
Soft quilts on quilts, on carpets carpets spread,
And couches stretched around in seemly band ;
And endless pillows rise to prop the head ;
So that each spacious room was one full-swelling
    bed ;

And everywhere huge covered tables stood,
With wines high-flavored and rich viands
    crowned ;
Whatever sprightly juice or tasteful food
On the green bosom of this earth are found,
And all old ocean 'genders in his round :
Some hand unseen these silently displayed,
Even undemanded by a sign or sound ;
You need but wish, and instantly obeyed,
Fair ranged the dishes rose, and thick the glasses
    played.

Here freedom reigned, without the least alloy ;
Nor gossip's tale, nor ancient maiden's gall,
Nor saintly spleen durst murmur at our joy,
And with envenomed tongue our pleasures pall.
For why ? there was but one great rule for all ;
To wit, that each should work his own desire,
And eat, drink, study, sleep, as it may fall,
Or melt the time in love, or wake the lyre,
And carol what, unbid, the Muses might in-
    spire.

The rooms with costly tapestry were hung,
Where was inwoven many a gentle tale ;
Such as of old the rural poets sung,
Or of Arcadian or Sicilian vale :

Reclining lovers, in the lonely dale,
Poured forth at large the sweetly tortured
   heart ;
Or, sighing tender passion, swelled the gale,
And taught charmed echo to resound their
   smart ;
While flocks, woods, streams around, repose and
   peace impart.

    .   .   .   .

Each sound too here to languishment inclined,
Lulled the weak bosom, and induced ease ;
Aerial music in the warbling wind,
At distance rising oft, by small degrees,
Nearer and nearer came, till o'er the trees
It hung, and breathed such soul-dissolving airs,
As did, alas ! with soft perdition please :
Entangled deep in its enchanting snares,
The listening heart forgot all duties and all cares.

A certain music, never known before,
Here lulled the pensive, melancholy mind ;
Full easily obtained. Behooves no more,
But sidelong, to the gently waving wind,
To lay the well-tuned instrument reclined ;
From which, with airy flying fingers light,
Beyond each mortal touch the most refined,
The god of winds drew sounds of deep delight :
Whence, with just cause, the harp of Æolus it
   hight.

Ah me! what hand can touch the string so fine ?
Who up the lofty diapason roll
Such sweet, such sad, such solemn airs divine,
Then let them down again into the soul :
Now rising love they fanned; now pleasing dole
They breathed, in tender musings, through the
   heart ;
And now a graver sacred strain they stole,
As when seraphic hands a hymn impart :
Wild warbling nature all, above the reach of art !
                      JAMES THOMSON.

---◆---

KUBLA KHAN.*

IN Xanadu did Kubla Khan
A stately pleasure-dome decree
Where Alph, the sacred river, ran,
Through caverns measureless to man,
Down to a sunless sea.

So twice five miles of fertile ground
With walls and towers were girdled round ;
And there were gardens, bright with sinuous rills,
Where blossomed many an incense-bearing tree ;
And here were forests ancient as the hills,
Infolding sunny spots of greenery.

But O that deep romantic chasm, which slanted
Down the green hill athwart a cedarn cover !
A savage place ! as holy and enchanted
As e'er beneath a waning moon was haunted
By woman wailing for her demon-lover !
And from this chasm, with ceaseless turmoil
   seething,
As if this earth in fast thick pants were breathing,
A mighty fountain momently was forced,
Amid whose swift, half-intermitted burst
Huge fragments vaulted like rebounding hail,
Or chaffy grain beneath the thresher's flail ;
And mid these dancing rocks at once and ever
It flung up momently the sacred river.
Five miles, meandering with a mazy motion
Through wood and dale, the sacred river ran, —
Then reached the caverns measureless to man,
And sank in tumult to a lifeless ocean,
And mid this tumult Kubla heard from far
Ancestral voices prophesying war.

   The shadow of the dome of pleasure
   Floated midway on the waves
   Where was heard the mingled measure
   From the fountain and the caves.
It was a miracle of rare device, —
A sunny pleasure-dome with caves of ice !
   A damsel with a dulcimer
   In a vision once I saw ;
   It was an Abyssinian maid,
   And on her dulcimer she played,
   Singing of Mount Abora.
   Could I revive within me
   Her symphony and song,
   To such a deep delight 't would win me
That, with music loud and long,
I would build that dome in air, —
That sunny dome ! those caves of ice !

---

* "In the summer of the year 1797 the author, then in ill-health, had retired to a lonely farm-house between Porlock and Linton, on the Exmoor confines of Somerset and Devonshire. In consequence of a slight indisposition, an anodyne had been prescribed, from the effect of which he fell asleep in his chair at the moment he was reading the following sentence, or words of the same substance, in *Purchas's Pilgrimage:* ' Here the Khan Kubla commanded a palace to be built, and a stately garden thereunto : and thus ten miles of fertile ground were enclosed with a wall.' The author continued for about three hours in a profound sleep, at least of the external senses, during which time he has the most vivid confidence that he could not have composed less than from two to three hundred lines ; if that indeed can be called composition in which all the images rose up before him as things, with a parallel production of the correspondent expressions, without any sensation or consciousness of effort. On awaking he appeared to himself to have a distinct recollection of the whole, and, taking his pen, ink, and paper, instantly and eagerly wrote down the lines that are here preserved. At this moment he was unfortunately called out by a person on business from Porlock, and detained by him above an hour, and on his return to his room found, to his no small surprise and mortification, that though he still retained some vague and dim recollection of the general purport of the vision, yet, with the exception of some eight or ten scattered lines and images, all the rest had passed away, like the images on the surface of a stream into which a stone had been cast, but, alas ! without the after restoration of the latter."— THE AUTHOR. 1816.

And all who heard should see them there,
And all should cry, Beware ! beware
His flashing eyes, his floating hair !
Weave a circle round him thrice,
And close your eyes with holy dread,
For he on honey-dew hath fed,
And drunk the milk of Paradise.
                              SAMUEL TAYLOR COLERIDGE.

SONG OF WOOD-NYMPHS.

COME here, come here, and dwell
In forest deep !
Come here, come here, and tell
Why thou dost weep !
Is it for love (sweet pain !)
That thus thou dar'st complain
Unto our pleasant shades, our summer leaves,
Where naught else grieves ?

Come here, come here, and lie
By whispering stream !
Here no one dares to die
For love's sweet dream ;
But health all seek, and joy,
And shun perverse annoy,
And race along green paths till close of day,
And laugh — alway !

Or else, through half the year,
On rushy floor,
We lie by waters clear,
While skylarks pour
Their songs into the sun !
And when bright day is done,
We hide 'neath bells of flowers or nodding corn,
And dream — till morn !
                      BRYAN WALLER PROCTER (*Barry Cornwall*).

THE FAIRIES' LULLABY.

FROM "MIDSUMMER NIGHT'S DREAM," ACT II. SC. 3.

Enter TITANIA, *with her train.*

TITANIA. Come, now a roundel, and a fairy
    song ;
Then, for the third part of a minute, hence ; —
Some, to kill cankers in the musk-rose buds ;
Some war with rear-mice for their leathern wings,
To make my small elves coats ; and some keep
    back
The clamorous owl, that nightly hoots, and
    wonders
At our quaint spirits.   Sing me now asleep ;
Then to your offices, and let me rest.

SONG.

1 FAIRY. *You spotted snakes, with double tongue,
    Thorny hedgehogs, be not seen ;
    Newts and blind-worms, do no wrong :
    Come not near our fairy queen.*

CHORUS. *Philomel, with melody,
    Sing in our sweet lullaby ;
Lulla, lulla, lullaby ; lulla, lulla, lullaby :
    Never harm,
    Nor spell nor charm,
    Come our lovely lady nigh ;
    So, good-night, with lullaby.*

2 FAIRY. *Weaving spiders, come not here,
    Hence, you long-legged spinners,
        hence !
    Beetles black, approach not near ;
    Worm, nor snail, do no offence.*

CHORUS. *Philomel, with melody,* etc.

1 FAIRY. Hence away ; now all is well :
    One, aloof, stand sentinel.
        [*Exeunt Fairies.* TITANIA *sleeps.*
                              SHAKESPEARE.

FAIRIES' SONG.

WE the fairies blithe and antic,
Of dimensions not gigantic,
Though the moonshine mostly keep us,
Oft in orchards frisk and peep us.

Stolen sweets are always sweeter ;
Stolen kisses much completer ;
Stolen looks are nice in chapels ;
Stolen, stolen be your apples.

When to bed the world are bobbing,
Then 's the time for orchard-robbing ;
Yet the fruit were scarce worth peeling
Were it not for stealing, stealing.
            From the Latin of THOMAS RANDOLPH.*
            Translation of LEIGH HUNT.

COMPLIMENT TO QUEEN ELIZABETH.

FROM "MIDSUMMER NIGHT'S DREAM," ACT II. SC. 2.

OBERON. My gentle Puck, come hither. Thou
    remember'st
Since once I sat upon a promontory,
And heard a mermaid, on a dolphin's back,
Uttering such dulcet and harmonious breath,

---

* Randolph was a masterly scholar, and a profound student of
the Greek and Latin poets, whose writings he imitated in those languages, and whose influence was marked in his English writings.
He died (1634) at the age of twenty-nine, not fulfilling the fame
promised by his early years.

That the rude sea grew civil at her song,
And certain stars shot madly from their spheres,
To hear the sea-maid's music.
    PUCK.   I remember.
    OBE. That very time I saw (but thou couldst
      not),
Flying between the cold moon and the earth,
Cupid all armed : a certain aim he took
At a fair vestal thronèd by the west,
And loosed his love-shaft smartly from his bow,
As it should pierce a hundred thousand hearts :
But I might see young Cupid's fiery shaft
Quenched in the chaste beams of the watery moon,
And the imperial votaress passed on,
In maiden meditation, fancy free.
Yet marked I where the bolt of Cupid fell :
It fell upon a little western flower
Before milk-white, now purple with love's wound,
And maidens call it Love-in-idleness.
Fetch me that flower.
                        SHAKESPEARE.

QUEEN MAB.

FROM "ROMEO AND JULIET," ACT I. SC. 4.

O, THEN, I see, Queen Mab hath been with you.
She is the fairies' midwife ; and she comes
In shape no bigger than an agate-stone
On the fore-finger of an alderman,
Drawn with a team of little atomies
Athwart men's noses as they lie asleep :
Her wagon-spokes made of long spinners' legs ;
The cover, of the wings of grasshoppers ;
The traces, of the smallest spider's web ;
The collars, of the moonshine's watery beams ;
Her whip, of cricket's bone ; the lash, of film ;
Her wagoner, a small gray-coated gnat,
Not half so big as a round little worm
Pricked from the lazy finger of a maid :
Her chariot is an empty hazel-nut,
Made by the joiner squirrel, or old grub,
Time out of mind the fairies' coach-makers.
And in this state she gallops night by night
Through lovers' brains, and then they dream of
    love ;
On courtiers' knees, that dream on court'sies
    straight ;
O'er lawyers' fingers, who straight dream on fees ;
O'er ladies' lips, who straight on kisses dream, —
Which oft the angry Mab with blisters plagues,
Because their breaths with sweetmeats tainted are :
Sometime she gallops o'er a courtier's nose,
And then dreams he of smelling out a suit ;
And sometime comes she with a tithe-pig's tail,
Tickling a parson's nose as 'a lies asleep,
Then dreams he of another benefice :

Sometime she driveth o'er a soldier's neck,
And then dreams he of cutting foreign throats,
Of breaches, ambuscadoes, Spanish blades,
Of healths five fathom deep ; and then anon
Drums in his ear, at which he starts, and wakes ;
And, being thus frighted, swears a prayer or two,
And sleeps again. This is that very Mab
That plats the manes of horses in the night :
And bakes the elf-locks in foul sluttish hairs,
Which, once untangled, much misfortune bodes :
This is the hag, when maids lie on their backs,
That presses them, and learns them first to bear,
Making them women of good carriage.
                        SHAKESPEARE.

THE FAIRIES.

UP the airy mountain,
    Down the rushy glen,
We daren't go a hunting
    For fear of little men ;
Wee folk, good folk,
    Trooping all together ;
Green jacket, red cap,
    And white owl's feather !

Down along the rocky shore
    Some make their home, —
They live on crispy pancakes
    Of yellow tide-foam ;
Some in the reeds
    Of the black mountain-lake,
With frogs for their watch-dogs,
    All night awake.

High on the hill-top
    The old King sits ;
He is now so old and gray
    He's nigh lost his wits.
With a bridge of white mist
    Columbkill he crosses,
On his stately journeys
    From Slieveleague to Rosses :
Or going up with music
    On cold starry nights,
To sup with the queen
    Of the gay Northern Lights.

They stole little Bridget
    For seven years long ;
When she came down again
    Her friends were all gone.
They took her lightly back,
    Between the night and morrow ;
They thought that she was fast asleep,
    But she was dead with sorrow.

They have kept her ever since
  Deep within the lakes,
On a bed of flag-leaves,
  Watching till she wakes.

By the craggy hillside,
  Through the mosses bare,
They have planted thorn-trees
  For pleasure here and there.
Is any man so daring
  To dig one up in spite,
He shall find the thornies set
  In his bed at night.

Up the airy mountain,
  Down the rushy glen,
We dare n't go a hunting
  For fear of little men ;
Wee folk, good folk,
  Trooping all together ;
Green jacket, red cap,
  And white owl's feather !
             WIILLIAM ALLINGHAM.

KILMENY.

FROM "THE QUEEN'S WAKE."

BONNY Kilmeny gaed up the glen ;
But it wasna to meet Duneira's men,
Nor the rosy monk of the isle to see,
For Kilmeny was pure as pure could be.
It was only to hear the yorlin sing,
And pu' the cress-flower round the spring, —
The scarlet hypp, and the hindberrye,
And the nut that hang frae the hazel-tree ;
For Kilmeny was pure as pure could be.
But lang may her minny look o'er the wa',
And lang may she seek i' the green-wood shaw ;
Lang the laird of Duneira blame,
And lang, lang greet or Kilmeny come hame.

When many a day had come and fled,
When grief grew calm, and hope was dead,
When mass for Kilmeny's soul had been sung,
When the bedesman had prayed, and the dead-
    bell rung ;
Late, late in a gloamin, when all was still,
When the fringe was red on the westlin hill,
The wood was sear, the moon i' the wane,
The reek o' the cot hung over the plain, —
Like a little wee cloud in the world its lane ;
When the ingle lowed with an eiry leme,
Late, late in the gloamin Kilmeny came hame !

" Kilmeny, Kilmeny, where have you been ?
Lang hae we sought baith holt and den, —
By linn, by ford, and green-wood tree ;
Yet you are halesome and fair to see.

Where got you that joup o' the lily sheen ?
That bonny snood of the birk sae green ?
And these roses, the fairest that ever was seen ?
Kilmeny, Kilmeny, where have you been ?"

Kilmeny looked up with a lovely grace,
But nae smile was seen on Kilmeny's face ;
As still was her look, and as still was her ee,
As the stillness that lay on the emerant lea,
Or the mist that sleeps on a waveless sea.
For Kilmeny had been she knew not where,
And Kilmeny had seen what she could not
    declare.
Kilmeny had been where the cock never crew,
Where the rain never fell, and the wind never
    blew ;
But it seemed as the harp of the sky had rung,
And the airs of heaven played round her tongue,
When she spake of the lovely forms she had seen,
And a land where sin had never been, —
A land of love, and a land of light,
Withouten sun or moon or night ;
Where the river swa'd a living stream,
And the light a pure celestial beam :
The land of vision it would seem,
A still, an everlasting dream.
In yon green-wood there is a waik,
And in that waik there is a wene,
And in that wene there is a maike,
That neither has flesh, blood, nor bane ;
And down in yon green-wood he walks his lane.
In that green wene Kilmeny lay,
Her bosom happed wi' the flowerets gay ;
But the air was soft, and the silence deep,
And bonny Kilmeny fell sound asleep ;
She kend nae mair, nor opened her ee,
Till waked by the hymns of a far countrye.

She awaked on a couch of the silk sae slim,
All striped wi' the bars of the rainbow's rim ;
And lovely beings around were rife,
Who erst had travelled mortal life ;
And aye they smiled, and 'gan to speer :
" What spirit has brought this mortal here ?"

" Lang have I journeyed the world wide,"
A meek and reverend fere replied ;
" Baith night and day I have watched the fair
Eident a thousand years and mair.
Yes, I have watched o'er ilk degree,
Wherever blooms femenitye ;
But sinless virgin, free of stain,
In mind and body, fand I nane.
Never, since the banquet of time,
Found I a virgin in her prime,
Till late this bonny maiden I saw,
As spotless as the morning snaw.

Full twenty years she has lived as free
As the spirits that sojourn in this countrye.
I have brought her away frae the snares of men,
That sin or death she may never ken."

They clasped her waist and her hands sae fair ;
They kissed her cheek, and they kemed her hair ;
And round came many a blooming fere,
Saying, " Bonny Kilmeny, ye 're welcome here ;
Women are freed of the littand scorn ;
O, blest be the day Kilmeny was born !
Now shall the land of the spirits see,
Now shall it ken, what a woman may be !
Many a lang year in sorrow and pain,
Many a lang year through the world we 've gane,
Commissioned to watch fair womankind,
For it 's they who nurice the immortal mind.
We have watched their steps as the dawning
        shone,
And deep in the greenwood walks alone ;
By lily bower and silken bed
The viewless tears have o'er them shed ;
Have soothed their ardent minds to sleep,
Or left the couch of love to weep.
We have seen ! we have seen ! but the time must
        come,
And the angels will weep at the day of doom !

'·O, would the fairest of mortal kind
Aye keep the holy truths in mind,
That kindred spirits their motions see,
Who watch their ways with anxious e'e,
And grieve for the guilt of humanitye !
O, sweet to Heaven the maiden's prayer,
And the sigh that heaves a bosom sae fair !
And dear to Heaven the words of truth
And the praise of virtue frae beauty's mouth !
And dear to the viewless forms of air
The minds that kythe as the body fair !

" O bonny Kilmeny ! free frae stain,
If ever you seek the world again, —
That world of sin, of sorrow and fear, —
O, tell of the joys that are waiting here ;
And tell of the signs you shall shortly see ;
Of the times that are now, and the times that
        shall be."

They lifted Kilmeny, they led her away,
And she walked in the light of a sunless day ;
The sky was a dome of crystal bright,
The fountain of vision, and fountain of light ;
The emerald fields were of dazzling glow,
And the flowers of everlasting blow.
Then deep in the stream her body they laid,
That her youth and beauty never might fade ;
And they smiled on heaven, when they saw her lie
    In the stream of life that wandered by.

And she heard a song, — she heard it sung,
She kend not where ; but sae sweetly it rung,
It fell on her ear like a dream of the morn, —
" O, blest be the day Kilmeny was born !
Now shall the land of the spirits see,
Now shall it ken, what a woman may be !
The sun that shines on the world sae bright,
A borrowed gleid frae the fountain of light ;
And the moon that sleeks the sky sae dun,
Like a gouden bow, or a beamless sun,
Shall wear away, and be seen nae mair ;
And the angels shall miss them, travelling the air.
But lang, lang after baith night and day,
When the sun and the world have edyed away,
When the sinner has gane to his waesome doom,
Kilmeny shall smile in eternal bloom ! "

They bore her away, she wist not how,
For she felt not arm nor rest below ;
But so swift they wained her through the light,
'T was like the motion of sound or sight ;
They seemed to split the gales of air,
And yet nor gale nor breeze was there.
Unnumbered groves below them grew ;
They came, they past, and backward flew,
Like floods of blossoms gliding on,
In moment seen, in moment gone.
O, never vales to mortal view
Appeared like those o'er which they flew,
That land to human spirits given,
The lowermost vales of the storied heaven ;
From whence they can view the world below,
And heaven's blue gates with sapphires glow, —
More glory yet unmeet to know.

They bore her far to a mountain green,
To see what mortal never had seen ;
And they seated her high on a purple sward,
And bade her heed what she saw and heard,
And note the changes the spirits wrought ;
For now she lived in the land of thought. —
She looked, and she saw nor sun nor skies,
But a crystal dome of a thousand dyes ;
She looked, and she saw nae land aright,
But an endless whirl of glory and light ;
And radiant beings went and came,
Far swifter than wind or the linkèd flame ;
She hid her een frae the dazzling view ;
She looked again, and the scene was new.

She saw a sun on a summer sky,
And clouds of amber sailing by ;
A lovely land beneath her lay,
And that land had glens and mountains gray ;
And that land had valleys and hoary piles,
And marlèd seas, and a thousand isles ;
Its fields were speckled, its forests green,
And its lakes were all of the dazzling sheen,

Like magic mirrors, where slumbering lay
The sun and the sky and the cloudlet gray,
Which heaved and trembled, and gently swung ;
On every shore they seemed to be hung ;
For there they were seen on their downward plain
A thousand times and a thousand again ;
In winding lake and placid firth, —
Little peaceful heavens in the bosom of earth.

Kilmeny sighed and seemed to grieve,
For she found her heart to that land did cleave ;
She saw the corn wave on the vale ;
She saw the deer run down the dale ;
She saw the plaid and the broad claymore,
And the brows that the badge of freedom bore ;
And she thought she had seen the land before.

She saw a lady sit on a throne,
The fairest that ever the sun shone on :
A lion licked her hand of milk,
And she held him in a leish of silk ;
And a leifu' maiden stood at her knee,
With a silver wand and melting ee ;
Her sovereign shield till love stole in,
And poisoned all the fount within.

Then a gruff untoward bedesman came,
And hundit the lion on his dame ;
And the guardian maid wi' the dauntless ee,
She dropped a tear, and left her knee ;
And she saw till the queen frae the lion fled,
Till the bonniest flower of the world lay dead ;
A coffin was set on a distant plain,
And she saw the red blood fall like rain :
Then bonny Kilmeny's heart grew sair,
And she turned away, and could look nae mair.

Then the gruff grim carle girnèd amain,
And they trampled him down, but he rose again ;
And he baited the lion to deeds of weir,
Till he lapped the blood to the kingdom dear ;
And weening his head was danger-preef,
When crowned with the rose and clover leaf,
He gowled at the carle, and chased him away
To feed wi' the deer on the mountain gray.
He gowled at the carle, and he gecked at Heaven ;
But his mark was set, and his arles given.   .
Kilmeny a while her een withdrew ;
She looked again, and the scene was new.

She saw below her fair unfurled
One half of all the glowing world,
Where oceans rolled, and rivers ran,
To bound the aims of sinful man.
She saw a people, fierce and fell,
Burst frae their bounds like fiends of hell ;
There lilies grew, and the eagle flew,
And she herked on her ravening crew,

Till the cities and towers were wrapt in a blaze,
And the thunder it roared o'er the lands and the
  seas.
The widows they wailed, and the red blood ran,
And she threatened an end to the race of man :
She never lened, nor stood in awe,
Till caught by the lion's deadly paw.
Oh ! then the eagle swinked for life,
And brainzelled up a mortal strife ;
But flew she north, or flew she south,
She met wi' the gowl of the lion's mouth.

With a mooted wing and waefu' maen,
The eagle sought her eiry again ;
But lang may she cower in her bloody nest,
And lang, lang sleek her wounded breast,
Before she sey another flight,
To play wi' the norland lion's might.

But to sing the sights Kilmeny saw,
So far surpassing nature's law,
The singer's voice wad sink away,
And the string of his harp wad cease to play.
But she saw till the sorrows of man were by,
And all was love and harmony ; —
Till the stars of heaven fell calmly away,
Like the flakes of snaw on a winter's day.

Then Kilmeny begged again to see
The friends she had left in her own countrye,
To tell the place where she had been,
And the glories that lay in the land unseen ;
To warn the living maidens fair,
The loved of heaven, the spirits' care,
That all whose minds unmeled remain
Shall bloom in beauty when time is gane.

With distant music, soft and deep,
They lulled Kilmeny sound asleep ;
And when she awakened, she lay her lane,
All happed with flowers in the green-wood wene.
When seven long years had come and fled ;
When grief was calm, and hope was dead ;
When scarce was remembered Kilmeny's name,
Late, late in a gloamin, Kilmeny came hame !
And O, her beauty was fair to see,
But still and steadfast was her ee !
Such beauty bard may never declare,
For there was no pride nor passion there ;
And the soft desire of maidens' een
In that mild face could never be seen.
Her seymar was the lily flower,
And her cheek the moss-rose in the shower ;
And her voice like the distant melodye
That floats along the twilight sea.
But she loved to raike the lanely glen,
And keeped afar frae the haunts of men ;

Her holy hymns unheard to sing,
To suck the flowers and drink the spring.
But wherever her peaceful form appeared,
The wild beasts of the hills were cheered;
The wolf played blythely round the field;
The lordly byson lowed and kneeled;
The dun deer wooed with manner bland,
And cowered aneath her lily hand.
And when at even the woodlands rung,
When hymns of other worlds she sung
In ecstasy of sweet devotion,
O, then the glen was all in motion!
The wild beasts of the forest came,
Broke from their bughts and faulds the tame,
And goved around, charmed and amazed;
Even the dull cattle crooned, and gazed,
And murmured, and looked with anxious pain
For something the mystery to explain.
The buzzard came with the throstle-cock,
The corby left her houf in the rock;
The blackbird alang wi' the eagle flew;
The hind came tripping o'er the dew;
The wolf and the kid their raike began;
And the tod, and the lamb, and the leveret ran;
The hawk and the hern attour them hung,
And the merl and the mavis forhooyed their
                young;
And all in a peaceful ring were hurled:
It was like an eve in a sinless world!

When a month and day had come and gane,
Kilmeny sought the green-wood wene;
There laid her down on the leaves sae green,
And Kilmeny on earth was never mair seen.
But O the words that fell from her mouth
Were words of wonder, and words of truth!
But all the land were in fear and dread,
For they kend na whether she was living or dead.
It wasna her hame, and she couldna remain;
She left this world of sorrow and pain,
And returned to the land of thought again.

                        JAMES HOGG.

THE FAIRY CHILD.

THE summer sun was sinking
    With a mild light, calm and mellow;
It shone on my little boy's bonnie cheeks,
    And his loose locks of yellow.

The robin was singing sweetly,
    And his song was sad and tender;
And my little boy's eyes, while he heard the song,
    Smiled with a sweet, soft splendor.

My little boy lay on my bosom
    While his soul the song was quaffing;
The joy of his soul had tinged his cheek,
    And his heart and his eye were laughing.

I sate alone in my cottage,
    The midnight needle plying;
I feared for my child, for the rush's light
    In the socket now was dying;

There came a hand to my lonely latch,
    Like the wind at midnight moaning;
I knelt to pray, but rose again,
    For I heard my little boy groaning.

I crossed my brow and I crossed my breast,
    But that night my child departed, —
They left a weakling in his stead,
    And I am broken-hearted!

O, it cannot be my own sweet boy,
    For his eyes are dim and hollow;
My little boy is gone — is gone,
    And his mother soon will follow.

The dirge for the dead will be sung for me,
    And the mass be chanted meetly,
And I shall sleep with my little boy,
    In the moonlight churchyard sweetly.

                        JOHN ANSTER.

THE CULPRIT FAY.

" My visual orbs are purged from film, and, lo!
    Instead of Anster's turnip-bearing vales,
    I see old fairy land's miraculous show!
    Her trees of tinsel kissed by freakish gales,
    Her ouphs that, cloaked in leaf-gold, skim the breeze,
    And fairies, swarming ——————."

                TENNANT'S ANSTER FAIR.

'T IS the middle watch of a summer's night, —
The earth is dark, but the heavens are bright;
Naught is seen in the vault on high
But the moon, and the stars, and the cloudless
            sky,
And the flood which rolls its milky hue,
A river of light on the welkin blue.
The moon looks down on old Cro'nest;
She mellows the shades on his shaggy breast,
And seems his huge gray form to throw
In a silver cone on the wave below.
His sides are broken by spots of shade,
By the walnut bough and the cedar made;
And through their clustering branches dark
Glimmers and dies the firefly's spark, —
Like starry twinkles that momently break
Through the rifts of the gathering tempest's rack

The stars are on the moving stream,
    And fling, as its ripples gently flow,
A burnished length of wavy beam
    In an eel-like, spiral line below;

The winds are whist, and the owl is still ;
  The bat in the shelvy rock is hid ;
And naught is heard on the lonely hill
But the cricket's chirp, and the answer shrill
  Of the gauze-winged katydid ;
And the plaint of the wailing whippoorwill,
  Who moans unseen, and ceaseless sings
  Ever a note of wail and woe,
    Till morning spreads her rosy wings,
And earth and sky in her glances glow.

'T is the hour of fairy ban and spell :
The wood-tick has kept the minutes well ;
He has counted them all with click and stroke
Deep in the heart of the mountain-oak,
And he has awakened the sentry elve
  Who sleeps with him in the haunted tree,
To bid him ring the hour of twelve,
  And call the fays to their revelry ;
Twelve small strokes on his tinkling bell
('T was made of the white snail's pearly shell) :
" Midnight comes, and all is well !
Hither, hither wing your way !
'T is the dawn of the fairy-day."

They come from beds of lichen green,
They creep from the mullein's velvet screen ;
  Some on the backs of beetles fly
From the silver tops of moon-touched trees,
  Where they swung in their cobweb hammocks high,
And rocked about in the evening breeze ;
  Some from the hum-bird's downy nest, —
They had driven him out by elfin power,
  And, pillowed on plumes of his rainbow breast,
Had slumbered there till the charmèd hour ;
  Some had lain in the scoop of the rock,
With glittering ising-stars inlaid ;
  And some had opened the four-o'clock,
And stole within its purple shade.
  And now they throng the moonlight glade,
Above, below, on every side, —
  Their little minim forms arrayed
In the tricksy pomp of fairy pride !

They come not now to print the lea,
In freak and dance around the tree,
Or at the mushroom board to sup,
And drink the dew from the buttercup :
A scene of sorrow waits them now,
For an ouphe has broken his vestal vow ;
He has loved an earthly maid,
And left for her his woodland shade ;
He has lain upon her lip of dew,
And sunned him in her eye of blue,
Fanned her cheek with his wing of air,
Played in the ringlets of her hair,

And, nestling on her snowy breast,
Forgot the lily-king's behest.
For this the shadowy tribes of air
  To the elfin court must haste away :
And now they stand expectant there,
  To hear the doom of the culprit fay.

The throne was reared upon the grass,
Of spice-wood and of sassafras ;
On pillars of mottled tortoise-shell
  Hung the burnished canopy, —
And o'er it gorgeous curtains fell
  Of the tulip's crimson drapery.
The monarch sat on his judgment-seat,
  On his brow the crown imperial shone,
The prisoner fay was at his feet,
  And his peers were ranged around the throne.
He waved his sceptre in the air,
  He looked around and calmly spoke ;
His brow was grave and his eye severe,
  But his voice in a softened accent broke :

" Fairy ! fairy ! list and mark :
Thou hast broke thine elfin chain ;
Thy flame-wood lamp is quenched and dark,
  And thy wings are dyed with a deadly stain, —
Thou hast sullied thine elfin purity
  In the glance of a mortal maiden's eye ;
Thou hast scorned our dread decree,
  And thou shouldst pay the forfeit high.
But well I know her sinless mind
  Is pure as the angel forms above,
Gentle and meek, and chaste and kind,
  Such as a spirit well might love.
Fairy ! had she spot or taint,
Bitter had been thy punishment :
Tied to the hornet's shardy wings ;
Tossed on the pricks of nettles' stings ;
Or seven long ages doomed to dwell
With the lazy worm in the walnut-shell
Or every night to writhe and bleed
Beneath the tread of the centipede ;
Or bound in a cobweb-dungeon dim,
Your jailer a spider, huge and grim,
Amid the carrion bodies to lie
Of the worm, and the bug, and the murdered fly :
These it had been your lot to bear,
Had a stain been found on the earthly fair.
Now list, and mark our mild decree, —
Fairy, this your doom must be :

" Thou shalt seek the beach of sand
Where the water bounds the elfin land ;
Thou shalt watch the oozy brine
Till the sturgeon leaps in the bright moonshine,
Then dart the glistening arch below,
And catch a drop from his silver bow.

The water-sprites will wield their arms
  And dash around, with roar and rave,
And vain are the woodland spirits' charms ;
  They are the imps that rule the wave.
Yet trust thee in thy single might :
If thy heart be pure and thy spirit right,
Thou shalt win the warlock fight.

" If the spray-bead gem be won,
  The stain of thy wing is washed away ;
But another errand must be done
  Ere thy crime be lost for aye :
Thy flame-wood lamp is quenched and dark,
Thou must re-illume its spark.
Mount thy steed, and spur him high
To the heaven's blue canopy ;
And when thou seest a shooting star,
Follow it fast, and follow it far, —
The last faint spark of its burning train
Shall light the elfin lamp again.
Thou hast heard our sentence, fay ;
Hence ! to the water-side, away ! "

The goblin marked his monarch well ;
  He spake not, but he bowed him low,
Then plucked a crimson colen-bell,
  And turned him round in act to go.
The way is long, he cannot fly,
  His soilèd wing has lost its power,
And he winds adown the mountain high,
  For many a sore and weary hour.
Through dreary beds of tangled fern,
Through groves of nightshade dark and dern,
Over the grass and through the brake,
Where toils the ant and sleeps the snake ;
  Now o'er the violet's azure flush
He skips along in lightsome mood ;
  And now he thrids the bramble-bush,
Till its points are dyed in fairy blood.
He has leaped the bog, he has pierced the brier,
He has swum the brook, and waded the mire,
Till his spirits sank, and his limbs grew weak,
And the red waxed fainter in his cheek.
He had fallen to the ground outright,
  For rugged and dim was his onward track,
But there came a spotted toad in sight,
  And he laughed as he jumped upon her back ;
He bridled her mouth with a silkweed twist,
  He lashed her sides with an osier thong ;
And now, through evening's dewy mist,
  With leap and spring they bound along,
Till the mountain's magic verge is past,
And the beach of sand is reached at last.

Soft and pale is the moony beam,
Moveless still the glassy stream ;

The wave is clear, the beach is bright
  With snowy shells and sparkling stones ;
The shore-surge comes in ripples light,
  In murmurings faint and distant moans ;
And ever afar in the silence deep
Is heard the splash of the sturgeon's leap,
And the bend of his graceful bow is seen, —
A glittering arch of silver sheen,
Spanning the wave of burnished blue,
And dripping with gems of the river-dew.

The elfin cast a glance around,
  As he lighted down from his courser toad,
Then round his breast his wings he wound,
  And close to the river's brink he strode ;
He sprang on a rock, he breathed a prayer,
  Above his head his arms he threw,
Then tossed a tiny curve in air,
  And headlong plunged in the waters blue.

Up sprung the spirits of the waves
From the sea-silk beds in their coral caves ;
With snail-plate armor, snatched in haste,
They speed their way through the liquid waste ;
Some are rapidly borne along
On the mailèd shrimp or the prickly prong ;
Some on the blood-red leeches glide,
Some on the stony star-fish ride,
Some on the back of the lancing squab,
Some on the sideling soldier-crab ;
And some on the jellied quarl, that flings
At once a thousand streamy stings ;
They cut the wave with the living oar,
And hurry on to the moonlight shore,
To guard their realms and chase away
The footsteps of the invading fay.

Fearlessly he skims along,
His hope is high, and his limbs are strong ;
He spreads his arms like the swallow's wing,
And throws his feet with a frog-like fling ;
His locks of gold on the waters shine,
  At his breast the tiny foam-bees rise,
His back gleams bright above the brine,
  And the wake-line foam behind him lies.
But the water-sprites are gathering near
  To check his course along the tide ;
Their warriors come in swift career
  And hem him round on every side ;
On his thigh the leech has fixed his hold,
The quarl's long arms are round him rolled,
The prickly prong has pierced his skin,
And the squab has thrown his javelin ;
The gritty star has rubbed him raw,
And the crab has struck with his giant claw,
He howls with rage, and he shrieks with pain ;
He strikes around, but his blows are vain ;

Hopeless is the unequal fight,
Fairy ! naught is left but flight.

He turned him round, and fled amain,
With hurry and dash, to the beach again ;
He twisted over from side to side,
And laid his cheek to the cleaving tide ;
The strokes of his plunging arms are fleet,
And with all his might he flings his feet,
But the water-sprites are round him still,
To cross his path and work him ill.
They bade the wave before him rise ;
They flung the sea-fire in his eyes ;
And they stunned his ears with the scallop-stroke,
With the porpoise heave and the drum-fish croak.
O, but a weary wight was he
When he reached the foot of the dogwood-tree.
Gashed and wounded, and stiff and sore,
He laid him down on the sandy shore ;
He blessed the force of the charmèd line,
   And he banned the water-goblins' spite,
For he saw around in the sweet moonshine
Their little wee faces above the brine,
   Giggling and laughing with all their might
   At the piteous hap of the fairy wight.

Soon he gathered the balsam dew
   From the sorrel-leaf and the henbane bud ;
Over each wound the balm he drew,
   And with cobweb lint he stanched the blood.
The mild west-wind was soft and low,
It cooled the heat of his burning brow ;
And he felt new life in his sinews shoot,
As he drank the juice of the calamus-root ;
And now he treads the fatal shore
As fresh and vigorous as before.

Wrapped in musing stands the sprite ;
'T is the middle wane of night ;
   His task is hard, his way is far,
But he must do his errand right
   Ere dawning mounts her beamy car,
And rolls her chariot wheels of light ;
And vain are the spells of fairy-land, —
He must work with a human hand.

He cast a saddened look around ;
   But he felt new joy his bosom swell,
When, glittering on the shadowed ground,
   He saw a purple muscle-shell ;
Thither he ran, and he bent him low,
He heaved at the stern and he heaved at the bow,
And he pushed her over the yielding sand
Till he came to the verge of the haunted land.
She was as lovely a pleasure-boat
   As ever fairy had paddied in,
For she glowed with purple paint without,
   And shone with silvery pearl within ;

A sculler's notch in the stern he made,
An oar he shaped of the bootle-blade ;
Then sprung to his seat with a lightsome leap,
And launched afar on the calm, blue deep.

The imps of the river yell and rave.
They had no power above the wave ;
But they heaved the billow before the prow,
   And they dashed the surge against her side,
And they struck her keel with jerk and blow,
   Till the gunwale bent to the rocking tide.
She wimpled about to the pale moonbeam,
Like a feather that floats on a wind-tossed stream ;
And momently athwart her track
The quarl upreared his island back,
And the fluttering scallop behind would float,
And patter the water about the boat ;
But he bailed her out with his colen-bell,
   And he kept her trimmed with a wary tread,
While on every side, like lightning, fell
   The heavy strokes of his bootle-blade.

Onward still he held his way,
Till he came where the column of moonshine lay,
And saw beneath the surface dim
The brown-backed sturgeon slowly swim ;
Around him were the goblin train, —
But he sculled with all his might and main,
And followed wherever the sturgeon led,
Till he saw him upward point his head ;
Then he dropped his paddle-blade,
And held his colen-goblet up
To catch the drop in its crimson cup.

With sweeping tail and quivering fin
   Through the wave the sturgeon flew ;
And, like the heaven-shot javelin,
   He sprung above the waters blue.
Instant as the star-fall light
   He plunged him in the deep again,
But he left an arch of silver bright,
   The rainbow of the moony main.
It was a strange and lovely sight
   To see the puny goblin there ;
He seemed an angel form of light,
   With azure wing and sunny hair,
   Throned on a cloud of purple fair,
Circled with blue and edged with white
And sitting, at the fall of even,
Beneath the bow of summer heaven.

A moment, and its lustre fell ;
   But ere it met the billow blue
He caught within his crimson bell
   A droplet of its sparkling dew ! —
Joy to thee, fay ! thy task is done,
Thy wings are pure, for the gem is won, —

Cheerly ply thy dripping oar,
And haste away to the elfin shore.

He turns, and, lo ! on either side
The ripples on his path divide ;
And the track o'er which his boat must pass
Is smooth as a sheet of polished glass.
Around, their limbs the sea-nymphs lave,
  With snowy arms half swelling out,
While on the glossed and gleamy wave
  Their sea-green ringlets loosely float.
They swim around with smile and song ;
  They press the bark with pearly hand,
And gently urge her course along
  Toward the beach of speckled sand,
  And, as he lightly leaped to land,
They bade adieu with nod and bow ;
  Then gayly kissed each little hand,
And dropped in the crystal deep below.

A moment stayed the fairy there ;
He kissed the beach and breathed a prayer ;
Then spread his wings of gilded blue,
And on to the elfin court he flew.
As ever ye saw a bubble rise,
And shine with a thousand changing dyes,
Till, lessening far, through ether driven,
It mingles with the hues of heaven ;
As, at the glimpse of morning pale,
The lance-fly spreads his silken sail,
And gleams with blendings soft and bright
Till lost in the shades of fading night, —
So rose from earth the lovely fay ;
So vanished, far in heaven away !

   *   *   *   *   *

Up, fairy ! quit thy chickweed bower,
The cricket has called the second hour ;
Twice again, and the lark will rise
To kiss the streaking of the skies, —
Up ! thy charmèd armor don,
Thou 'lt need it ere the night be gone.

He put his acorn helmet on ;
It was plumed of the silk of the thistle-down ;
The corselet plate that guarded his breast
Was once the wild bee's golden vest ;
His cloak, of a thousand mingled dyes,
Was formed of the wings of butterflies ;
His shield was the shell of a lady-bug queen,
Studs of gold on a ground of green ;
And the quivering lance which he brandished
    bright
Was the sting of a wasp he had slain in fight.
Swift he bestrode his firefly steed ;
  He bared his blade of the bent-grass blue ;
He drove his spurs of the cockle-seed,
  And away like a glance of thought he flew

To skim the heavens, and follow far
The fiery trail of the rocket-star.

The moth-fly, as he shot in air,
Crept under the leaf, and hid her there ;
The katydid forgot its lay,
The prowling gnat fled fast away,
The fell mosquito checked his drone
And folded his wings till the fay was gone.
And the wily beetle dropped his head,
And fell on the ground as if he were dead ;
They crouched them close in the darksome shade,
  They quaked all o'er with awe and fear,
For they had felt the blue-bent blade,
  And writhed at the prick of the elfin spear.
Many a time, on a summer's night,
When the sky was clear, and the moon was bright,
They had been roused from the haunted ground
By the yelp and bay of the fairy hound ;
  They had heard the tiny bugle-horn,
They had heard the twang of the maize-silk string,
When the vine-twig bows were tightly drawn,
  And the needle-shaft through air was borne,
Feathered with down of the hum-bird's wing.
And now they deemed the courier ouphe
  Some hunter-sprite of the elfin ground,
And they watched till they saw him mount the roof
  That canopies the world around ;
Then glad they left their covert lair,
And freaked about in the midnight air.

Up to the vaulted firmament
His path the firefly courser bent,
And at every gallop on the wind
He flung a glittering spark behind ;
He flies like a feather in the blast
Till the first light cloud in heaven is past.
  But the shapes of air have begun their work,
And a drizzly mist is round him cast ;
  He cannot see through the mantle murk ;
He shivers with cold, but he urges fast ;
  Through storm and darkness, sleet and shade,
He lashes his steed, and spurs amain, —
For shadowy hands have twitched the rein,
  And flame-shot tongues around him played,
And near him many a fiendish eye
Glared with a fell malignity,
And yells of rage, and shrieks of fear,
Came screaming on his startled ear.

His wings are wet around his breast,
The plume hangs dripping from his crest,
His eyes are blurred with the lightning's glare,
And his ears are stunned with the thunder's blare.
But he gave a shout, and his blade he drew,
  He thrust before and he struck behind,
Till he pierced their cloudy bodies through,
  And gashed their shadowy limbs of wind :

Howling the misty spectres flew,
  They rend the air with frightful cries ;
For he has gained the welkin blue,
  And the land of clouds beneath him lies.

Up to the cope careering swift,
  In breathless motion fast,
Fleet as the swallow cuts the drift,
  Or the sea-roc rides the blast,
The sapphire sheet of eve is shot,
  The spherèd moon is past,
The earth but seems a tiny blot
  On a sheet of azure cast.
O, it was sweet, in the clear moonlight,
  To tread the starry plain of even !
To meet the thousand eyes of night,
  And feel the cooling breath of heaven !
But the elfin made no stop or stay
Till he came to the bank of the Milky Way ;
Then he checked his courser's foot,
And watched for the glimpse of the planet-shoot.

Sudden along the snowy tide
  That swelled to meet their footsteps' fall,
The sylphs of heaven were seen to glide,
  Attired in sunset's crimson pall ;
Around the fay they weave the dance,
  They skip before him on the plain,
And one has taken his wasp-sting lance,
  And one upholds his bridle-rein ;
With warblings wild they lead him on
To where, through clouds of amber seen,
Studded with stars, resplendent shone
  The palace of the sylphid queen.
Its spiral columns, gleaming bright,
Were streamers of the northern light ;
Its curtain's light and lovely flush
Was of the morning's rosy blush ;
And the ceiling fair that rose aboon,
The white and feathery fleece of noon.

But, O, how fair the shape that lay
  Beneath a rainbow bending bright !
She seemed to the entrancèd fay
  The loveliest of the forms of light ;
Her mantle was the purple rolled
  At twilight in the west afar ;
'T was tied with threads of dawning gold,
  And buttoned with a sparkling star.
Her face was like the lily roon
  That veils the vestal planet's hue ;
Her eyes, two beamlets from the moon,
  Set floating in the welkin blue.
Her hair is like the sunny beam,
And the diamond gems which round it gleam
Are the pure drops of dewy even
That ne'er have left their native heaven.

She raised her eyes to the wondering sprite,
  And they leaped with smiles ; for well I ween
Never before in the bowers of light
  Had the form of an earthly fay been seen.
Long she looked in his tiny face ;
  Long with his butterfly cloak she played ;
She smoothed his wings of azure lace,
  And handled the tassel of his blade ;
And as he told, in accents low,
The story of his love and woe,
She felt new pains in her bosom rise,
And the tear-drop started in her eyes.
And "O, sweet spirit of earth," she cried,
  "Return no more to your woodland height,
But ever here with me abide
  In the land of everlasting light !
Within the fleecy drift we 'll lie,
  We 'll hang upon the rainbow's rim ;
And all the jewels of the sky
  Around thy brow shall brightly beam !
And thou shalt bathe thee in the stream
  That rolls its whitening foam aboon,
And ride upon the lightning's gleam,
  And dance upon the orbèd moon !
We 'll sit within the Pleiad ring,
  We 'll rest on Orion's starry belt,
And I will bid my sylphs to sing
  The song that makes the dew-mist melt ;
Their harps are of the umber shade
  That hides the blush of waking day,
And every gleamy string is made
  Of silvery moonshine's lengthened ray ;
And thou shalt pillow on my breast,
  While heavenly breathings float around,
And, with the sylphs of ether blest,
  Forget the joys of fairy ground."

She was lovely and fair to see,
And the elfin's heart beat fitfully ;
But lovelier far, and still more fair,
The earthly form imprinted there ;
Naught he saw in the heavens above
Was half so dear as his mortal love,
For he thought upon her looks so meek,
And he thought of the light flush on her cheek
Never again might he bask and lie
On that sweet cheek and moonlight eye ;
But in his dreams her form to see,
To clasp her in his revery,
To think upon his virgin bride,
Was worth all heaven, and earth beside.

"Lady," he cried, " I have sworn to-night,
On the word of a fairy knight,
To do my sentence-task aright ;
My honor scarce is free from stain, —
I may not soil its snows again :

Betide me weal, betide me woe,
Its mandate must be answered now."
Her bosom heaved with many a sigh,
The tear was in her drooping eye ;
But she led him to the palace gate,
    And called the sylphs who hovered there,
And bade them fly and bring him straight,
    Of clouds condensed, a sable car.
With charm and spell she blessed it there,
From all the fiends of upper air ;
Then round him cast the shadowy shroud,
And tied his steed behind the cloud ;
And pressed his hand as she bade him fly
Far to the verge of the northern sky,
For by its wane and wavering light
There was a star would fall to-night.

Borne afar on the wings of the blast,
Northward away he speeds him fast,
And his courser follows the cloudy wain
Till the hoof-strokes fall like pattering rain.
The clouds roll backward as he flies,
Each flickering star behind him lies,
And he has reached the northern plain,
And backed his firefly steed again,
Ready to follow in its flight
The streaming of the rocket-light.

The star is yet in the vault of heaven,
    But it rocks in the summer gale ;
And now 't is fitful and uneven,
    And now 't is deadly pale ;
And now 't is wrapped in sulphur-smoke,
    And quenched is its rayless beam ;
And now with a rattling thunder-stroke
    It bursts in flash and flame.
As swift as the glance of the arrowy lance
    That the storm-spirit flings from high,
The star-shot flew o'er the welkin blue,
    As it fell from the sheeted sky.
As swift as the wind in its train behind
    The elfin gallops along :
The fiends of the clouds are bellowing loud,
    But the sylphid charm is strong ;
He gallops unhurt in the shower of fire,
    While the cloud-fiends fly from the blaze ;
He watches each flake till its sparks expire,
    And rides in the light of its rays.
But he drove his steed to the lightning's speed,
    And caught a glimmering spark ;
Then wheeled around to the fairy ground,
    And sped through the midnight dark.
        *   *   *   *   *
Ouphe and goblin ! imp and sprite !
    Elf of eve ! and starry fay !
Ye that love the moon's soft light,
    Hither, — hither wend your way ;

Twine ye in a jocund ring,
    Sing and trip it merrily,
Hand to hand, and wing to wing,
    Round the wild witch-hazel tree.

Hail the wanderer again
    With dance and song, and lute and lyre ;
Pure his wing and strong his chain,
    And doubly bright his fairy fire.
Twine ye in an airy round,
    Brush the dew and print the lea ;
Skip and gambol, hop and bound,
    Round the wild witch-hazel tree.

The beetle guards our holy ground,
    He flies about the haunted place,
And if mortal there be found,
    He hums in his ears and flaps his face ;
The leaf-harp sounds our roundelay,
    The owlet's eyes our lanterns be ;
Thus we sing and dance and play
    Round the wild witch-hazel tree.

But hark ! from tower to tree-top high,
    The sentry-elf his call has made ;
A streak is in the eastern sky,
    Shapes of moonlight ! flit and fade !
The hill-tops gleam in morning's spring,
The skylark shakes his dappled wing,
The day-glimpse glimmers on the lawn,
The cock has crowed, and the fays are gone.
                    JOSEPH RODMAN DRAKE.

———◆———

FAIRY SONG.

SHED no tear ! O, shed no tear !
The flower will bloom another year.
Weep no more ! O, weep no more !
Young buds sleep in the root's white core.
Dry your eyes ! O, dry your eyes !
For I was taught in Paradise
To ease my breast of melodies, —
                    Shed no tear.

Overhead ! look overhead !
'Mong the blossoms white and red, —
Look up, look up ! I flutter now
On this fresh pomegranate bough.
See me ! 't is this silvery bill
Ever cures the good man's ill,
Shed no tear ! O, shed no tear !
The flower will bloom another year.
Adieu, adieu — I fly — adieu !
I vanish in the heaven's blue, —
                    Adieu, adieu !
                    JOHN KEATS

FAREWELL TO THE FAIRIES.

FAREWELL rewards and fairies,
  Good housewifes now may say,
For now foul sluts in dairies
  Do fare as well as they.
And though they sweep their hearths no less
  Than maids were wont to do,
Yet who of late, for cleanliness,
  Finds sixpence in her shoe?

Lament, lament, old Abbeys,
  The fairies' lost command:
They did but change priests' babies,
  But some have changed your land;
And all your children sprung from thence
  Are now grown Puritans,
Who live as changelings ever since,
  For love of your domains.

At morning and at evening both,
  You merry were and glad,
So little care of sleep or sloth
  These pretty ladies had;
When Tom came home from labor,
  Or Cis to milking rose,
Then merrily went their tabor,
  And nimbly went their toes.

Witness those rings and roundelays
  Of theirs, which yet remain,
Were footed in Queen Mary's days
  On many a grassy plain;
But since of late Elizabeth,
  And later, James came in,
They never danced on any heath
  As when the time hath been.

By which we note the fairies
  Were of the old profession,
Their songs were Ave-Maries,
  Their dances were procession:
But now, alas! they all are dead,
  Or gone beyond the seas;
Or farther for religion fled,
  Or else they take their ease.

A tell-tale in their company
  They never could endure,
And whoso kept not secretly
  Their mirth, was punished sure;
It was a just and Christian deed,
  To pinch such black and blue:
O, how the commonwealth doth need
  Such justices as you!
                        RICHARD CORBET.

TAM O'SHANTER.

A TALE.

"Of Brownyis and of Bogilis full is this Buke."
                        GAWIN DOUGLASS.

WHEN chapman billies leave the street,
And drouthy neebors neebors meet,
As market-days are wearing late,
An' folk begin to tak the gate;
While we sit bousing at the nappy,
An' getting fou and unco happy,
We think na on the lang Scots miles,
The mosses, waters, slaps, and styles,
That lie between us and our hame,
Whare sits our sulky, sullen dame,
Gathering her brows like gathering storm,
Nursing her wrath to keep it warm.
  This truth fand honest Tam O'Shanter,
As he frae Ayr ae night did canter
(Auld Ayr, wham ne'er a town surpasses,
For honest men and bonnie lasses).
  O Tam! hadst thou been but sae wise
As taen thy ain wife Kate's advice!
She tauld thee weel thou was a skellum,
A blethering, blustering, drunken blellum:
That frae November till October,
Ae market-day thou was na sober;
That ilka melder, wi' the miller,
Thou sat as lang as thou had siller;
That every naig was ca'd a shoe on,
The smith and thee gat roaring fou on;
That at the L—d's house, ev'n on Sunday,
Thou drank wi' Kirton Jean till Monday.
She prophesied that, late or soon,
Thou would be found deep drowned in Doon;
Or catched wi' warlocks in the mirk,
By Alloway's auld haunted kirk.
  Ah, gentle dames! it gars me greet
To think how monie counsels sweet,
How monie lengthened sage advices,
The husband frae the wife despises!
  But to our tale: Ae market night
Tam had got planted unco right,
Fast by an ingle, bleezing finely,
Wi' reaming swats, that drank divinely;
And at his elbow souter Johnny,
His ancient, trusty, drouthy crony.
Tam lo'ed him like a vera brither;
They had been fou for weeks thegither.
The night drave on wi' sangs and clatter,
And aye the ale was growing better;
The landlady and Tam grew gracious,
Wi' favors secret, sweet, and precious;
The souter tauld his queerest stories;
The landlord's laugh was ready chorus;
The storm without might rair and rustle,
Tam did na mind the storm a whistle.

Care, mad to see a man sae happy,
E'en drowned himself amang the nappy ;
As bees flee hame wi' lades o' treasure,
The minutes winged their way wi' pleasure ;
Kings may be blest, but Tam was glorious,
O'er a' the ills o' life victorious.

But pleasures are like poppies spread ;
You seize the flower, its bloom is shed ;
Or like the snow-fall in the river,
A moment white, — then melts forever ;
Or like the borealis race,
That flit ere you can point their place ;
Or like the rainbow's lovely form
Evanishing amid the storm.
Nae man can tether time or tide ;
The hour approaches Tam maun ride ;
That hour o' night's black arch the keystane,
That dreary hour he mounts his beast in ;
And sic a night he takes the road in
As ne'er poor sinner was abroad in.

The wind blew as 't wad blawn its last ;
The rattling showers rose on the blast ;
The speedy gleams the darkness swallowed ;
Loud, deep, and lang the thunder bellowed ;
That night a child might understand
The Deil had business on his hand.

Weel mounted on his gray mare, Meg,
(A better never lifted leg,)
Tam skelpit on thro' dub and mire,
Despising wind and rain and fire, —
Whyles holding fast his guid blue bonnet,
Whyles crooning o'er some auld Scots sonnet,
Whyles glowering round wi' prudent cares,
Lest bogles catch him unawares ;
Kirk-Alloway was drawing nigh,
Whare ghaists and houlets nightly cry.

By this time he was cross the ford,
Whare in the snaw the chapman smoored ;
And past the birks and meikle stane,
Whare drunken Charlie brak 's neck-bane ;
And through the whins, and by the cairn,
Whare hunters fand the murdered bairn ;
And near the thorn, aboon the well,
Whare Mungo's mither hanged hersel'.
Before him Doon pours all his floods ;
The doubling storm roars through the woods ;
The lightnings flash from pole to pole ;
Near and more near the thunders roll ;
When, glimmering through the groaning trees,
Kirk-Alloway seemed in a bleeze !
Through ilka bore the beams were glancing,
And loud resounded mirth and dancing.

Inspiring bold John Barleycorn !
What dangers thou canst make us scorn !
Wi' tippenny we fear nae evil ;
Wi' usquebae we 'll face the Devil ! —
The swats sae reamed in Tammie's noddle,

Fair play, he cared na Deils a bodle.
But Maggie stood right sair astonished,
Till, by the heel and hand admonished,
She ventured forward on the light ;
And, wow ! Tam saw an unco sight !
Warlocks and witches in a dance :
Nae cotillon brent new frae France,
But hornpipes, jigs, strathspeys, and reels
Put life and mettle in their heels.
A winnock-bunker in the east,
There sat auld Nick, in shape o' beast, —
A towzie tyke, black, grim, and large, —
To gie them music was his charge :
He screwed the pipes and gart them skirl
Till roof an' rafters a' did dirl.
Coffins stood round like open presses,
That shawed the dead in their last dresses ;
And by some devilish cantrip sleight,
Each in its cauld hand held a light, —
By which heroic Tam was able
To note, upon the haly table,
A murderer's banes, in gibbet airns ;
Twa span-lang, wee, unchristened bairns ;
A thief, new cutted frae a rape,
Wi' his last gasp his gab did gape ;
Five tomahawks, wi' bluid red rusted ;
Five scymitars, wi' murder crusted ;
A garter, which a babe had strangled ;
A knife, a father's throat had mangled,
Whom his ain son o' life bereft, —
The gray hairs yet stack to the heft ;
Three lawyers' tongues turned inside out,
Wi' lies seamed like a beggar's clout ;
And priests' hearts, rotten, black as muck,
Lay stinking, vile, in every neuk :
Wi' mair o' horrible and awfu'
Which even to name wad be unlawfu'.

As Tammie glowered, amazed and curious,
The mirth and fun grew fast and furious ;
The piper loud and louder blew ;
The dancers quick and quicker flew ;
They reeled, they set, they crossed, they cleekit,
Till ilka carlin swat and reekit,
And coost her duddies to the wark,
And linket at it in her sark !

Now Tam, O Tam ! had they been queans,
A' plump and strapping in their teens :
Their sarks, instead of creeshie flannen,
Been snaw-white seventeen-hunder linen ;
Thir breeks o' mine, my only pair,
That ance were plush, o' guid blue hair,
I wad hae gi'en them aff my hurdies
For ae blink o' the bonnie burdies !
But withered beldams, auld and droll,
Rigwoodie hags wad spean a foal,
Lowping an' flinging on a crummock, —
I wonder didna turn thy stomach.

But Tam kenn'd what was what fu' brawlie.
There was ae winsome wench and walie,
That night inlisted in the core
(Lang after kenn'd on Carrick shore ;
For monie a beast to dead she shot,
And perished monie a bonnie boat,
And shook baith meikle corn and bear,
And kept the country-side in fear).
Her cutty-sark o' Paisley harn,
That while a lassie she had worn,
In longitude though sorely scanty, —
It was her best, and she was vaunty. —
Ah ! little kenned thy reverend grannie
That sark she coft for her wee Nannie
Wi' twa pund Scots ('t was a' her riches)
Wad ever graced a dance o' witches !

But here my Muse her wing maun cower,
Sic flights are far beyond her power ;
To sing how Nannie lap and flang
(A souple jade she was and strang),
And how Tam stood like ane bewitched,
And thought his very een enriched.
Ev'n Satan glowered, and fidged fu' fain,
And hotched and blew wi' might and main ;
Till first ae caper, syne anither, —
Tam tint his reason a' thegither,
And roars out, " Weel done, Cutty-sark !"
And in an instant a' was dark ;
And scarcely had he Maggie rallied,
When out the hellish legion sallied.
As bees bizz out wi' angry fyke,
When plundering herds assail their byke ;
As open pussie's mortal foes,
When, pop ! she starts before their nose ;
As eager runs the market-crowd,
When *Catch the thief !* resounds aloud ;
So Maggie runs, — the witches follow,
Wi' monie an eldritch skreech and hollow.
Ah, Tam ! ah, Tam ! thou 'll get thy fairin' !
In hell they 'll roast thee like a herrin' !
In vain thy Kate awaits thy comin' —
Kate soon will be a woefu' woman !
Now, do thy speedy utmost, Meg,
And win the key-stane of the brig ;
There at them thou thy tail may toss, -
A running stream they dare na cross.
But ere the key-stane she could make,
The fient a tail she had to shake !
For Nannie, far before the rest,
Hard upon noble Maggie prest,
And flew at Tam wi' furious ettle :
But little wist she Maggie's mettle, —
Ae spring brought aff her master hale,
But left behind her ain gray tail :
The carlin claught her by the rump,
And left poor Maggie scarce a stump.

Now, wha this tale o' truth shall read,
Ilk man and mother's son take heed ;
Whene'er to drink you are inclined,
Or cutty-sarks run in your mind,
Think, ye may buy the joys o'er dear,
Remember Tam O'Shanter's mare.

ROBERT BURNS.

THE PIED PIPER OF HAMELIN.

HAMELIN Town 's in Brunswick,
By famous Hanover City ;
  The river Weser, deep and wide,
  Washes its wall on the southern side ;
A pleasanter spot you never spied ;
But when begins my ditty,
  Almost five hundred years ago,
  To see the townsfolk suffer so
From vermin was a pity.

  Rats !
They fought the dogs, and killed the cats,
  And bit the babies in the cradles,
And ate the cheeses out of the vats,
  And licked the soup from the cook's own ladles,
Split open the kegs of salted sprats,
Made nests inside men's Sunday hats,
And even spoiled the women's chats,
    By drowning their speaking
    With shrieking and squeaking
In fifty different sharps and flats.

At last the people in a body
  To the Town Hall came flocking :
" 'T is clear," cried they, " our Mayor 's a noddy ;
  And as for our Corporation, — shocking
To think we buy gowns lined with ermine
For dolts that can't or won't determine
What 's best to rid us of our vermin !"
At this the Mayor and Corporation
Quaked with a mighty consternation.

An hour they sate in counsel, —
  At length the Mayor broke silence :
" For a guilder I 'd my ermine gown sell ;
  I wish I were a mile hence !
It 's easy to bid one rack one's brain, —
I 'm sure my poor head aches again.
I 've scratched it so, and all in vain.
O for a trap, a trap, a trap !"
Just as he said this, what should hap
At the chamber door but a gentle tap ?
" Bless us," cried the Mayor, " what 's that ?"
" Come in !" — the Mayor cried, looking bigger ;
And in did come the strangest figure ;
He advanced to the council-table :
And, " Please your honors," said he, " I 'm able,

By means of a secret charm, to draw
All creatures living beneath the sun,
That creep or swim or fly or run,
After me so as you never saw !
    Yet," said he, " poor piper as I am,
In Tartary I freed the Cham,
Last June, from his huge swarm of gnats ;
I eased in Asia the Nizam
Of a monstrous brood of vampire-bats ;
And as for what your brain bewilders, —
If I can rid your town of rats,
Will you give me a thousand guilders ?"
" One ? fifty thousand !" was the exclamation
Of the astonished Mayor and Corporation.

Into the street the piper stept,
    Smiling first a little smile,
As if he knew what magic slept
    In his quiet pipe the while ;
Then, like a musical adept,
To blow the pipe his lips he wrinkled,
And green and blue his sharp eyes twinkled,
Like a candle flame where salt is sprinkled ;
And ere three shrill notes the pipe uttered,
You heard as if an army muttered ;
And the muttering grew to a grumbling ;
And the grumbling grew to a mighty rumbling ;
And out of the houses the rats came tumbling.
Great rats, small rats, lean rats, brawny rats,
Brown rats, black rats, gray rats, tawny rats,
Grave old plodders, gay young friskers,
    Fathers, mothers, uncles, cousins,
Cocking tales and pricking whiskers ;
    Families by tens and dozens,
Brothers, sisters, husbands, wives, —
Followed the piper for their lives.
From street to street he piped advancing,
And step for step they followed dancing,
Until they came to the river Weser,
Wherein all plunged and perished
Save one who, stout as Julius Cæsar,
Swam across and lived to carry
(As he the manuscript he cherished)
To Rat-land home his commentary,
Which was : " At the first shrill notes of the pipe,
I heard a sound as of scraping tripe,
And putting apples, wondrous ripe,
Into a cider-press's gripe, —
And a moving away of pickle-tub-boards,
And a leaving ajar of conserve-cupboards,
And a drawing the corks of train-oil-flasks,
And a breaking the hoops of butter-casks ;
And it seemed as if a voice
(Sweeter far than by harp or by psaltery
Is breathed) called out, O rats, rejoice !
The world is grown to one vast drysaltery !
So munch on, crunch on, take your nuncheon,

Breakfast, supper, dinner, luncheon !
And just as a bulky sugar-puncheon,
Already staved, like a great sun shone
Glorious scarce an inch before me,
Just as methought it said, Come, bore me ! —
I found the Weser rolling o'er me."

You should have heard the Hamelin people
Ringing the bells till they rocked the steeple ;
" Go," cried the Mayor, " and get long poles !
Poke out the nests and block up the holes !
Consult with carpenters and builders,
And leave in our town not even a trace
Of the rats ! " — when suddenly, up the face
Of the piper perked in the market-place,
With a " First, if you please, my thousand guil-
    ders ! "

A thousand guilders ! the Mayor looked blue ;
So did the Corporation too.
For council-dinners made rare havoc
With Claret, Moselle, Vin-de-Grave, Hock ;
And half the money would replenish
Their cellar's biggest butt with Rhenish,
To pay this sum to a wandering fellow
With a gypsy coat of red and yellow !
" Beside," quoth the Mayor, with a knowing
    wink,
" Our business was done at the river's brink ;
We saw with our eyes the vermin sink,
And what 's dead can't come to life, I think.
So, friend, we 're not the folks to shrink
From the duty of giving you something to drink,
And a matter of money to put in your poke ;
But as for the guilders, what we spoke
Of them, as you very well know, was in joke.
Beside, our losses have made us thrifty ;
A thousand guilders ! Come, take fifty ! "

The piper's face fell, and he cried,
" No trifling ! I can't wait ! beside,
I 've promised to visit by dinner time
Bagdat, and accept the prime
Of the head cook's pottage, all he 's rich in,
For having left, in the Caliph's kitchen,
Of a nest of scorpions no survivor, —
With him I proved no bargain-driver ;
With you, don't think I 'll bate a stiver !
And folks who put me in a passion
May find me pipe to another fashion."

" How ? " cried the Mayor, " d' ye think I 'll
    brook
Being worse treated than a cook ?
Insulted by a lazy ribald
With idle pipe and vesture piebald ?
You threaten us, fellow ? Do your worst,
Blow your pipe there till you burst ! "

Once more he stept into the street ;
  And to his lips again
Laid his long pipe of smooth straight cane ;
  And ere he blew three notes (such sweet
Soft notes as yet musician's cunning
  Never gave the enraptured air)
There was a rustling that seemed like a bustling
Of merry crowds justling at pitching and hustling ;
Small feet were pattering, wooden shoes clatter-
      ing,
Little hands clapping, and little tongues chat-
      tering ;
And, like fowls in a farm-yard when barley is
      scattering,
Out came the children running :
All the little boys and girls,
With rosy cheeks and flaxen curls,
And sparkling eyes and teeth like pearls,
Tripping and skipping, ran merrily after
The wonderful music with shouting and laughter.

The Mayor was dumb, and the Council stood
As if they were changed into blocks of wood,
Unable to move a step, or cry
To the children merrily skipping by, —
And could only follow with the eye
That joyous crowd at the piper's back.
But how the Mayor was on the rack,
And the wretched Council's bosoms beat,
As the piper turned from the High Street
To where the Weser rolled its waters
Right in the way of their sons and daughters !
However, he turned from south to west,
And to Koppelberg Hill his steps addressed,
And after him the children pressed ;
Great was the joy in every breast.
" He never can cross that mighty top !
He 's forced to let the piping drop,
And we shall see our children stop ! "
When, lo, as they reached the mountain's side,
A wondrous portal opened wide,
As if a cavern was suddenly hollowed ;
And the piper advanced and the children followed ;
And when all were in, to the very last,
The door in the mountain-side shut fast.
Did I say all ? No ! One was lame,
And could not dance the whole of the way ;
And in after years, if you would blame
His sadness, he was used to say, —
" It 's dull in our town since my playmates left !
I can't forget that I 'm bereft
Of all the pleasant sights they see,
Which the piper also promised me ;
For he led us, he said, to a joyous land,
Joining the town and just at hand,
Where waters gushed, and fruit-trees grew,
And flowers put forth a fairer hue,
And everything was strange and new ;

The sparrows were brighter than peacocks here,
And their dogs outran our fallow deer,
And honey-bees had lost their stings,
And horses were born with eagles' wings ;
And just as I became assured
My lame foot would be speedily cured,
The music stopped and I stood still,
And found myself outside the Hill,
Left alone against my will,
To go now limping as before,
And never hear of that country more ! "
                    ROBERT BROWNING.

THE TOAD'S JOURNAL.

[It is said that Belzoni, the traveller in Egypt, discovered a living toad in a temple, which had been for ages buried in the sand.]

In a land for antiquities greatly renowned
A traveller had dug wide and deep under ground,
A temple, for ages entombed, to disclose, —
When, lo ! he disturbed, in its secret repose,
A toad, from whose journal it plainly appears
It had lodged in that mansion some thousands
      of years.
The roll which this reptile's long history records,
A treat to the sage antiquarian affords :
The sense by obscure hieroglyphics concealed,
Deep learning at length, with long labor, revealed.
The first thousand years as a specimen take, —
The dates are omitted for brevity's sake :
" Crawled forth from some rubbish, and winked
      with one eye ;
Half opened the other, but could not tell why ;
Stretched out my left leg, as it felt rather queer.
Then drew all together and slept for a year.
Awakened, felt chilly, — crept under a stone ;
Was vastly contented with living alone.
One toe became wedged in the stone like a peg,
Could not get it away, — had the cramp in my leg,
Began half to wish for a neighbor at hand
To loosen the stone, which was fast in the sand ;
Pulled harder, then dozed, as I found 't was no
      use ; —
Awoke the next summer, and lo ! it was loose.
Crawled forth from the stone when completely
      awake ;
Crept into a corner and grinned at a snake.
Retreated, and found that I needed repose ;
Curled up my damp limbs and prepared for a doze ;
Fell sounder to sleep than was usual before,
And did not awake for a century or more ;
But had a sweet dream, as I rather believe :
Methought it was light, and a fine summer's eve ;
And I in some garden deliciously fed
In the pleasant moist shade of a strawberry-bed.
There fine speckled creatures claimed kindred
      with me,
And others that hopped, most enchanting to see.

Here long I regaled with emotion extreme ; —
Awoke, — disconcerted to find it a dream ;
Grew pensive, — discovered that life is a load ;
Began to get weary of being a toad ;
Was fretful at first, and then shed a few tears "—
Here ends the account of the first thousand years.

MORAL.

It seems that life is all a void,
On selfish thoughts alone employed ;
That length of days is not a good,
Unless their use be understood.

JANE TAYLOR.

———◆———

THE RAVEN.

ONCE upon a midnight dreary, while I pondered,
    weak and weary,
Over many a quaint and curious volume of for-
    gotten lore, —
While I nodded, nearly napping, suddenly there
    came a tapping,
As of some one gently rapping, rapping at my
    chamber door.
" 'T is some visitor," I muttered, "tapping at
    my chamber door ;
    Only this, and nothing more."

Ah, distinctly I remember, it was in the bleak
    December,
And each separate dying ember wrought its ghost
    upon the floor.
Eagerly I wished the morrow ; vainly I had
    sought to borrow
From my books surcease of sorrow, — sorrow for
    the lost Lenore, —
For the rare and radiant maiden whom the angels
    named Lenore, —
    Nameless here forevermore.

And the silken, sad, uncertain rustling of each
    purple curtain
Thrilled me, — filled me with fantastic terrors
    never felt before ;
So that now, to still the beating of my heart, I
    stood repeating,
" 'T is some visitor entreating entrance at my
    chamber door, —
Some late visitor entreating entrance at my
    chamber door ;
    That it is, and nothing more."

Presently my soul grew stronger ; hesitating then
    no longer,
" Sir," said I, "or madam, truly your forgive-
    ness I implore ;
But the fact is, I was napping, and so gently you
    came rapping,

And so faintly you came tapping, tapping at m
    chamber door,
That I scarce was sure I heard you " — Here
    opened wide the door ;
    Darkness there, and nothing more.

Deep into that darkness peering, long I stood
    there, wondering, fearing,
Doubting, dreaming dreams no mortal ever dared
    to dream before ;
But the silence was unbroken, and the darkness
    gave no token,
And the only word there spoken was the whis-
    pered word " Lenore ! "
This I whispered, and an echo murmured back
    the word " Lenore ! "
    Merely this, and nothing more.

Back into the chamber turning, all my soul within
    me burning,
Soon again I heard a tapping, something louder
    than before :
" Surely," said I, "surely that is something at
    my window-lattice ;
Let me see then what thereat is, and this mys-
    tery explore, —
Let my heart be still a moment, and this mystery
    explore ; —
    'T is the wind, and nothing more."

Open then I flung the shutter, when, with many
    a flirt and flutter,
In there stepped a stately raven of the saintly
    days of yore.
Not the least obeisance made he ; not an instant
    stopped or stayed he ;
But, with mien of lord or lady, perched above
    my chamber door, —
Perched upon a bust of Pallas, just above my
    chamber door, —
    Perched, and sat, and nothing more.

Then this ebony bird beguiling my sad fancy into
    smiling,
By the grave and stern decorum of the counte-
    nance it wore,
" Though thy crest be shorn and shaven, thou,"
    I said, "art sure no craven ;
Ghastly, grim, and ancient raven, wandering
    from the nightly shore,
Tell me what thy lordly name is on the night's
    Plutonian shore ? "
    Quoth the raven, " Nevermore ! "

Much I marvelled this ungainly fowl to hear
    discourse so plainly,
Though its answer little meaning, little rele-
    vancy bore ;

For we cannot help agreeing that no living human being
Ever yet was blessed with seeing bird above his chamber door,
Bird or beast upon the sculptured bust above his chamber door,
   With such name as " Nevermore ! "

But the raven, sitting lonely on the placid bust, spoke only
That one word, as if his soul in that one word he did outpour.
Nothing further then he uttered, — not a feather then he fluttered, —
Till I scarcely more than muttered, " Other friends have flown before, —
On the morrow he will leave me, as my hopes have flown before."
   Then the bird said, " Nevermore ! "

Startled at the stillness, broken by reply so aptly spoken,
"Doubtless," said I, " what it utters is its only stock and store,
Caught from some unhappy master, whom unmerciful disaster
Followed fast and followed faster, till his song one burden bore,
Till the dirges of his hope that melancholy burden bore, —
   Of ' Nevermore, — nevermore ! ' "

But the raven still beguiling all my sad soul into smiling,
Straight I wheeled a cushioned seat in front of bird and bust and door,
Then, upon the velvet sinking, I betook myself to linking
Fancy unto fancy, thinking what this ominous bird of yore —
What this grim, ungainly, ghastly, gaunt, and ominous bird of yore —
   Meant in croaking " Nevermore ! "

This I sat engaged in guessing, but no syllable expressing
To the fowl whose fiery eyes now burned into my bosom's core ;
This and more I sat divining, with my head at ease reclining
On the cushion's velvet lining that the lamplight gloated o'er,
But whose velvet violet lining, with the lamplight gloating o'er,
   She shall press — ah ! nevermore !

Then methought the air grew denser, perfumed from an unseen censer,
Swung by seraphim, whose footfalls tinkled on the tufted floor.
" Wretch," I cried, " thy God hath lent thee, — by these angels he hath sent thee
Respite, — respite and nepenthe from the memories of Lenore !
Quaff, O, quaff this kind nepenthe, and forget this lost Lenore ! "
   Quoth the raven, " Nevermore ! "

" Prophet ! " said I, " thing of evil ! — prophet still, if bird or devil !
Whether tempter sent, or whether tempest tossed thee here ashore,
Desolate yet all undaunted, on this desert land enchanted, —
On this home by horror haunted, — tell me truly, I implore, —
Is there — is there balm in Gilead ? — tell me, — tell me, I implore ! "
   Quoth the raven, " Nevermore ! "

" Prophet ! " said I, " thing of evil ! — prophet still, if bird or devil !
By that heaven that bends above us, — by that God we both adore,
Tell this soul with sorrow laden, if, within the distant Aidenn,
It shall clasp a sainted maiden, whom the angels name Lenore,
Clasp a fair and radiant maiden, whom the angels name Lenore ! "
   Quoth the raven, " Nevermore ! "

" Be that word our sign of parting, bird or fiend ! " I shrieked, upstarting, —
" Get thee back into the tempest and the night's Plutonian shore !
Leave no black plume as a token of that lie thy soul hath spoken !
Leave my loneliness unbroken ! — quit the bust above my door !
Take thy beak from out my heart, and take thy form from off my door ! "
   Quoth the raven, " Nevermore ! "

And the raven, never flitting, still is sitting, still is sitting
On the pallid bust of Pallas, just above my chamber door ;
And his eyes have all the seeming of a demon that is dreaming,
And the lamplight o'er him streaming throws his shadow on the floor ;
And my soul from out that shadow that lies floating on the floor
   Shall be lifted — *nevermore !*

                EDGAR ALLAN POE.

RIME OF THE ANCIENT MARINER.

PART I.

An Ancient Mariner meeteth three gallants bidden to a wedding feast, and detaineth one.

IT is an Ancient Mariner,
And he stoppeth one of three.
" By thy long gray beard and glittering
    eye,
Now wherefore stopp'st thou me ?
The Bridegroom's doors are opened wide,
And I am next of kin ;
The guests are met, the feast is set, —
Mayst hear the merry din."

He holds him with his skinny hand :
" There was a ship," quoth he.
" Hold off ! unhand me, graybeard
    loon ! " —
Eftsoons his hand dropt he.

The Wedding-Guest is spellbound by the eye of the old seafaring man, and constrained to hear his tale.

He holds him with his glittering eye, —
The Wedding-Guest stood still ;
He listens like a three years' child ;
The Mariner hath his will.

The Wedding-Guest sat on a stone, —
He cannot choose but hear ;
And thus spake on that ancient man,
The bright-eyed Mariner :

" The ship was cheered, the harbor
    cleared ;
Merrily did we drop
Below the kirk, below the hill,
Below the light-house top.

The Mariner tells how the ship sailed southward, with a good wind and fair weather, till it reached the line.

The sun came up upon the left,
Out of the sea came he ;
And he shone bright, and on the right
Went down into the sea ;

Higher and higher every day,
Till over the mast at noon — "
The Wedding-Guest here beat his breast,
For he heard the loud bassoon.

The Wedding-Guest heareth the bridal music ; but the Mariner continueth his tale.

The Bride hath paced into the hall —
Red as a rose is she ;
Nodding their heads before her goes
The merry minstrelsy.

The Wedding-Guest he beat his breast,
Yet he cannot choose but hear ;
And thus spake on that ancient man,
The bright-eyed Mariner :

The ship drawn by a storm toward the south pole.

" And now the Storm-blast came, and he
Was tyrannous and strong ;
He struck with his o'ertaking wings,
And chased us south along.

With sloping masts and dipping prow —
As who pursued with yell and blow
Still treads the shadow of his foe,
And forward bends his head —
The ship drove fast ; loud roared the
    blast,
And southward aye we fled.

And now there came both mist and snow,
And it grew wondrous cold ;
And ice, mast-high, came floating by,
As green as emerald.

The land of ice and of fearful sounds, where no living thing was to be seen.

And through the drifts the snowy cliffs
Did send a dismal sheen ;
Nor shapes of men nor beasts we ken —
The ice was all between.

The ice was here, the ice was there,
The ice was all around ;
It cracked and growled, and roared and
    howled,
Like noises in a swound !

Till a great sea-bird, called the Albatross, came through the snow-fog, and was received with great joy and hospitality.

At length did cross an Albatross —
Thorough the fog it came ;
As if it had been a Christian soul,
We hailed it in God's name.

It ate the food it ne'er had eat,
And round and round it flew.
The ice did split with a thunder-fit ;
The helmsman steered us through !

And lo ! the Albatross proveth a bird of good omen, and followeth the ship as it returned northward through fog and floating ice.

And a good south wind sprung up be-
    hind ;
The Albatross did follow,
And every day, for food or play,
Came to the mariners' hollo !

In mist or cloud, on mast or shroud,
It perched for vespers nine ;
Whiles all the night, through fog-smoke
    white,
Glimmered the white moonshine."

The Ancient Mariner inhospitably killeth the pious bird of good omen.

" God save thee, Ancient Mariner !
From the fiends, that plague thee thus ! —
Why look'st thou so ? " — " With my
    cross-bow
I shot the Albatross.

PART II.

THE Sun now rose upon the right :
Out of the sea came he,
Still hid in mist, and on the left
Went down into the sea.

And the good south wind still blew
    behind,
But no sweet bird did follow,

Nor any day, for food or play,
Came to the mariners' hollo !

His shipmates cry out against the Ancient Mariner, for killing the bird of good luck.

And I had done an hellish thing,
And it would work 'em woe :
For all averred, I had killed the bird
That made the breeze to blow.
Ah wretch ! said they, the bird to slay,
That made the breeze to blow !

But when the fog cleared off, they justify the same, and thus make themselves accomplices in the crime.

Nor dim nor red, like God's own head
The glorious Sun uprist :
Then all averred, I had killed the bird
That brought the fog and mist.
'T was right, said they, such birds to slay,
That bring the fog and mist.

The fair breeze continues ; the ship enters the Pacific Ocean, and sails northward, even till it reaches the line.

The fair breeze blew, the white foam flew,
The furrow followed free ;
We were the first that ever burst
Into that silent sea.

The ship hath been suddenly becalmed ;

Down dropt the breeze, the sails dropt
        down, —
'T was sad as sad could be ;
And we did speak only to break
The silence of the sea.

All in a hot and copper sky
The bloody Sun, at noon,
Right up above the mast did stand,
No bigger than the Moon.

Day after day, day after day,
We stuck, — nor breath nor motion ;
As idle as a painted ship
Upon a painted ocean.

and the Albatross begins to be avenged.

Water, water everywhere,
And all the boards did shrink ;
Water, water everywhere,
Nor any drop to drink.

The very deep did rot : O Christ !
That ever this should be !
Yea, slimy things did crawl with legs
Upon the slimy sea !

About, about, in reel and rout,
The death-fires danced at night ;
The water, like a witch's oils,
Burnt green, and blue, and white.

A Spirit had followed them ; one of the invisible inhabitants of this planet, neither departed souls nor angels ; concerning whom the learned Jew Josephus, and the Platonic Constantinopolitan, Michael Psellus, may be consulted. They are very numerous, and there is no climate or element without one or more.

And some in dreams assurèd were
Of the Spirit that plagued us so ;
Nine fathom deep he had followed us
From the land of mist and snow.

And every tongue, through utter
        drought,
Was withered at the root ;
We could not speak, no more than if
We had been choked with soot.

The shipmates, in their sore distress, would fain throw the whole guilt on the Ancient Mariner : in sign whereof they hang the dead sea-bird round his neck.

Ah ! well-a-day ! what evil looks
Had I from old and young !
Instead of the cross the Albatross
About my neck was hung.

PART III.

THERE passed a weary time. Each
        throat
Was parched, and glazed each eye —
A weary time ! a weary time !
How glazed each weary eye ! —
When, looking westward, I beheld
A something in the sky.

The Ancient Mariner beholdeth a sign in the element afar off.

At first it seemed a little speck,
And then it seemed a mist ;
It moved and moved, and took at last
A certain shape, I wist —

A speck, a mist, a shape, I wist !
And still it neared and neared ;
As if it dodged a water-sprite,
It plunged and tacked and veered.

At its nearer approach it seemeth him to be a ship ; and at a dear ransom he freeth his speech from the bonds of thirst.

With throats unslaked, with black lips
        baked,
We could nor laugh nor wail ;
Through utter drought all dumb we
        stood !
I bit my arm, I sucked the blood,
And cried, 'A sail ! a sail !'

A flash of joy.

With throats unslaked, with black lips
        baked,
Agape they heard me call ;
Gramercy ! they for joy did grin,
And all at once their breath drew in,
As they were drinking all.

And horror follows. For can it be a ship that comes onward without wind or tide ?

'See ! see !' I cried, 'she tacks no more !
Hither to work us weal —
Without a breeze, without a tide,
She steadies with upright keel !'

The western wave was all a-flame ;
The day was well nigh done !
Almost upon the western wave
Rested the broad bright sun,
When that strange shape drove suddenly
Betwixt us and the Sun.

It seemeth him but the skeleton of a ship.

And straight the Sun was flecked with
        bars,
(Heaven's Mother send us grace !)

As if through a dungeon-grate he peered
With broad and burning face.

Alas ! thought I — and my heart beat
    loud —
How fast she nears and nears !
Are those her sails that glance in the sun,
Like restless gossameres ?

And its ribs are seen as bars on the face of the setting sun. The spectre-woman and her death-mate, and no other on board the skeleton ship.

Are those her ribs through which the Sun
Did peer, as through a grate ?
And is that woman all her crew ?
Is that a death ? and are there two ?
Is Death that woman's mate ?

Like vessel, like crew !

Her lips were red, her looks were free,
Her locks were yellow as gold ;
Her skin was as white as leprosy :
The night-mare, Life-in-Death, was she,
Who thicks man's blood with cold.

Death and Life-in-Death have diced for the ship's crew, and she (the latter) winneth the Ancient Mariner.

The naked hulk alongside came,
And the twain were casting dice :
'The game is done. I've won ! I've
    won ! '
Quoth she, and whistles thrice.

No twilight within the courts of the Sun.

The Sun's rim dips ; the stars rush out ;
At one stride comes the dark ;
With far-heard whisper, o'er the sea,
Off shot the spectre-bark.

At the rising of the Moon,

We listened and looked sideways up !
Fear at my heart, as at a cup ;
My life-blood seemed to sip !
The stars were dim, and thick the night,
The steersman's face by his lamp
    gleamed white ;
From the sails the dew did drip —
Till clombe above the eastern bar,
The hornèd Moon, with one bright star
Within the nether tip.

one after another,

One after one, by the star-dogged Moon,
Too quick for groan or sigh,
Each turned his face with a ghastly pang,
And cursed me with his eye.

his shipmates drop down dead.

Four times fifty living men
(And I heard nor sigh nor groan),
With heavy thump, a lifeless lump,
They dropped down one by one.

But Life-in-Death begins her work on the Ancient Mariner.

The souls did from their bodies fly, —
They fled to bliss or woe !
And every soul, it passed me by,
Like the whizz of my cross-bow ! "

PART IV.

The Wedding-Guest feareth that a spirit is talking to him ;

" I FEAR thee, Ancient Mariner !
I fear thy skinny hand !
And thou art long, and lank, and
    brown,
As is the ribbed sea-sand.

I fear thee and thy glittering eye,
And thy skinny hand so brown." —

but the Ancient Mariner assureth him of his bodily life, and proceedeth to relate his horrible penance.

" Fear not, fear not, thou Wedding-
    Guest !
This body dropt not down.

Alone, alone, all, all alone,
Alone on a wide, wide sea !
And never a saint took pity on
My soul in agony.

He despiseth the creatures of the calm ;

The many men so beautiful !
And they all dead did lie :
And a thousand thousand slimy things
Lived on ; and so did I.

and envieth that they should live, and so many lie dead.

I looked upon the rotting sea,
And drew my eyes away ;
I looked upon the rotting deck,
And there the dead men lay.

I looked to heaven, and tried to pray ;
But, or ever a prayer had gusht,
A wicked whisper came, and made
My heart as dry as dust.

I closed my lids, and kept them close,
And the balls like pulses beat ;
For the sky and the sea, and the sea
    and the sky,
Lay like a load on my weary eye,
And the dead were at my feet.

But the curse liveth for him in the eye of the dead men.

The cold sweat melted from their limbs,
Nor rot nor reek did they :
The look with which they looked on me
Had never passed away.

An orphan's curse would drag to hell
A spirit from on high ;
But oh ! more horrible than that
Is a curse in a dead man's eye !
Seven days, seven nights, I saw that
    curse,
And yet I could not die.

In his loneliness and fixedness he yearneth towards the journeying Moon, and everywhere the blue sky belongs to them, and is their appointed rest, and their native country, and their own natural homes, which they enter unannounced, as lords that are certainly expected, and yet there is a silent joy at their arrival.

The moving Moon went up the sky,
And nowhere did abide :
Softly she was going up,
And a star or two beside —

Her beams bemocked the sultry main,
Like April hoar-frost spread ;
But where the ship's huge shadow lay
The charmèd water burnt alway,
A still and awful red.

By the light of the Moon he beholdeth God's creatures of the great calm.

Beyond the shadow of the ship
I watched the water-snakes ,
They moved in tracks of shining white ;
And when they reared, the elfish light
Fell off in hoary flakes.

Within the shadow of the ship
I watched their rich attire —
Blue, glossy green, and velvet black,
They coiled and swam ; and every track
Was a flash of golden fire.

Their beauty and their happiness.

O happy living things ! no tongue
Their beauty might declare ;
A spring of love gushed from my heart,

He blesseth them in his heart.

And I blessed them unaware —
Sure my kind saint took pity on me,
And I blessed them unaware.

The spell begins to break.

The selfsame moment I could pray ;
And from my neck so free
The Albatross fell off, and sank
Like lead into the sea.

PART V.

O SLEEP ! it is a gentle thing,
Beloved from pole to pole !
To Mary Queen the praise be given !
She sent the gentle sleep from heaven
That slid into my soul.

By grace of the holy Mother, the Ancient Mariner is refreshed with rain.

The silly buckets on the deck,
That had so long remained,
I dreamt that they were filled with dew;
And when I awoke, it rained.

My lips were wet, my throat was cold,
My garments all were dank ;
Sure I had drunken in my dreams,
And still my body drank.

I moved, and could not feel my limbs ;
I was so light — almost
I thought that I had died in sleep,
And was a blessèd ghost.

He heareth sounds and seeth strange sights and commotions in the sky and the element.

And soon I heard a roaring wind —
It did not come anear ;
But with its sound it shook the sails,
That were so thin and sere.

The upper air burst into life ;
And a hundred fire-flags sheen,
To and fro they were hurried about ;

And to and fro, and in and out,
The wan stars danced between.

And the coming wind did roar more loud,
And the sails did sigh like sedge ;
And the rain poured down from one
    black cloud —
The Moon was at its edge.

The thick black cloud was cleft, and still
The Moon was at its side ;
Like waters shot from some high crag,
The lightning fell with never a jag —
A river steep and wide.

The bodies of the ship's crew are inspired, and the ship moves on ;

The loud wind never reached the ship,
Yet now the ship moved on !
Beneath the lightning and the Moon
The dead men gave a groan.

They groaned, they stirred, they all
    uprose —
Nor spake, nor moved their eyes ;
It had been strange, even in a dream,
To have seen those dead men rise.

The helmsman steered, the ship moved
    on ;
Yet never a breeze up blew ;
The mariners all 'gan work the ropes,
Where they were wont to do ;
They raised their limbs like· lifeless
    tools —
We were a ghastly crew.

The Body of my brother's son
Stood by me, knee to knee :
The Body and I pulled at one rope,
But he said naught to me."

but not by the souls of the men, nor by dæmons of earth or middle air, but by a blessed troop of angelic spirits, sent down by the invocation of the guardian saint.

" I fear thee, Ancient Mariner ! "
" Be calm, thou Wedding-Guest !
'T was not those souls that fled in pain,
Which to their corses came again,
But a troop of spirits blest :

For when it dawned — they dropped
    their arms,
And clustered round the mast ;
Sweet sounds rose slowly through their
    mouths,
And from their bodies passed.

Around, around, flew each sweet sound,
Then darted to the Sun ;
Slowly the sounds came back again,
Now mixed, now one by one.

Sometimes a-dropping from the sky,
I heard the skylark sing ;
Sometimes all little birds that are,
How they seemed to fill the sea and air
With their sweet jargoning !

And now 't was like all instruments,
Now like a lonely flute ;
And now it is an angel's song
That makes the heavens be mute.

It ceased ; yet still the sails made on
A pleasant noise till noon,
A noise like of a hidden brook
In the leafy month of June,
That to the sleeping woods all night
Singeth a quiet tune.

Till noon we quietly sailed on,
Yet never a breeze did breathe :
Slowly and smoothly went the ship,
Moved onward from beneath.

The lonesome spirit from the south pole carries on the ship as far as the line, in obedience to the angelic troop, but still requireth vengeance.

Under the keel nine fathom deep,
From the land of mist and snow,
The Spirit slid : and it was he
That made the ship to go.
The sails at noon left off their tune,
And the ship stood still also.

The Sun, right up above the mast,
Had fixed her to the ocean :
But in a minute she 'gan stir,
With a short uneasy motion —
Backwards and forwards half her length
With a short uneasy motion.

Then like a pawing horse let go,
She made a sudden bound :
It flung the blood into my head
And I fell down in a swound.

The Polar Spirit's fellow-dæmons, the invisible inhabitants of the element, take part in his wrong ; and two of them relate, one to the other, that penance long and heavy for the Ancient Mariner hath been accorded to the Polar Spirit, who returneth southward.

How long in that same fit I lay,
I have not to declare ;
But ere my living life returned,
I heard, and in my soul discerned
Two voices in the air.

'Is it he ?' quoth one, 'Is this the man?
By Him who died on cross,
With his cruel bow he laid full low
The harmless Albatross !

The Spirit who bideth by himself
In the land of mist and snow,
He loved the bird that loved the man
Who shot him with his bow.'

The other was a softer voice,
As soft as honey-dew :
Quoth he, 'The man hath penance done,
And penance more will do.'

PART VI.

FIRST VOICE.

'BUT tell me, tell me ! speak again,
Thy soft response renewing —
What makes that ship drive on so fast ?
What is the ocean doing ?'

SECOND VOICE.

'Still as a slave before his lord,
The ocean hath no blast ;
His great bright eye most silently
Up to the Moon is cast —

If he may know which way to go ;
For she guides him smooth or grim.
See, brother, see ! how graciously
She looketh down on him.'

FIRST VOICE.

'But why drives on that ship so fast,
Without or wave or wind ?'

SECOND VOICE.

'The air is cut away before,
And closes from behind.

Fly, brother, fly ! more high, more high !
Or we shall be belated ;
For slow and slow that ship will go,
When the Mariner's trance is abated.'

The Mariner hath been cast into a trance ; for the angelic power causeth the vessel to drive northward faster than human life could endure

I woke, and we were sailing on
As in a gentle weather ;
'T was night, calm night — the moon
was high ;
The dead men stood together.

The supernatural motion is retarded ; the Mariner awakes, and his penance begins anew.

All stood together on the deck,
For a charnel-dungeon fitter ;
All fixed on me their stony eyes,
That in the Moon did glitter.

The pang, the curse, with which they
died,
Had never passed away ;
I could not draw my eyes from theirs,
Nor turn them up to pray.

And now this spell was snapt ; once more
I viewed the ocean green,
And looked far forth, yet little saw
Of what had else been seen —

The curse is finally expiated.

Like one that on a lonesome road
Doth walk in fear and dread,

And, having once turned round, walks on,
And turns no more his head ;
Because he knows a frightful fiend
Doth close behind him tread.

But soon there breathed a wind on me,
Nor sound nor motion made ;
Its path was not upon the sea,
In ripple or in shade.

It raised my hair, it fanned my cheek,
Like a meadow-gale of Spring —
It mingled strangely with my fears,
Yet it felt like a welcoming.

Swiftly, swiftly flew the ship,
Yet she sailed softly too ;
Sweetly, sweetly blew the breeze —
On me alone it blew.

And the Ancient Mariner beholdeth his native country.

O dream of joy ! is this indeed
The light-house top I see ?
Is this the hill ? is this the kirk ?
Is this mine own countree ?

We drifted o'er the harbor-bar,
And I with sobs did pray —
O let me be awake, my God !
Or let me sleep alway.

The harbor-bay was clear as glass,
So smoothly it was strewn !
And on the bay the moonlight lay,
And the shadow of the moon.

The rock shone bright, the kirk no less
That stands above the rock ;
The moonlight steeped in silentness
The steady weathercock.

The angelic spirits leave the dead bodies,

And the bay was white with silent light,
Till rising from the same,
Full many shapes, that shadows were,
In crimson colors came.

and appear in their own forms of light.

A little distance from the prow
Those crimson shadows were :
I turned my eyes upon the deck —
O Christ ! what saw I there !

Each corse lay flat, lifeless and flat,
And, by the holy rood !
A man all light, a seraph man,
On every corse there stood.

This seraph-band, each waved his hand :
It was a heavenly sight !

They stood as signals to the land,
Each one a lovely light ;

This seraph-band, each waved his hand,
No voice did they impart —
No voice ; but oh ! the silence sank
Like music on my heart.

But soon I heard the dash of oars,
I heard the pilot's cheer ;
My head was turned perforce away,
And I saw a boat appear.

The pilot and the pilot's boy,
I heard them coming fast :
Dear Lord in Heaven ! it was a joy
The dead men could not blast.

I saw a third — I heard his voice :
It is the hermit good !
He singeth loud his godly hymns
That he makes in the wood.
He 'll shrieve my soul, he 'll wash away
The Albatross's blood.

PART VII.

The hermit of the wood

This hermit good lives in that wood
Which slopes down to the sea.
How loudly his sweet voice he rears !
He loves to talk with marineres
That come from a far countree.

He kneels at morn, and noon, and eve —
He hath a cushion plump :
It is the moss that wholly hides
The rotted old oak-stump.

The skiff-boat neared : I heard them talk,
' Why, this is strange, I trow !
Where are those lights so many and fair,
That signal made but now ? '

approacheth the ship with wonder.

' Strange, by my faith ! ' the hermit said —
' And they answered not our cheer !
The planks look'd warped ! and see those sails
How thin they are and sere !
I never saw aught like to them,
Unless perchance it were

Brown skeletons of leaves that lag
My forest-brook along ;
When the ivy-tod is heavy with snow,

And the owlet whoops to the wolf below,
That eats the she-wolf's young.'

'Dear Lord ! it hath a fiendish look
(The pilot made reply) —
I am a-feared.' — ' Push on, push on !'
Said the hermit cheerily.

The boat came closer to the ship,
But I nor spake nor stirred ;
The boat came close beneath the ship,
And straight a sound was heard.

The ship suddenly sinketh. Under the water it rumbled on,
Still louder and more dread :
It reached the ship, it split the bay ;
The ship went down like lead.

The Ancient Mariner is saved in the pilot's boat. Stunned by that loud and dreadful
                              sound,
Which sky and ocean smote,
Like one that hath been seven days
                              drowned
My body lay afloat ;
But swift as dreams, myself I found
Within the pilot's boat.

Upon the whirl where sank the ship
The boat spun round and round ;
And all was still, save that the hill
Was telling of the sound.

I moved my lips — the pilot shrieked
And fell down in a fit ;
The holy hermit raised his eyes,
And prayed where he did sit.

I took the oars ; the pilot's boy,
Who now doth crazy go,
Laughed loud and long; and all the while
His eyes went to and fro :
'Ha ! ha !' quoth he, 'full plain I see,
The Devil knows how to row.'

And now, all in my own countree,
I stood on the firm land !
The hermit stepped forth from the boat,
And scarcely he could stand.

The Ancient Mariner earnestly entreateth the hermit to shrieve him: and the penance of life falls on him. 'O shrieve me, shrieve me, holy
                              man !' —
The hermit crossed his brow :
'Say quick,' quoth he, ' I bid thee
                              say —
What manner of man art thou ?'

Forthwith this frame of mine was
                              wrenched
With a woful agony,

Which forced me to begin my tale —
And then it left me free.

Since then, at an uncertain hour,
That agony returns ;
And till my ghastly tale is told
This heart within me burns.

And ever and anon throughout his future life an agony constraineth him to travel from land to land.

I pass, like night, from land to land ;
I have strange power of speech ;
That moment that his face I see
I know the man that must hear me —
To him my tale I teach.

What loud uproar bursts from that
                              door !
The wedding-guests are there ;
But in the garden-bower the Bride
And bride-maids singing are ;
And hark the little vesper bell,
Which biddeth me to prayer !

O Wedding-Guest ! this soul hath been
Alone on a wide, wide sea —
So lonely 't was, that God himself
Scarce seemed there to be.

O sweeter than the marriage-feast,
'T is sweeter far to me,
To walk together to the kirk
With a goodly company ! —

To walk together to the kirk,
And all together pray,
While each to his great Father bends —
Old men, and babes, and loving friends,
And youths and maidens gay !

Farewell ! farewell ! but this I tell
To thee, thou Wedding-Guest !
He prayeth well who loveth well
Both man and bird and beast.

and to teach by his own example, love and reverence to all things, that God made and loveth.

He prayeth best who loveth best
All things both great and small ;
For the dear God who loveth us,
He made and loveth all."

The Mariner, whose eye is bright,
Whose beard with age is hoar,
Is gone. And now the Wedding-Guest
Turned from the Bridegroom's door.

He went like one that hath been
                              stunned,
And is of sense forlorn ;
A sadder and a wiser man
He rose the morrow morn.
                    SAMUEL TAYLOR COLERIDGE

ALONZO THE BRAVE AND THE FAIR IMOGINE.

A WARRIOR so bold, and a virgin so bright,
    Conversed as they sat on the green;
They gazed on each other with tender delight:
Alonzo the Brave was the name of the knight, —
    The maiden's, the Fair Imogine.

"And O," said the youth, "since to-morrow I go
    To fight in a far distant land,
Your tears for my absence soon ceasing to flow,
Some other will court you, and you will bestow
    On a wealthier suitor your hand!"

"O, hush these suspicions," Fair Imogine said,
    "Offensive to love and to me;
For, if you be living, or if you be dead,
I swear by the Virgin that none in your stead
    Shall husband of Imogine be.

"If e'er I, by lust or by wealth led aside,
    Forget my Alonzo the Brave,
God grant that, to punish my falsehood and pride,
Your ghost at the marriage may sit by my side,
May tax me with perjury, claim me as bride,
    And bear me away to the grave!"

To Palestine hastened the hero so bold,
    His love she lamented him sore;
But scarce had a twelvemonth elapsed when, be-
    hold!
A baron, all covered with jewels and gold,
    Arrived at Fair Imogine's door.

His treasures, his presents, his spacious domain,
    Soon made her untrue to her vows;
He dazzled her eyes, he bewildered her brain;
He caught her affections, so light and so vain,
    And carried her home as his spouse.

And now had the marriage been blest by the
    priest;
    The revelry now was begun;
The tables they groaned with the weight of the
    feast,
Nor yet had the laughter and merriment ceased,
    When the bell at the castle tolled — one.

Then first with amazement Fair Imogine found
    A stranger was placed by her side:
His air was terrific; he uttered no sound, —
He spake not, he moved not, he looked not
    around, —
    But earnestly gazed on the bride.

His visor was closed, and gigantic his height,
    His armor was sable to view;
All pleasure and laughter were hushed at his
    sight;

The dogs, as they eyed him, drew back in affright;
    The lights in the chamber burned blue!

His presence all bosoms appeared to dismay;
    The guests sat in silence and fear;
At length spake the bride, — while she trembled,
    — "I pray,
Sir knight, that your helmet aside you would lay,
    And deign to partake of our cheer."

The lady is silent; the stranger complies —
    His visor he slowly unclosed;
O God! what a sight met Fair Imogine's eyes!
What words can express her dismay and surprise,
    When a skeleton's head was exposed!

All present then uttered a terrified shout,
    All turned with disgust from the scene;
The worms they crept in, and the worms they
    crept out,
And sported his eyes and his temples about
    While the spectre addressed Imogine:

"Behold me, thou false one, behold me!" he
    cried,
    "Remember Alonzo the Brave!
God grants that, to punish thy falsehood and pride,
My ghost at thy marriage should sit by thy side;
Should tax thee with perjury, claim thee as bride,
    And bear thee away to the grave!"

Thus saying his arms round the lady he wound,
    While loudly she shrieked in dismay;
Then sunk with his prey through the wide-
    yawning ground,
Nor ever again was Fair Imogine found,
    Or the spectre that bore her away.

Not long lived the baron; and none, since that
    time,
    To inhabit the castle presume;
For chronicles tell that, by order sublime,
There Imogine suffers the pain of her crime,
    And mourns her deplorable doom.

At midnight, four times in each year, does her
    sprite,
    When mortals in slumber are bound,
Arrayed in her bridal apparel of white,
Appear in the hall with the skeleton knight,
    And shriek as he whirls her around!

While they drink out of skulls newly torn from
    the grave,
    Dancing round them the spectres are seen;
Their liquor is blood, and this horrible stave
They howl: "To the health of Alonzo the Brave,
    And his consort, the Fair Imogine!"

               MATTHEW GREGORY LEWIS.

THE KING OF THULE.

MARGARET'S SONG IN "FAUST."

There was a king in Thule,
Was faithful till the grave, —
To whom his mistress, dying,
A golden goblet gave.

Naught was to him more precious ;
He drained it at every bout :
His eyes with tears ran over,
As oft as he drank thereout.

When came his time of dying,
The towns in his land he told,
Naught else to his heir denying
Except the goblet of gold.

He sat at the royal banquet
With his knights of high degree,
In the lofty hall of his fathers,
In the Castle by the Sea.

There stood the old carouser,
And drank the last life-glow ;
And hurled the hallowed goblet
Into the tide below.

He saw it plunging and filling,
And sinking deep in the sea, —
Then fell his eyelids forever,
And never more drank he.

From the German of GOETHE. Translation of BAYARD TAYLOR.

THE PHILOSOPHER'S SCALES.

A MONK, when his rites sacerdotal were o'er,
In the depth of his cell with its stone-covered
     floor,
Resigning to thought his chimerical brain,
Once formed the contrivance we now shall explain;
But whether by magic's or alchemy's powers
We know not ; indeed, 't is no business of ours.

Perhaps it was only by patience and care,
At last, that he brought his invention to bear.
In youth 't was projected, but years stole away,
And ere 't was complete he was wrinkled and
     gray ;
But success is secure, unless energy fails ;
And at length he produced THE PHILOSOPHER'S
SCALES.

"What were they ?" you ask.   You shall pres-
     ently see ;
These scales were not made to weigh sugar and tea.

O no ; for such properties wondrous had they,
That qualities, feelings, and thoughts they could
     weigh,
Together with articles small or immense,
From mountains or planets to atoms of sense.

Naught was there so bulky but there it would lay,
And naught so ethereal but there it would stay,
And naught so reluctant but in it must go :
All which some examples more clearly will show.

The first thing he weighed was the head of Vol-
     taire,
Which retained all the wit that had ever been
     there ;
As a weight, he threw in the torn scrap of a leaf
Containing the prayer of the penitent thief ;
When the skull rose aloft with so sudden a spell
That it bounced like a ball on the roof of the cell.

One time he put in Alexander the Great,
With the garment that Dorcas had made, for a
     weight ;
And though clad in armor from sandals to crown,
The hero rose up, and the garment went down.

A long row of almshouses, amply endowed
By a well-esteemed Pharisee, busy and proud,
Next loaded one scale ; while the other was
     pressed
By those mites the poor widow dropped into the
     chest :
Up flew the endowment, not weighing an ounce,
And down, down the farthing-worth came with
     a bounce.

By further experiments (no matter how)
He found that ten chariots weighed less than one
     plough ;
A sword with gilt trapping rose up in the scale,
Though balanced by only a ten-penny nail ;
A shield and a helmet, a buckler and spear,
Weighed less than a widow's uncrystallized tear.
A lord and a lady went up at full sail,
When a bee chanced to light on the opposite
     scale ;
Ten doctors, ten lawyers, two courtiers, one earl,
Ten counsellors' wigs, full of powder and curl,
All heaped in one balance and swinging from
     thence,
Weighed less than a few grains of candor and
     sense ;
A first-water diamond, with brilliants begirt,
Than one good potato just washed from the dirt ;
Yet not mountains of silver and gold could suffice
One pearl to outweigh, — 't was THE PEARL OF
     GREAT PRICE.

Last of all, the whole world was bowled in at the
grate,
With the soul of a beggar to serve for a weight,
When the former sprang up with so strong a re-
buff
That it made a vast rent and escaped at the roof !
When balanced in air, it ascended on high,
And sailed up aloft, a balloon in the sky ;
While the scale with the soul in 't so mightily
fell
That it jerked the philosopher out of his cell.

JANE TAYLOR.

THE NIGHTINGALE AND GLOW-WORM.

A NIGHTINGALE, that all day long
Had cheered the village with his song,
Nor yet at eve his note suspended,
Nor yet when eventide was ended,
Began to feel — as well he might —
The keen demands of appetite ;
When, looking eagerly around,
He spied, far off, upon the ground,
A something shining in the dark,
And knew the glow-worm by his spark ;
So, stooping down from hawthorn top,
He thought to put him in his crop.
The worm, aware of his intent,
Harangued him thus, quite eloquent, —
    " Did you admire my lamp," quoth he,
" As much as I your minstrelsy,
You would abhor to do me wrong,
As much as I to spoil your song ;
For 't was the self-same Power divine
Taught you to sing, and me to shine ;
That you with music, I with light,
Might beautify and cheer the night."
The songster heard his short oration,
And, warbling out his approbation,
Released him, as my story tells,
And found a supper somewhere else.

WILLIAM COWPER.

THE PETRIFIED FERN.

IN a valley, centuries ago,
  Grew a little fern-leaf, green and slender,
  Veining delicate and fibres tender ;
Waving when the wind crept down so low.
  Rushes tall, and moss, and grass grew round it,
  Playful sunbeams darted in and found it,
Drops of dew stole in by night, and crowned it,
But no foot of man e'er trod that way ;
Earth was young, and keeping holiday

Monster fishes swam the silent main,
  Stately forests waved their giant branches,
  Mountains hurled their snowy avalanches,
Mammoth creatures stalked across the plain ;
  Nature revelled in grand mysteries,
  But the little fern was not of these,
  Did not number with the hills and trees ;
  Only grew and waved its wild sweet way,
  No one came to note it day by day.

Earth, one time, put on a frolic mood,
  Heaved the rocks and changed the mighty
    motion
Of the deep, strong currents of the ocean ;
Moved the plain and shook the haughty wood,
  Crushed the little fern in soft moist clay, —
  Covered it, and hid it safe away.
  O, the long, long centuries since that day !
  O, the changes ! O, life's bitter cost,
  Since that useless little fern was lost !

Useless ? Lost ? There came a thoughtful man
  Searching Nature's secrets, far and deep ;
  From a fissure in a rocky steep
He withdrew a stone, o'er which there ran
  Fairy pencillings, a quaint design,
  Veinings, leafage, fibres clear and fine.
  And the fern's life lay in every line !
  So, I think, God hides some souls away,
  Sweetly to surprise us, the last day.

MARY L. BOLLES BRANCH.

THE COMET.

OCTOBER, 1858.

ERRATIC Soul of some great Purpose, doomed
To track the wild illimitable space,
Till sure propitiation has been made
For the divine commission unperformed !
What was thy crime ? Ahasuerus' curse
Were not more stern on earth than thine in
    heaven !

Art thou the Spirit of some Angel World,
For grave rebellion banished from thy peers,
Compelled to watch the calm, immortal stars
Circling in rapture the celestial void,
While the avenger follows in thy train
To spur thee on to wretchedness eterne ?

Or one of Nature's wildest fantasies,
From which she flies in terror so profound,
And with such whirl of torment in her breast,
That mighty earthquakes yawn where'er she
    treads ;
While War makes red its terrible right hand,
And Famine stalks abroad all lean and wan ?

To us thou art as exquisitely fair
As the ideal visions of the seer,
Or gentlest fancy that e'er floated down
Imagination's bright, unruffled stream,
Wedding the thought that was too deep for words
To the low breathings of inspirèd song.

When the stars sang together o'er the birth
Of the poor Babe at Bethlehem, that lay
In the coarse manger at the crowded Inn,
Didst thou, perhaps a bright exalted star,
Refuse to swell the grand, harmonious lay,
Jealous as Herod of the birth divine?

Or when the crown of thorns on Calvary
Pierced the Redeemer's brow, didst thou disdain
To weep, when all the planetary worlds
Were blinded by the fulness of their tears?
E'en to the flaming sun, that hid his face
At the loud cry, "Lama Sabachthani!"

No rest! No rest! the very damned have that
In the dark councils of remotest Hell,
Where the dread scheme was perfected that sealed
Thy disobedience and accruing doom.
Like Adam's sons, hast thou, too, forfeited
The blest repose that never pillowed Sin?

No! none can tell thy fate, thou wandering
          Sphinx!
Pale Science, searching by the midnight lamp
Through the vexed mazes of the human brain,
Still fails to read the secret of its soul
As the superb enigma flashes by,
A loosed Prometheus burning with disdain.
                                    CHARLES SANGSTER.

SONG OF THE LIGHTNING.

"PUCK.   I'll put a girdle round about the earth
In forty minutes."
                              Midsummer's Night Dream.

AWAY! away! through the sightless air
    Stretch forth your iron thread!
For I would not dim my sandals fair
    With the dust ye tamely tread!
Ay, rear it up on its million piers,
    Let it circle the world around,
And the journey ye make in a hundred years
    I'll clear at a single bound!

Though I cannot toil, like the groaning slave
    Ye have fettered with iron skill
To ferry you over the boundless wave,
    Or grind in the noisy mill,
Let him sing his giant strength and speed!
    Why, a single shaft of mine

Would give that monster a flight indeed, —
    To the depths of the ocean's brine!

No! no! I'm the spirit of light and love!
    To my unseen hand 't is given
To pencil the ambient clouds above
    And polish the stars of heaven!
I scatter the golden rays of fire
    On the horizon far below,
And deck the sky where storms expire
    With my red and dazzling glow.

With a glance I cleave the sky in twain;
    I light it with a glare,
When fall the boding drops of rain
    Through the darkly curtained air!
The rock-built towers, the turrets gray,
    The piles of a thousand years,
Have not the strength of potter's clay
    Beneath my glittering spears.

From the Alps' or the Andes' highest crag,
    From the peaks of eternal snow,
The blazing folds of my fiery flag
    Illume the world below.
The earthquake heralds my coming power,
    The avalanche bounds away,
And howling storms at midnight's hour
    Proclaim my kingly sway.

Ye tremble when my legions come, —
    When my quivering sword leaps out
O'er the hills that echo my thunder down,
    And rend with my joyous shout.
Ye quail on the land, or upon the sea
    Ye stand in your fear aghast,
To see me burn the stalworth trees,
    Or shiver the stately mast.

The hieroglyphs on the Persian wall, —
    The letters of high command, —
Where the prophet read the tyrant's fall,
    Were traced by my burning hand.
And oft in fire have I wrote since then
    What angry Heaven decreed;
But the sealèd eyes of sinful men
    Were all too blind to read.

At length the hour of light is here,
    And kings no more shall bind,
Nor bigots crush with craven fear
    The forward march of mind.
The words of Truth and Freedom's rays
    Are from my pinions hurled;
And soon the light of better days
    Shall rise upon the world.
                                    GEORGE W. CUTTER.

ORIGIN OF THE OPAL.

A DEW-DROP came, with a spark of flame
  He had caught from the sun's last ray,
To a violet's breast, where he lay at rest
  Till the hours brought back the day.

The rose looked down, with a blush and frown ;
  But she smiled all at once, to view
Her own bright form, with its coloring warm,
  Reflected back by the dew.

Then the stranger took a stolen look
  At the sky, so soft and blue ;
And a leaflet green, with its silver sheen,
  Was seen by the idler too.

A cold north-wind, as he thus reclined,
  Of a sudden raged around ;
And a maiden fair, who was walking there,
  Next morning, an *opal* found.
                              ANONYMOUS.

THE ORIGIN OF THE HARP.

'T is believed that this harp, which I wake now
      for thee,
Was a Siren of old, who sung under the sea ;
And who often, at eve, through the bright billow
      roved,
To meet, on the green shore, a youth whom she
      loved.

But she loved him in vain, for he left her to
      weep,
And in tears, all the night, her gold ringlets to
      steep,
Till Heaven looked with pity on true-love so
      warm,
And changed to this soft harp the sea-maiden's
      form.

Still her bosom rose fair — still her cheek smiled
      the same —
While her sea-beauties gracefully curled round
      the frame ;
And her hair, shedding tear-drops from all its
      bright rings,
Fell o'er her white arm, to make the gold strings !

Hence it came, that this soft harp so long hath
      been known
To mingle love's language with sorrow's sad tone ;
Till *thou* didst divide them, and teach the fond
      lay
To be love when I'm near thee, and grief when
      away !
                          THOMAS MOORE.

ECHO AND SILENCE.*

IN eddying course when leaves began to fly,
And Autumn in her lap the store to strew,
As mid wild scenes I chanced the Muse to woo,
Through glens untrod, and woods that frowned
      on high,
Two sleeping nymphs with wonder mute I spy !
And, lo, she 's gone ! — In robe of dark-green hue,
'T was Echo from her sister Silence flew,
For quick the hunter's horn resounded to the sky !
In shade affrighted Silence melts away.
Not so her sister.   Hark ! for onward still,
With far-heard step, she takes her listening way,
Bounding from rock to rock, and hill to hill.
Ah, mark the merry maid in mockful play
With thousand mimic tones the laughing forest
      fill !
              SIR SAMUEL EGERTON BRYDGES.

A MUSICAL INSTRUMENT.

WHAT was he doing, the great god Pan,
  Down in the reeds by the river ?
Spreading ruin and scattering ban,
Splashing and paddling with hoofs of a goat,
And breaking the golden lilies afloat
  With the dragon-fly on the river ?

He tore out a reed, the great god Pan,
  From the deep, cool bed of the river,
The limpid water turbidly ran,
And the broken lilies a-dying lay,
And the dragon-fly had fled away,
  Ere he brought it out of the river.

High on the shore sat the great god Pan,
  While turbidly flowed the river,
And hacked and hewed as a great god can
With his hard, bleak steel at the patient reed,
Till there was not a sign of a leaf indeed
  To prove it fresh from the river.

He cut it short, did the great god Pan,
  (How tall it stood in the river !)
Then drew the pith like the heart of a man,
Steadily from the outside ring,
Then notched the poor dry empty thing
  In holes, as he sate by the river.

"This is the way," laughed the great god Pan,
  (Laughed while he sate by the river !)
"The only way since gods began
To make sweet music, they could succeed."
Then dropping his mouth to a hole in the reed,
  He blew in power by the river.

* Declared by Wordsworth to be the best Sonnet in the English
language.

Sweet, sweet, sweet, O Pan,
  Piercing sweet by the river !
Blinding sweet, O great god Pan !
The sun on the hill forgot to die,
And the lilies revived, and the dragon-fly
  Came back to dream on the river.

Yet half a beast is the great god Pan,
  To laugh, as he sits by the river,
Making a poet out of a man.
The true gods sigh for the cost and the pain, —
For the reed that grows nevermore again
  As a reed with the reeds of the river.

            ELIZABETH BARRETT BROWNING.

THE CALIPH AND SATAN.

VERSIFIED FROM THOLUCK'S TRANSLATION OUT OF THE
PERSIAN.

In heavy sleep the Caliph lay,
When some one called, " Arise, and pray ! "

The angry Caliph cried, " Who dare
Rebuke his king for slighted prayer ? "

Then, from the corner of the room,
A voice cut sharply through the gloom :

" My name is Satan. Rise ! obey
Mohammed's law ; awake, and pray ! "

" Thy *words* are good," the Caliph said,
" But their intent I somewhat dread.

For matters cannot well be worse
Than when the thief says, ' Guard your purse ! '

I cannot trust your counsel, friend,
It surely hides some wicked end."

Said Satan, " Near the throne of God,
In ages past, we devils trod ;

Angels of light, to us 't was given
To guide each wandering foot to heaven.

Not wholly lost is that first love,
Nor those pure tastes we knew above.

Roaming across a continent,
The Tartar moves his shifting tent,

But never quite forgets the day
When in his father's arms he lay ;

So we, once bathed in love divine,
Recall the taste of that rich wine.

God's finger rested on my brow, —
That magic touch, I feel it now !

I fell, 't is true — O, ask not why,
For still to God I turn my eye.

It was a chance by which I fell,
Another takes me back from hell.

'T was but my envy of mankind,
The envy of a loving mind.

Jealous of men, I could not bear
God's love with this new race to share.

But yet God's tables open stand,
His guests flock in from every land ;

Some kind act toward the race of men
May toss us into heaven again.

A game of chess is all we see, —
And God the player, pieces we.

White, black — queen, pawn, — 't is all the same,
For on both sides he plays the game.

Moved to and fro, from good to ill,
We rise and fall as suits his will."

The Caliph said, " If this be so,
I know not, but thy guile I know ;

For how can I thy words believe,
When even God thou didst deceive ?

A sea of lies art thou, — our sin
Only a drop that sea within."

" Not so," said Satan, " I serve God,
His angel now, and now his rod.

In tempting I both bless and curse,
Make good men better, bad men worse.

Good coin is mixed with bad, my brother,
I but distinguish one from the other."

" Granted," the Caliph said, " but still
You never tempt to good, but ill.

Tell then the truth, for well I know
You come as my most deadly foe."

Loud laughed the fiend. " You know me well,
Therefore my purpose I will tell.

If you had missed your prayer, I knew
A swift repentance would ensue ;

And such repentance would have been
A good, outweighing far the sin.

FROM "CORN."

Look, out of line one tall corn-captain
    stands
Advanced beyond the foremost of his
    bands,
  And waves his blades upon the very edge
  And hottest thicket of the battling hedge.
Thou lustrous stalk, that ne'er mayst walk
    nor talk,
  Still shalt thou type the poet-soul sublime
  That leads the vanward of his timid time
  And sings up cowards with commanding
    rhyme —
Soul-calm, like thee, yet fain, like thee, to
    grow
By double increment, above, below;
  Soul-homely, as thou art, yet rich in grace
    like thee,
  Teaching the yeomen selfless chivalry
  That moves in gentle curves of courtesy;
Soul-filled like thy long veins with sweet-
    ness tense,
    By every godlike sense
  Transmuted from the four wild elements.
    Drawn to high plans,
Thou lift'st more stature than a mortal
    man's,
Yet ever piercest downward in the mould
    And keepest hold
Upon the reverend and steadfast earth
    That gave thee birth;
Yea, standest smiling in thy very grave,
    Serene and brave,
  With unremitting breath
  Inhaling life from death,
Thine epitaph writ fair in fruitage eloquent
  Thy living self thy monument.

Sidney Lanier

FROM "WORDSWORTH'S GRAVE."

Poet who sleepest by this wandering wave!
    When thou wast born, what birth-gift hadst thou then?
To thee what wealth was that the Immortals gave,
    The wealth thou gavest in thy turn to men?

Not Milton's keen, translunar music thine;
    Not Shakespeare's cloudless, boundless human view;
Not Shelley's flush of rose on peaks divine;
    Nor yet the wizard twilight Coleridge knew.

What hadst thou that could make so large amends
    For all thou hadst not and thy peers possessed,
Motion and fire, swift means to radiant ends?—
    Thou hadst for weary feet the gift of rest.

From Shelley's dazzling glow or thunderous haze,
    From Byron's tempest-anger, tempest-mirth,
Men turned to thee and found—not blast and blaze,
    Tumult of tottering heavens, but peace on earth.

Nor peace that grows by Lethe, scentless flower,
    There in white languors to decline and cease;
But peace whose names are also rapture, power,
    Clear sight, and love: for these are parts of peace.

WILLIAM WATSON.

I chose this humbleness divine,
Borne out of fault, should not be thine,

Preferring prayers elate with pride
To sin with penitence allied."

JAMES FREEMAN CLARKE.

AIRY NOTHINGS.

FROM "THE TEMPEST," ACT IV. SC. 1.

OUR revels now are ended.   These our actors,
As I foretold you, were all spirits, and
Are melted into air, into thin air ;
And, like the baseless fabric of this vision,
The cloud-capped towers, the gorgeous palaces,
The solemn temples, the great globe itself,
Yea, all which it inherit, shall dissolve,
And, like this insubstantial pageant faded,
Leave not a rack behind.   We are such stuff
As dreams are made on, and our little life
Is rounded with a sleep.

SHAKESPEARE.

FRAGMENTS.

IMAGINATION.

Within the soul a faculty abides,
That with interpositions, which would hide
And darken, so can deal that they become
Contingencies of pomp ; and serve to exalt
Her native brightness.   As the ample moon,
In the deep stillness of a summer even
Rising behind a thick and lofty grove,
Burns, like an unconsuming fire of light,
In the green trees ; and, kindling on all sides
Their leafy umbrage, turns the dusky veil
Into a substance glorious as her own.

The Excursion, Book iv.　　　　WORDSWORTH.

And, as imagination bodies forth
The forms of things unknown, the poet's pen
Turns them to shapes, and gives to airy nothing
A local habitation and a name.

Midsummer Night's Dream. Act v. *Sc.* 1.　　SHAKESPEARE.

O for a muse of fire, that would ascend
The brightest heaven of invention !

King Henry V., Chorus.　　　SHAKESPEARE.

Hark, his hands the lyre explore !
Bright-eyed Fancy, hovering o'er,
Scatters from her pictured urn
Thoughts that breathe and words that burn.

Progress of Poesy.　　　　T. GRAY.

CONCEPTION AND EXECUTION.

We figure to ourselves
The thing we like, and then we build it up
As chance will have it, on the rock or sand ;
For thought is tired of wandering o'er the world,
And home-bound Fancy runs her bark ashore.

Philip Van Artevelde, Part I. Act i. *Sc.* 5.　　SIR H. TAYLOR.

Of its own beauty is the mind diseased,
And fevers into false creation : — where,
Where are the forms the sculptor's soul hath
  seized ?
In him alone.   Can Nature show so fair ?
Where are the charms and virtues which we
  dare
Conceive in boyhood and pursue as men,
The unreached Paradise of our despair,
Which o'er-informs the pencil and the pen,
And overpowers the page where it would bloom
  again ?

Childe Harold, Cant. iv.　　　　BYRON.

CLOUD-VISIONS.

A step,
A single step, that freed me from the skirts
Of the blind vapor, opened to my view
Glory beyond all glory ever seen
By waking sense or by the dreaming soul !
The appearance, instantaneously disclosed,
Was of a mighty city, — boldly say
A wilderness of building, sinking far
And self-withdrawn into a boundless depth,
Far sinking into splendor, — without end !
Fabric it seemed of diamond and of gold,
With alabaster domes, and silver spires,
And blazing terrace upon terrace, high
Uplifted ; here, serene pavilions bright,
In avenues disposed ; there, towers begirt
With battlements that on their restless fronts
Bore stars, — illumination of all gems !

The Excursion, Book ii.　　　　WORDSWORTH.

THE MIND'S EYE.

HAMLET.   My father, — methinks I see my
  father.
HORATIO.   O ! where, my lord !
HAM.　　　　In my mind's eye, Horatio.

Hamlet, Act i. *Sc.* 2.　　　　SHAKESPEARE.

On man, on nature, and on human life,
Musing in solitude, I oft perceive
Fair trains of imagery before me rise,
Accompanied by feelings of delight,
Pure, or with no unpleasing sadness mixed.

The Excursion : Prelude.　　　WORDSWORTH.

But O, what solemn scenes on Snowdon's height
　Descending slow their glittering skirts unroll?
Visions of glory, spare my aching sight!
　Ye unborn ages, crowd not on my soul!
The Bard.　　　　　　　　　　　　T. GRAY.

SPIRITS.

Millions of spiritual creatures walk the earth
Unseen, both when we wake, and when we sleep.
　Paradise Lost, Book iv.　　　　　　　MILTON.

　　　　　　　Spirits when they please
Can either sex assume, or both,
　.　　　.　　　.　　　.
Can execute their airy purposes,
And works of love or enmity fulfil.
　Paradise Lost, Book i.　　　　　　　MILTON.

　　　　　　　　　　　　　Worse
Than fables yet have feigned, or fear conceived,
Gorgons, and Hydras, and Chimæras dire.
　Paradise Lost, Book ii.　　　　　　MILTON.

'T is the djinns' wild-streaming swarm
Whistling in their tempest-flight;
Snap the tall yews 'neath the storm,
Like a pine-flame crackling bright;
Swift and heavy, low, their crowd
Through the heavens rushing loud! —
Like a lurid thunder-cloud
With its bolt of fiery night!
　The Djinns. Trans. of J. L. O'SULLIVAN.　V. HUGO.

But shapes that come not at an earthly call
Will not depart when mortal voices bid;
Lords of the visionary eye, whose lid,
Once raised, remains aghast, and will not fall!
　Dion.　　　　　　　　　　WORDSWORTH.

GHOSTS OF THE DEAD.

MACBETH.　Thou canst not say I did it; never
　shake thy gory locks at me.
　.　　　.　　　.
LADY MACBETH.　　　　　O proper stuff!
This is the very painting of your fear;
This is the air-drawn dagger which, you said,
Led you to Duncan.
　.　　　.　　　.
MACBETH.　Pr'ythee, see there! behold! look!
　lo! how say you?
　.　　　.　　　.
　　　　　　　　The times have been,
That, when the brains were out, the man would
　die,
And there an end; but now they rise again,
With twenty mortal murders on their crowns,
And push us from our stools.
　.　　　.　　　.

Avaunt! and quit my sight. Let the earth hide
　thee!
Thy bones are marrowless, thy blood is cold;
Thou hast no speculation in those eyes,
Which thou dost glare with!
　.　　　.　　　.
　　　　　　　Hence, horrible shadow!
Unreal mockery, hence!
　Macbeth, Act iii. *Sc.* 4.　　　　SHAKESPEARE.

And then it started, like a guilty thing
Upon a fearful summons. I have heard,
The cock, that is the trumpet to the morn,
Doth with his lofty and shrill-sounding throat
Awake the god of day; and at his warning,
Whether in sea or fire, in earth or air,
The extravagant and erring spirit hies
To his confine.
　Hamlet, Act i. *Sc.* 1.　　　　SHAKESPEARE.

This is the very coinage of your brain.
　Hamlet, Act iii. *Sc.* 4.　　　　SHAKESPEARE.

By the apostle Paul, shadows to-night
Have struck more terror to the soul of Richard
Than can the substance of ten thousand soldiers.
　King Richard III., Act v. *Sc.* 3.　　SHAKESPEARE.

WITCHES.

BANQUO.　　　　　What are these,
So withered, and so wild in their attire;
That look not like the inhabitants o' the earth,
And yet are on 't?
　.　　　.　　　.
The earth hath bubbles, as the water has,
And these are of them. — Whither have they
　vanished?
MACBETH.　Into the air, and what seemed
　corporal melted
As breath into the wind.
　Macbeth, Act i. *Sc.* 3.　　　　SHAKESPEARE.

Show his eyes, and grieve his heart;
Come like shadows, so depart.
　Macbeth, Act iv. *Sc.* 1.　　　　SHAKESPEARE.

FAIRIES.

They're fairies! he that speaks to them shall die:
I'll wink and couch; no man their sports must
　eye.
Merry Wives of Windsor, Act v. *Sc.* 5.　SHAKESPEARE

This is the fairy land: O, spite of spites!
We talk with goblins, owls, and elvish sprites.
　Comedy of Errors, Act ii. *Sc.* 2.　SHAKESPEARE

I took it for a faery vision
Of some gay creatures of the element,
That in the colors of the rainbow live
And play i' th' plighted clouds.
Comus.   MILTON.

ARIEL. Where the bee sucks, there suck I :
In a cowslip's bell I lie ;
There I couch when owls do cry.
On the bat's back I do fly
After summer, merrily.
Merrily, merrily, shall I live now,
Under the blossom that hangs on the bough.
The Tempest, Act v _Sc._ 1.   SHAKESPEARE.

PUCK. How now, spirit, whither wander you ?
FAIRY. Over hill, over dale,
Thorough bush, thorough brier,
Over park, over pale,
Thorough flood, thorough fire,
I do wander everywhere,
Swifter than the moon's sphere ;
And I serve the fairy queen,
To dew her orbs upon the green :
The cowslips tall her pensioners be ;
In their gold coats spots you see ;
Those be rubies, fairy favors,
In those freckles live their savors :
I must go seek some dewdrops here,
And hang a pearl in every cowslip's ear.
Midsummer Night's Dream, Act ii. _Sc._ 1 SHAKESPEARE.

Fairies use flowers for their charactery.
Merry Wives of Windsor, Act v. _Sc._ 5.   SHAKESPEARE

WATER SPRITES.

Come unto these yellow sands,
    And then take hands ;
Court'sied when you have, and kissed
    The wild waves whist,
Foot it featly here and there ;
And, sweet sprites, the burden bear.
    Hark, hark !
        Bowgh, wowgh.
    The watch-dogs bark :
        Bowgh, wowgh.
Hark, hark ! I hear
The strain of strutting chanticleer
Cry, Cock-a-doodle-doo.

Full fathom five thy father lies
    Of his bones are coral made :

Those are pearls that were his eyes :
    Nothing of him that doth fade,
But doth suffer a sea-change
Into something rich and strange.
Sea-nymphs hourly ring his knell :
            [_Burden_] Ding-dong.
Hark ! now I hear them, — Ding-dong, bell.
    The Tempest, Act i. _Sc._ 1.   SHAKESPEARE

Sabrina fair,
    Listen where thou art sitting,
Under the glassy, cool, translucent wave,
    In twisted braids of lilies knitting
The loose train of thy amber-dropping hair.
    Listen for dear honor's sake,
    Goddess of the silver lake,
        Listen and save.
Comus.   MILTON.

WOOD-NYMPHS.

Egeria ! sweet creation of some heart
Which found no mortal resting-place so fair
As thine ideal breast ; whate'er thou art
Or wert, — a young Aurora of the air,
The nympholepsy of some fond despair ;
Or, it might be, a beauty of the earth,
Who found a more than common votary there
Too much adoring ; whatsoe'er thy birth,
Thou wert a beautiful thought, and softly bodied
    forth.
Childe Harold, Cant. iv.   BYRON.

Quite spent and out of breath he reached the
    tree,
And, listening fearfully, he heard once more
The low voice murmur "Rhœcus !" close at hand :
Whereat he looked around him, but could see
Naught but the deepening glooms beneath the
    oak.
Then sighed the voice, "O Rhœcus ! nevermore
Shalt thou behold me or by day or night,
Me, who would fain have blessed thee with a love
More ripe and bounteous than ever yet
Filled up with nectar any mortal heart ;
But thou didst scorn my humble messenger,
And sent'st him back to me with bruisèd wings.
We spirits only show to gentle eyes,
We ever ask an undivided love.
And he who scorns the least of Nature's works
Is thenceforth exiled and shut out from all.
Farewell ! for thou canst never see me more."
    Rhœcus.   J. R. LOWELL.

And through the land is throngéd again, O Sea!
Strange sadness thrills all that go with thee.
The small birds plaining note, the wind's strange call,
I hear this own spirit, it is indeed all!
How dark & stern upon the waves looks down
Yonder bold bluff! – be with this isle common
And I see! Those noble pines along the steep
Are come to join thy requiem, gloomy deep!!
Like stoled monks they stand & chant the dirge
Down the dark waters they low-chanting surge –

—

Obienk H. Dunn

POEMS OF TRAGEDY

This is love, who, deaf to prayers,
Floats with blessings unawares.
Draw, if thou canst, the mystic line
Severing rightly his from thine,
Which is human, which divine.

R W Emerson

POEMS OF TRAGEDY.

IPHIGENEIA AND AGAMEMNON.

IPHIGENEIA, when she heard her doom
At Aulis, and when all beside the king
Had gone away, took his right hand, and said :
' O father ! I am young and very happy.
I do not think the pious Calchas heard
Distinctly what the goddess spake ; old age
Obscures the senses.   If my nurse, who knew
My voice so well, sometimes misunderstood,
While I was resting on her knee both arms,
And hitting it to make her mind my words,
And looking in her face, and she in mine,
Might not he, also, hear one word amiss,
Spoken from so far off, even from Olympus ?"
The father placed his cheek upon her head,
And tears dropt down it ; but the king of men
Replied not.   Then the maiden spake once more :
" O father ! sayest thou nothing ? Hearest thou
            not
Me, whom thou ever hast, until this hour,
Listened to fondly, and awakened me
To hear my voice amid the voice of birds,
When it was inarticulate as theirs,
And the down deadened it within the nest ?"
He moved her gently from him, silent still ;
And this, and this alone, brought tears from her,
Although she saw fate nearer.   Then with sighs :
" I thought to have laid down my hair before
Benignant Artemis, and not dimmed
Her polished altar with my virgin blood ;
I thought to have selected the white flowers
To please the nymphs, and to have asked of each
By name, and with no sorrowful regret,
Whether, since both my parents willed the change,
I might at Hymen's feet bend my clipt brow ;
And (after these who mind us girls the most)
Adore our own Athene, that she would
Regard me mildly with her azure eyes, —
But, father, to see you no more, and see
Your love, O father ! go ere I am gone ! "
Gently he moved her off, and drew her back,
Bending his lofty head far over hers ;
And the dark depths of nature heaved and burst.
He turned away, — not far, but silent still.

She now first shuddered ; for in him, so nigh,
So long a silence seemed the approach of death,
And like it.   Once again she raised her voice :
" O father ! if the ships are now detained,
And all your vows move not the gods above,
When the knife strikes me there will be one prayer
The less to them ; and purer can there be
Any, or more fervent, than the daughter's prayer
For her dear father's safety and success ? "
A groan that shook him shook not his resolve.
An aged man now entered, and without
One word stepped slowly on, and took the wrist
Of the pale maiden.   She looked up, and saw
The fillet of the priest and calm, cold eyes.
Then turned she where her parent stood, and cried :
" O father ! grieve no more ; the ships can sail."
                    WALTER SAVAGE LANDOR.

THE ROMAN FATHER'S SACRIFICE.

FROM "VIRGINIA."

STRAIGHTWAY Virginius led the maid
    A little space aside,
To where the reeking shambles stood,
    Piled up with horn and hide ;
Close to yon low dark archway,
    Where, in a crimson flood,
Leaps down to the great sewer
    The gurgling stream of blood.

Hard by, a flesher on a block
    Had laid his whittle down :
Virginius caught the whittle up,
    And hid it in his gown.
And then his eyes grew very dim,
    And his throat began to swell,
And in a hoarse, changed voice he spake,
    " Farewell, sweet child ! Farewell !

" O, how I loved my darling !
    Though stern I sometimes be,
To thee, thou know'st, I was not so, —
    Who could be so to thee ?

And how my darling loved me !
　　How glad she was to hear
My footstep on the threshold
　　When I came back last year !

" And how she danced with pleasure
　　To see my civic crown,
And took my sword, and hung it up,
　　And brought me forth my gown !
Now, all those things are over, —
　　Yes, all thy pretty ways,
Thy needlework, thy prattle,
　　Thy snatches of old lays ;

" And none will grieve when I go forth,
　　Or smile when I return,
Or watch beside the old man's bed,
　　Or weep upon his urn.
The house that was the happiest
　　Within the Roman walls,
The house that envied not the wealth
　　Of Capua's marble halls,

" Now, for the brightness of thy smile,
　　Must have eternal gloom,
And for the music of thy voice,
　　The silence of the tomb.
The time is come !　See how he points
　　His eager hand this way !
See how his eyes gloat on thy grief,
　　Like a kite's upon the prey !

" With all his wit, he little deems
　　That, spurned, betrayed, bereft,
Thy father hath, in his despair,
　　One fearful refuge left.
He little deems that in this hand
　　I clutch what still can save
Thy gentle youth from taunts and blows,
　　The portion of the slave ;

" Yea, and from nameless evil,
　　That passeth taunt and blow, —
Foul outrage which thou knowest not,
　　Which thou shalt never know.
Then clasp me round the neck once more,
　　And give me one more kiss ;
And now, mine own dear little girl,
　　There is no way but this."

With that he lifted high the steel,
　　And smote her in the side,
And in her blood she sank to earth,
　　And with one sob she died.
Then, for a little moment,
　　All people held their breath ;
And through the crowded forum
　　Was stillness as of death ;

And in another moment
　　Brake forth, from one and all,
A cry as if the Volscians
　　Were coming o'er the wall.
Some with averted faces
　　Shrieking fled home amain ;
Some ran to call a leech ; and some
　　Ran to lift up the slain.

Some felt her lips and little wrist,
　　If life might there be found ;
And some tore up their garments fast,
　　And strove to stanch the wound.
In vain they ran, and felt, and stanched ;
　　For never truer blow
That good right arm had dealt in fight
　　Against a Volscian foe.

When Appius Claudius saw that deed,
　　He shuddered and sank down,
And hid his face some little space
　　With the corner of his gown ;
Till, with white lips and bloodshot eyes,
　　Virginius tottered nigh,
And stood before the judgment-seat,
　　And held the knife on high.

" O dwellers in the nether gloom,
　　Avengers of the slain,
By this dear blood I cry to you
　　Do right between us twain ;
And even as Appius Claudius
　　Hath dealt by me and mine,
Deal you by Appius Claudius,
　　And all the Claudian line ! "

So spake the slayer of his child,
　　And turned and went his way ;
But first he cast one haggard glance
　　To where the body lay,
And writhed, and groaned a fearful groan,
　　And then, with steadfast feet,
Strode right across the market-place
　　Unto the Sacred Street.

Then up sprang Appius Claudius :
　　" Stop him ; alive or dead !
Ten thousand pounds of copper
　　To the man who brings his head."
He looked upon his clients ;
　　But none would work his will.
He looked upon his lictors ;
　　But they trembled, and stood still.

And as Virginius through the press
　　His way in silence cleft,
Ever the mighty multitude
　　Fell back to right and left.

And he hath passed in safety
    Unto his woful home,
And there ta'en horse to tell the camp
    What deeds are done in Rome.

THOMAS BABINGTON MACAULAY.

LUCIUS JUNIUS BRUTUS OVER THE BODY OF LUCRETIA.

FROM "BRUTUS."

WOULD you know why I summoned you together?
Ask ye what brings me here? Behold this dagger,
Clotted with gore! Behold that frozen corse!
See where the lost Lucretia sleeps in death!
She was the mark and model of the time,
The mould in which each female face was formed,
The very shrine and sacristy of virtue!
Fairer than ever was a form created
By youthful fancy when the blood strays wild,
And never-resting thought is all on fire!
The worthiest of the worthy! Not the nymph
Who met old Numa in his hallowed walks,
And whispered in his ear her strains divine,
Can I conceive beyond her; — the young choir
Of vestal virgins bent to her. 'T is wonderful
Amid the darnel, hemlock, and base weeds,
Which now spring rife from the luxurious com-
    post
Spread o'er the realm, how this sweet lily rose, —
How from the shade of those ill-neighboring
    plants
Her father sheltered her, that not a leaf
Was blighted, but, arrayed in purest grace,
She bloomed unsullied beauty. Such perfections
Might have called back the torpid breast of age
To long-forgotten rapture; such a mind
Might have abashed the boldest libertine
And turned desire to reverential love
And holiest affection! O my countrymen!
You all can witness when that she went forth
It was a holiday in Rome; old age
Forgot its crutch, labor its task, — all ran,
And mothers, turning to their daughters, cried,
"There, there 's Lucretia!" Now look ye where
    she lies!
That beauteous flower, that innocent sweet rose,
Torn up by ruthless violence, — gone! gone! gone!
    Say, would you seek instruction? would ye ask
What ye should do? Ask ye yon conscious walls,
Which saw his poisoned brother, —
Ask yon deserted street, where Tullia drove
O'er her dead father's corse, 't will cry, Revenge!
Ask yonder senate-house, whose stones are purple
With human blood, and it will cry, Revenge!
Go to the tomb where lies his murdered wife,

And the poor queen, who loved him as her son,
Their unappeasèd ghosts will shriek, Revenge!
The temples of the gods, the all-viewing heavens,
The gods themselves, shall justify the cry,
And swell the general sound, Revenge! Revenge!
    And we will be revenged, my countrymen!
Brutus shall lead you on; Brutus, a name
Which will, when you 're revenged, be dearer to
    him
Than all the noblest titles earth can boast.
    Brutus your king! — No, fellow-citizens!
If mad ambition in this guilty frame
Had strung one kingly fibre, yea, but one, —
By all the gods, this dagger which I hold
Should rip it out, though it intwined my heart.
    Now take the body up. Bear it before us
To Tarquin's palace; there we 'll light our torches,
And in the blazing conflagration rear
A pile, for these chaste relics, that shall send
Her soul amongst the stars. On! Brutus leads
    you!

JOHN HOWARD PAYNE.

ANTONY'S ORATION OVER THE BODY OF CÆSAR.

FROM "JULIUS CÆSAR," ACT III. SC. 2.

ANTONY. O mighty Cæsar! dost thou lie so low?
Are all thy conquests, glories, triumphs, spoils,
Shrunk to this little measure? — Fare thee well. —

(*To the people.*)

Friends, Romans, countrymen, lend me your
    ears;
I come to bury Cæsar, not to praise him.
The evil that men do lives after them;
The good is oft interrèd with their bones;
So let it be with Cæsar. The noble Brutus
Hath told you Cæsar was ambitious:
If it were so, it was a grievous fault;
And grievously hath Cæsar answered it.
Here, under leave of Brutus and the rest,
(For Brutus is an honorable man;
So are they all, all honorable men,)
Come I to speak in Cæsar's funeral.
He was my friend, faithful and just to me:
But Brutus says he was ambitious;
And Brutus is an honorable man.
He hath brought many captives home to Rome,
Whose ransoms did the general coffers fill:
Did this in Cæsar seem ambitious?
When that the poor have cried, Cæsar hath wept:
Ambition should be made of sterner stuff:
Yet Brutus says he was ambitious;
And Brutus is an honorable man.
You all did see that on the Lupercal

I thrice presented him a kingly crown,
Which he did thrice refuse : was this ambition ?
Yet Brutus says he was ambitious ;
And, sure, he is an honorable man.
I speak not to disprove what Brutus spoke,
But here I am to speak what I do know.
You all did love him once, — not without cause ·
What cause withholds you, then, to mourn for
    him ?
O judgment, thou art fled to brutish beasts,
And men have lost their reason !— Bear with me ;
My heart is in the coffin there with Cæsar,
And I must pause till it come back to me.

      ·   ·   ·   ·   ·

    But yesterday, the word of Cæsar might
Have stood against the world · now lies he there,
And none so poor to do him reverence.
O masters ! if I were disposed to stir
Your hearts and minds to mutiny and rage,
I should do Brutus wrong, and Cassius wrong,
Who, you all know, are honorable men :
I will not do them wrong ; I rather choose
To wrong the dead, to wrong myself, and you,
Than I will wrong such honorable men.
But here 's a parchment, with the seal of Cæsar, —
I found it in his closet, — 't is his will :
Let but the commons hear this testament,
(Which, pardon me, I do not mean to read,)
And they would go and kiss dead Cæsar's wounds,
And dip their napkins in his sacred blood :
Yea, beg a hair of him for memory,
And, dying, mention it within their wills,
Bequeathing it, as a rich legacy,
Unto their issue.
    4 CITIZEN. We 'll hear the will : read it, Mark
      Antony.
    CITIZENS. The will, the will ! we will hear
      Cæsar's will.
    ANT. Have patience, gentle friends, I must
      not read it ;
It is not meet you know how Cæsar loved you.
You are not wood, you are not stones, but men ;
And, being men, hearing the will of Cæsar,
It will inflame you, it will make you mad :
'T is good you know not that you are his heirs,
For if you should, O, what would come of it !
    4 CIT. Read the will ; we 'll hear it, Antony ;
You shall read us the will, — Cæsar's will.
    ANT. Will you be patient ? Will you stay
      awhile ?
I have o'ershot myself to tell you of it.
I fear I wrong the honorable men
Whose daggers have stabbed Cæsar ; I do fear it.
    4 CIT. They were traitors : honorable men !
    CIT. The will ! the testament !
    2 CIT. They were villains, murderers : the
      will ! read the will !

    ANT. You will compel me, then, to read the
      will ?
Then make a ring about the corse of Cæsar,
And let me show you him that made the will.
Shall I descend ? and will you give me leave ?
    CITIZENS. Come down.
    ANT. Nay, press not so upon me ; stand far off.
    CITIZENS. Stand back ; room ; bear back.
    ANT. If you have tears, prepare to shed them
      now.
You all do know this mantle : I remember
The first time ever Cæsar put it on ;
'T was on a summer's evening, in his tent ;
That day he overcame the Nervii : —
Look, in this place ran Cassius' dagger through :
See what a rent the envious Casca made :
Through this the well-belovèd Brutus stabbed ;
And, as he plucked his cursèd steel away,
Mark how the blood of Cæsar followed it,
As rushing out of doors, to be resolved
If Brutus so unkindly knocked, or no ;
For Brutus, as you know, was Cæsar's angel :
Judge, O you gods, how dearly Cæsar loved him !
This was the most unkindest cut of all ;
For when the noble Cæsar saw him stab,
Ingratitude, more strong than traitors' arms,
Quite vanquished him : then burst his mighty
    heart ;
And, in his mantle muffling up his face,
Even at the base of Pompey's statua,
Which all the while ran blood, great Cæsar fell.
O, what a fall was there, my countrymen !
Then I, and you, and all of us fell down,
Whilst bloody treason flourished over us.
O, now you weep ; and, I perceive, you feel
The dint of pity : these are gracious drops.
Kind souls, what, weep you when you but behold
Our Cæsar's vesture wounded ? Look you here,
Here is himself, marred, as you see, with traitors.

    ·   ·   ·   ·   ·

    Good friends, sweet friends, let me not stir
      you up
To such a sudden flood of mutiny.
They that have done this deed are honorable ; —
What private griefs they have, alas, I know not,
That made them do it ; — they are wise and
    honorable,
And will, no doubt, with reasons answer you.
I come not, friends, to steal away your hearts ;
I am no orator, as Brutus is ;
But, as you know me all, a plain blunt man,
That love my friend ; and that they know full
    well
That gave me public leave to speak of him :
For I have neither wit, nor words, nor worth,
Action, nor utterance, nor the power of speech,
To stir men's blood : I only speak right on ;

I tell you that which you yourselves do know ;
Show you sweet Cæsar's wounds, poor, poor
    dumb mouths,
And bid them speak for me : but were I Brutus,
And Brutus Antony, there were an Antony
Would ruffle up your spirits, and put a tongue
In every wound of Cæsar, that should move
The stones of Rome to rise in mutiny.
      .   .

   Here is the will, and under Cæsar's seal : —
To every Roman citizen he gives,
To every several man, seventy-five drachmas.
  2 CIT. Most noble Cæsar ! — we 'll revenge
    his death.
  3 CIT. O royal Cæsar !
  ANT. Hear me with patience.
  CITIZENS. Peace, ho !
  ANT. Moreover, he hath left you all his walks,
His private arbors, and new-planted orchards,
On this side Tiber ; he hath left them you,
And to your heirs forever, — common pleasures,
To walk abroad, and recreate yourselves.
Here was a Cæsar ! when comes such another ?
  1 CIT. Never, never ! — Come away, away !
We 'll burn his body in the holy place,
And with the brands fire the traitors' houses.
Take up the body.
                      SHAKESPEARE.

OTHELLO'S REMORSE.

FROM "OTHELLO," ACT V. SC. 2.

      BEHOLD, I have a weapon ;
A better never did itself sustain
Upon a soldier's thigh : I have seen the day,
That, with this little arm and this good sword,
I have made my way through more impediments
Than twenty times your stop : — but, O vain
    boast !
Who can control his fate ? 't is not so now. —
Be not afraid, though you do see me weaponed ;
Here is my journey's end, here is my butt,
And very sea-mark of my utmost sail.
Do you go back dismayed ? 't is a lost fear ;
Man but a rush against Othello's breast,
And he retires : — where should Othello go ? —
Now, how dost thou look now ? O ill-starred
    wench !
Pale as thy smock ! when we shall meet at compt,
This look of thine will hurl my soul from heaven,
And fiends will snatch at it. Cold, cold, my girl?
Even like thy chastity — O, cursed slave ! —
Whip me, ye devils,
From the possession of this heavenly sight !
Blow me about in winds ! roast me in sulphur !
Wash me in steep-down gulfs of liquid fire ! —
O Desdemona ! Desdemona ! dead ? O ! O !
                      SHAKESPEARE.

THE EXECUTION OF MONTROSE.

[James Graham, Marquis of Montrose, was executed in Edinburgh, May 21, 1650, for an attempt to overthrow the Commonwealth, and restore Charles II.]

COME hither, Evan Cameron !
  Come, stand behind my knee —
I hear the river roaring down
  Toward the wintry sea.
There 's shouting on the mountain-side,
  There 's war within the blast —
Old faces look upon me,
  Old forms go trooping past.
I hear the pibroch wailing
  Amidst the din of fight,
And my dim spirit wakes again
  Upon the verge of night.

'T was I that led the Highland host
  Through wild Lochaber's snows,
What time the plaided clans came down
  To battle with Montrose.
I 've told thee how the Southrons fell
  Beneath the broad claymore,
And how we smote the Campbell clan
  By Inverlochy's shore.
I 've told thee how we swept Dundee,
  And tamed the Lindsays' pride ;
But never have I told thee yet
  How the great Marquis died.

A traitor sold him to his foes ; —
  O deed of deathless shame !
I charge thee, boy, if e'er thou meet
  With one of Assynt's name —
Be it upon the mountain's side,
  Or yet within the glen,
Stand he in martial gear alone,
  Or backed by armèd men —
Face him as thou wouldst face the man
  Who wronged thy sire's renown ;
Remember of what blood thou art,
  And strike the caitiff down !

They brought him to the Watergate,
  Hard bound with hempen span,
As though they held a lion there,
  And not a 'fenceless man.
They set him high upon a cart —
  The hangman rode below —
They drew his hands behind his back,
  And bared his noble brow.
Then, as a hound is slipped from leash,
  They cheered the common throng,
And blew the note with yell and shout,
  And bade him pass along.

It would have made a brave man's heart
   Grow sad and sick that day,
To watch the keen, malignant eyes
   Bent down on that array.
There stood the Whig west-country lords
   In balcony and bow ;
There sat their gaunt and withered dames,
   And their daughters all a-row.
And every open window
   Was full as full might be
With black-robed Covenanting carles,
   That goodly sport to see !

But when he came, though pale and wan,
   He looked so great and high,
So noble was his manly front,
   So calm his steadfast eye ; —
The rabble rout forbore to shout,
   And each man held his breath,
For well they knew the hero's soul
   Was face to face with death.
And then a mournful shudder
   Through all the people crept,
And some that came to scoff at him
   Now turned aside and wept.

But onward — always onward,
   In silence and in gloom,
The dreary pageant labored,
   Till it reached the house of doom.
Then first a woman's voice was heard
   In jeer and laughter loud,
And an angry cry and a hiss arose
   From the heart of the tossing crowd :
Then, as the Græme looked upward,
   He saw the ugly smile
Of him who sold his king for gold —
   The master-fiend Argyle !

The Marquis gazed a moment,
   And nothing did he say,
But the cheek of Argyle grew ghastly pale,
   And he turned his eyes away.
The painted harlot by his side,
   She shook through every limb,
For a roar like thunder swept the street,
   And hands were clenched at him ;
And a Saxon soldier cried aloud,
   "Back, coward, from thy place !
For seven long years thou hast not dared
   To look him in the face."

Had I been there with sword in hand,
   And fifty Camerons by,
That day through high Dunedin's streets
   Had pealed the slogan-cry.

Not all their troops of trampling horse,
   Nor might of mailèd men —
Not all the rebels in the south
   Had borne us backward then !
Once more his foot on Highland heath
   Had trod as free as air,
Or I, and all who bore my name,
   Been laid around him there !

It might not be. They placed him next
   Within the solemn hall,
Where once the Scottish kings were throned
   Amidst their nobles all.
But there was dust of vulgar feet
   On that polluted floor,
And perjured traitors filled the place
   Where good men sate before.
With savage glee came Warriston
   To read the murderous doom ;
And then uprose the great Montrose
   In the middle of the room :

"Now, by my faith as belted knight
   And by the name I bear,
And by the bright St. Andrew's cross
   That waves above us there —
Yea, by a greater, mightier oath —
   And O that such should be ! —
By that dark stream of royal blood
   That lies 'twixt you and me —
I have not sought in battle-field
   A wreath of such renown,
Nor dared I hope on my dying day
   To win the martyr's crown !

"There is a chamber far away
   Where sleep the good and brave,
But a better place ye have named for me
   Than by my fathers' grave.
For truth and right, 'gainst treason's might,
   This hand hath always striven,
And ye raise it up for a witness still
   In the eye of earth and heaven.
Then nail my head on yonder tower —
   Give every town a limb —
And God who made shall gather them :
   I go from you to Him !"

The morning dawned full darkly,
   The rain came flashing down,
And the jagged streak of the levin-bolt
   Lit up the gloomy town.
The thunder crashed across the heaven,
   The fatal hour was come ;
Yet aye broke in, with muffled beat,
   The 'larum of the drum.

There was madness on the earth below
  And anger in the sky,
And young and old, and rich and poor,
  Came forth to see him die.

Ah God ! that ghastly gibbet !
  How dismal 't is to see
The great tall spectral skeleton,
  The ladder and the tree !
Hark ! hark ! it is the clash of arms, —
  The bells begin to toll, —
" He is coming ! he is coming !
  God's mercy on his soul ! "
One last long peal of thunder, —
  The clouds are cleared away,
And the glorious sun once more looks down
  Amidst the dazzling day.

" He is coming ! he is coming ! "
  Like a bridegroom from his room
Came the hero from his prison
  To the scaffold and the doom.
There was glory on his forehead,
  There was lustre in his eye,
And he never walked to battle
  More proudly than to die.
There was color in his visage,
  Though the cheeks of all were wan ;
And they marvelled as they saw him pass,
  That great and goodly man !

He mounted up the scaffold,
  And he turned him to the crowd ;
But they dared not trust the people,
  So he might not speak aloud.
But he looked upon the heavens,
  And they were clear and blue,
And in the liquid ether
  The eye of God shone through :
Yet a black and murky battlement
  Lay resting on the hill,
As though the thunder slept within, —
  All else was calm and still.

The grim Geneva ministers
  With anxious scowl drew near,
As you have seen the ravens flock
  Around the dying deer.
He would not deign them word nor sign,
  But alone he bent the knee ;
And veiled his face for Christ's dear grace
  Beneath the gallows-tree.
Then, radiant and serene, he rose,
  And cast his cloak away ;
For he had ta'en his latest look
  Of earth and sun and day.

A beam of light fell o'er him,
  Like a glory round the shriven,
And he climbed the lofty ladder
  As it were the path to heaven.
Then came a flash from out the cloud,
  And a stunning thunder-roll ;
And no man dared to look aloft, —
  Fear was on every soul.
There was another heavy sound,
  A hush, and then a groan ;
And darkness swept across the sky, —
  The work of death was done !
                WILLIAM EDMONDSTOUNE AYTOUN.

GOD'S JUDGMENT ON A WICKED BISHOP.

[Hatto, Archbishop of Mentz, in the year 914, barbarously murdered a number of poor people to prevent their consuming a portion of the food during that year of famine. He was afterwards devoured by rats in his tower on an island in the Rhine. — *Old Legend.*]

THE summer and autumn had been so wet,
That in winter the corn was growing yet :
'T was a piteous sight to see all around
The grain lie rotting on the ground.

Every day the starving poor
Crowded around Bishop Hatto's door ;
For he had a plentiful last-year's store,
And all the neighborhood could tell
His granaries were furnished well.

At last Bishop Hatto appointed a day
To quiet the poor without delay ;
He bade them to his great barn repair,
And they should have food for the winter there.

Rejoiced the tidings good to hear,
The poor folks flocked from far and near ;
The great barn was full as it could hold
Of women and children, and young and old.

Then, when he saw it could hold no more,
Bishop Hatto he made fast the door ;
And whilst for mercy on Christ they call,
He set fire to the barn, and burnt them all.

" I' faith 't is an excellent bonfire ! " quoth he ;
" And the country is greatly obliged to me
For ridding it, in these times forlorn,
Of rats that only consume the corn."

So then to his palace returnèd he,
And he sate down to supper merrily,
And he slept that night like an innocent man ;
But Bishop Hatto never slept again.

In the morning, as he entered the hall,
Where his picture hung against the wall,
A sweat like death all over him came,
For the rats had eaten it out of the frame.

As he looked, there came a man from his farm, —
He had a countenance white with alarm :
" My lord, I opened your granaries this morn,
And the rats had eaten all your corn."

Another came running presently,
And he was pale as pale could be.
" Fly ! my lord bishop, fly !" quoth he,
"Ten thousand rats are coming this way, —
The Lord forgive you for yesterday !"

" I 'll go to my tower in the Rhine," replied he ;
"'T is the safest place in Germany, —
The walls are high, and the shores are steep,
And the tide is strong, and the water deep."

Bishop Hatto fearfully hastened away ;
And he crossed the Rhine without delay,
And reached his tower, and barred with care
All the windows, doors, and loop-holes there.

He laid him down and closed his eyes,
But soon a scream made him arise ;
He started, and saw two eyes of flame
On his pillow, from whence the screaming came.

He listened and looked, — it was only the cat ;
But the bishop he grew more fearful for that,
For she sate screaming, mad with fear,
At the army of rats that were drawing near.

For they have swum over the river so deep,
And they have climbed the shores so steep,
And now by thousands up they crawl
To the holes and the windows in the wall.

Down on his knees the bishop fell,
And faster and faster his beads did he tell,
As louder and louder, drawing near,
The saw of their teeth without he could hear.

And in at the windows, and in at the door,
And through the walls, by thousands they pour ;
And down from the ceiling and up through the
floor,
From the right and the left, from behind and
before,
From within and without, from above and be-
low, —
And all at once to the bishop they go.

They have whetted their teeth against the stones,
And now they pick the bishop's bones ;
They gnawed the flesh from every limb,
For they were sent to do judgment on him !

ROBERT SOUTHEY.

THE SACK OF BALTIMORE.

[Baltimore is a small seaport in the barony of Carbery, in South Munster. It grew up around a castle of O'Driscoll's, and was, after his ruin, colonized by the English. On the 20th of June, 1631, the crews of two Algerine galleys landed in the dead of the night, sacked the town, and bore off into slavery all who were not too old, or too young, or too fierce, for their purpose. The pirates were steered up the intricate channel by one Hackett, a Dungarvan fisherman, whom they had taken at sea for the purpose. Two years after, he was convicted of the crime and executed. Baltimore never recovered from this.]

THE summer sun is falling soft on Carbery's
hundred isles,
The summer sun is gleaming still through
Gabriel's rough defiles, —
Old Inisherkin's crumbled fane looks like a
moulting bird ;
And in a calm and sleepy swell the ocean tide is
heard :
The hookers lie upon the beach ; the children
cease their play ;
The gossips leave the little inn ; the households
kneel to pray ;
And full of love and peace and rest, — its daily
labor o'er, —
Upon that cosy creek there lay the town of Balti-
more.

A deeper rest, a starry trance, has come with
midnight there ;
No sound, except that throbbing wave, in earth
or sea or air.
The massive capes and ruined towers seem con-
scious of the calm ;
The fibrous sod and stunted trees are breathing
heavy balm.
So still the night, these two long barks round
Dunashad that glide
Must trust their oars — methinks not few —
against the ebbing tide.
O, some sweet mission of true love must urge
them to the shore, —
They bring some lover to his bride, who sighs in
Baltimore !

All, all asleep within each roof along that rocky
street,
And these must be the lover's friends, with gently gliding feet.
A stifled gasp ! a dreamy noise ! The roof is in
a flame !
From out their beds, and to their doors, rush
maid and sire and dame,
And meet, upon the threshold stone, the gleaming sabre's fall,
And o'er each black and bearded face the white
or crimson shawl.
The yell of " Allah !" breaks above the prayer
and shriek and roar —
O blessèd God ! the Algerine is lord of Baltimore !

Then flung the youth his naked hand against the
    shearing sword ;
Then sprung the mother on the brand with which
    her son was gored ;
Then sunk the grandsire on the floor, his grand-
    babes clutching wild ;
Then fled the maiden moaning faint, and nestled
    with the child.
But see, yon pirate strangling lies, and crushed
    with splashing heel,
While o'er him in an Irish hand there sweeps his
    Syrian steel ;
Though virtue sink, and courage fail, and misers
    yield their store,
There's *one* hearth well avenged in the sack of
    Baltimore !

Midsummer morn, in woodland nigh, the birds
    begin to sing ;
They see not now the milking-maids, deserted is
    the spring !
Midsummer day, this gallant rides from distant
    Bandon's town,
These hookers crossed from stormy Skull, that
    skiff from Affadown.
They only found the smoking walls with neigh-
    bors' blood besprent,
And on the strewed and trampled beach awhile
    they wildly went,
Then dashed to sea, and passed Cape Clear, and
    saw, five leagues before,
The pirate-galleys vanishing that ravaged Balti-
    more.

O, some must tug the galley's oar, and some
    must tend the steed, —
This boy will bear a Scheik's chibouk, and that
    a Bey's jerreed.
O, some are for the arsenals by beauteous Darda-
    nelles,
And some are in the caravan to Mecca's sandy
    dells.
The maid that Bandon gallant sought is chosen
    for the Dey,
She's safe, — she's dead, — she stabbed him in
    the midst of his Serai ;
And when to die a death of fire that noble maid
    they bore,
She only smiled, — O'Driscoll's child, — she
    thought of Baltimore.

'T is two long years since sunk the town beneath
    that bloody band,
And all around its trampled hearths a larger
    concourse stand,
Where high upon a gallows-tree a yelling wretch
    is seen, —

'T is Hackett of Dungarvan, — he who steered
    the Algerine !
He fell amid a sullen shout, with scarce a passing
    prayer,
For he had slain the kith and kin of many a
    hundred there :
Some muttered of MacMorrogh, who had brought
    the Norman o'er,
Some cursed him with Iscariot, that day in Bal-
    timore.

THOMAS DAVIS.

PARRHASIUS.

PARRHASIUS stood, gazing forgetfully
Upon the canvas. There Prometheus lay,
Chained to the cold rocks of Mount Caucasus,
The vulture at his vitals, and the links
Of the lame Lemnian festering in his flesh ;
And, as the painter's mind felt through the dim
Rapt mystery, and plucked the shadows forth
With its far-reaching fancy, and with form
And color clad them, his fine, earnest eye
Flashed with a passionate fire, and the quick curl
Of his thin nostril, and his quivering lip,
Were like the winged god's breathing from his
    flights.

"Bring me the captive now !
My hand feels skilful, and the shadows lift
From my waked spirit airily and swift ;
    And I could paint the bow
Upon the bended heavens, — around me play
Colors of such divinity to-day.

"Ha ! bind him on his back !
Look ! as Prometheus in my picture here ;
Quick, — or he faints ! — stand with the cordial
    near !
    Now, — bend him to the rack !
Press down the poisoned links into his flesh !
And tear agape that healing wound afresh !

"So, — let him writhe ! How long
Will he live thus ? Quick, my good pencil, now !
What a fine agony works upon his brow !
    Ha ! gray-haired, and so strong !
How fearfully he stifles that short moan !
Gods ! if I could but paint a dying groan !

"Pity thee ! so I do !
I pity the dumb victim at the altar,
But does the robed priest for his pity falter ?
    I'd rack thee, though I knew
A thousand lives were perishing in thine ;
What were ten thousand to a fame like mine ?

"Ah! there's a deathless name! —
A spirit that the smothering vaults shall spurn,
And, like a steadfast planet, mount and burn ;
    And though its crown of flame
Consumed my brain to ashes as it shone,
By all the fiery stars, I 'd bind it on !

    "Ay! though it bid me rifle
My heart's last fount for its insatiate thirst, —
Though every life-strung nerve be maddened
    first, —
    Though it should bid me stifle
The yearnings in my heart for my sweet child,
And taunt its mother till my brain went wild, —

    "All, — I would do it all, —
Sooner than die, like a dull worm, to rot
Thrust foully in the earth to be forgot.
    O Heavens! — but I appall
Your heart, old man! — forgive — ha! on your
    lives
Let him not faint! rack him till he revives !

    "Vain, — vain, — give o'er.   His eye
Glazes apace.   He does not feel you now, —
Stand back! I 'll paint the death-dew on his brow!
    Gods ! if he do not die,
But for one moment — one — till I eclipse
Conception with the scorn of those calm lips !

    "Shivering !   Hark ! he mutters
Brokenly now, — that was a difficult breath, —
Another ?   Wilt thou never come, O Death ?
    Look ! how his temple flutters !
Is his heart still ?   Aha ! lift up his head !
He shudders, — gasps, — Jove help him ! — so,
    — he 's dead ! "

How like a mounting devil in the heart
Rules the unreined ambition !   Let it once
But play the monarch, and its haughty brow
Glows with a beauty that bewilders thought
And unthrones peace forever.   Putting on
The very pomp of Lucifer, it turns
The heart to ashes, and with not a spring
Left in the bosom for the spirit's lip,
We look upon our splendor, and forget
The thirst of which we perish !

NATHANIEL PARKER WILLIS.

———◆———

A DAGGER OF THE MIND.

FROM "MACBETH," ACT II. SC. 1.

[MACBETH before the murder of Duncan, meditating alone, sees
the image of a dagger in the air, and thus soliloquizes :]

Is this a dagger which I see before me,
The handle toward my hand ?   Come, let me
    clutch thee : —
I have thee not, and yet I see thee still.

Art thou not, fatal vision, sensible
To feeling as to sight ? or art thou but
A dagger of the mind, a false creation,
Proceeding from the heat-oppressèd brain ?
I see thee yet, in form as palpable
As this which now I draw.
Thou marshal'st me the way that I was going ;
And such an instrument I was to use.
Mine eyes are made the fools o' the other senses,
Or else worth all the rest : I see thee still ;
And on thy blade and dudgeon gouts of blood,
Which was not so before. — There 's no such
    thing :
It is the bloody business, which informs
Thus to mine eyes. — Now o'er the one half
    world
Nature seems dead, and wicked dreams abuse
The curtained sleep ; witchcraft celebrates
Pale Hecate's offerings ; and withered murder,
Alarumed by his sentinel, the wolf,
Whose howl 's his watch, thus with his stealthy
    pace,
With Tarquin's ravishing strides, towards his
    design
Moves like a ghost. — Thou sure and firm-set
    earth,
Hear not my steps, which way they walk, for
    fear
The very stones prate of my whereabout,
And take the present horror from the time,
Which now suits with it. — Whiles I threat, he
    lives :
Words to the heat of deeds too cold breath gives.
        (*A bell rings.*)
I go, and it is done ; the bell invites me.
Hear it not, Duncan ; for it is a knell
That summons thee to heaven or to hell.
                                SHAKESPEARE.

———◆———

THE MURDER.

FROM "MACBETH," ACT II. SC. 2.

SCENE *in the Castle.   Enter* LADY MACBETH.

LADY MACBETH.   That which hath made them
        drunk hath made me bold ,
What hath quenched them hath given me fire.
        Hark ! — Peace !
It was the owl that shrieked, the fatal bellman,
Which gives the stern'st good night.   He is
        about it :
The doors are open ; and the surfeited grooms
Do mark their charge with snores : I have
        drugged their possets,
That death and nature do contend about them,
Whether they live or die.

MACBETH (*within*).   Who 's there ?   What, ho !

LADY M. Alack, I am afraid they have awaked
And 't is not done : — the attempt and not the deed
Confounds us. — Hark ! — I laid their daggers ready ;
He could not miss them. — Had he not resembled
My father, as he slept, I had done 't. — My husband !
  MACB. I have done the deed. Didst thou not hear a noise ?
  LADY M. I heard the owl scream, and the crickets cry.
Did not you speak ?
  MACB.   When ?
  LADY M.   Now.
  MACB.   As I descended ?
  LADY M. Ay.
  MACB. Hark ! —
Who lies i' the second chamber ?
  LADY M.   Donalbain.
  MACB. (*looking on his hands*). This is a sorry sight.
  LADY M. A foolish thought, to say a sorry sight.
  MACB. There 's one did laugh in 's sleep, and one cried, " Murder ! "
That they did wake each other : I stood and heard them :
But they did say their prayers, and addressed them
Again to sleep.
  LADY M.   There are two lodged together.
  MACB. One cried, " God bless us ! " and, " Amen," the other ;
As they had seen me with these hangman's hands.
Listening their fear, I could not say, " Amen,"
When they did say, " God bless us."
  LADY M.   Consider it not so deeply.
  MACB. But wherefore could not I pronounce " Amen " ?
I had most need of blessing, and " Amen "
Stuck in my throat.
  LADY M.   These deeds must not be thought
After these ways ; so, it will make us mad.
  MACB. Methought I heard a voice cry, "Sleep no more !
Macbeth does murder sleep," — the innocent sleep,
Sleep that knits up the ravelled sleave of care,
The death of each day's life, sore labor's bath,
Balm of hurt minds, great nature's second course,
Chief nourisher in life's feast, —
  LADY M.   What do you mean ?
  MACB. Still it cried, " Sleep no more ! " to all the house :

" Glamis hath murdered sleep ; and therefore Cawdor
Shall sleep no more, — Macbeth shall sleep no more ! "
  LADY M. Who was it that thus cried ? Why, worthy thane,
You do unbend your noble strength, to think
So brainsickly of things. — Go, get some water,
And wash this filthy witness from your hand.
Why did you bring these daggers from the place ?
They must lie there : go carry them ; and smear
The sleepy grooms with blood.
  MACB.   I 'll go no more !
I am afraid to think what I have done ;
Look on 't again, I dare not.
  LADY M.   Infirm of purpose !
Give me the daggers : the sleeping, and the dead,
Are but as pictures : 't is the eye of childhood
That fears a painted devil. If he do bleed,
I 'll gild the faces of the grooms withal ;
For it must seem their guilt.
          [*Exit. Knocking within.*
  MACB.   Whence is that knocking !
How is 't with me, when every noise appalls me?
What hands are here ! Ha ! they pluck out mine eyes !
Will all great Neptune's ocean wash this blood
Clean from my hand ? No ; this my hand will rather
The multitudinous seas incarnadine,
Making the green — one red.
      (*Re-enter* LADY MACBETH.)
  LADY M. My hands are of your color ; but I shame
To wear a heart so white. (*Knocking.*) I hear a knocking
At the south entry : — retire we to our chamber:
A little water clears us of this deed :
How easy is it, then ! Your constancy
Hath left you unattended. (*Knocking.*) Hark, more knocking.
Get on your nightgown, lest occasion call us,
And show us to be watchers : — be not lost
So poorly in your thoughts.
  MACB. To know my deed, 't were best not know myself. (*Knocking.*)
Wake Duncan with thy knocking ! I would thou couldst.
              SHAKESPEARE.

RIDING TOGETHER.

FOR many, many days together
  The wind blew steady from the east ;
For many days hot grew the weather,
  About the time of our Lady's feast.

For many days we rode together,
   Yet met we neither friend nor foe ;
Hotter and clearer grew the weather,
   Steadily did the east-wind blow.

We saw the trees in the hot, bright weather,
   Clear-cut, with shadows very black,
As freely we rode on together
   With helms unlaced and bridles slack.

And often as we rode together,
   We, looking down the green-banked stream,
Saw flowers in the sunny weather,
   And saw the bubble-making bream.

And in the night lay down together,
   And hung above our heads the rood,
Or watched night-long in the dewy weather,
   The while the moon did watch the wood.

Our spears stood bright and thick together,
   Straight out the banners streamed behind,
As we galloped on in the sunny weather,
   With faces turned towards the wind.

Down sank our threescore spears together,
   As thick we saw the pagans ride ;
His eager face in the clear fresh weather
   Shone out that last time by my side.

Up the sweep of the bridge we dashed together,
   It rocked to the crash of the meeting spears,
Down rained the buds of the dear spring weather,
   The elm-tree flowers fell like tears.

There, as we rolled and writhed together,
   I threw my arms above my head,
For close by my side, in the lovely weather,
   I saw him reel and fall back dead.

I and the slayer met together,
   He waited the death-stroke there in his place,
With thoughts of death, in the lovely weather
   Gapingly mazed at my maddened face.

Madly I fought as we fought together ;
   In vain : the little Christian band
The pagans drowned, as in stormy weather,
   The river drowns low-lying land.

They bound my blood-stained hands together,
   They bound his corpse to nod by my side :
Then on we rode, in the bright March weather,
   With clash of cymbals did we ride.

We ride no more, no more together ;
   My prison-bars are thick and strong,
I take no heed of any weather,
   The sweet Saints grant I live not long.
            WILLIAM MORRIS.

THE ROSE AND THE GAUNTLET.

Low spake the knight to the peasant maid,
" O, be not thus of my suit afraid !
Fly with me from this garden small,
And thou shalt sit in my castle hall.

" Thou shalt have pomp and wealth and pleasure,
Joys beyond thy fancy's measure ;
Here with my sword and horse I stand,
To bear thee away to my distant land.

" Take, thou fairest ! this full-blown rose
A token of love that as ripely blows."
With his glove of steel he plucked the token,
And it fell from the gauntlet crushed and broken.

The maiden exclaimed, " Thou seest, Sir Knight,
Thy fingers of iron can only smite ;
And, like the rose thou hast torn and scattered,
I in thy grasp should be wrecked and shattered ! "

She trembled and blushed, and her glances fell,
But she turned from the knight, and said, " Fare-
   well."
" Not so," he cried, " will I lose my prize ;
I heed not thy words, but I read thine eyes."

He lifted her up in his grasp of steel,
And he mounted and spurred with fiery heel ;
But her cry drew forth her hoary sire,
Who snatched his bow from above the fire.

Swift from the valley the warrior fled,
But swifter the bolt of the cross-bow sped ;
And the weight that pressed on the fleet-foot
   horse
Was the living man and the woman's corse.

That morning the rose was bright of hue,
That morning the maiden was sweet to view ;
But the evening sun its beauty shed
On the withered leaves and the maiden dead.
       JOHN WILSON (*Christopher North*).

THE KING IS COLD.

RAKE the embers, blow the coals,
   Kindle at once a roaring fire ;
   Here 's some paper — 't is nothing, sir —
Light it (they 've saved a thousand souls),
Run for fagots, ye scurvy knaves,
   There are plenty out in the public square,
   You know they fry the heretics there.
(But God remember their nameless graves !)
Fly, fly, or the king may die !

Ugh ! his royal feet are like snow,
And the cold is mounting up to his heart.
  (But that was frozen long ago !)
Rascals, varlets, do as you are told, —
    The king is cold.

His bed of state is a grand affair,
  With sheets of satin and pillows of down,
  And close beside it stands the crown, —
But that won't keep him from dying there !
His hands are wrinkled, his hair is gray,
  And his ancient blood is sluggish and thin ;
  When he was young it was hot with sin, —
But that is over this many a day !
Under these sheets of satin and lace
He slept in the arms of his concubines ;
Now they carouse with the prince instead,
  Drinking the maddest, merriest wines ;
It's pleasant to hear such catches trolled,
    Now the king is cold !

What shall I do with His Majesty now ?
  For, thanks to my potion, the man is dead ;
  Suppose I bolster him up in bed,
And fix the crown again on his brow ?
That would be merry ! but then the prince
  Would tumble it down, I know, in a trice ;
  'T would puzzle the Devil to name a vice
That would make his Excellent Highness wince !
Hark ! he's coming, I know his step ;
  He's stealing to see if his wishes are true ;
Sire, may your father's end be yours !
  (With just such a son to murder you !)
Peace to the dead !   Let the bells be tolled —
    The king is cold !
                              ROBERT BROWNING.

FRA GIACOMO.

ALAS, Fra Giacomo,
  Too late ! — but follow me ;
Hush ! draw the curtain, — so ! —
She is dead, quite dead, you see.
Poor little lady ! she lies
With the light gone out of her eyes,
But her features still wear that soft
  Gray meditative expression,
Which you must have noticed oft,
  And admired too, at confession.
How saintly she looks, and how meek !
  Though this be the chamber of death,
  I fancy I feel her breath
As I kiss her on the cheek.
With that pensive religious face,
She has gone to a holier place !
And I hardly appreciated her, —
  Her praying, fasting, confessing,
Poorly, I own, I mated her ;

I thought her too cold, and rated her
  For her endless image-caressing.
Too saintly for me by far,
As pure and as cold as a star,
  Not fashioned for kissing and pressing, —
But made for a heavenly crown.
Ay, father, let us go down, —
  But first, if you please, your blessing.

Wine ? No ?   Come, come, you must !
  You'll bless it with your prayers,
And quaff a cup, I trust,
  To the health of the saint up stairs ?
My heart is aching so !
  And I feel so weary and sad,
  Through the blow that I have had, —
You'll sit, Fra Giacomo ?
My friend ! (and a friend I rank you
  For the sake of that saint,) — nay, nay !
  Here's the wine, — as you love me, stay ! —
'T is Montepulciano ! — Thank you.

Heigh-ho !   'T is now six summers
  Since I won that angel and married her :
  I was rich, not old, and carried her
Off in the face of all comers.
So fresh, yet so brimming with soul !
  A tenderer morsel, i swear,
Never made the dull black coal
  Of a monk's eye glitter and glare.
  Your pardon ! — nay, keep your chair !
I wander a little, but mean
No offence to the gray gaberdine ;
Of the church, Fra Giacomo,
I'm a faithful upholder, you know,
But (humor me !) she was as sweet
  As the saints in your convent windows,
So gentle, so meek, so discreet,
  She knew not what lust does or sin does.
I'll confess, though, before we were one,
  I deemed her less saintly, and thought
  The blood in her veins had caught
Some natural warmth from the sun.
I was wrong, — I was blind as a bat, —
  Brute that I was, how I blundered !
Though such a mistake as that
Might have occurred as pat
  To ninety-nine men in a hundred.
Yourself, for example ? you've seen her ?
Spite her modest and pious demeanor,
And the manners so nice and precise,
  Seemed there not color and light,
  Bright motion and appetite,
That were scarcely consistent with *ice ?*
Externals implying, you see,
  Internals less saintly than human ? —
Pray speak, for between you and me
  You're not a bad judge of a woman !

A jest, — but a jest ! — Very true :
'T is hardly becoming to jest,
And that saint up stairs at rest, —
Her soul may be listening, too ?
I was always a brute of a fellow !
Well may your visage turn yellow, —
To think how I doubted and doubted,
Suspected, grumbled at, flouted
That golden-haired angel, — and solely
Because she was zealous and holy !
Noon and night and morn
  She devoted herself to piety ;
Not that she seemed to scorn
  Or dislike her husband's society ;
But the claims of her *soul* superseded
All that I asked for or needed,
And her thoughts were far away
From the level of sinful clay,
And she trembled if earthly matters
Interfered with her *aves* and *paters.*
Poor dove, she so fluttered in flying
Above the dim vapors of hell —
Bent on self-sanctifying —
That she never thought of trying
  To save her husband as well.
And while she was duly elected
  For place in the heavenly roll,
I (brute that I was !) suspected
  Her manner of saving her soul.
So, half for the fun of the thing,
What did I (blasphemer !) but fling
On my shoulders the gown of a monk —
  Whom I managed for that very day
  To get safely out of the way —
And seat me, half sober, half drunk,
With the cowl thrown over my face,
In the father confessor's place.
Eheu ! benedicite !
In her orthodox sweet simplicity,
With that pensive gray expression,
She sighfully knelt at confession,
While I bit my lips till they bled,
And dug my nails in my hand,
And heard with averted head
  What I 'd guessed and could understand.
Each word was a serpent's sting,
  But, wrapt in my gloomy gown,
I sat, like a marble thing,
  As she told me all ! — SIT DOWN.

More wine, Fra Giacomo !
One cup, — if you love me ! No ?
What, have these dry lips drank
So deep of the sweets of pleasure —
  Sub rosa, but quite without measure —
That Montepulciano tastes rank ?
Come, drink ! 't will bring the streaks

Of crimson back to your cheeks ;
Come, drink again to the saint
Whose virtues you loved to paint,
Who, stretched on her wifely bed,
  With the tender, grave expression
  You used to admire at confession,
Lies poisoned, overhead !

Sit still, — or by heaven, you die !
Face to face, soul to soul, you and I
Have settled accounts, in a fine
Pleasant fashion, over our wine.
Stir not, and seek not to fly, —
Nay, whether or not, you are mine !
Thank Montepulciano for giving
  You death in such delicate sips ;
'T is not every monk ceases living
  With so pleasant a taste on his lips ;
But, lest Montepulciano unsurely should kiss,
  Take this ! and this ! and this !

Cover him over, Pietro,
And bury him in the court below, —
You can be secret, lad, I know !
And, hark you, then to the convent go, —
Bid every bell of the convent toll,
And the monks say mass for your mistress' soul.

ROBERT BUCHANAN.

COUNTESS LAURA.

IT was a dreary day in Padua.
The Countess Laura, for a single year
Fernando's wife, upon her bridal bed,
Like an uprooted lily on the snow,
The withered outcast of a festival,
Lay dead. She died of some uncertain ill,
That struck her almost on her wedding day,
And clung to her, and dragged her slowly down,
Thinning her cheeks and pinching her full lips,
Till, in her chance, it seemed that with a year
Full half a century was overpast.
In vain had Paracelsus taxed his art,
And feigned a knowledge of her malady ;
In vain had all the doctors, far and near,
Gathered around the mystery of her bed,
Draining her veins, her husband's treasury,
And physic's jargon, in a fruitless quest
For causes equal to the dread result.
The Countess only smiled when they were gone,
Hugged her fair body with her little hands,
And turned upon her pillows wearily,
As though she fain would sleep no common sleep,
But the long, breathless slumber of the grave.
She hinted nothing. Feeble as she was,
The rack could not have wrung her secret out.
The Bishop, when he shrived her, coming forth,

Cried, in a voice of heavenly ecstasy,
"O blessèd soul ! with nothing to confess
Save virtues and good deeds, which she mis-
    takes —
So humble is she — for our human sins !"
Praying for death, she tossed upon her bed
Day after day ; as might a shipwrecked bark
That rocks upon one billow, and can make
No onward motion towards her port of hope.
At length, one morn, when those around her said,
"Surely the Countess mends, so fresh a light
Beams from her eyes and beautifies her face," —
One morn in spring, when every flower of earth
Was opening to the sun, and breathing up
Its votive incense, her impatient soul
Opened itself, and so exhaled to heaven.
When the Count heard it, he reeled back a pace ;
Then turned with anger on the messenger ;
Then craved his pardon, and wept out his heart
Before the menial ; tears, ah me ! such tears
As love sheds only, and love only once.
Then he bethought him, "Shall this wonder die,
And leave behind no shadow ? not a trace
Of all the glory that environed her,
That mellow nimbus circling round my star ?"
So, with his sorrow glooming in his face,
He paced along his gallery of art,
And strode among the painters, where they stood,
With Carlo, the Venetian, at their head,
Studying the Masters by the dawning light
Of his transcendent genius. Through the groups
Of gayly vestured artists moved the Count,
As some lone cloud of thick and leaden hue,
Packed with the secret of a coming storm,
Moves through the gold and crimson evening
    mists,
Deadening their splendor. In a moment still
Was Carlo's voice, and still the prattling crowd ;
And a great shadow overwhelmed them all,
As their white faces and their anxious eyes
Pursued Fernando in his moody walk.
He paused, as one who balances a doubt,
Weighing two courses, then burst out with this :
"Ye all have seen the tidings in my face ;
Or has the dial ceased to register
The workings of my heart ? Then hear the bell,
That almost cracks its frame in utterance ;
The Countess, — she is dead !" "Dead !" Carlo
    groaned.
And if a bolt from middle heaven had struck
His splendid features full upon the brow,
He could not have appeared more scathed and
    blanched.
"Dead ! — dead !" He staggered to his easel-
    frame,
And clung around it, buffeting the air
With one wild arm, as though a drowning man

Hung to a spar and fought against the waves.
The Count resumed : "I came not here to grieve,
Nor see my sorrow in another's eyes.
Who 'll paint the Countess, as she lies to-night
In state within the chapel ? Shall it be
That earth must lose her wholly ? that no hint
Of her gold tresses, beaming eyes, and lips
That talked in silence, and the eager soul
That ever seemed outbreaking through her clay,
And scattering glory round it, — shall all these
Be dull corruption's heritage, and we,
Poor beggars, have no legacy to show
That love she bore us ? That were shame to love,
And shame to you, my masters." Carlo stalked
Forth from his easel stiffly as a thing
Moved by mechanic impulse. His thin lips,
And sharpened nostrils, and wan, sunken cheeks,
And the cold glimmer in his dusky eyes,
Made him a ghastly sight. The throng drew
    back
As though they let a spectre through. Then he,
Fronting the Count, and speaking in a voice
Sounding remote and hollow, made reply :
"Count, I shall paint the Countess. 'T is my
    fate, —
Not pleasure, — no, nor duty." But the Count,
Astray in woe, but understood assent,
Not the strange words that bore it ; and he flung
His arm round Carlo, drew him to his breast,
And kissed his forehead. At which Carlo shrank;
Perhaps 't was at the honor. Then the Count,
A little reddening at his public state, —
Unseemly to his near and recent loss, —
Withdrew in haste between the downcast eyes
That did him reverence as he rustled by.

Night fell on Padua. In the chapel lay
The Countess Laura at the altar's foot.
Her coronet glittered on her pallid brows ;
A crimson pall, weighed down with golden work,
Sown thick with pearls, and heaped with early
    flowers,
Draped her still body almost to the chin ;
And over all a thousand candles flamed
Against the winking jewels, or streamed down
The marble aisle, and flashed along the guard
Of men-at-arms that slowly wove their turns,
Backward and forward, through the distant
    gloom.
When Carlo entered, his unsteady feet
Scarce bore him to the altar, and his head
Drooped down so low that all his shining curls
Poured on his breast, and veiled his countenance.
Upon his easel a half-finished work,
The secret labor of his studio,
Said from the canvas, so that none might err,
"I am the Countess Laura." Carlo kneeled,

And gazed upon the picture ; as if thus,
Through those clear eyes, he saw the way to
    heaven.
Then he arose ; and as a swimmer comes
Forth from the waves, he shook his locks aside,
Emerging from his dream, and standing firm
Upon a purpose with his sovereign will.
He took his palette, murmuring, " Not yet !"
Confidingly and softly to the corpse ,
And as the veriest drudge, who plies his art
Against his fancy, he addressed himself
With stolid resolution to his task,
Turning his vision on his memory,
And shutting out the present, till the dead,
The gilded pall, the lights, the pacing guard,
And all the meaning of that solemn scene
Became as nothing, and creative Art
Resolved the whole to chaos, and reformed
The elements according to her law :
So Carlo wrought, as though his eye and hand
Were Heaven's unconscious instruments, and
    worked
The settled purpose of Omnipotence.
And it was wondrous how the red, the white,
The ochre, and the umber, and the blue,
From mottled blotches, hazy and opaque,
Grew into rounded forms and sensuous lines ;
How just beneath the lucid skin the blood
Glimmered with warmth ; the scarlet lips apart
Bloomed with the moisture of the dews of life ;
How the light glittered through and underneath
The golden tresses, and the deep, soft eyes
Became intelligent with conscious thought,
And somewhat troubled underneath the arch
Of eyebrows but a little too intense
For perfect beauty ; how the pose and poise
Of the lithe figure on its tiny foot
Suggested life just ceased from motion ; so
That any one might cry, in marvelling joy,
" That creature lives, — has senses, mind, a soul
To win God's love or dare hell's subtleties !"
The artist paused. The ratifying "Good !"
Trembled upon his lips. He saw no touch
To give or soften. " It is done," he cried, —
" My task, my duty ! Nothing now on earth
Can taunt me with a work left unfulfilled !"
The lofty flame, which bore him up so long,
Died in the ashes of humanity ;
And the mere man rocked to and fro again
Upon the centre of his wavering heart.
He put aside his palette, as if thus
He stepped from sacred vestments, and assumed
A mortal function in the common world.
" Now for my rights !" he muttered, and ap-
    proached
The noble body. " O lily of the world !
So withered, yet so lovely ! what wast thou

To those who came thus near thee — for I stood
Without the pale of thy half-royal rank —
When thou wast budding, and the streams of life
Made eager struggles to maintain thy bloom,
And gladdened heaven dropped down in gracious
    dews
On its transplanted darling ? Hear me now !
I say this but in justice, not in pride,
Not to insult thy high nobility,
But that the poise of things in God's own sight
May be adjusted ; and hereafter I
May urge a claim that all the powers of heaven
Shall sanction, and with clarions blow abroad. —
Laura, you loved me ! Look not so severe,
With your cold brows, and deadly, close-drawn
    lips !
You proved it, Countess, when you died for it, —
Let it consume you in the wearing strife
It fought with duty in your ravaged heart.
I knew it ever since that summer day
I painted Lilla, the pale beggar's child,
At rest beside the fountain ; when I felt —
O Heaven ! — the warmth and moisture of your
    breath
Blow through my hair, as with your eager soul —
Forgetting soul and body go as one —
You leaned across my easel till our cheeks —
Ah me ! 't was not your purpose — touched, and
    clung !
Well, grant 't was genius ; and is genius naught ?
I ween it wears as proud a diadem —
Here, in this very world — as that you wear.
A king has held my palette, a grand-duke
Has picked my brush up, and a pope has begged
The favor of my presence in his Rome.
I did not go ; I put my fortune by.
I need not ask you why : you knew too well.
It was but natural, it was no way strange,
That I should love you. Everything that saw,
Or had its other senses, loved you, sweet,
And I among them. Martyr, holy saint, —
I see the halo curving round your head, —
I loved you once ; but now I worship you,
For the great deed that held my love aloof,
And killed you in the action ! I absolve
Your soul from any taint. For from the day
Of that encounter by the fountain-side
Until this moment, never turned on me
Those tender eyes, unless they did a wrong
To nature by the cold, defiant glare
With which they chilled me. Never heard I word
Of softness spoken by those gentle lips ;
Never received a bounty from that hand
Which gave to all the world. I know the cause.
You did your duty, — not for honor's sake,
Nor to save sin, or suffering, or remorse,
Or all the ghosts that haunt a woman's shame,

But for the sake of that pure, loyal love
Your husband bore you. Queen, by grace of God,
I bow before the lustre of your throne !
I kiss the edges of your garment-hem,
And hold myself ennobled ! Answer me, — .
If I had wronged you, you would answer me
Out of the dusty porches of the tomb : —
Is this a dream, a falsehood ? or have I
Spoken the very truth ?" "The very truth !"
A voice replied ; and at his side he saw
A form, half shadow and half substance, stand,
Or, rather, rest ; for on the solid earth
It had no footing, more than some dense mist
That wavers o'er the surface of the ground
It scarcely touches. With a reverent look
The shadow's waste and wretched face was bent
Above the picture ; as though greater awe
Subdued its awful being, and appalled,
With memories of terrible delight
And fearful wonder, its devouring gaze.
"You make what God makes, — beauty," said
    the shape.
"And might not this, this second Eve, console
The emptiest heart ? Will not this thing outlast
The fairest creature fashioned in the flesh ?
Before that figure, Time, and Death himself,
Stand baffled and disarmed. What would you
    ask
More than God's power, from nothing to create ?"
The artist gazed upon the boding form,
And answered : "Goblin, if you had a heart,
That were an idle question. What to me
Is my creative power, bereft of love ?
Or what to God would be that self-same power,
If so bereaved ?" "And yet the love, thus
    mourned,
You calmly forfeited. For had you said
To living Laura — in her burning ears —
One half that you professed to Laura dead,
She would have been your own. These contraries
Sort not with my intelligence. But speak,
Were Laura living, would the same stale play
Of raging passion tearing out its heart
Upon the rock of duty be performed ?"
"The same, O phantom, while the heart I bear
Trembled, but turned not its magnetic faith
From God's fix'd centre." "If I wake for you
This Laura, — give her all the bloom and glow
Of that midsummer day you hold so dear, —
The smile, the motion, the impulsive soul,
The love of genius, — yea, the very love,
The mortal, hungry, passionate, hot love,
She bore you, flesh to flesh, — would you receive
That gift, in all its glory, at my hands ?"
A smile of malice curled the tempter's lips,
And glittered in the caverns of his eyes,
Mocking the answer. Carlo paled and shook ;

A woful spasm went shuddering through his
    frame,
Curdling his blood, and twisting his fair face
With nameless torture. But he cried aloud,
Out of the clouds of anguish, from the smoke
Of very martyrdom, " O God, she is thine !
Do with her at thy pleasure !" Something grand,
And radiant as a sunbeam, touched the head
He bent in awful sorrow. "Mortal, see—"
"Dare not ! As Christ was sinless, I abjure
These vile abominations ! Shall she bear
Life's burden twice, and life's temptations twice,
While God is justice ?" "Who has made you
    judge
Of what you call God's good, and what you think
God's evil ? One to him, the source of both,
The God of good and of permitted ill.
Have you no dream of days that might have been,
Had you and Laura filled another fate ? —
Some cottage on the sloping Apennines,
Roses and lilies, and the rest all love ?
I tell you that this tranquil dream may be
Filled to repletion. Speak, and in the shade
Of my dark pinions I shall bear you hence,
And land you where the mountain-goat himself
Struggles for footing." He outspread his wings,
And all the chapel darkened, as though hell
Had swallowed up the tapers ; and the air
Grew thick, and, like a current sensible,
Flowed round the person, with a wash and dash,
As of the waters of a nether sea.
Slowly and calmly through the dense obscure,
Dove-like and gentle, rose the artist's voice :
"I dare not bring her spirit to that shame !
Know my full meaning, — I who neither fear
Your mystic person nor your dreadful power.
Nor shall I now invoke God's potent name
For my deliverance from your toils. I stand
Upon the founded structure of his law,
Established from the first, and thence defy
Your arts, reposing all my trust in that !"
The darkness eddied off ; and Carlo saw
The figure gathering, as from outer space,
Brightness on brightness ; and his former shape
Fell from him, like the ashes that fall off,
And show a core of mellow fire within.
Adown his wings there poured a lambent flood,
That seemed as molten gold, which plashing fell
Upon the floor, enringing him with flame ;
And o'er the tresses of his beaming head
Arose a stream of many-colored light,
Like that which crowns the morning. Carlo stood
Steadfast, for all the splendor, reaching up
The outstretched palms of his untainted soul
Towards heaven for strength. A moment thus
    then asked,
With reverential wonder quivering through

His sinking voice, " Who, spirit, and what, art
thou ? "
" I am that blessing which men fly from, —
Death."
" Then take my hand, if so God orders it ;
For Laura waits me." " But, bethink thee, man,
What the world loses in the loss of thee !
What wondrous art will suffer with eclipse !
What unwon glories are in store for thee !
What fame, outreaching time and temporal shocks,
Would shine upon the letters of thy name
Graven in marble, or the brazen height
Of columns wise with memories of thee ! "
" Take me ! If I outlived the Patriarchs,
I could but paint those features o'er and o'er :
Lo ! that is done." A smile of pity lit
The seraph's features, as he looked to heaven,
With deep inquiry in his tender eyes.
The mandate came. He touched with downy wing
The sufferer lightly on his aching heart ;
And gently, as the skylark settles down
Upon the clustered treasures of her nest,
So Carlo softly slid along the prop
Of his tall easel, nestling at the foot
As though he slumbered ; and the morning broke
In silver whiteness over Padua.

GEORGE HENRY BOKER.

GINEVRA.

IF thou shouldst ever come by choice or chance
To Modena, where still religiously
Among her ancient trophies is preserved
Bologna's bucket (in its chain it hangs
Within that reverend tower, the Guirlandina),
Stop at a palace near the Reggio gate,
Dwelt of old by one of the Orsini.
Its noble gardens, terrace above terrace,
And rich in fountains, statues, cypresses,
Will long detain thee ; through their archèd
walks,
Dim at noonday, discovering many a glimpse
Of knights and dames, such as in old romance,
And lovers, such as in heroic song,
Perhaps the two, for groves were their delight,
That in the spring-time, as alone they sat,
Venturing together on a tale of love,
Read only part that day. — A summer sun
Sets ere one half is seen ; but ere thou go,
Enter the house — prythee, forget it not —
And look awhile upon a picture there.

'T is of a Lady in her earliest youth,
The last of that illustrious race ;
Done by Zampieri — but I care not whom.
He who observes it, ere he passes on,
Gazes his fill, and comes and comes again,
That he may call it up when far away.

She sits inclining forward as to speak,
Her lips half open, and her finger up,
As though she said " Beware !" her vest of gold
Broidered with flowers, and clasped from head to
foot,
An emerald stone in every golden clasp ;
And on her brow, fairer than alabaster,
A coronet of pearls. But then her face,
So lovely, yet so arch, so full of mirth,
The overflowings of an innocent heart, —
It haunts me still, though many a year has fled,
Like some wild melody !

Alone it hangs
Over a mouldering heirloom, its companion,
An oaken chest, half eaten by the worm,
But richly carved by Antony of Trent
With Scripture stories from the life of Christ ;
A chest that came from Venice, and had held
The ducal robes of some old Ancestor,
That, by the way — it may be true or false —
But don't forget the picture ; and thou wilt not
When thou hast heard the tale they told me there.

She was an only child ; from infancy
The joy, the pride, of an indulgent Sire ;
Her Mother dying of the gift she gave,
That precious gift, what else remained to him ?
The young Ginevra was his all in life,
Still as she grew, for ever in his sight ;
And in her fifteenth year became a bride,
Marrying an only son, Francesco Doria,
Her playmate from her birth, and her first love.

Just as she looks there in her bridal dress,
She was all gentleness, all gayety,
Her pranks the favorite theme of every tongue.
But now the day was come, the day, the hour ;
Now, frowning, smiling, for the hundredth time,
The nurse, that ancient lady, preached decorum ;
And, in the lustre of her youth, she gave
Her hand, with her heart in it, to Francesco.

Great was the joy ; but at the Bridal-feast,
When all sate down, the bride was wanting
there,
Nor was she to be found ! Her Father cried,
" 'T is but to make a trial of our love !"
And filled his glass to all ; but his hand shook,
And soon from guest to guest the panic spread.
'T was but that instant she had left Francesco,
Laughing and looking back, and flying still,
Her ivory tooth imprinted on his finger.
But now, alas, she was not to be found ;
Nor from that hour could anything be guessed,
But that she was not !

Weary of his life,
Francesco flew to Venice, and, forthwith,
Flung it away in battle with the Turk.
Orsini lived, — and long mightst thou have seen
An old man wandering as in quest of something,
Something he could not find, he knew not what.
When he was gone, the house remained awhile
Silent and tenantless, — then went to strangers.

Full fifty years were past, and all forgot,
When, on an idle day, a day of search
Mid the old lumber in the Gallery,
That mouldering chest was noticed ; and 't was
    said
By one as young, as thoughtless as Ginevra,
"Why not remove it from its lurking-place ? "
'T was done as soon as said ; but on the way
It burst, it fell ; and lo, a skeleton,
With here and there a pearl, an emerald s'..n ,
A golden clasp, clasping a shred of gold !
All else had perished, — save a nuptial-ring,
And a small seal, her mother's legacy,
Engraven with a name, the name of both,
"Ginevra."

There then had she found a grave !
Within that chest had she concealed herself,
Fluttering with joy, the happiest of the happy ;
When a spring-lock, that lay in ambush there,
Fastened her down for ever !
Samuel Rogers.

THE MISTLETOE BOUGH.

The mistletoe hung in the castle hall,
The holly branch shone on the old oak wall ;
And the baron's retainers were blithe and gay,
And keeping their Christmas holiday.
The baron beheld with a father's pride
His beautiful child, young Lovell's bride ;
While she with her bright eyes seemed to be
The star of the goodly company.

"I 'm weary of dancing now," she cried ;
"Here tarry a moment, — I 'll hide, I 'll hide !
And, Lovell, be sure thou 'rt first to trace
The clew to my secret lurking-place."
Away she ran, — and her friends began
Each tower to search, and each nook to scan ;
And young Lovell cried, "O, where dost thou
    hide ?
I 'm lonesome without thee, my own dear bride."

They sought her that night, and they sought her
    next day,
And they sought her in vain when a week passed
    away :
In the highest, the lowest, the loneliest spot,
Young Lovell sought wildly, — but found her not.

And years flew by, and their grief at last
Was told as a sorrowful tale long past ;
And when Lovell appeared, the children cried,
"See ! the old man weeps for his fairy bride."

At length an oak chest, that had long lain hid,
Was found in the castle, — they raised the lid,
And a skeleton form lay mouldering there
In the bridal wreath of that lady fair !
O, sad was her fate ! —in sportive jest
She hid from her lord in the old oak chest.
It closed with a spring ! — and, dreadful doom,
The bride lay clasped in her living tomb !
Thomas Haynes Bayly.

THE YOUNG GRAY HEAD.

Grief hath been known to turn the young head
    gray, —
To silver over in a single day
The bright locks of the beautiful, their prime
Scarcely o'erpast ; as in the fearful time
Of Gallia's madness, that discrowned head
Serene, that on the accursèd altar bled
Miscalled of Liberty. O martyred Queen !
What must the sufferings of that night have
    been —
That one — that sprinkled thy fair tresses o'er
With time's untimely snow ! But now no more,
Lovely, august, unhappy one ! of thee —
I have to tell a humbler history ;
A village tale, whose only charm, in sooth
(If any), will be sad and simple truth.

"Mother," quoth Ambrose to his thrifty dame, —
So oft our peasant's use his wife to name,
"Father " and "Master " to himself applied,
As life's grave duties matronize the bride, —
"Mother," quoth Ambrose, as he faced the north
With hard-set teeth, before he issued forth
To his day labor, from the cottage door, —
"I 'm thinking that, to-night, if not before,
There 'll be wild work.   Dost hear old Chewton *
    roar ?
It 's brewing up, down westward ; and look there,
One of those sea-gulls ! ay, there goes a pair ;
And such a sudden thaw ! If rain comes on,
As threats, the waters will be out anon.
That path by the ford 's a nasty bit of way, —
Best let the young ones bide from school to-day."

"Do, mother, do !" the quick-eared urchins cried ;
Two little lasses to the father's side

* A fresh-water spring rushing into the sea, called Chewton
Bunny.

Close clinging, as they looked from him, to spy
The answering language of the mother's eye.
There was denial, and she shook her head :
" Nay, nay, — no harm will come to them," she
          said,
" The mistress lets them off these short dark days
An hour the earlier ; and our Liz, she says,
May quite be trusted — and I know 't is true —
To take care of herself and Jenny too.
And so she ought, — she 's seven come first of
          May, —
Two years the oldest ; and they give away
The Christmas bounty at the school to-day."

The mother's will was law (alas, for her
That hapless day, poor soul !) — *she* could not err,
Thought Ambrose ; and his little fair-haired Jane
(Her namesake) to his heart he hugged again,
When each had had her turn ; she clinging so
As if that day she could not let him go.
But Labor's sons must snatch a hasty bliss
In nature's tenderest mood.   One last fond kiss,
" God bless my little maids ! " the father said,
And cheerly went his way to win their bread.
Then might be seen, the playmate parent gone,
What looks demure the sister pair put on, —
Not of the mother as afraid, or shy,
Or questioning the love that could deny ;
But simply, as their simple training taught,
In quiet, plain straightforwardness of thought
(Submissively resigned the hope of play)
Towards the serious business of the day.

To me there 's something touching, I confess,
In the grave look of early thoughtfulness,
Seen often in some little childish face
Among the poor.   Not that wherein we trace
(Shame to our land, our rulers, and our race !)
The unnatural sufferings of the factory child,
But a staid quietness, reflective, mild,
Betokening, in the depths of those young eyes,
Sense of life's cares, without its miseries.

So to the mother's charge, with thoughtful brow,
The docile Lizzy stood attentive now,
Proud of her years and of imputed sense,
And prudence justifying confidence, —
And little Jenny, more *demurely* still,
Beside her waited the maternal will.
So standing hand in hand, a lovelier twain
Gainsborough ne'er painted : no — nor he of
          Spain,
Glorious Murillo ! — and by contrast shown
More beautiful.   The younger little one,
With large blue eyes and silken ringlets fair,
By nut-brown Lizzy, with smooth parted hair,
Sable and glossy as the raven's wing,
And lustrous eyes as dark.

            " Now, mind and bring
Jenny safe home," the mother said, — " don't
          stay
To pull a bough or berry by the way :
And when you come to cross the ford, hold fast
Your little sister's hand, till you 're quite past, —
That plank 's so crazy, and so slippery
(If not o'erflowed) the stepping-stones will be.
But you 're good children — steady as old folk —
I 'd trust ye anywhere."   Then Lizzy's cloak,
A good gray duffle, lovingly she tied,
And amply little Jenny's lack supplied
With her own warmest shawl.   " Be sure," said
          she,
" To wrap it round and knot it carefully
(Like this), when you come home, just leaving
          free
One hand to hold by.   Now, make haste away —
Good will to school, and then good right to play."

Was there no sinking at the mother's heart
When, all equipt, they turned them to depart ?
When down the lane she watched them as they
          went
Till out of sight, was no forefeeling sent
Of coming ill ?   In truth I cannot tell :
Such warnings *have been* sent, we know full well
And must believe — believing that they are —
In mercy then — to rouse, restrain, prepare.

And now I mind me, something of the kind
Did surely haunt that day the mother's mind,
Making it irksome to bide all alone
By her own quiet hearth.   Though never known
For idle gossipry was Jenny Gray,
Yet so it was, that morn she could not stay
At home with her own thoughts, but took her
          way
To her next neighbor's, half a loaf to borrow, —
Yet might her store have lasted out the mor-
          row, —
And with the loan obtained, she lingered still.
Said she, " My master, if he 'd had his will,
Would have kept back our little ones from school
This dreadful morning ; and I 'm such a fool,
Since they 've been gone, I 've wished them back.
          But then
It won't do in such things to humor men, —
Our Ambrose specially.   If let alone
He 'd spoil those wenches.   But it 's coming on,
That storm he said was brewing, sure enough, —
Well ! what of that ?   To think what idle stuff
Will come into one's head !   And here with you
I stop, as if I 'd nothing else to do —
And they 'll come home, drowned rats.   I must
          be gone
To get dry things, and set the kettle on."

His day's work done, three mortal miles, and
　　more,
Lay between Ambrose and his cottage-door.
A weary way, God wot, for weary wight !
But yet far off the curling smoke in sight
From his own chimney, and his heart felt light.
How pleasantly the humble homestead stood,
Down the green lane, by sheltering Shirley wood!
How sweet the wafting of the evening breeze,
In spring-time, from his two old cherry-trees,
Sheeted with blossom !　And in hot July,
From the brown moor-track, shadowless and dry,
How grateful the cool covert to regain
Of his own *avenue*, — that shady lane,
With the white cottage, in a slanting glow
Of sunset glory, gleaming bright below,
And jasmine porch, his rustic portico !

With what a thankful gladness in his face,
(Silent heart-homage, — plant of special grace !)
At the lane's entrance, slackening oft his pace,
Would Ambrose send a loving look before,
Conceiting the caged blackbird at the door ;
The very blackbird strained its little throat,
In welcome, with a more rejoicing note ;
And honest Tinker, dog of doubtful breed,
All bristle, back, and tail, but "good at need,"
Pleasant his greeting to the accustomed ear ;
But of all welcomes pleasantest, most dear,
The ringing voices, like sweet silver bells,
Of his two little ones.　How fondly swells
The father's heart, as, dancing up the lane,
Each clasps a hand in her small hand again,
And each must tell her tale and "say her say,"
Impeding as she leads with sweet delay
(Childhood's blest thoughtlessness !) his onward
　　way.

And when the winter day closed in so fast ;
Scarce for his task would dreary daylight last ;
And in all weathers — driving sleet and snow —
Home by that bare, bleak moor-track must he go,
Darkling and lonely.　O, the blessed sight
(His polestar) of that little twinkling light
From one small window, through the leafless
　　trees,—
Glimmering so fitfully ; no eye but his
Had spied it so far off.　And sure was he,
Entering the lane, a steadier beam to see,
Ruddy and broad as peat-fed hearth could pour,
Streaming to meet him from the open door.
Then, though the blackbird's welcome was un-
　　heard, —
Silenced by winter, — note of summer bird
Still hailed him from no mortal fowl alive,
But from the cuckoo clock just striking five.
And Tinker's ear and Tinker's nose were keen,—
Off started he, and then a form was seen

Darkening the doorway ; and a smaller sprite,
And then another, peered into the night,
Ready to follow free on Tinker's track,
But for the mother's hand that held her back :
And yet a moment — a few steps — and there,
Pulled o'er the threshold by that eager pair,
He sits by his own hearth, in his own chair ;
Tinker takes post beside with eyes that say,
" Master, we 've done our business for the day."
The kettle sings, the cat in chorus purrs,
The busy housewife with her tea-things stirs ;
The door 's made fast, the old stuff curtain
　　drawn ;
How the hail clatters !　Let it clatter on !
How the wind raves and rattles !　What cares he ?
Safe housed and warm beneath his own roof-tree,
With a wee lassie prattling on each knee.

Such was the hour — hour sacred and apart —
Warmed in expectancy the poor man's heart
Summer and winter, as his toil he plied,
To him and his the literal doom applied,
Pronounced on Adam.　But the bread was sweet
So earned, for such dear mouths.　The weary feet,
Hope-shod, stept lightly on the homeward way ;
So specially it fared with Ambrose Gray
That time I tell of.　He had worked all day
At a great clearing ; vigorous stroke on stroke
Striking, till, when he stopt, his back seemed
　　broke,
And the strong arms dropt nerveless.　What of
　　that ?
There was a treasure hidden in his hat, —
A plaything for the young ones.　He had found
A dormouse nest ; the living ball coiled round
For its long winter sleep ; and all his thought,
As he trudged stoutly homeward, was of naught
But the glad wonderment in Jenny's eyes,
And graver Lizzy's quieter surprise,
When he should yield, by guess and kiss and
　　prayer
Hard won, the frozen captive to their care.

'T was a wild evening, — wild and rough.　"I
　　knew,"
Thought Ambrose, "those unlucky gulls spoke
　　true,
And Gaffer Chewton never growls for naught, —
I should be mortal 'mazed now if I thought
My little maids were not safe housed before
That blinding hail-storm, — ay, this hour and
　　more, —
Unless by that old crazy bit of board,
They 've not passed dry-foot over Shallow ford,
That I 'll be bound for, — swollen as it must
　　be —
Well ! if my mistress had been ruled by me — "
But, checking the half-thought as heresy,

He looked out for the Home Star. There it
   shone,
And with a gladdened heart he hastened on.

He 's in the lane again, — and there below,
Streams from the open doorway that red glow,
Which warms him but to look at. For his prize
Cautious he feels, — all safe and snug it lies. —
"Down, Tinker ! down, old boy ! — not quite so
   free, —
The thing thou sniffest is no game for thee. —
But what 's the meaning ? no lookout to-night !
No living soul astir ! Pray God, all 's right !
Who 's flittering round the peat-stack in such
   weather ?
Mother !" you might have felled him with a
   feather,
When the short answer to his loud "Hillo !"
And hurried question, "Are they come ?" was
   "No."

To throw his tools down, hastily unhook
The old cracked lantern from its dusty nook,
And, while he lit it, speak a cheering word,
That almost choked him, and was scarcely heard,
Was but a moment's act, and he was gone
To where a fearful foresight led him on.
Passing a neighbor's cottage in his way, —
Mark Fenton's, — him he took with short delay
To bear him company, — for who could say
What need might be ? They struck into the track
The children should have taken coming back
From school that day ; and many a call and shout
Into the pitchy darkness they sent out,
And, by the lantern light, peered all about,
In every roadside thicket, hole, and nook,
Till suddenly — as nearing now the brook —
Something brushed past them. That was Tink-
   er's bark, —
Unheeded, he had followed in the dark,
Close at his master's heels ; but, swift as light,
Darted before them now. "Be sure he 's right, —
He 's on the track," cried Ambrose. "Hold the
   light
Low down, — he 's making for the water. Hark !
I know that whine, — the old dog 's found them,
   Mark."
So speaking, breathlessly he hurried on
Toward the old crazy foot-bridge. It was gone !
And all his dull contracted light could show
Was the black void and dark swollen stream below.
"Yet there 's life somewhere, — more than Tink-
   er's whine, —
That s sure," said Mark. "So, let the lantern
   shine
Down yonder. There 's the dog, — and, hark !"
   "O dear !"
And a low sob came faintly on the ear,

Mocked by the sobbing gust. Down, quick as
   thought,
Into the stream leapt Ambrose, where he caught
Fast hold of something, — a dark huddled heap, —
Half in the water, where 't was scarce knee-deep
For a tall man, and half above it, propped
By some old ragged side-piles, that had stopt
Endways the broken plank, when it gave way
With the two little ones that luckless day !
"My babes ! — my lambkins !" was the father's
   cry.
One little voice made answer, "Here am I !"
'T was Lizzy's. There she crouched with face as
   white,
More ghastly by the flickering lantern-light
Than sheeted corpse. The pale blue lips drawn
   tight,
Wide parted, showing all the pearly teeth,
And eyes on some dark object underneath,
Washed by the turbid water, fixed as stone, —
One arm and hand stretched out, and rigid
   grown,
Grasping, as in the death-gripe, Jenny's frock.
There she lay drowned. Could he sustain that
   shock,
The doting father ? Where 's the unriven rock
Can bide such blasting in its flintiest part
As that soft sentient thing, — the human heart ?

They lifted her from out her watery bed, —
Its covering gone, the lovely little head
Hung like a broken snowdrop all aside ;
And one small hand, — the mother's shawl was
   tied,
Leaving *that* free, about the child's small form,
As was her last injunction — "*fast* and warm " —
Too well obeyed, — too fast ! A fatal hold
Affording to the scrag by a thick fold
That caught and pinned her in the river's bed,
While through the reckless water overhead
Her life-breath bubbled up.
                "She might have lived,
Struggling like Lizzy," was the thought that
   rived
The wretched mother's heart, when she knew all,
" But for my foolishness about that shawl !
And Master would have kept them back the day ;
But I was wilful, — driving them away
In such wild weather !"
             Thus the tortured heart
Unnaturally against itself takes part,
Driving the sharp edge deeper of a woe
Too deep already. They had raised her now,
And parting the wet ringlets from her brow,
To that, and the cold cheek, and lips as cold,
The father glued his warm ones, ere they rolled
Once more the fatal shawl — her winding-sheet —
About the precious clay. One heart still beat,

Warmed by *his heart's* blood.   To his *only child*
He turned him, but her piteous moaning mild
Pierced him afresh, — and now she knew him not.
"Mother !" she murmured, "who says I forgot ?
Mother ! indeed, indeed, I kept fast hold,
And tied the shawl quite close—she can't be cold—
But she won't move — we slipt — I don't know
        how —
But I held on — and I 'm so weary now —
And it 's so dark and cold ! O dear ! O dear ! —
And she won't move ; — if daddy was but here !"
  .   .   .   .   .   .
Poor lamb ! she wandered in her mind, 't was
        clear ;
But soon the piteous murmur died away,
And quiet in her father's arms she lay, —
They their dead burden had resigned, to take
The living, so near lost.   For her dear sake,
And one at home, he armed himself to bear
His misery like a man, — with tender care
Doffing his coat her shivering form to fold
(His neighbor bearing that which felt no cold),
He clasped her close, and so, with little said,
Homeward they bore the living and the dead.

From Ambrose Gray's poor cottage all that night
Shone fitfully a little shifting light,
Above, below, — for all were watchers there,
Save one sound sleeper.   *Her*, parental care,
Parental watchfulness, availed not now.
But in the young survivor's throbbing brow,
And wandering eyes, delirious fever burned ;
And all night long from side to side she turned,
Piteously plaining like a wounded dove,
With now and then the murmur, "She won't
        move."
And lo ! when morning, as in mockery, bright
Shone on that pillow, passing strange the sight, —
That young head's raven hair was streaked with
        white !
No idle fiction this.   Such things have been,
We know.   And now *I tell what I have seen.*

Life struggled long with death in that small frame,
But it was strong, and conquered.   All became
As it had been with the poor family, —
All, saving that which nevermore might be :
There was an empty place, — they were but three.
                CAROLINE BOWLES SOUTHEY.

———◆———

THE DREAM OF EUGENE ARAM.

'T WAS in the prime of summer time,
    An evening calm and cool,
And four-and-twenty happy boys
    Came bounding out of school ;

There were some that ran, and some that leapt
    Like troutlets in a pool.

Away they sped with gamesome minds
    And souls untouched by sin ;
To a level mead they came, and there
    They drave the wickets in :
Pleasantly shone the setting sun
    Over the town of Lynn.

Like sportive deer they coursed about,
    And shouted as they ran,
Turning to mirth all things of earth
    As only boyhood can ;
But the usher sat remote from all,
    A melancholy man !

His hat was off, his vest apart,
    To catch heaven's blessèd breeze ;
For a burning thought was in his brow,
    And his bosom ill at ease ;
So he leaned his head on his hands, and read
    The book between his knees.

Leaf after leaf he turned it o'er,
    Nor ever glanced aside, —
For the peace of his soul he read that book
    In the golden eventide ;
Much study had made him very lean,
    And pale, and leaden-eyed.

At last he shut the ponderous tome ;
    With a fast and fervent grasp
He strained the dusky covers close,
    And fixed the brazen hasp :
"O God ! could I so close my mind,
    And clasp it with a clasp !"

Then leaping on his feet upright,
    Some moody turns he took, —
Now up the mead, then down the mead,
    And past a shady nook, —
And, lo ! he saw a little boy
    That pored upon a book.

"My gentle lad, what is 't you read, —
    Romance or fairy fable ?
Or is it some historic page,
    Of kings and crowns unstable ?"
The young boy gave an upward glance, —
    "It is 'The Death of Abel.'"

The usher took six hasty strides,
    As smit with sudden pain, —
Six hasty strides beyond the place,
    Then slowly back again ;
And down he sat beside the lad,
    And talked with him of Cain ;

And, long since then, of bloody men,
  Whose deeds tradition saves ;
And lonely folk cut off unseen,
  And hid in sudden graves ;
And horrid stabs, in groves forlorn ;
  And murders done in caves ;

And how the sprites of injured men
  Shriek upward from the sod ;
Ay, how the ghostly hand will point
  To show the burial clod ;
And unknown facts of guilty acts
  Are seen in dreams from God.

He told how murderers walk the earth
  Beneath the curse of Cain, —
With crimson clouds before their eyes,
  And flames about their brain ;
For blood has left upon their souls
  Its everlasting stain !

"And well," quoth he, "I know for truth
  Their pangs must be extreme —
Woe, woe, unutterable woe ! —
  Who spill life's sacred stream.
For why ? Methought, last night I wrought
  A murder, in a dream !

"One that had never done me wrong, —
  A feeble man and old ;
I led him to a lonely field, —
  The moon shone clear and cold :
Now here, said I, this man shall die,
  And I will have his gold !

"Two sudden blows with a ragged stick,
  And one with a heavy stone,
One hurried gash with a hasty knife, —
  And then the deed was done :
There was nothing lying at my feet
  But lifeless flesh and bone !

"Nothing but lifeless flesh and bone,
  That could not do me ill ;
And yet I feared him all the more
  For lying there so still :
There was a manhood in his look
  That murder could not kill !

"And, lo ! the universal air
  Seemed lit with ghastly flame, —
Ten thousand thousand dreadful eyes
  Were looking down in blame ;
I took the dead man by his hand,
  And called upon his name.

"O God ! it made me quake to see
  Such sense within the slain ;

But, when I touched the lifeless clay,
  The blood gushed out amain !
For every clot a burning spot
  Was scorching in my brain !

"My head was like an ardent coal,
  My heart as solid ice ;
My wretched, wretched soul, I knew,
  Was at the Devil's price.
A dozen times I groaned, — the dead
  Had never groaned but twice.

"And now, from forth the frowning sky,
  From the heaven's topmost height,
I heard a voice, — the awful voice
  Of the blood-avenging sprite :
'Thou guilty man ! take up thy dead,
  And hide it from my sight !'

"And I took the dreary body up,
  And cast it in a stream, —
The sluggish water black as ink,
  The depth was so extreme : —
My gentle boy, remember, this
  Is nothing but a dream !

"Down went the corse with a hollow plunge,
  And vanished in the pool ;
Anon I cleansed my bloody hands,
  And washed my forehead cool,
And sat among the urchins young,
  That evening, in the school.

"O Heaven ! to think of their white souls,
  And mine so black and grim !
I could not share in childish prayer,
  Nor join in evening hymn ;
Like a devil of the pit I seemed,
  Mid holy cherubim !

"And Peace went with them, one and all,
  And each calm pillow spread ;
But Guilt was my grim chamberlain,
  That lighted me to bed,
And drew my midnight curtains round
  With fingers bloody red !

"All night I lay in agony,
  In anguish dark and deep ;
My fevered eyes I dared not close,
  But stared aghast at Sleep ;
For Sin had rendered unto her
  The keys of hell to keep !

"All night I lay in agony,
  From weary chime to chime ;
With one besetting horrid hint
  That racked me all the time,

A mighty yearning, like the first
  Fierce impulse unto crime, —

" One stern tyrannic thought, that made
  All other thoughts its slave !
Stronger and stronger every pulse
  Did that temptation crave, —
Still urging me to go and see
  The dead man in his grave !

" Heavily I rose up, as soon
  As light was in the sky,
And sought the black accursèd pool
  With a wild, misgiving eye ;
And I saw the dead in the river-bed,
  For the faithless stream was dry.

" Merrily rose the lark, and shook
  The dew-drop from its wing ;
But I never marked its morning flight,
  I never heard it sing,
For I was stooping once again
  Under the horrid thing.

" With breathless speed, like a soul in chase,
  I took him up and ran ;
There was no time to dig a grave
  Before the day began, —
In a lonesome wood, with heaps of leaves,
  I hid the murdered man !

" And all that day I read in school,
  But my thought was otherwhere ;
As soon as the midday task was done,
  In secret I was there, —
And a mighty wind had swept the leaves,
  And still the corse was bare !

" Then down I cast me on my face,
  And first began to weep,
For I knew my secret then was one
  That earth refused to keep, —
Or land or sea, though he should be
  Ten thousand fathoms deep.

" So wills the fierce avenging sprite,
  Till blood for blood atones !
Ay, though he 's buried in a cave,
  And trodden down with stones,
And years have rotted off his flesh, —
  The world shall see his bones !

" O God ! that horrid, horrid dream
  Besets me now awake !
Again — again, with dizzy brain,
  The human life I take ;
And my red right hand grows raging hot,
  Like Cranmer's at the stake.

" And still no peace for the restless clay
  Will wave or mould allow ;
The horrid thing pursues my soul, —
  It stands before me now ! "
The fearful boy looked up, and saw
  Huge drops upon his brow.

That very night, while gentle sleep
  The urchin's eyelids kissed,
Two stern-faced men set out from Lynn
  Through the cold and heavy mist ;
And Eugene Aram walked between,
  With gyves upon his wrist.
                    THOMAS HOOD.

RAMON.

REFUGIO MINE, NORTHERN MEXICO.

DRUNK and senseless in his place,
Prone and sprawling on his face,
More like brute than any man
    Alive or dead, —
By his great pump out of gear,
Lay the peon engineer,
Waking only just to hear,
    Overhead,
Angry tones that called his name,
Oaths and cries of bitter blame, —
Woke to hear all this, and waking, turned and
    fled !

" To the man who 'll bring to me,"
  Cried Intendant Harry Lee, —
Harry Lee, the English foreman of the mine, —
" Bring the sot alive or dead,
I will give to him," he said,
" Fifteen hundred *pesos* down,
Just to set the rascal's crown
Underneath this heel of mine :
    Since but death
Deserves the man whose deed,
Be it vice or want of heed,
Stops the pumps that give us breath, —
Stops the pumps that suck the death
From the poisoned lower levels of the mine ! "

No one answered, for a cry
  From the shaft rose up on high ;
And shuffling, scrambling, tumbling from below,
  Came the miners each, the bolder
  Mounting on the weaker's shoulder,
  Grappling, clinging to their hold or
    Letting go,
  As the weaker gasped and fell
  From the ladder to the well, —
  To the poisoned pit of hell
    Down below !

"To the man who sets them free,"
Cried the foreman, Harry Lee, —
Harry Lee, the English foreman of the mine, —
"Brings them out and sets them free,
I will give that man," said he,
"Twice that sum, who with a rope
Face to face with death shall cope :
Let him come who dares to hope ! "
"Hold your peace ! " some one replied,
Standing by the foreman's side ;
"There has one already gone, whoe'er he be ! "

Then they held their breath with awe,
Pulling on the rope, and saw
Fainting figures reappear,
On the black rope swinging clear,
Fastened by some skilful hand from below ;
Till a score the level gained,
And but one alone remained, —
He the hero and the last,
He whose skilful hand made fast
The long line that brought them back to hope
    and cheer !

Haggard, gasping, down dropped he
At the feet of Harry Lee, —
Harry Lee, the English foreman of the mine ;
"I have come," he gasped, "to claim
Both rewards, Señor, — my name
    Is Ramon !
I'm the drunken engineer, —
I'm the coward, Señor — " Here
He fell over, by that sign
    Dead as stone !

                              BRET HARTE.

REVELRY OF THE DYING.

[Supposed to be written in India, while the plague was raging,
and playing havoc among the British residents and troops stationed
there.   This has been attributed to Alfred Domett and to Bartholomew Dowling, but was written by neither of them.   It first
appeared in the *New York Albion*, but the author is absolutely unknown.]

WE meet 'neath the sounding rafter,
    And the walls around are bare ;
As they shout to our peals of laughter,
    It seems that the dead are there.
But stand to your glasses, steady !
    We drink to our comrades' eyes ;
Quaff a cup to the dead already —
    And hurrah for the next that dies !

Not here are the goblets glowing,
    Not here is the vintage sweet ;
'T is cold, as our hearts are growing,
    And dark as the doom we meet.

But stand to your glasses, steady !
    And soon shall our pulses rise ;
A cup to the dead already—
    Hurrah for the next that dies !

Not a sigh for the lot that darkles,
    Not a tear for the friends that sink ;
We 'll fall, midst the wine-cup's sparkles,
    As mute as the wine we drink.
So stand to your glasses, steady !
    'T is this that the respite buys ;
One cup to the dead already —
    Hurrah for the next that dies !

Time was when we frowned at others ;
    We thought we were wiser then ;
Ha ! ha ! let those think of their mothers,
    Who hope to see them again.
No ! stand to your glasses, steady !
    The thoughtless are here the wise ;
A cup to the dead already —
    Hurrah for the next that dies !

There 's many a hand that 's shaking,
    There 's many a cheek that 's sunk ;
But soon, though our hearts are breaking,
    They 'll burn with the wine we 've drunk
So stand to your glasses, steady !
    'T is here the revival lies ;
A cup to the dead already —
    Hurrah for the next that dies !

There 's a mist on the glass congealing,
    'T is the hurricane's fiery breath ;
And thus does the warmth of feeling
    Turn ice in the grasp of Death.
Ho ! stand to your glasses, steady !
    For a moment the vapor flies ;
A cup to the dead already —
    Hurrah for the next that dies !

Who dreads to the dust returning ?
    Who shrinks from the sable shore,
Where the high and haughty yearning
    Of the soul shall sting no more !
Ho ! stand to your glasses, steady !
    The world is a world of lies ;
A cup to the dead already —
    Hurrah for the next that dies !

Cut off from the land that bore us,
    Betrayed by the land we find,
Where the brightest have gone before us,
    And the dullest remain behind —
Stand, stand to your glasses, steady !
    'T is all we have left to prize ;
A cup to the dead already —
    And hurrah for the next that dies !

FRAGMENTS.

The First Tragedy.

So saying, her rash hand in evil hour
Forth reaching to the fruit, she plucked, she eat :
Earth felt the wound ; and Nature from her seat,
Sighing through all her works, gave signs of woe,
That all was lost.

Paradise Lost, Book ix.   MILTON.

He scrupled not to eat
Against his better knowledge, not deceived,
But fondly overcome with female charm.
Earth trembled from her entrails, as again
In pangs, and Nature gave a second groan.

Paradise Lost, Book ix.   MILTON.

Death
Grinned horrible a ghastly smile, to hear
His famine should be filled, and blessed his maw
Destined to that good hour.

Paradise Lost, Book ii.   MILTON.

Effects of Crime and Grief.

The stings of Falsehood those shall try,
And hard Unkindness' altered eye,
  That mocks the tear it forced to flow ;
And keen Remorse with blood defiled,
And moody Madness laughing wild
  Amid severest woe.

On a Distant Prospect of Eton College.   T. GRAY.

My heart is as an anvil unto sorrow,
Which beats upon it like a Cyclop's hammer,
And with the noise turns up my giddy brain
And makes me frantic !

Edward II.   C. MARLOWE.

Every sense
Had been o'erstrung by pangs intense ;
And each frail fibre of her brain
(As bowstrings, when relaxed by rain,
The erring arrow launch aside)
Sent forth her thoughts all wild and wide.

Parisina.   BYRON.

I am not mad ; — I would to heaven I were !
For then, 't is like I should forget myself ;
O, if I could, what grief I should forget !

King John, Act iii. *Sc.* 4.   SHAKESPEARE.

Portents and Fears.

CÆSAR.   Speak ! Cæsar is turned to hear.
SOOTHSAYER.   Beware the Ides of March !

Julius Cæsar, Act i. *Sc.* 2.   SHAKESPEARE.

Fierce fiery warriors fought upon the clouds,
In ranks and squadrons, and right form of war,
Which drizzled blood upon the Capitol.
O Cæsar ! these things are beyond all use,
And I do fear them.

.   .   .   .   .

When beggars die there are no comets seen ;
The heavens themselves blaze forth the death of
    princes.

Julius Cæsar, Act ii. *Sc.* 2.   SHAKESPEARE.

Danger knows full well
That Cæsar is more dangerous than he.
We are two lions littered in one day,
And I the elder and more terrible.

Julius Cæsar, Act ii. *Sc.* 2.   SHAKESPEARE.

What is danger
More than the weakness of our apprehensions ?
A poor cold part o' th' blood ; who takes it hold of ?
Cowards and wicked livers : valiant minds
Were made the masters of it.

Chances.   BEAUMONT and FLETCHER.

CÆSAR. The Ides of March are come.
SOOTHSAYER. Ay, Cæsar ; but not gone.

Julius Cæsar, Act iii. *Sc.* 1.   SHAKESPEARE.

Eyes, look your last :
Arms, take your last embrace ; and lips,
            O ! you,
The doors of breath, seal with a righteous kiss
A dateless bargain to engrossing death.

Romeo and Juliet, Act v. *Sc.* 3.   SHAKESPEARE.

The King's Enemy.

Thou art a traitor. —
Off with his head ! — now by Saint Paul I swear
I will not dine until I see the same.

King Richard III., Act iii. *Sc.* 4.   SHAKESPEARE.

Off with his head ! so much for Buckingham !

Shakespeare's Richard III. (Altered), Act iv. *Sc.* 3.
C. CIBBER.

Revenge.

And if we do but watch the hour,
There never yet was human power
Which could evade, if unforgiven,
The patient search and vigil long
Of him who treasures up a wrong.

Mazeppa.   BYRON.

I will feed fat the ancient grudge I bear him.

Merchant of Venice, Act i. *Sc.* 2.   SHAKESPEARE.

If it will feed nothing else, it will feed my re-
    venge.

Merchant of Venice, Act iii. *Sc.* 1.   SHAKESPEARE.

Vengeance to God alone belongs ;
But when I think on all my wrongs,
My blood is liquid flame.

Marmion, Cant. vi.   SCOTT.

FORETHOUGHT OF MURDER.

There shall be done
A deed of dreadful note.

Macbeth, Act iii. *Sc.* 2.   SHAKESPEARE.

Between the acting of a dreadful thing,
And the first motion, all the interim is
Like a phantasma, or a hideous dream :
The Genius, and the mortal instruments,
Are then in council ; and the state of man,
Like to a little kingdom, suffers then
The nature of an insurrection.

Julius Cæsar, Act i. *Sc.* 1.   SHAKESPEARE.

If it were done, when 't is done, then 't were well
It were done quickly : if the assassination
Could trammel up the consequence, and catch
With his surcease, success ; that but this blow
Might be the be-all and the end-all here,
But here, upon this bank and shoal of time, —
We 'd jump the life to come.

.   .   .   .

Besides, this Duncan
Hath borne his faculties so meek, hath been
So clear in his great office, that his virtues
Will plead like angels, trumpet-tongued, against
The deep damnation of his taking-off.

Macbeth, Act i. *Sc.* 7.   SHAKESPEARE.

Put out the light, and then — put out the light.
If I quench thee, thou flaming minister,
I can again thy former light restore,
Should I repent me ; but once put out thy light,
Thou cunning'st pattern of excelling nature,
I know not where is that Promethean heat,
That can thy light relume. When I have plucked
thy rose
I cannot give it vital growth again,
It needs must wither.

Othello, Act v. *Sc.* 2.   SHAKESPEARE.

Stop up th' access and passage to remorse,
That no compunctious visitings of nature
Shake my fell purpose, nor keep peace between
Th' effect and it.

Macbeth, Act i. *Sc.* 5.   SHAKESPEARE.

Let 's kill him boldly, but not wrathfully ;
Let 's carve him as a dish fit for the gods,
Not hew him as a carcase fit for hounds.

Julius Cæsar, Act ii. *Sc.* 1.   SHAKESPEARE.

AFTERWARDS.

O, my offence is rank, it smells to heaven ;
It hath the primal eldest curse upon 't,
A brother's murder.

Hamlet, Act iii. *Sc.* 3.   SHAKESPEARE.

O horror ! horror ! horror ! Tongue nor heart
Cannot conceive nor name thee.

.   .   .   .

Confusion now hath made his master-piece.
Most sacrilegious murder hath broke ope
The Lord's anointed temple, and stole thence
The life o' the building.

Macbeth, Act ii. *Sc.* 2.   SHAKESPEARE.

Blood, though it sleep a time, yet never dies :
The gods on murderers fix revengeful eyes.

Widow's Tears.   CHAPMAN.

Foul deeds will rise,
Though all the earth o'erwhelm them, to men's
eyes.

Hamlet, Act i. *Sc.* 2.   SHAKESPEARE.

O blisful God, that art so just and trewe !
Lo, howe that thou biwreyest mordre alway !
Mordre wol out, that se we day by day.

The Nonnes Preestes Tale.   CHAUCER.

For murder, though it have no tongue, will speak
With most miraculous organ.

Hamlet, Act ii. *Sc.* 1.   SHAKESPEARE.

THE HARDENED CRIMINAL.

I have almost forgot the taste of fear.
The time has been, my senses would have quailed
To hear a night-shriek ; and my fell of hair
Would at a dismal treatise rouse, and stir,
As life were in 't.   I have supped full with hor-
rors :
Direness, familiar to my slaughterous thoughts,
Cannot once start me.

Macbeth, Act v. *Sc.* 4.   SHAKESPEARE.

SUICIDE.

All mankind
Is one of these two cowards ;
Either to wish to die
When he should live, or live when he should die.

The Blind Lady.   SIR R. HOWARD.

Our enemies have beat us to the hip :
It is more worthy to leap in ourselves
Than tarry till they push us.

Julius Cæsar, Act v. *Sc.* 5.   SHAKESPEARE.

He
That kills himself t' avoid misery, fears it,
And at the best shows but a bastard valor :
This life 's a fort committed to my trust,
Which I must not yield up, till it be forced ;
Nor will I : he 's not valiant that dares die,
But he that boldly bears calamity.

The Maid of Honor.   P. MASSINGER.

PERSONAL POEMS

Epitaph.

Here rests his Head upon the Lap of Earth
A Youth, to Fortune & to Fame unknown:
Fair Science frown'd not on his humble Birth,
And Melancholy mark'd him for her own.

Large was his Bounty, & his Soul sincere;
Heav'n did a Recompense as largely send:
He gave to Mis'ry all, he had, a Tear,
He gain'd from Heav'n ('twas all he wish'd) a Friend

No farther seek his Merits to disclose,
Or draw his Frailties from their dread Abode,
(There they alike in trembling Hope repose)
The Bosom of his Father, & his God.

T. Gray.

———————

One year, one year, one little year
And so much gone
And yet the even flow of life
Moves calmly on:

H B Stowe

———————

Hark! to the tolling bells
In echoes deep and slow,
While on the breeze our banner floats
Draped in the weeds of woe.

L. Huntley Sigourney.

PERSONAL POEMS.

PRAXITELES.

FROM THE GREEK.

VENUS (*loquitur*). Paris, Anchises, and Adonis
   — three,
Three only, did me ever naked see ;
But this Praxiteles — when, where, did he ?

DIRGE OF ALARIC THE VISIGOTH.

[Alaric stormed and spoiled the city of Rome, and was afterwards
buried in the channel of the river Busentius, the water of which
had been diverted from its course that the body might be interred.]

WHEN I am dead, no pageant train
  Shall waste their sorrows at my bier,
Nor worthless pomp of homage vain
  Stain it with hypocritic tear ;
For I will die as I did live,
Nor take the boon I cannot give.

Ye shall not raise a marble bust
  Upon the spot where I repose ;
Ye shall not fawn before my dust,
  In hollow circumstance of woes ;
Nor sculptured clay, with lying breath,
Insult the clay that moulds beneath.

Ye shall not pile with servile toil
  Your monuments upon my breast,
Nor yet within the common soil
  Lay down the wreck of power to rest ;
Where man can boast that he has trod
On him that was "the scourge of God."

But ye the mountain-stream shall turn,
  And lay its secret channel bare
And hollow, for your sovereign's urn
  A resting-place forever there :
Then bid its everlasting springs
Flow back upon the king of kings ;
And never be the secret said,
Until the deep give up his dead.

My gold and silver ye shall fling
  Back to the clods that gave them birth ; –
The captured crowns of many a king,
  The ransom of a conquered earth ;
For e'en though dead will I control
The trophies of the capitol.

But when, beneath the mountain-tide,
  Ye 've laid your monarch down to rot,
Ye shall not rear upon its side
  Pillar or mound to mark the spot ;
For long enough the world has shook
Beneath the terrors of my look ;
And now, that I have run my race,
The astonished realms shall rest a space.

My course was like a river deep,
  And from the northern hills I burst,
Across the world in wrath to sweep,
  And where I went the spot was cursed.
Nor blade of grass again was seen
Where Alaric and his hosts had been.

See how their haughty barriers fail
  Beneath the terror of the Goth,
Their iron-breasted legions quail
  Before my ruthless sabaoth,
And low the queen of empires kneels,
And grovels at my chariot-wheels.

Not for myself did I ascend
  In judgment my triumphal car ;
'T was God alone, on high, did send
  The avenging Scythian to the war,
To shake abroad, with iron hand,
The appointed scourge of his command.

With iron hand that scourge I reared
  O'er guilty king and guilty realm ;
Destruction was the ship I steered,
  And Vengeance sat upon the helm,
When, launched in fury on the flood,
I ploughed my way through seas of blood,
And, in the stream their hearts had spilt,
Washed out the long arrears of guilt.

Across the everlasting Alp
  I poured the torrent of my powers,
And feeble Cæsars shrieked for help,
  In vain, within their seven-hilled towers !
I quenched in blood the brightest gem
That glittered in their diadem,
And struck a darker, deeper dye
In the purple of their majesty,
And bade my Northern banners shine
Upon the conquered Palatine.

My course is run, my errand done ;
  I go to Him from whom I came ;
But never yet shall set the sun
  Of glory that adorns my name ;
And Roman hearts shall long be sick,
When men shall think of Alaric.

My course is run, my errand done ;
  But darker ministers of fate,
Impatient, round the eternal throne,
  And in the caves of vengeance, wait ;
And soon mankind shall blench away
Before the name of Attila.

                          EDWARD EVERETT.

———◆———

THE COMPLEYNTE OF CHAUCER TO HIS PURSE.*

To you, my purse, and to noon other wight
  Compleyn I, for ye be my lady dere !
I am so sorry now that ye been lyght,
  For certes, but-yf ye make me hevy chere,
  Me were as leaf be layde upon my bere,
For whiche unto your mercy thus I crye, —
Beeth hevy ageyne, or ellès mote I dye !

Now voucheth sauf this day, or it be nyghte,
  That I of you the blissful soune may here,
Or see your colour lyke the sonnè bryghte,
  That of yelownesse haddè never pere,
  Ye be my lyfe ! ye be myn hertys stere ! †
Quene of comfort and good companye !
Beth hevy ageyne, or ellès mote I dye.

Now, purse, that ben to me my lyves lyght
  And saveour, as doun in this worlde here,
Oute of this toune helpe me thurgh your myght,

* " From this unique petition," says Mr. Gilman in his "River-
side" *Chaucer,* "there seems to have resulted an additional pension
of forty marks a year, on the strength of which Chaucer took a lease
of a house in the garden of St. Mary's Chapel, Westminster, for
fifty-three years, at an annual rent of two pounds thirteen shillings
and fourpence, the lease to be void on the poet's death." So that
the practical results of this poetical plaint show that Chaucer well
described one of his own characteristics in his description of the
MARCHANT, among his *Canterbury Pilgrims,* —

  " This worthy man ful wel his wit bisette [used]."

‡ guide.

Syn that ye wole not ben my tresorere ;
  For I am shave as nye as is a frere.
But I praye unto your curtesye
Beth hevy ageyn, or ellès moote I dye !

L'ENVOYE DE CHAUCER.

O conquerour of Brutes Albyoun,*
Whiche that by lygne and free eleccioun
  Been verray Kynge,† this song to you I sende,
  And ye that mowen ‡ alle myn harme amende,
Have mynde upon my supplicacioun !
                          GEOFFREY CHAUCER.

———◆———

SIR PHILIP SIDNEY.

FROM "AN ELEGY ON A FRIEND'S PASSION FOR HIS
ASTROPHILL."

WITHIN these woods of Arcadie
He chiefe delight and pleasure tooke,
And on the mountaine Parthenie,
Upon the chrystall liquid brooke,
  The Muses met him ev'ry day,
  That taught him sing, to write, and say.

When he descended downe to the mount,
His personage seemed most divine,
A thousand graces one might count
Upon his lovely, cheerfull eine ;
  To heare him speake and sweetly smile,
  You were in Paradise the while.

A sweet attractive kinde of grace,
A full assurance given by lookes,
Continuall comfort in a face,
The lineaments of Gospell bookes ;
  I trowe that countenance cannot lie,
  Whose thoughts are legible in the eie.

Was never eie did see that face,
Was never eare did heare that tong,
Was never minde did minde his grace,
That ever thought the travell long ;
  But eies, and eares, and ev'ry thought,
  Were with his sweete perfections caught.
                          MATTHEW ROYDEN.

———◆———

ANNE HATHAWAY.

TO THE IDOL OF MY EYE AND DELIGHT OF MY HEART,
ANNE HATHAWAY

WOULD ye be taught, ye feathered throng,
With love's sweet notes to grace your song,
To pierce the heart with thrilling lay,
Listen to mine Anne Hathaway !

* The Albion of Brutus, a descendant of Eneas.
† King Henry IV. seems to be meant.   ‡ may

She hath a way to sing so clear,
Phœbus might wondering stop to hear.
To melt the sad, make blithe the gay,
And nature charm, Anne hath a way ;
    She hath a way,
     Anne Hathaway ;
To breathe delight Anne hath a way.

When Envy's breath and rancorous tooth
Do soil and bite fair worth and truth,
And merit to distress betray,
To soothe the heart Anne hath a way ;
She hath a way to chase despair,
To heal all grief, to cure all care,
Turn foulest night to fairest day.
Thou know'st, fond heart, Anne hath a way ;
    She hath a way,
     Anne Hathaway ;
To make grief bliss, Anne hath a way.

Talk not of gems, the orient list,
The diamond, topaz, amethyst,
The emerald mild, the ruby gay ;
Talk of my gem, Anne Hathaway !
She hath a way, with her bright eye,
Their various lustres to defy, —
The jewels she, and the foil they,
So sweet to look Anne hath a way ;
    She hath a way,
     Anne Hathaway ;
To shame bright gems, Anne hath a way.

But were it to my fancy given
To rate her charms, I 'd call them heaven ;
For, though a mortal made of clay,
Angels must love Anne Hathaway ;
She hath a way so to control,
To rapture, the imprisoned soul,
And sweetest heaven on earth display,
That to be heaven Anne hath a way ;
    She hath a way,
     Anne Hathaway ;
To be heaven's self, Anne hath a way.
        ANONYMOUS *

ON THE PORTRAIT † OF SHAKESPEARE.

This figure, that thou here seest put,
It was for gentle Shakespeare cut ;
Wherein the Graver had a strife
With Nature to outdo the life :
O, could he but have drawn his wit
As well in brass, as he hath hit

* This poem has sometimes, but without much reason, been attributed to Shakespeare.
† The engraving by Martin Droeshout.

His face ; the Print would then surpass
All that was ever writ in brass.
But since he cannot, Reader, look
Not at his picture, but his book.
        BEN JONSON

SHAKESPEARE.

FROM " PROLOGUE " SPOKEN BY MR. GARRICK AT THE OPEN-
ING OF THE THEATRE IN DRURY LANE, IN 1747.

When Learning's triumph o'er her barbarous
    foes
First reared the stage, immortal Shakespeare rose ;
Each change of many-colored life he drew,
Exhausted worlds, and then imagined new :
Existence saw him spurn her bounded reign,
And panting Time toiled after him in vain :
His powerful strokes presiding Truth impressed,
And unresisted Passion stormed the breast.
        DR. SAMUEL JOHNSON.

TO THE MEMORY OF MY BELOVED MASTER, WILLIAM SHAKESPEARE, AND WHAT HE HATH LEFT US.

To draw no envy, Shakespeare, on thy name,
Am I thus ample to thy book and fame ;
While I confess thy writings to be such
As neither man nor Muse can praise too much.
'T is true, and all men's suffrage. But these ways
Were not the paths I meant unto thy praise ;
For silliest ignorance on these would light,
Which, when it sounds at best, but echoes right ;
Or blind affection, which doth ne'er advance
The truth, but gropes, and urges all by chance ;
Or crafty malice might pretend this praise,
And think to ruin, where it seemed to raise.

  .   .   .   .

But thou art proof against them, and, indeed,
Above the ill fortune of them, or the need.
I therefore will begin : Soul of the age !
The applause, delight, the wonder of our stage !
My Shakespeare, rise ! I will not lodge thee by
Chaucer, or Spenser, or bid Beaumont lie
A little further off, to make thee room :
Thou art a monument without a tomb,
And art alive still, while thy book doth live,
And we have wits to read, and praise to give.
That I not mix thee so, my brain excuses,
I mean with great but disproportioned Muses :
For if I thought my judgment were of years,
I should commit thee surely with thy peers,
And tell how far thou didst our Lyly outshine,
Or sporting Kyd or Marlowe's mighty line.
And though thou had small Latin and less Greek,
From thence to honour thee I will not seek
For names ; but call forth thundering Eschylus,
Euripides, and Sophocles to us,

Pacuvius, Accius, him of Cordova dead,
To live again, to hear thy buskin tread,
And shake a stage : or when thy socks were on,
Leave thee alone for the comparison
Of all, that insolent Greece or haughty Rome
Sent forth, or since did from their ashes come.
Triumph, my Britain, thou hast one to show,
To whom all scenes of Europe homage owe.
He was not of an age, but for all time !
And all the Muses still were in their prime,
When, like Apollo, he came forth to warm
Our ears, or like a Mercury, to charm !
Nature herself was proud of his designs,
And joyed to wear the dressing of his lines !
Which were so richly spun, and woven so fit,
As, since, she will vouchsafe no other wit.
The merry Greek, tart Aristophanes,
Neat Terence, witty Plautus, now not please :
But antiquated and deserted lie,
As they were not of nature's family.
Yet must I not give nature all ; thy art,
My gentle Shakespeare, must enjoy a part.
For though the poet's matter nature be,
His art doth give the fashion ; and, that he
Who casts to write a living line, must sweat
(Such as thine are) and strike the second heat
Upon the Muses' anvil ; turn the same,
And himself with it, that he thinks to frame ;
Or for the laurel, he may gain a scorn ;
For a good poet 's made as well as born.
And such wert thou !   Look how the father's face
Lives in his issue, even so the race
Of Shakespeare's mind and manners brightly
    shines
In his well turned and true filed lines :
In each of which he seems to shake a lance,
As brandished at the eyes of ignorance.
Sweet Swan of Avon ! what a sight it were
To see thee in our water yet appear,
And make those flights upon the banks of Thames
That so did take Eliza and our James !
But stay, I see thee in the hemisphere
Advanced, and made a constellation there !
Shine forth, thou Star of Poets, and with rage,
Or influence, chide, or cheer the drooping stage
Which since thy flight from hence hath mourned
    like night,
And despairs day, but for thy volume's light !
                                    BEN JONSON.

SHAKESPEARE.

THE soul of man is larger than the sky,
Deeper than ocean, or the abysmal dark
Of the unfathomed centre.   Like that ark,
Which in its sacred hold uplifted high,
O'er the drowned hills, the human family,

And stock reserved of every living kind,
So, in the compass of the single mind,
The seeds and pregnant forms in essence lie,
That make all worlds.   Great poet, 't was th
    art
To know thyself, and in thyself to be
Whate'er love, hate, ambition, destiny,
Or the firm fatal purpose of the heart
Can make of man.   Yet thou wert still the
    same,
Serene of thought, unhurt by thy own flame.
                            HARTLEY COLERIDGE.

AN   EPITAPH   ON   THE   ADMIRABLE DRAMATIC POET, W. SHAKESPEARE.

WHAT needs my Shakespeare for his honored
    bones,
The labor of an age in pilèd stones ?
Or that his hallowed relics should be hid
Under a star-y-pointing pyramid ?
Dear son of memory, great heir of fame,
What need'st thou such weak witness of thy
    name ?
Thou in our wonder and astonishment
Hast built thyself a livelong monument.
For whilst to the shame of slow-endeavoring art
Thy easy numbers flow, and that each heart
Hath from the leaves of thy unvalued book
Those Delphic lines with deep impression took,
Then thou our fancy of itself bereaving,
Dost make us marble with too much conceiv-
    ing ;
And so sepúlchred in such pomp dost lie,
That kings for such a tomb would wish to die.
                                    MILTON.

TO THE MEMORY OF BEN JONSON.

THE Muse's fairest light in no dark time,
The wonder of a learnèd age ; the line
Which none can pass ! the most proportioned
    wit, —
To nature, the best judge of what was fit ;
The deepest, plainest, highest, clearest pen ;
The voice most echoed by consenting men ;
The soul which answered best to all well said
By others, and which most requital made ;
Tuned to the highest key of ancient Rome,
Returning all her music with his own ;
In whom, with nature, study claimed a part,
And yet who to himself owed all his art :
Here lies Ben Jonson ! every age will look
With sorrow here, with wonder on his book.
                            JOHN CLEVELAND.

ODE TO BEN JONSON.

Ah Ben !
Say how or when
Shall we, thy guests,
Meet at those lyric feasts,
Made at the Sun,
The Dog, the Triple Tun ;
Where we such clusters had
As made us nobly wild, not mad ;
And yet each verse of thine
Outdid the meat, outdid the frolic wine.

My Ben !
Or come again,
Or send to us
Thy wit's great overplus ;
But teach us yet
Wisely to husband it,
Lest we that talent spend :
And having once brought to an end
That precious stock, the store
Of such a wit, the world should have no more.

ROBERT HERRICK.

BEN JONSON'S COMMONPLACE BOOK.

His learning such, no author, old or new,
Escaped his reading that deserved his view ;
And such his judgment, so exact his taste,
Of what was best in books, or what books best,
That had he joined those notes his labors took
From each most praised and praise-deserving
        book,
And could the world of that choice treasure boast,
It need not care though all the rest were lost.

LUCIUS CARY (LORD FALKLAND).

EPITAPH ON THE COUNTESS OF PEMBROKE.

Underneath this sable hearse
Lies the subject of all verse,
Sydney's sister, — Pembroke's mother.
Death, ere thou hast slain another
Fair and wise and good as she,
Time shall throw a dart at thee !

Marble piles let no man raise
To her name in after days ;
Some kind woman, born as she,
Reading this, like Niobe
Shall turn marble, and become
Both her mourner and her tomb.

BEN JONSON.

EPITAPH ON ELIZABETH L. H.

Wouldst thou heare what man can say
In a little ? — reader, stay !
Underneath this stone doth lye
As much beauty as could dye, —
Which in life did harbor give
To more vertue than doth live.
If at all she had a fault,
Leave it buried in this vault.
One name was Elizabeth, —
The other, let it sleep with death :
Fitter where it dyed to tell,
Than that it lived at all.   Farewell !

BEN JONSON.

UNDER THE PORTRAIT OF JOHN MILTON.

PREFIXED TO "PARADISE LOST."

Three Poets, in three distant ages born,
Greece, Italy, and England did adorn.
The first in loftiness of thought surpassed ;
The next in majesty ; in both the last.
The force of nature could no further go ;
To make a third, she joined the former two.

JOHN DRYDEN

TO MILTON.

"LONDON, 1802."

Milton ! thou shouldst be living at this hour :
England hath need of thee : she is a fen
Of stagnant waters : altar, sword, and pen,
Fireside, the heroic wealth of hall and bower,
Have forfeited their ancient English dower
Of inward happiness.   We are selfish men ;
Oh ! raise us up, return to us again ;
And give us manners, virtue, freedom, power.
Thy soul was like a star, and dwelt apart :
Thou hadst a voice whose sound was like the sea
Pure as the naked heavens, majestic, free,
So didst thou travel on life's common way,
In cheerful godliness ; and yet thy heart
The lowliest duties on herself did lay.

WILLIAM WORDSWORTH.

THE SONNET.

Scorn not the sonnet ; critic, you have frowned,
Mindless of its just honors ; with this key
Shakespeare unlocked his heart ; the melody
Of this small lute gave ease to Petrarch's wound ;
A thousand times this pipe did Tasso sound ;
With it Camoëns soothed an exile's grief ;
The sonnet glittered a gay myrtle leaf

Amid the cypress with which Dante crowned
His visionary brow; a glow-worm lamp,
It cheered mild Spenser, called from fairy-land
To struggle through dark ways ; and when a damp
Fell round the path of Milton, in his hand
The thing became a trumpet ; whence he blew
Soul-animating strains, — alas ! too few.

WILLIAM WORDSWORTH.

ON A BUST OF DANTE.

SEE, from this counterfeit of him
Whom Arno shall remember long,
How stern of lineament, how grim,
The father was of Tuscan song !
There but the burning sense of wrong,
Perpetual care, and scorn, abide —
Small friendship for the lordly throng,
Distrust of all the world beside.

Faithful if this wan image be,
No dream his life was — but a fight ;
Could any Beatrice see
A lover in that anchorite ?
To that cold Ghibeline's gloomy sight
Who could have guessed the visions came
Of beauty, veiled with heavenly light,
In circles of eternal flame ?

The lips as Cumæ's cavern close,
The cheeks with fast and sorrow thin,
The rigid front, almost morose,
But for the patient hope within,
Declare a life whose course hath been
Unsullied still, though still severe,
Which, through the wavering days of sin,
Kept itself icy-chaste and clear.

Not wholly such his haggard look
When wandering once, forlorn, he strayed,
With no companion save his book,
To Corvo's hushed monastic shade ;
Where, as the Benedictine laid
His palm upon the pilgrim guest,
The single boon for which he prayed
The convent's charity was rest.

Peace dwells not here — this rugged face
Betrays no spirit of repose ;
The sullen warrior sole we trace,
The marble man of many woes.
Such was his mien when first arose
The thought of that strange tale divine —
When hell he peopled with his foes,
The scourge of many a guilty line.

War to the last he waged with all
The tyrant canker-worms of earth ;
Baron and duke, in hold and hall,
Cursed the dark hour that gave him birth ;
He used Rome's harlot for his mirth ;
Plucked bare hypocrisy and crime ;
But valiant souls of knightly worth
Transmitted to the rolls of time.

O time ! whose verdicts mock our own,
The only righteous judge art thou ;
That poor, old exile, sad and lone,
Is Latium's other Virgil now.
Before his name the nations bow ;
His words are parcel of mankind,
Deep in whose hearts, as on his brow,
The marks have sunk of Dante's mind.

THOMAS WILLIAM PARSONS.

WALTON'S BOOK OF LIVES.

FROM "ECCLESIASTICAL SONNETS," PART III.

THERE are no colors in the fairest sky
So fair as these.   The feather, whence the pen
Was shaped that traced the lives of these good
men,
Dropped from an angel's wing.   With moistened
eye
We read of faith and purest charity
In statesman, priest, and humble citizen :
O, could we copy their mild virtues, then
What joy to live, what blessedness to die !
Methinks their very names shine still and bright ;
Apart, — like glow-worms on a summer night ;
Or lonely tapers when from far they fling
A guiding ray ; or seen, like stars on high,
Satellites burning in a lucid ring
Around meek Walton's heavenly memory.

WILLIAM WORDSWORTH.

CHARACTER OF THE EARL OF SHAFTESBURY.

FROM "ABSALOM AND ACHITOPHEL," PART I.

FOR close designs and crooked councils fit ;
Sagacious, bold, and turbulent of wit ;
Restless, unfixed in principles and place ;
In power unpleased, impatient of disgrace :
A fiery soul, which, working out its way,
Fretted the pygmy-body to decay,
And o'er informed the tenement of clay.
A daring pilot in extremity ;
Pleased with the danger, when the waves went
high

He sought the storms ; but for a calm unfit,
Would steer too nigh the sands to boast his wit.
Great wits are sure to madness near allied,
And thin partitions do their bounds divide.

JOHN DRYDEN.

ZIMRI.

[GEORGE VILLIERS, DUKE OF BUCKINGHAM, 1682.]

FROM "ABSALOM AND ACHITOPHEL," PART I.

SOME of their chiefs were princes of the land ;
In the first rank of these did Zimri stand ;
A man so various, that he seemed to be
Not one, but all mankind's epitome :
Stiff in opinions, always in the wrong ;
Was everything by starts, and nothing long ;
But, in the course of one revolving moon,
Was chymist, fiddler, statesman, and buffoon ;
Then all for women, painting, rhyming, drinking,
Besides ten thousand freaks that died in thinking.
Blest madman, who could every hour employ,
With something new to wish or to enjoy !
Railing and praising were his usual themes ;
And both, to show his judgment, in extremes :
So over-violent or over-civil,
That every man with him was god or devil.
In squandering wealth was his peculiar art ;
Nothing went unrewarded but desert.
Beggared by fools, whom still he found too late :
He had his jest, and they had his estate.
He laughed himself from court, then sought relief
By forming parties, but could ne'er be chief ;
For, spite of him, the weight of business fell
On Absalom, and wise Achitophel.
Thus, wicked but in will, of means bereft,
He left no faction, but of that was left.

JOHN DRYDEN.

CHARLES XII.

FROM "VANITY OF HUMAN WISHES."

ON what foundations stands the warrior's pride,
How just his hopes, let Swedish Charles decide:
A frame of adamant, a soul of fire,
No dangers fright him, and no labors tire ;
O'er love, o'er fear, extends his wide domain,
Unconquered lord of pleasure and of pain.
No joys to him pacific sceptres yield,
War sounds the trump, he rushes to the field ;
Behold surrounding kings their power combine,
And one capitulate, and one resign ;
Peace courts his hand, but spreads her charms in
vain ;
"Think nothing gained," he cries, "till naught
remain,

On Moscow's walls till Gothic standards fly,
And all be mine beneath the polar sky."
The march begins in military state,
And nations on his eye suspended wait ;
Stern famine guards the solitary coast,
And winter barricades the realms of frost.
He comes, nor want nor cold his course delay,
Hide, blushing glory, hide Pultowa's day !
The vanquished hero leaves his broken bands,
And shows his miseries in distant lands ;
Condemned a needy supplicant to wait,
While ladies interpose and slaves debate.
But did not chance at length her error mend ?
Did no subverted empire mark his end ?
Did rival monarchs give the fatal wound,
Or hostile millions press him to the ground ?
His fall was destined to a barren strand,
A petty fortress, and a dubious hand ;
He left the name, at which the world grew pale,
To point a moral or adorn a tale.

DR. SAMUEL JOHNSON.

TO THE LORD-GENERAL CROMWELL.

CROMWELL, our chief of men, who through a
cloud,
Not of war only, but detractions rude,
Guided by faith and matchless fortitude,
To peace and truth thy glorious way hast
ploughed,
And on the neck of crownèd fortune proud
Hast reared God's trophies, and his work pur-
sued,
While Darwen stream, with blood of Scots im-
bued,
And Dunbar field resounds thy praises loud,
And Worcester's laureate wreath. Yet much re-
mains
To conquer still ; Peace hath her victories
No less renowned than War : new foes arise,
Threatening to bind our souls with secular chains:
Help us to save free conscience from the paw
Of hireling wolves, whose gospel is their maw.

MILTON.

SPORUS.

[LORD HERVEY.]

FROM THE "PROLOGUE TO THE SATIRES."

LET Sporus tremble. — A.* What ? that thing
of silk,
Sporus, that mere white curd of asses' milk ·
Satire or sense, alas ! can Sporus feel ?
Who breaks a butterfly upon a wheel ?

* Arbuthnot.

P.* Yet let me flap this bug with gilded
   wings,
This painted child of dirt that stinks and stings ;
Whose buzz the witty and the fair annoys,
Yet wit ne'er tastes, and beauty ne'er enjoys :
So well-bred spaniels civilly delight
In mumbling of the game they dare not bite.
Eternal smiles his emptiness betray,
As shallow streams run dimpling all the way.
Whether in florid impotence he speaks,
And, as the prompter breathes, the puppet
   squeaks,
Or at the ear of Eve, familiar toad,
Half froth, half venom, spits himself abroad,
In puns, or politics, or tales, or lies,
Or spite, or smut, or rhymes, or blasphemies ;
His wit all seesaw, between that and this,
Now high, now low, now master up, now miss,
And he himself one vile antithesis.
Amphibious thing ! that, acting either part,
The trifling head, or the corrupted heart,
Fop at the toilet, flatterer at the board,
Now trips a lady, and now struts a lord.
Eve's tempter thus the rabbins have exprest,
A cherub's face, a reptile all the rest ;
Beauty that shocks you, parts that none will trust,
Wit that can creep, and pride that licks the dust.

                              ALEXANDER POPE.

ADDISON.

FROM THE "PROLOGUE TO THE SATIRES."

PEACE to all such ! but were there one whose fires
True genius kindles, and fair fame inspires ;
Blest with each talent and each art to please,
And born to write, converse, and live with ease :
Should such a man, too fond to rule alone,
Bear, like the Turk, no brother near the throne,
View him with scornful, yet with jealous eyes,
And hate for arts that caused himself to rise ;
Damn with faint praise, assent with civil leer,
And, without sneering, teach the rest to sneer ;
Willing to wound, and yet afraid to strike,
Just hint a fault, and hesitate dislike ;
Alike reserved to blame, or to commend,
A timorous foe, and a suspicious friend ;
Dreading even fools, by flatterers besieged,
And so obliging that he ne'er obliged ;
Like Cato, give his little senate laws,
And sit attentive to his own applause ;
Whilst wits and templars every sentence raise,
And wonder with a foolish face of praise : —
Who but must laugh, if such a one there be ?
Who would not weep, if Atticus were he ?

                              ALEXANDER POPE.

* Pope.

TO THE EARL OF WARWICK, ON THE DEATH OF ADDISON.

IF, dumb too long, the drooping Muse hath
   stayed,
And left her debt to Addison unpaid,
Blame not her silence, Warwick, but bemoan,
And judge, O, judge my bosom by your own.
What mourner ever felt poetic fires !
Slow comes the verse that real woe inspires :
Grief unaffected suits but ill with art,
Or flowing numbers with a bleeding heart.

Can I forget the dismal night that gave
My soul's best part forever to the grave ?
How silent did his old companions tread,
By midnight lamps, the mansions of the dead,
Through breathing statues, then unheeded things,
Through rows of warriors and through walks of
   kings !
What awe did the slow, solemn knell inspire ;
The pealing organ, and the pausing choir ;
The duties by the lawn-robed prelate paid ;
And the last words, that dust to dust conveyed !
While speechless o'er thy closing grave we bend,
Accept these tears, thou dear departed friend.
O, gone forever ! take this long adieu ;
And sleep in peace next thy loved Montague.
To strew fresh laurels let the task be mine,
A frequent pilgrim at thy sacred shrine ;
Mine with true sighs thy absence to bemoan,
And grave with faithful epitaphs thy stone.
If e'er from me thy loved memorial part,
May shame afflict this alienated heart ;
Of thee forgetful if I form a song,
My lyre be broken, and untuned my tongue,
My grief be doubled, from thy image free,
And mirth a torment, unchastised by thee !

Oft let me range the gloomy aisles alone,
Sad luxury ! to vulgar minds unknown,
Along the walls where speaking marbles show
What worthies form the hallowed mould below ;
Proud names, who once the reins of empire held ;
In arms who triumphed, or in arts excelled ;
Chiefs, graced with scars, and prodigal of blood,
Stern patriots, who for sacred freedom stood ;
Just men, by whom impartial laws were given ;
And saints, who taught and led the way to
   heaven !
Ne'er to these chambers, where the mighty rest,
Since their foundation came a nobler guest ;
Nor e'er was to the bowers of bliss conveyed
A fairer spirit or more welcome shade.

In what new region, to the just assigned,
What new employments please the unbodied
   mind ?

A wingèd Virtue, through the ethereal sky,
From world to world unwearied does he fly ?
Or curious trace the long laborious maze
Of Heaven's decrees, where wondering angels
  gaze ?
Does he delight to hear bold seraphs tell
How Michael battled and the dragon fell ;
Or, mixed with milder cherubim, to glow
In hymns of love, not ill-essayed below ?
Or dost thou warn poor mortals left behind,
A task well suited to thy gentle mind ?
O, if sometimes thy spotless form descend,
To me thy aid, thou guardian genius, lend !
When rage misguides me, or when fear alarms,
When pain distresses, or when pleasure charms,
In silent whisperings purer thoughts impart,
And turn from ill a frail and feeble heart ;
Lead through the paths thy virtue trod before,
Till bliss shall join, nor death can part us more.

That awful form which, so the heavens decree,
Must still be loved and still deplored by me,
In nightly visions seldom fails to rise,
Or, roused by fancy, meets my waking eyes.
If business calls, or crowded courts invite,
The unblemished statesman seems to strike my
  sight ;
If in the stage I seek to soothe my care,
I meet his soul which breathes in Cato there ;
If pensive to the rural shades I rove,
His shape o'ertakes me in the lonely grove ;
'T was there of just and good he reasoned strong,
Cleared some great truth, or raised some serious
  song :
There patient showed us the wise course to steer,
A candid censor and a friend severe ;
There taught us how to live, and (O, too high
The price for knowledge !) taught us how to die.

Thou Hill, whose brow the antique structures
  grace,
Reared by bold chiefs of Warwick's noble race,
Why, once so loved, whene'er thy bower ap-
  pears,
O'er my dim eyeballs glance the sudden tears ?
How sweet were once thy prospects fresh and fair,
Thy sloping walks, and unpolluted air !
How sweet the glooms beneath thy aged trees,
Thy noontide shadow, and thy evening breeze !
His image thy forsaken bowers restore ;
Thy walks and airy prospects charm no more ;
No more the summer in thy glooms allay,
Thy evening breezes, and thy noonday shade.

From other hills, however fortune frowned,
Some refuge in the Muse's art I found ;
Reluctant now I touch the trembling string,
Bereft of him who taught me how to sing ;

And these sad accents, murmured o'er his urn,
Betray that absence they attempt to mourn.
O, must I then (now fresh my bosom bleeds,
And Craggs in death to Addison succeeds)
The verse, begun to one lost friend, prolong,
And weep a second in the unfinished song !

These works divine, which on his death-bed laid
To thee, O Craggs ! the expiring sage conveyed,
Great, but ill-omened, monument of fame,
Nor he survived to give, nor thou to claim.
Swift after him thy social spirit flies,
And close to his, how soon ! thy coffin lies.
Blest pair ! whose union future bards shall tell
In future tongues : each other's boast ! farewell !
Farewell ! whom, joined in fame, in friendship
  tried,
No chance could sever, nor the grave divide.

THOMAS TICKELL.

THE POET'S FRIEND.

[LORD BOLINGBROKE.]

FROM "AN ESSAY ON MAN," EPISTLE IV.

COME then, my friend ! my genius ! come along;
O master of the poet, and the song !
And while the muse now stoops, or now ascends,
To man's low passions, or their glorious ends,
Teach me, like thee, in various nature wise,
To fall with dignity, with temper rise ;
Formed by thy converse happily to steer
From grave to gay, from lively to severe ;
Correct with spirit, eloquent with ease,
Intent to reason, or polite to please.
O, while along the stream of time thy name
Expanded flies, and gathers all its fame ;
Say, shall my little bark attendant sail,
Pursue the triumph, and partake the gale ?
When statesmen, heroes, kings, in dust repose,
Whose sons shall blush their fathers were thy foes,
Shall then this verse to future age pretend
Thou wert my guide, philosopher, and friend !
That, urged by thee, I turned the tuneful art
From sounds to things, from fancy to the heart :
For wit's false mirror held up Nature's light ;
Showed erring pride, WHATEVER IS, IS RIGHT.

ALEXANDER POPE.

NAPOLEON.

FROM "CHILDE HAROLD," CANTO III.

THERE sunk the greatest, nor the worst of men,
Whose spirit antithetically mixed
One moment of the mightiest, and again
On little objects with like firmness fixed,

Extreme in all things ! hadst thou been betwixt,
Thy throne had still been thine, or never been ;
For daring made thy rise as fall : thou seek'st
Even now to reassume the imperial mien,
And shake again the world, the Thunderer of the
   scene !

Conqueror and captive of the earth art thou !
She trembles at thee still, and thy wild name
Was ne'er more bruited in men's minds than
   now
That thou art nothing, save the jest of Fame,
Who wooed thee once, thy vassal, and became
The flatterer of thy fierceness, till thou wert
A god unto thyself : nor less the same
To the astounded kingdoms all inert,
Who deemed thee for a time whate'er thou didst
   assert.

O more or less than man — in high or low,
Battling with nations, flying from the field ;
Now making monarchs' necks thy footstool,
   now
More than thy meanest soldier taught to yield :
An empire thou couldst crush, command, re-
   build,
But govern not thy pettiest passion, nor
However deeply in men's spirits skilled,·
Look through thine own, nor curb the lust of
   war,
Nor learn that tempted Fate will leave the lofti-
   est star.

Yet well thy soul hath brooked the turning
   tide
With that untaught innate philosophy,
Which, be it wisdom, coldness, or deep pride,
Is gall and wormwood to an enemy.
When the whole host of hatred stood hard by,
To watch and mock thee shrinking, thou hast
   smiled
With a sedate and all-enduring eye, —
When Fortune fled her spoiled and favorite
   child,
He stood unbowed beneath the ills upon him
   piled.

Sager than in thy fortunes ; for in them
Ambition steeled thee on too far to show
That just habitual scorn which could contemn
Men and their thoughts ; 't was wise to feel,
   not so
To wear it ever on thy lip and brow,
And spurn the instruments thou wert to use
Till they were turned unto thine overthrow ;
'T is but a worthless world to win or lose ;
So hath it proved to thee, and all such lot who
   choose.

If, like a tower upon a headlong rock,
Thou hadst been made to stand or fall alone,
Such scorn of man had helped to brave the
   shock ;
But men's thoughts were the steps which paved
   thy throne,
Their admiration thy best weapon shone ;
The part of Philip's son was thine, not then
(Unless aside thy purple had been thrown)
Like stern Diogenes to mock at men ;
For sceptred cynics earth were far too wide a
   den.

But quiet to quick bosoms is a hell,
And *there* hath been thy vane ; there is a fire
And motion of the soul which will not dwell
In its own narrow being, but aspire
Beyond the fitting medium of desire ;
And, but once kindled, quenchless evermore,
Preys upon high adventure, nor can tire
Of aught but rest ; a fever at the core,
Fatal to him who bears, to all who ever bore.

This makes the madmen who have made men
   mad
By their contagion ! Conquerors and Kings,
Founders of sects and systems, to whom add
Sophists, Bards, Statesmen, all unquiet things
Which stir too strongly the soul's secret springs,
And are themselves the fools to those they
   fool ;
Envied, yet how unenviable ! what stings
Are theirs ! One breast laid open were a school
Which would unteach mankind the lust to shine
   or rule.

Their breath is agitation, and their life
A storm whereon they ride, to sink at last,
And yet so nursed and bigoted to strife,
That should their days, surviving perils past,
Melt to calm twilight, they feel overcast
With sorrow and supineness, and so die ;
Even as a flame, unfed, which runs to waste
With its own flickering, or a sword laid by,
Which eats into itself, and rusts ingloriously.

He who ascends to mountain-tops shall find
The loftiest peaks most wrapt in clouds and
   snow ;
He who surpasses or subdues mankind
Must look down on the hate of those below.
Though high above the sun of glory glow,
And far beneath the earth and ocean spread,
Round him are icy rocks, and loudly blow
Contending tempests on his naked head,
And thus reward the toils which to those sum-
   mits led.
                    LORD BYRON.

POPULAR RECOLLECTIONS OF BONAPARTE.

A RENDERING OF BÉRANGER'S "SOUVENIRS DU PEUPLE."

THEY 'll talk of him for years to come,
  In cottage chronicle and tale ;
When, for aught else, renown is dumb,
  His legend shall prevail !
When in the hamlet's honored chair
  Shall sit some aged dame,
Teaching to lowly clown and villager
  That narrative of fame.
" 'T is true," they 'll say, "his gorgeous throne
  France bled to raise ;
But he was all our own ! "
  " Mother, say something in his praise, —
  O, speak of him always ! "

" I saw him pass, — his was a host
  Countless beyond your young imaginings, —
My children, he could boast
  A train of conquered kings !
And when he came this road,
  'T was on my bridal day,
He wore, for near to him I stood,
  Cocked hat and surcoat gray.
I blushed ; he said, ' Be of good cheer !
Courage, my dear ! '
  That was his very word."
  " Mother ! O, then, this really occurred,
And you his voice could hear."

" A year rolled on, when next at Paris I,
  Lone woman that I am,
Saw him pass by,
  Girt with his peers to kneel at Notre Dame,
I knew, by merry chime and signal gun,
God granted him a son,
  And O, I wept for joy !
For why not weep when warrior men did,
Who gazed upon that sight so splendid,
  And blessed the imperial boy ?
Never did noonday sun shine out so bright !
O, what a sight ! "
  " Mother, for you that must have been
  A glorious scene."

" But when all Europe's gathered strength
Burst o'er the French frontier at length,
  'T will scarcely be believed
  What wonders, single-handed, he achieved ;
  Such general ne'er lived !
One evening on my threshold stood
  A guest, — 't was he ! Of warriors few
He had a toil-worn retinue.
He flung himself into this chair of wood,

Muttering, meantime, with fearful air,
' Quelle guerre ! O, quelle guerre ! ' "
" Mother ! and did our emperor sit there,
Upon that very chair ? "

" He said, ' Give me some food.'
  Brown loaf I gave, and homely wine,
  And made the kindling fire-blocks shine
To dry his cloak with wet bedewed.
  Soon by the bonny blaze he slept,
  Then waking chid me, — for I wept ;
' Courage ! ' he cried, ' I 'll strike for all
Under the sacred wall
  Of France's noble capital ! '
  Those were his words : I 've treasured up
  With pride that same wine-cup ;
And for its weight in gold
It never shall be sold ! "
  " Mother, on that proud relic let us gaze.
  O, keep that cup always ! "

" But through some fatal witchery
  He, whom a pope had crowned and blest,
Perished, my sons, by foulest treachery,
  Cast on an isle far in the lonely West !
Long time sad rumors were afloat, —
  The fatal tidings we would spurn,
Still hoping from that isle remote
  Once more our hero would return.
But when the dark announcement drew
  Tears from the virtuous and the brave,
When the sad whisper proved too true,
  A flood of grief I to his memory gave.
Peace to the glorious dead ! "
  " Mother, may God his fullest blessing shed
  Upon your aged head ! "

FRANCIS MAHONY (Father Prout)

MURAT.

FROM "ODE FROM THE FRENCH."

THERE, where death's brief pang was quickest,
And the battle's wreck lay thickest,
Strewed beneath the advancing banner
  Of the eagle's burning crest —
(There with thunder-clouds to fan her,
Who could then her wing arrest —
  Victory beaming from her breast ?)
While the broken line enlarging
  Fell, or fled along the plain : —
There be sure Murat was charging !
  There he ne'er shall charge again !

LORD BYRON

TO MADAME DE SEVIGNÉ,

PLAYING BLIND-MAN'S-BUFF.

You charm when you talk, walk, or move,
    Still more on this day than another :
When blinded — you're taken for Love ;
    When the bandage is off — for his mother !
                      DE MONTREUIL.

ON A PORTRAIT OF WORDSWORTH,

BY R. B. HAYDON.

WORDSWORTH upon Helvellyn !   Let the cloud
Ebb audibly along the mountain-wind,
Then break against the rock, and show behind
The lowland valleys floating up to crowd
The sense with beauty.   *He*, with forehead bowed
And humble-lidded eyes, as one inclined
Before the sovran thought of his own mind,
And very meek with inspirations proud, —
Takes here his rightful place as poet-priest
By the high-altar, singing prayer and prayer
To the higher Heavens.   A noble vision free,
Our Haydon's hand hath flung out from the mist !
No portrait this, with Academic air, —
This is the poet and his poetry.
               ELIZABETH BARRETT BROWNING.

BURNS.

A POET'S EPITAPH.

STOP, mortal !   Here thy brother lies, —
    The poet of the poor.
His books were rivers, woods, and skies,
    The meadow and the moor ;
His teachers were the torn heart's wail,
    The tyrant, and the slave,
The street, the factory, the jail,
    The palace, — and the grave !
Sin met thy brother everywhere !
    And is thy brother blamed ?
From passion, danger, doubt, and care
    He no exemption claimed.
The meanest thing, earth's feeblest worm,
    He feared to scorn or hate ;
But, honoring in a peasant's form
    The equal of the great,
He blessed the steward, whose wealth makes
    The poor man's little more ;
Yet loathed the haughty wretch that takes
    From plundered labor's store.
A hand to do, a head to plan,
    A heart to feel and dare, —
Tell man's worst foes, here lies the man
    Who drew them as they are.
                  EBENEZER ELLIOTT.

BURNS.

ON RECEIVING A SPRIG OF HEATHER IN BLOSSOM

No more these simple flowers belong
    To Scottish maid and lover ;
Sown in the common soil of song,
    They bloom the wide world over.

In smiles and tears, in sun and showers,
    The minstrel and the heather,
The deathless singer and the flowers
    He sang of live together.

Wild heather-bells and Robert Burns !
    The moorland flower and peasant !
How, at their mention, memory turns
    Her pages old and pleasant !

The gray sky wears again its gold
    And purple of adorning,
And manhood's noonday shadows hold
    The dews of boyhood's morning :

The dews that washed the dust and soil
    From off the wings of pleasure,
The sky, that flecked the ground of toil
    With golden threads of leisure.

I call to mind the summer day,
    The early harvest mowing,
The sky with sun and clouds at play,
    And flowers with breezes blowing.

I hear the blackbird in the corn,
    The locust in the haying ;
And, like the fabled hunter's horn,
    Old tunes my heart is playing.

How oft that day, with fond delay,
    I sought the maple's shadow,
And sang with Burns the hours away,
    Forgetful of the meadow !

Bees hummed, birds twittered, overhead
    I heard the squirrels leaping ;
The good dog listened while I read,
    And wagged his tail in keeping.

I watched him while in sportive mood
    I read " The Twa Dogs' " story,
And half believed he understood
    The poet's allegory.

Sweet day, sweet songs ! — The golden hours
    Grew brighter for that singing,
From brook and bird and meadow flowers
    A dearer welcome bringing.

New light on home-seen Nature beamed,
New glory over Woman ;
And daily life and duty seemed
No longer poor and common.

I woke to find the simple truth
Of fact and feeling better
Than all the dreams that held my youth
A still repining debtor :

That Nature gives her handmaid, Art,
The themes of sweet discoursing ;
The tender idyls of the heart
In every tongue rehearsing.

Why dream of lands of gold and pearl,
Of loving knight and lady,
When farmer boy and barefoot girl
Were wandering there already ?

I saw through all familiar things
The romance underlying ;
The joys and griefs that plume the wings
Of Fancy skyward flying.

I saw the same blithe day return,
The same sweet fall of even,
That rose on wooded Craigie-burn,
And sank on crystal Devon.

I matched with Scotland's heathery hills
The sweet-brier and the clover ;
With Ayr and Doon, my native rills,
Their wood-hymns chanting over.

O'er rank and pomp, as he had seen,
I saw the Man uprising ;
No longer common or unclean,
The child of God's baptizing.

With clearer eyes I saw the worth
Of life among the lowly ;
The Bible at his Cotter's hearth
Had made my own more holy.

And if at times an evil strain,
To lawless love appealing,
Broke in upon the sweet refrain
Of pure and healthful feeling,

It died upon the eye and ear,
No inward answer gaining ;
No heart had I to see or hear
The discord and the staining.

Let those who never erred forget
His worth, in vain bewailings ;
Sweet Soul of Song ! — I own my debt
Uncancelled by his failings !

Lament who will the ribald line
Which tells his lapse from duty,
How kissed the maddening lips of wine,
Or wanton ones of beauty ;

But think, while falls that shade between
The erring one and Heaven,
That he who loved like Magdalen,
Like her may be forgiven.

Not his the song whose thunderous chime
Eternal echoes render, —
The mournful Tuscan's haunted rhyme,
And Milton's starry splendor ;

But who his human heart has laid
To Nature's bosom nearer ?
Who sweetened toil like him, or paid
To love a tribute dearer ?

Through all his tuneful art, how strong
The human feeling gushes !
The very moonlight of his song
Is warm with smiles and blushes !

Give lettered pomp to teeth of Time,
So " Bonny Doon " but tarry ;
Blot out the Epic's stately rhyme,
But spare his " Highland Mary " !

JOHN GREENLEAF WHITTIER.

BURNS.

TO A ROSE BROUGHT FROM NEAR ALLOWAY KIRK, IN AYR
SHIRE, IN THE AUTUMN OF 1822.

WILD rose of Alloway ! my thanks :
Thou 'mind'st me of that autumn noon
When first we met upon "the banks
And braes o' bonny Doon."

Like thine, beneath the thorn-tree's bough,
My sunny hour was glad and brief ;
We 've crossed the winter sea, and thou
Art withered — flower and leaf.

And will not thy death-doom be mine —
The doom of all things wrought of clay ?
And withered my life's leaf like thine,
Wild rose of Alloway ?

Not so his memory for whose sake
My bosom bore thee far and long —
His, who a humbler flower could make
Immortal as his song,

The memory of Burns — a name
That calls, when brimmed her festal cup,
A nation's glory and her shame,
In silent sadness up.

A nation's glory — be the rest
　　Forgot — she 's canonized his mind,
And it is joy to speak the best
　　We may of humankind.

I 've stood beside the cottage-bed
　　Where the bard-peasant first drew breath ;
A straw-thatched roof above his head,
　　A straw-wrought couch beneath.

And I have stood beside the pile,
　　His monument — that tells to Heaven
The homage of earth's proudest isle
　　To that bard-peasant given.

Bid thy thoughts hover o'er that spot,
　　Boy-minstrel, in thy dreaming hour ;
And know, however low his lot,
　　A poet's pride and power ;

The pride that lifted Burns from earth,
　　The power that gave a child of song
Ascendency o'er rank and birth,
　　The rich, the brave, the strong ;

And if despondency weigh down
　　Thy spirit's fluttering pinions then,
Despair — thy name is written on
　　The roll of common men.

There have been loftier themes than his,
　　And longer scrolls, and louder lyres,
And lays lit up with Poesy's
　　Purer and holier fires ;

Yet read the names that know not death ;
　　Few nobler ones than Burns are there ;
And few have won a greener wreath
　　Than that which binds his hair.

His is that language of the heart
　　In which the answering heart would speak,
Thought, word, that bids the warm tear start,
　　Or the smile light the cheek ;

And his that music to whose tone
　　The common pulse of man keeps time,
In cot or castle's mirth or moan,
　　In cold or sunny clime.

And who hath heard his song, nor knelt
　　Before its spell with willing knee,
And listened and believed, and felt
　　The poet's mastery

O'er the mind's sea, in calm and storm,
　　O'er the heart's sunshine and its showers,
O'er Passion's moments, bright and warm,
　　O'er Reason's dark, cold hours ;

On fields where brave men "die or do,"
　　In halls where rings the banquet's mirth,
Where mourners weep, where lovers woo,
　　From throne to cottage hearth ?

What sweet tears dim the eye unshed,
　　What wild vows falter on the tongue,
When "Scots wha hae wi' Wallace bled,"
　　Or "Auld Lang Syne," is sung !

Pure hopes, that lift the soul above,
　　Come with his Cotter's hymn of praise,
And dreams of youth, and truth, and love
　　With "Logan's" banks and braes.

And when he breathes his master-lay
　　Of Alloway's witch-haunted wall,
All passions in our frames of clay
　　Come thronging at his call.

Imagination's world of air,
　　And our own world, its gloom and glee,
Wit, pathos, poetry, are there,
　　And death's sublimity.

And Burns — though brief the race he ran,
　　Though rough and dark the path he trod —
Lived, died, in form and soul a man,
　　The image of his God.

Through care, and pain, and want, and woe,
　　With wounds that only death could heal,
Tortures the poor alone can know,
　　The proud alone can feel ;

He kept his honesty and truth,
　　His independent tongue and pen,
And moved, in manhood as in youth,
　　Pride of his fellow-men.

Strong sense, deep feeling, passions strong,
　　A hate of tyrant and of knave,
A love of right, a scorn of wrong,
　　Of coward and of slave ;

A kind, true heart, a spirit high,
　　That could not fear, and would not bow,
Were written in his manly eye
　　And on his manly brow.

Praise to the bard ! his words are driven,
　　Like flower-seeds by the far winds sown,
Where'er, beneath the sky of heaven,
　　The birds of fame have flown.

Praise to the man ! a nation stood
　　Beside his coffin with wet eyes,
Her brave, her beautiful, her good,
　　As when a loved one dies.

And still, as on his funeral-day,
  Men stand his cold earth-couch around,
With the mute homage that we pay
  To consecrated ground.

And consecrated ground it is,
  The last, the hallowed home of one
Who lives upon all memories,
  Though with the buried gone.

Such graves as his are pilgrim-shrines,
  Shrines to no code or creed confined —
The Delphian vales, the Palestines,
  The Meccas, of the mind.

Sages, with Wisdom's garland wreathed,
  Crowned kings, and mitred priests of power,
And warriors with their bright swords sheathed,
  The mightiest of the hour ;

And lowlier names, whose humble home
  Is lit by Fortune's dimmer star,
Are there — o'er wave and mountain come,
  From countries near and far ;

Pilgrims, whose wandering feet have pressed
  The Switzer's snow, the Arab's sand,
Or trod the piled leaves of the West,
  My own green forest-land.

All ask the cottage of his birth,
  Gaze on the scenes he loved and sung,
And gather feelings not of earth
  His fields and streams among.

They linger by the Doon's low trees,
  And pastoral Nith, and wooded Ayr,
And round thy sepulchres, Dumfries !
  The Poet's tomb is there.

But what to them the sculptor's art,
  His funeral columns, wreaths, and urns ?
Wear they not graven on the heart
  The name of Robert Burns ?

                              FITZ-GREENE HALLECK.

———◆———

A BARD'S EPITAPH.

Is there a whim-inspirèd fool,
Owre fast for thought, owre hot for rule,
Owre blate * to seek, owre proud to snool ; †
            Let him draw near,
And owre this grassy heap sing dool,
            And drap a tear.

  * bashful.   † tamely submit.

Is there a bard of rustic song,
Who, noteless, steals the crowd **among**,
That weekly this area throng ;
            O, pass not by ;
But, with a frater-feeling strong,
            Here heave a sigh !

Is there a man whose judgment clear
Can others teach the course to steer,
Yet runs himself life's mad career,
            Wild as the wave ;
Here pause, and, through the starting tear,
            Survey this grave.

The poor inhabitant below
Was quick to learn and wise to know,
And keenly felt the friendly glow,
            And sober flame ;
But thoughtless follies laid him low,
            And stained his name !

Reader, attend, — whether thy soul
Soars fancy's flights beyond the pole,
Or **darkly** grubs this earthly hole,
            In low pursuit ;
Know, prudent, cautious self-control
            Is wisdom's root.
                              ROBERT BURNS

———◆———

ELEGY ON CAPTAIN MATTHEW HENDERSON.

HE 's gane, he 's gane ! he 's frae us torn
The ae best fellow e'er was born !
Thee, Matthew, Nature's sel' shall mourn
            By wood and wild,
Where, haply, pity strays forlorn,
            Frae man exiled.

  Ye hills, near neebors o' the starns,
That proudly cock your cresting cairns !
Ye cliffs, the haunts of sailing yearns,*
            Where echo slumbers !
Come join, ye Nature's sturdiest bairns,
            My wailing numbers !

  Mourn, ilka grove the cushat kens !
Ye hazelly shaws and briery dens !
Ye burnies, wimplin' down your glens,
            Wi' toddlin' din.
Or foaming strang, wi' hasty stens,
            Frae lin to lin !

  Mourn, little harebells o'er the lea,
Ye stately foxgloves fair to see ;
Ye woodbines hanging bonnilie

            * eagles.

In scented bowers ;
Ye roses on your thorny tree,
  The first o' flowers.

At dawn, when every grassy blade
Droops with a diamond at his head,
At even, when beans their fragrance shed,
  I' the rustling gale,
Ye maukins whiddin through the glade,
  Come join my wail.

Mourn, ye wee songsters o' the wood ;
Ye grouse that crap the heather bud ;
Ye curlews calling through a clud ;
  Ye whistling plover ;
And mourn, ye whirring paitrick brood ;
  He 's gane forever !

Mourn, sooty coots, and speckled teals,
Ye fisher herons, watching eels ;
Ye duck and drake, wi' airy wheels
  Circling the lake ;
Ye bitterns, till the quagmire reels,
  Rair for his sake.

Mourn, clamoring craiks at close o' day,
'Mang fields o' flowering clover gay ;
And when ye wing your annual way
  Frae our cauld shore,
Tell thae far warlds wha lies in clay,
  Wham we deplore.

Ye houlets, frae your ivy bower,
In some auld tree, or eldritch tower,
What time the moon, wi' silent glower,
  Sets up her horn,
Wail thro' the dreary midnight hour
  Till waukrife morn.

O rivers, forests, hills and plains !
Oft have ye heard my canty strains :
But now, what else for me remains
  But tales of wo ?
And frae my een the drapping rains
  Maun ever flow.

Mourn, Spring, thou darling of the year !
Ilk cowslip cup shall keep a tear :
Thou, Simmer, while each corny spear
  Shoots up its head,
Thy gay, green flowery tresses shear,
  For him that 's dead !

Thou, Autumn, wi' thy yellow hair,
In grief thy sallow mantle tear !
Thou, Winter, hurling through the air
  The roaring blast,
Wide o'er the naked world declare
  The worth we 've lost.

Mourn him, thou sun, great source of light !
Mourn, empress of the silent night !
And you, ye twinkling starnies bright,
  My Matthew mourn !
For thro' your orbs he 's ta'en his flight,
  Ne'er to return.

O Henderson, the man ! the brother !
And art thou gone, and gone forever !
And hast thou crost that unknown river,
  Life's dreary bound !
Like thee where shall I find another,
  The world around !

Go to your sculptured tombs, ye great,
In a' the tinsel trash o' state !
But by thy honest turf I 'll wait,
  Thou man of worth !
And weep the ae best fellow's fate
  E'er lay in earth.

ROBERT BURNS.

BYRON.

FROM "THE COURSE OF TIME," BOOK IV

TAKE one example — to our purpose quite.
A man of rank, and of capacious soul,
Who riches had, and fame, beyond desire,
An heir of flattery, to titles born,
And reputation, and luxurious life :
Yet, not content with ancestorial name,
Or to be known because his fathers were,
He on this height hereditary stood,
And, gazing higher, purposed in his heart
To take another step. Above him seemed
Alone, the mount of song, the lofty seat
Of canonizèd bards ; and thitherward,
By nature taught, and inward melody,
In prime of youth, he bent his eagle eye.
No cost was spared. What books he wished, ne
  read ;
What sage to hear, he heard ; what scenes to see,
He saw. And first, in rambling school-boy days,
Britannia's mountain-walks, and heath-girt lakes,
And story-telling glens, and founts, and brooks,
And maids, as dew-drops pure and fair, his soul
With grandeur filled, and melody, and love.
Then travel came, and took him where he wished :
He cities saw, and courts, and princely pomp ;
And mused alone on ancient mountain-brows ;
And mused on battle-fields, where valor fought
In other days ; and mused on ruins gray
With years ; and drank from old and fabulous
  wells,
And plucked the vine that first-born prophets
  plucked ;

And mused on famous tombs, and on the wave
Of ocean mused, and on the desert waste ;
The heavens and earth of every country saw :
Where'er the old inspiring Genii dwelt,
Aught that could rouse, expand, refine the soul,
Thither he went, and meditated there.
   He touched his harp, and nations heard en-
      tranced.
As some vast river of unfailing source,
Rapid, exhaustless, deep, his numbers flowed,
And openèd new fountains in the human heart.
Where Fancy halted, weary in her flight,
In other men, his fresh as morning rose,
And soared untrodden heights, and seemed at
    home,
Where angels bashful lookèd. Others, though
    great,
Beneath their argument seemed struggling ;
    whiles
He, from above descending, stooped to touch
The loftiest thought ; and proudly stooped, as
    though
It scarce deserved his verse. With Nature's self
He seemed an old acquaintance, free to jest
At will with all her glorious majesty.
He laid his hand upon " the Ocean's mane,"
And played familiar with his hoary locks ;
Stood on the Alps, stood on the Apennines,
And with the thunder talked as friend to friend ;
And wove his garland of the lightning's wing,
In sportive twist, — the lightning's fiery wing,
Which, as the footsteps of the dreadful God,
Marching upon the storm in vengeance, seemed ;
Then turned, and with the grasshopper, who
    sung
His evening song beneath his feet, conversed.
Suns, moons, and stars, and clouds his sisters
    were ;
Rocks, mountains, meteors, seas, and winds, and
    storms
His brothers, younger brothers, whom he scarce
As equals deemed. All passions of all men,
The wild and tame, the gentle and severe ;
All thoughts, all maxims, sacred and profane ;
All creeds ; all seasons, time, eternity ;
All that was hated, and all that was dear ;
All that was hoped, all that was feared, by man,—
He tossed about, as tempest-withered leaves ;
Then, smiling, looked upon the wreck he made.
With terror now he froze the cowering blood,
And now dissolved the heart in tenderness ;
Yet would not tremble, would not weep himself ;
But back into his soul retired, alone,
Dark, sullen, proud, gazing contemptuously
On hearts and passions prostrate at his feet.
So Ocean, from the plains his waves had late
To desolation swept, retired in pride,

Exulting in the glory of his might,
And seemed to mock the ruin he had wrought.
   As some fierce comet of tremendous size,
To which the stars did reverence as it passed,
So he, through learning and through fancy, took
His flight sublime, and on the loftiest top
Of Fame's dread mountain sat ; not soiled and
    worn,
As if he from the earth had labored up,
But as some bird of heavenly plumage fair
He looked, which down from higher regions came,
And perched it there, to see what lay beneath.
   The nations gazed, and wondered much and
    praised.
Critics before him fell in humble plight ;
Confounded fell ; and made debasing signs
To catch his eye ; and stretched and swelled
    themselves
To bursting nigh, to utter bulky words
Of admiration vast ; and many too,
Many that aimed to imitate his flight,
With weaker wing, unearthly fluttering made,
And gave abundant sport to after days.
   Great man ! the nations gazed and wondered
    much,
And praised ; and many called his evil good.
Wits wrote in favor of his wickedness ;
And kings to do him honor took delight.
Thus full of titles, flattery, honor, fame ;
Beyond desire, beyond ambition, full, —
He died, — he died of what ? Of wretchedness ;
Drank every cup of joy, heard every trump
Of fame ; drank early, deeply drank ; drank
    draughts
That common millions might have quenched, —
    then died
Of thirst, because there was no more to drink.
His goddess, Nature, wooed, embraced, enjoyed,
Fell from his arms, abhorred ; his passions died
Died, all but dreary, solitary Pride ;
And all his sympathies in being died.
As some ill-guided bark, well built and tall,
Which angry tides cast out on desert shore,
And then, retiring, left it there to rot
And moulder in the winds and rains of heaven ;
So he, cut from the sympathies of life,
And cast ashore from pleasure's boisterous surge,
A wandering, weary, worn, and wretched thing,
A scorched and desolate and blasted soul,
A gloomy wilderness of dying thought, —
Repined, and groaned, and withered from the
    earth.
His groanings filled the land his numbers filled ;
And yet he seemed ashamed to groan. — Poor
    man !
Ashamed to ask, and yet he needed help.
              ROBERT POLLOK.

TO CAMPBELL.

TRUE bard and simple, — as the race
  Of heaven-born poets always are,
When stooping from their starry place
  They 're children near, though gods afar.
                    THOMAS MOORE.

CAMP-BELL.

CHARADE.

COME from my first, ay, come !
  The battle-dawn is nigh ;
And the screaming trump and the thundering
    drum
  Are calling thee to die !

Fight as thy father fought ;
  Fall as thy father fell ;
Thy task is taught ; thy shroud is wrought ;
  So forward and farewell !

Toll ye my second, toll !
  Fling high the flambeau's light,
And sing the hymn for a parted soul
  Beneath the silent night !

The wreath upon his head,
  The cross upon his breast,
Let the prayer be said and the tear be shed,
  So, — take him to his rest !

Call ye my whole, — ay, call
  The lord of lute and lay ;
And let him greet the sable pall
  With a noble song to-day.

Go, call him by his name !
  No fitter hand may crave
To light the flame of a soldier's fame
  On the turf of a soldier's grave.
           WINTHROP MACKWORTH PRAED.

TO THOMAS MOORE.

MY boat is on the shore,
  And my bark is on the sea ;
But before I go, Tom Moore,
  Here 's a double health to thee !

Here 's a sigh to those who love me,
  And a smile to those who hate ;
And, whatever sky 's above me,
  Here 's a heart for every fate !

Though the ocean roar around me,
  Yet it still shall bear me on ;
Though a desert should surround me,
  It hath springs that may be won.

Were 't the last drop in the well,
  As I gasped upon the brink,
Ere my fainting spirit fell,
  'T is to thee that I would drink.

With that water, as this wine,
  The libation I would pour
Should be, — Peace with thine and mine,
  And a health to thee, Tom Moore !
                 LORD BYRON.

BURIAL OF SIR JOHN MOORE.

NOT a drum was heard, not a funeral note,
  As his corse to the rampart we hurried ;
Not a soldier discharged his farewell shot
  O'er the grave where our hero we buried.

We buried him darkly, at dead of night,
  The sods with our bayonets turning ;
By the struggling moonbeams' misty light,
  And the lantern dimly burning.

No useless coffin enclosed his breast,
  Not in sheet or in shroud we wound him ;
But he lay, like a warrior taking his rest,
  With his martial cloak around him.

Few and short were the prayers we said,
  And we spoke not a word of sorrow ;
But we steadfastly gazed on the face of the dead,
  And we bitterly thought of the morrow.

We thought, as we hollowed his narrow bed,
  And smoothed down his lonely pillow,
That the foe and the stranger would tread o'er
    his head,
  And we far away on the billow !

Lightly they 'll talk of the spirit that 's gone,
  And o'er his cold ashes upbraid him ;
But little he 'll reck, if they let him sleep on
  In the grave where a Briton has laid him !

But half of our heavy task was done,
  When the clock struck the hour for retiring ;
And we heard the distant and random gun
  That the foe was suddenly firing.

Slowly and sadly we laid him down,
  From the field of his fame fresh and gory !
We carved not a line, and we raised not a stone,
  But we left him alone with his glory.
                CHARLES WOLFE.

EMMET'S EPITAPH.

[Robert Emmet, the celebrated Irish Revolutionist, at his trial for high treason, which resulted in his conviction and execution, September 20, 1803, made an eloquent and pathetic defence, concluding with these words : "Let there be no inscription upon my tomb. Let no man write my epitaph. Let my character and my motives repose in security and peace till other times and other men can do them justice. Then shall my character be vindicated ; then may my epitaph be written. I have done." It was immediately upon reading this speech that the following lines were written.]

"LET no man write my epitaph ; let my grave
Be uninscribed, and let my memory rest
Till other times are come, and other men,
Who then may do me justice."
                    Emmet, no !
No withering curse hath dried my spirit up,
That I should now be silent, — that my soul
Should from the stirring inspiration shrink,
Now when it shakes her, and withhold her voice,
Of that divinest impulse nevermore
Worthy, if impious I withheld it now,
Hardening my heart. Here, here in this free Isle,
To which in thy young virtue's erring zeal
Thou wert so perilous an enemy,
Here in free England shall an English hand
Build thy imperishable monument ;
O, to thine own misfortune and to ours,
By thine own deadly error so beguiled,
Here in free England shall an English voice
Raise up thy mourning-song. For thou hast paid
The bitter penalty of that misdeed ;
Justice hath done her unrelenting part,
If she in truth be Justice who drives on,
Bloody and blind, the chariot-wheels of death.

So young, so glowing for the general good,
O, what a lovely manhood had been thine,
When all the violent workings of thy youth
Had passed away, hadst thou been wisely spared,
Left to the slow and certain influences
Of silent feeling and maturing thought !
How had that heart, — that noble heart of thine,
Which even now had snapped one spell, which
        beat
With such brave indignation at the shame
And guilt of France, and of her miscreant lord, —
How had it clung to England ! With what love,
What pure and perfect love, returned to her,
Now worthy of thy love, the champion now
For freedom, — yea, the only champion now,
And soon to be the avenger. But the blow
Hath fallen, the undiscriminating blow,
That for its portion to the grave consigned
Youth, Genius, generous Virtue. O, grief, grief !
O, sorrow and reproach ! Have ye to learn,
Deaf to the past, and to the future blind,
Ye who thus irremissibly exact
The forfeit life, how lightly life is staked,
When in distempered times the feverish mind

To strong delusion yields ? Have ye to learn
With what a deep and spirit-stirring voice
Pity doth call Revenge ? Have ye no hearts
To feel and understand how Mercy tames
The rebel nature, maddened by old wrongs,
And binds it in the gentle bands of love,
When steel and adamant were weak to hold
That Samson-strength subdued !
                    Let no man write
Thy epitaph ! Emmet, nay ; thou shalt not go
Without thy funeral strain ! O young and good,
And wise, though erring here, thou shalt not go
Unhonored or unsung. And better thus
Beneath that undiscriminating stroke,
Better to fall, than to have lived to mourn,
As sure thou wouldst, in misery and remorse,
Thine own disastrous triumph ; to have seen,
If the Almighty at that awful hour
Had turned away his face, wild Ignorance
Let loose, and frantic Vengeance, and dark zeal,
And all bad passions tyrannous, and the fires
Of Persecution once again ablaze.
How had it sunk into thy soul to see,
Last curse of all, the ruffian slaves of France
In thy dear native country lording it !
How happier thus, in that heroic mood
That takes away the sting of death, to die,
By all the good and all the wise forgiven !
Yea, in all ages by the wise and good
To be remembered, mourned, and honored still !
                            ROBERT SOUTHEY.

———◆———

O, BREATHE NOT HIS NAME !

ROBERT EMMET.

O, BREATHE not his name ! let it sleep in the
        shade,
Where cold and unhonored his relics are laid ;
Sad, silent, and dark be the tears that we shed,
As the night-dew that falls on the grave o'er his
        head.

But the night-dew that falls, though in silence
        it weeps,
Shall brighten with verdure the grave where he
        sleeps ;
And the tear that we shed, though in secret it
        rolls,
Shall long keep his memory green in our souls.
                            THOMAS MOORE.

———◆———

TO TOUSSAINT L'OUVERTURE.

TOUSSAINT ! the most unhappy man of men !
Whether the whistling rustic tend his plough
Within thy hearing, or thy head be now
Pillowed in some deep dungeon's earless den,

O miserable chieftain ! where and when
Wilt thou find patience ? Yet die not ; do
    thou
Wear rather in thy bonds a cheerful brow :
Though fallen thyself, never to rise again,
Live and take comfort. Thou hast left behind
Powers that will work for thee ; air, earth, and
    skies :
There 's not a breathing of the common wind
That will forget thee ; thou hast great allies ;
Thy friends are exultations, agonies,
And love, and man's unconquerable mind.

WILLIAM WORDSWORTH.

DEATH-BED OF BOMBA, KING OF NAPLES,

AT BARI, 1859.

COULD I pass those lounging sentries, through
    the aloe-bordered entries, up the sweep of
    squalid stair,
On through chamber after chamber, where the
    sunshine's gold and amber turn decay to
    beauty rare,
I should reach a guarded portal, where for strife
    of issue mortal, face to face two kings are
    met :
One the grisly King of Terrors ; one a Bourbon,
    with his errors, late to conscience-clearing
    set.
Well his fevered pulse may flutter, and the priests
    their mass may mutter with such fervor as
    they may :
Cross and chrism, and genuflection, mop and
    mow, and interjection, will not frighten
    Death away.
By the dying despot sitting, at the hard heart's
    portals hitting, shocking the dull brain to
    work,
Death makes clear what life has hidden, chides
    what life has left unchidden, quickens truth
    life tried to burke.
He but ruled within his borders after Holy
    Church's orders, did what Austria bade him
    do ;
By their guidance flogged and tortured ; high-
    born men and gently nurtured chained with
    crime's felonious crew.
What if summer fevers gripped them, what if
    winter freezings nipped them, till they rotted
    in their chains ?
He had word of Pope and Kaiser ; none could
    holier be or wiser ; theirs the counsel, his
    the reins.

So he pleads excuses eager, clutching, with his
    fingers meagre, at the bedclothes as he
    speaks ;
But King Death sits grimly grinning at the
    Bourbon's cobweb-spinning, — as each cob-
    web-cable breaks.
And the poor soul, from life's eylot, rudderless,
    without a pilot, drifteth slowly down the
    dark ;
While mid rolling incense vapor, chanted dirge,
    and flaring taper, lies the body, stiff and
    stark.

PUNCH.

TO THE MEMORY OF THOMAS HOOD.

TAKE back into thy bosom, earth,
    This joyous, May-eyed morrow,
The gentlest child that ever mirth
    Gave to be reared by sorrow !
'T is hard — while rays half green, half gold,
    Through vernal bowers are burning,
And streams their diamond mirrors hold
    To Summer's face returning —
To say we 're thankful that his sleep
    Shall nevermore be lighter,
In whose sweet-tongued companionship
    Stream, bower, and beam grow brighter !

But all the more intensely true
    His soul gave out each feature
Of elemental love, — each hue
    And grace of golden nature, —
The deeper still beneath it all
    Lurked the keen jags of anguish ;
The more the laurels clasped his brow
    Their poison made it languish.
Seemed it that, like the nightingale
    Of his own mournful singing,
The tenderer would his song prevail
    While most the thorn was stinging.

So never to the desert-worn
    Did fount bring freshness deeper
Than that his placid rest this morn
    Has brought the shrouded sleeper.
That rest may lap his weary head
    Where charnels choke the city,
Or where, mid woodlands, by his bed
    The wren shall wake its ditty ;
But near or far, while evening's star
    Is dear to hearts regretting,
Around that spot admiring thought
    Shall hover, unforgetting.

BARTHOLOMEW SIMMONS.

A VOICE, AND NOTHING ELSE.

"I WONDER if Brougham thinks as much as he
    talks,"
  Said a punster, perusing a trial :
"I vow, since his lordship was made Baron
    Vaux,
He 's been *Vaux et præterea nihil !* "
ANONYMOUS.

MACAULAY.

THE dreamy rhymer's measured snore
Falls heavy on our ears no more ;
And by long strides are left behind
The dear delights of womankind,
Who wage their battles like their loves,
In satin waistcoats and kid gloves,
And have achieved the crowning work
When they have trussed and skewered a Turk.
Another comes with stouter tread,
And stalks among the statelier dead.
He rushes on, and hails by turns
High-crested Scott, broad-breasted Burns ;
And shows the British youth, who ne'er
Will lag behind, what Romans were,
When all the Tuscans and their Lars
Shouted, and shook the towers of Mars.
WALTER SAVAGE LANDOR.

SONNETS TO GEORGE SAND.

A DESIRE.

THOU large-brained woman and large-hearted
    man,
Self-called George Sand ! whose soul amid the
    lions
Of thy tumultuous senses, moans defiance,
And answers roar for roar, as spirits can,
I would some mild miraculous thunder ran
Above the applauded circus, in appliance
Of thine own nobler nature's strength and sci-
    ence,
Drawing two pinions, white as wings of swan,
From thy strong shoulders, to amaze the place
With holier light ! that thou to woman's claim,
And man's, might join beside the angel's grace
Of a pure genius sanctified from blame ;
Till child and maiden pressed to thine embrace,
To kiss upon thy lips a stainless fame.

A RECOGNITION.

TRUE genius, but true woman ! dost deny
Thy woman's nature with a manly scorn,
And break away the gauds and armlets worn
By weaker women in captivity ?

Ah, vain denial ! that revolted cry
Is sobbed in by a woman's voice forlorn ;
Thy woman's hair, my sister, all unshorn,
Floats back dishevelled strength in agony,
Disproving thy man's name ; and while before
The world thou burnest in a poet-fire,
We see thy woman-heart beat evermore
Through the large flame. Beat purer, heart, and
    higher,
Till God unsex thee on the heavenly shore,
Where unincarnate spirits purely aspire.
ELIZABETH BARRETT BROWNING.

HEINE'S GRAVE.

"HENRI HEINE" — 't is here !
The black tombstone, the name
Carved there — no more ! and the smooth,
Swarded alleys, the limes
Touched with yellow by hot
Summer, but under them still
In September's bright afternoon
Shadow and verdure and cool !
Trim Montmartre ! the faint
Murmur of Paris outside ;
Crisp everlasting-flowers,
Yellow and black on the graves.

Half blind, palsied, in pain,
Hither to come, from the streets'
Uproar, surely not loath
Wast thou, Heine, — to lie
Quiet ! to ask for closed
Shutters, and darkened room,
And cool drinks, and an eased
Posture, and opium, no more !
Hither to come, and to sleep
Under the wings of Renown.

Ah ! not little, when pain
Is most quelling, and man
Easily quelled, and the fine
Temper of genius alive
Quickest to ill, is the praise
Not to have yielded to pain !
No small boast for a weak
Son of mankind, to the earth
Pinned by the thunder, to rear
His bolt-scathed front to the stars,
And, undaunted, retort
'Gainst thick-crashing, insane,
Tyrannous tempests of bale,
Arrowy lightnings of soul !

Hark ! through the alley resounds
Mocking laughter ! A film
Creeps o'er the sunshine ; a breeze
Ruffles the warm afternoon;

Saddens my soul with its chill.
Gibing of spirits in scorn
Shakes every leaf of the grove,
Mars the benignant repose
Of this amiable home of the dead.
Bitter spirits ! ye claim
Heine ? — Alas, he is yours !
Only a moment I longed
Here in the quiet to snatch
From such mates the outworn
Poet, and steep him in calm.
Only a moment !　I knew
Whose he was who is here
Buried ; I knew he was yours !
Ah, I knew that I saw
Here no sepulchre built
In the laurelled rock, o'er the blue
Naples bay, for a sweet
Tender Virgil ! no tomb
On Ravenna sands, in the shade
Of Ravenna pines, for a high
Austere Dante ! no grave
By the Avon side, in the bright
Stratford meadows, for thee,
Shakespeare ! loveliest of souls,
Peerless in radiance, in joy.

What so harsh and malign,
Heine ! distils from thy life,
Poisons the peace of thy grave ?
　.　　　　.　　　　.
Charm is the glory which makes
Song of the poet divine ;
Love is the fountain of charm.
How without charm wilt thou draw,
Poet, the world to thy way ?
Not by the lightnings of wit,
Not by the thunder of scorn !
These to the world, too, are given ;
Wit it possesses, and scorn, —
Charm is the poet's alone.
Hollow and dull are the great,
And artists envious, and the mob profane.
We know all this, we know !
Cam'st thou from heaven, O child
Of light ! but this to declare ?
Alas ! to help us forget
Such barren knowledge awhile,
God gave the poet his song.
Therefore a secret unrest
Tortured thee, brilliant and bold !
Therefore triumph itself
Tasted amiss to thy soul.
Therefore, with blood of thy foes,
Trickled in silence thine own.
Therefore the victor's heart
Broke on the field of his fame.

Ah ! as of old from the pomp
Of Italian Milan, the fair
Flower of marble of white
Southern palaces, — steps
Bordered by statues, and walks
Terraced, and orange bowers
Heavy with fragrance, — the blond
German Kaiser full oft
Longed himself back to the fields,
Rivers, and high-roofed towns
Of his native Germany ; so,
So, how often ! from hot
Paris drawing-rooms, and lamps
Blazing, and brilliant crowds,
Starred and jewelled, of men
Famous, of women the queens
Of dazzling converse, and fumes
Of praise, — hot, heady fumes, to the poor brain
That mount, that madden ! — how oft
Heine's spirit, outworn,
Longed itself out of the din
Back to the tranquil, the cool,
Far German home of his youth !
See ! in the May afternoon,
O'er the fresh short turf of the Hartz,
A youth, with the foot of youth,
Heine ! thou climbest again.
Up, through the tall dark firs
Warming their heads in the sun,
Checkering the grass with their shade,
Up, by the stream with its huge
Moss-hung bowlders and thin
Musical water half-hid,
Up o'er the rock-strewn slope,
With the sinking sun, and the air
Chill, and the shadows now
Long on the gray hillside,
To the stone-roofed hut at the top.

Or, yet later, in watch
On the roof of the Brocken tower
Thou standest, gazing ! to see
The broad red sun, over field,
Forest and city and spire
And mist-tracked stream of the wide,
Wide German land, going down
In a bank of vapors, — again
Standest ! at nightfall, alone ;
Or, next morning, with limbs
Rested by slumber, and heart
Freshened and light with the May,
O'er the gracious spurs coming down
Of the lower Hartz, among oaks,
And beechen coverts, and copse
Of hazels green in whose depth
Ilse, the fairy transformed,
In a thousand water-breaks light

Pours her petulant youth, —
Climbing the rock which juts
O'er the valley, the dizzily perched
Rock ! to its Iron Cross
Once more thou cling'st ; to the Cross
Clingest ! with smiles, with a sigh.

   .   .   .   .

But something prompts me : Not thus
Take leave of Heine, not thus
Speak the last word at his grave !
Not in pity, and not
With half-censure, — with awe
Hail, as it passes from earth,
Scattering lightnings, that soul !

The spirit of the world,
Beholding the absurdity of men, —
Their vaunts, their feats, — let a sardonic smile
For one short moment wander o'er his lips.
That smile was Heine ! for its earthly hour
The strange guest sparkled ; now 'tis passed away.

That was Heine ! and we,
Myriads who live, who have lived,
What are we all, but a mood,
A single mood, of the life
Of the Being in whom we exist,
Who alone is all things in one.
Spirit, who fillest us all !
Spirit, who utterest in each
New-coming son of mankind
Such of thy thoughts as thou wilt !
O thou, one of whose moods,
Bitter and strange, was the life
Of Heine, — his strange, alas !
His bitter life, — may a life
Other and milder be mine !
Mayst thou a mood more serene,
Happier, have uttered in mine !
Mayst thou the rapture of peace
Deep have embreathed at its core !
Made it a ray of thy thought,
Made it a beat of thy joy !
MATTHEW ARNOLD.

———◆———

A WELCOME TO "BOZ."

ON HIS FIRST VISIT TO THE WEST

Come as artist, come as guest,
Welcome to the expectant West,
Hero of the charmèd pen,
Loved of children, loved of men.
We have felt thy spell for years ;
Oft with laughter, oft with tears,
Thou hast touched the tenderest part
Of our inmost, hidden heart.
We have fixed our eager gaze
On thy pages nights and days,
Wishing, as we turned them o'er,
Like poor Oliver, for "more,"
And the creatures of thy brain
In our memory remain,
Till through them we seem to be
Old acquaintances of thee.
Much we hold it thee to greet,
Gladly sit we at thy feet ;
On thy features we would look,
As upon a living book,
And thy voice would grateful hear,
Glad to feel that Boz were near,
That his veritable soul
Held us by direct control :
Therefore, author loved the best.
Welcome, welcome to the West.

In immortal Weller's name,
By the rare Micawber's fame,
By the flogging wreaked on Squeers,
By Job Trotter's fluent tears,
By the beadle Bumble's fate
At the hands of shrewish mate,
By the famous Pickwick Club,
By the dream of Gabriel Grubb,
In the name of Snodgrass' muse,
Tupman's amorous interviews,
Winkle's ludicrous mishaps,
And the fat boy's countless naps ;
By Ben Allen and Bob Sawyer,
By Miss Sally Brass, the lawyer,
In the name of Newman Noggs,
River Thames, and London fogs,
Richard Swiveller's excess,
Feasting with the Marchioness,
By Jack Bunsby's oracles,
By the chime of Christmas bells,
By the cricket on the hearth,
By the sound of childish mirth,
By spread tables and good cheer.
Wayside inns and pots of beer,
Hostess plump and jolly host,
Coaches for the turnpike post,
Chambermaid in love with Boots,
Toodles, Traddles, Tapley, Toots,
Betsey Trotwood, Mister Dick,
Susan Nipper, Mistress Chick,
Snevellicci, Lilyvick,
Mantalini's predilections
To transfer his warm affections,
By poor Barnaby and Grip,
Flora, Dora Di, and Gip,
Peerybingle, Pinch, and Pip, —
Welcome, long-expected guest,
Welcome to the grateful West.

In the name of gentle Nell,
Child of light, belovèd well, —

Weeping, did we not behold
Roses on her bosom cold ?
Better we for every tear
Shed beside her snowy bier, —
By the mournful group that played
Round the grave where Smike was laid.
By the life of Tiny Tim,
And the lesson taught by him,
Asking in his plaintive tone
God to " bless us every one,"
By the sounding waves that bore
Little Paul to Heaven's shore,
By thy yearning for the human
Good in every man and woman,
By each noble deed and word
That thy story-books record,
And each noble sentiment
Dickens to the world hath lent,
By the effort thou hast made
Truth and true reform to aid,
By thy hope of man's relief
Finally from want and grief,
By thy never-failing trust
That the God of love is just, —
We would meet and welcome thee,
Preacher of humanity :
Welcome fills the throbbing breast
Of the sympathetic West.
                                        W. H. VENABLE.

DICKENS IN CAMP.

ABOVE the pines the moon was slowly drifting,
    The river sang below ;
The dim Sierras, far beyond, uplifting
    Their minarets of snow.

The roaring camp-fire, with rude humor, painted
    The ruddy tints of health
On haggard face and form that drooped and fainted
    In the fierce race for wealth ;

Till one arose, and from his pack's scant treasure
    A hoarded volume drew,
And cards were dropped from hands of listless
        leisure,
    To hear the tale anew ;

And then, while round them shadows gathered
        faster,
    And as the firelight fell,
He read aloud the book wherein the Master
    Had writ of " Little Nell."

Perhaps 't was boyish fancy, — for the reader
    Was youngest of them all, —
But, as he read, from clustering pine and cedar
    A silence seemed to fall :

The fir-trees, gathering closer in the shadows,
    Listened in every spray,
While the whole camp, with " Nell," on English
        meadows
    Wandered and lost their way.

And so in mountain solitudes — o'ertaken
    As by some spell divine —
Their cares dropped from them like the needles
        shaken
    From out the gusty pine.

Lost is that camp, and wasted all its fire ;
    And he who wrought that spell ? —
Ah, towering pine and stately Kentish spire,
    Ye have one tale to tell !

Lost is that camp ! but let its fragrant story
    Blend with the breath that thrills
With hop-vines' incense all the pensive glory
    That fills the Kentish hills.

And on that grave where English oak and holly
    And laurel wreaths intwine,
Deem it not all a too presumptuous folly, —
    This spray of Western pine.
                                        BRET HARTE.

TO VICTOR HUGO.

VICTOR in poesy !   Victor in romance !
    Cloud-weaver of phantasmal hopes and fears !
    French of the French and lord of human
        tears !
Child-lover, bard, whose fame-lit laurels glance,
Darkening the wreaths of all that would ad-
        vance
    Beyond our strait their claim to be thy peers !
    Weird Titan, by thy wintry weight of years
As yet unbroken !   Stormy voice of France,
Who does not love our England, so they say ;
    I know not ! England, France, all men to be,
    Will make one people, ere man's race be
        run ;
And I, desiring that diviner day,
    Yield thee full thanks for thy full courtesy
    To younger England in the boy, my son.
                                        ALFRED TENNYSON.

DANIEL BOONE.

FROM "DON JUAN."

OF all men, saving Sylla the man-slayer,
    Who passes for in life and death most lucky,
Of the great names which in our faces stare,
    The General Boone, backwoodsman of Ken-
        tucky,

Was happiest amongst mortals anywhere ;
  For, killing nothing but a bear or buck, he
Enjoyed the lonely, vigorous, harmless days
Of his old age in wilds of deepest maze.

Crime came not near him, she is not the child
  Of solitude ; Health shrank not from him, for
Her home is in the rarely trodden wild,
  Where if men seek her not, and death be more
Their choice than life, forgive them, as beguiled
  By habit to what their own hearts abhor,
In cities caged.   The present case in point I
Cite is, that Boone lived hunting up to ninety ;

And, what 's still stranger, left behind a name
  For which men vainly decimate the throng,
Not only famous, but of that *good* fame,
  Without which glory 's but a tavern song, —
Simple, serene, the antipodes of shame,
  Which hate nor envy e'er could tinge with
      wrong ;
An active hermit, even in age the child
Of nature, or the Man of Ross run wild.

'T is true he shrank from men, even of his nation ;
  When they built up unto his darling trees,
He moved some hundred miles off, for a station
  Where there were fewer houses and more ease ;
The inconvenience of civilization
  Is that you neither can be pleased nor please ;
But where he met the individual man,
He showed himself as kind as mortal can.

He was not all alone ; around him grew
  A sylvan tribe of children of the chase,
Whose young, unwakened world was ever new ;
  Nor sword nor sorrow yet had left a trace
On her unwrinkled brow, nor could you view
  A frown on nature's or on human face :
The freeborn forest found and kept them free,
And fresh as is a torrent or a tree.

And tall, and strong, and swift of foot, were they,
  Beyond the dwarfing city's pale abortions,
Because their thoughts had never been the prey
  Of care or gain : the green woods were their
      portions ;
No sinking spirits told them they grew gray ;
  No fashion made them apes of her distortions ;
Simple they were, not savage ; and their rifles,
Though very true, were not yet used for trifles.

Motion was in their days, rest in their slumbers,
  And cheerfulness the handmaid of their toil ;
Nor yet too many nor too few their numbers ;
  Corruption could not make their hearts her
      soil.

The lust which stings, the splendor which en-
      cumbers,
  With the free foresters divide no spoil :
Serene, not sullen, were the solitudes
Of this unsighing people of the woods.

                                    LORD BYRON.

WASHINGTON.

FROM " UNDER THE ELM," READ AT CAMBRIDGE, JULY 3,
1875, ON THE HUNDREDTH ANNIVERSARY OF WASHING-
TON'S TAKING COMMAND OF THE AMERICAN ARMY.

BENEATH our consecrated elm
A century ago he stood,
Famed vaguely for that old fight in the wood,
Which redly foamèd round him but could not
      overwhelm
The life foredoomed to wield our rough-hewn
      helm.
From colleges, where now the gown
To arms had yielded, from the town,
Our rude self-summoned levies flocked to see
The new-come chiefs and wonder which was he.
No need to question long ; close-lipped and tall,
Long trained in murder-brooding forests lone
To bridle others' clamors and his own,
Firmly erect, he towered above them all,
The incarnate discipline that was to free
With iron curb that armed democracy.

          .   .

Haughty they said he was, at first, severe,
But owned, as all men owned, the steady hand
Upon the bridle, patient to command,
Prized, as all prize, the justice pure from fear,
And learned to honor first, then love him, then
      revere.
Such power there is in clear-eyed self-restraint,
And purpose clean as light from every selfish
      taint.

Musing beneath the legendary tree,
The years between furl off : I seem to see
The sun-flecks, shaken the stirred foliage through,
Dapple with gold his sober buff and blue,
And weave prophetic aureoles round the head
That shines our beacon now, nor darkens with
      the dead.
O man of silent mood,
A stranger among strangers then,
How art thou since renowned the Great, the
      Good,
Familiar as the day in all the homes of men !
The wingèd years, that winnow praise and blame,
Blow many names out : they but fan to flame
The self-renewing splendors of thy fame.

          .   .   .

O, for a drop of that terse Roman's ink
Who gave Agricola dateless length of days.

To celebrate him fitly, neither swerve
To phrase unkempt, nor pass discretion's brink,
With him so statuelike in sad reserve,
So diffident to claim, so forward to deserve !
Nor need I shun due influence of his fame
Who, mortal among mortals, seemed as now
The equestrian shape with unimpassioned brow,
That paces silent on through vistas of acclaim.
What figure more immovably august
Than that grave strength so patient and so pure,
Calm in good fortune, when it wavered, sure,
That soul serene, impenetrably just,
Modelled on classic lines, so simple they endure ?
That soul so softly radiant and so white
The track it left seems less of fire than light,
Cold but to such as love distemperature ?
And if pure light, as some deem, be the force
That drives rejoicing planets on their course,
Why for his power benign seek an impurer
  source ?
His was the true enthusiasm that burns long,
Domestically bright,
Fed from itself and shy of human sight,
The hidden force that makes a lifetime strong,
And not the short-lived fuel of a song.
Passionless, say you ? What is passion for
But to sublime our natures and control
To front heroic toils with late return,
Or none, or such as shames the conqueror ?
That fire was fed with substance of the soul,
And not with holiday stubble, that could burn
Through seven slow years of unadvancing war,
Equal when fields were lost or fields were won,
With breath of popular applause or blame,
Nor fanned nor damped, unquenchably the same,
Too inward to be reached by flaws of idle fame.

Soldier and statesman, rarest unison;
High-poised example of great duties done
Simply as breathing, a world's honors worn
As life's indifferent gifts to all men born ;
Dumb for himself, unless it were to God,
But for his barefoot soldiers eloquent,
Tramping the snow to coral where they trod,
Held by his awe in hollow-eyed content ;
Modest, yet firm as Nature's self ; unblamed
Save by the men his nobler temper shamed ;
Not honored then or now because he wooed
The popular voice, but that he still withstood ;
Broad-minded, higher-souled, there is but one
Who was all this, and ours, and all men's, —
  Washington.

Minds strong by fits, irregularly great,
That flash and darken like revolving lights,
Catch more the vulgar eye unschooled to wait
On the long curve of patient days and nights,

Rounding a whole life to the circle fair
Of orbed completeness ; and this balanced soul,
So simple in its grandeur, coldly bare
Of draperies theatric, standing there
In perfect symmetry of self-control,
Seems not so great at first, but greater grows
Still as we look, and by experience learn
How grand this quiet is, how nobly stern
The discipline that wrought through life-long
  throes
This energetic passion of repose.
A nature too decorous and severe,
Too self-respectful in its griefs and joys
For ardent girls and boys,
Who find no genius in a mind so clear
That its grave depths seem obvious and near,
Nor a soul great that made so little noise.
They feel no force in that calm, cadenced phrase,
The habitual full-dress of his well-bred mind,
That seems to pace the minuet's courtly maze
And tell of ampler leisures, roomier length of
  days.
His broad-built brain, to self so little kind
That no tumultuary blood could blind,
Formed to control men, not amaze,
Looms not like those that borrow height of haze :
It was a world of statelier movement then
Than this we fret in, he a denizen
Of that ideal Rome that made a man for men.

Placid completeness, life without a fall
From faith or highest aims, truth's breachless
  wall,
Surely if any fame can bear the touch,
His will say " Here ! " at the last trumpet's call,
The unexpressive man whose life expressed so
  much.
                              JAMES RUSSELL LOWELL.

GEORGE WASHINGTON.

By broad Potomac's silent shore
  Better than Trajan lowly lies,
  Gilding her green declivities
With glory now and evermore ;
  Art to his fame no aid hath lent ;
  His country is his monument.
                              ANONYMOUS.

DANIEL WEBSTER.

When, stricken by the freezing blast,
  A nation's living pillars fall,
How rich the storied page, how vast,
  A word, a whisper, can recall !

No medal lifts its fretted face,
　Nor speaking marble cheats your eye ;
Yet, while these pictured lines I trace,
　A living image passes by :

A roof beneath the mountain pines ;
　The cloisters of a hill-girt plain ;
The front of life's embattled lines ;
　A mound beside the heaving main.

These are the scenes : a boy appears ;
　Set life's round dial in the sun,
Count the swift arc of seventy years,
　His frame is dust ; his task is done.

Yet pause upon the noontide hour,
　Ere the declining sun has laid
His bleaching rays on manhood's power,
　And look upon the mighty shade.

No gloom that stately shape can hide,
　No change uncrown his brow ; behold !
Dark, calm, large-fronted, lightning-eyed,
　Earth has no double from its mould !

Ere from the fields by valor won
　The battle-smoke had rolled away,
And bared the blood-red setting sun,
　His eyes were opened on the day.

His land was but a shelving strip,
　Black with the strife that made it free ;
He lived to see its banners dip
　Their fringes in the western sea.

The boundless prairies learned his name,
　His words the mountain echoes knew ;
The northern breezes swept his fame
　From icy lake to warm bayou.

In toil he lived ; in peace he died ;
　When life's full cycle was complete,
Put off his robes of power and pride,
　And laid them at his Master's feet.

His rest is by the storm-swept waves,
　Whom life's wild tempests roughly tried,
Whose heart was like the streaming caves
　Of ocean, throbbing at his side.

Death's cold white hand is like the snow
　Laid softly on the furrowed hill ;
It hides the broken seams below,
　And leaves the summit brighter still.

In vain the envious tongue upbraids ;
　His name a nation's heart shall keep,
Till morning's latest sunlight fades
　On the blue tablet of the deep !
　　　　　　　　OLIVER WENDELL HOLMES.

ICHABOD.

DANIEL WEBSTER. 1850.

So fallen ! so lost ! the light withdrawn,
　Which once he wore !
The glory from his gray hairs gone
　Forevermore !

Revile him not, — the Tempter hath
　A snare for all !
And pitying tears, not scorn and wrath,
　Befit his fall !

O, dumb be passion's stormy rage,
　When he who might
Have lighted up and led his age
　Falls back in night !

Scorn ! would the angels laugh to mark
　A bright soul driven,
Fiend-goaded, down the endless dark,
　From hope and heaven ?

Let not the land, once proud of him,
　Insult him now ;
Nor brand with deeper shame his dim,
　Dishonored brow.

But let its humbled sons instead,
　From sea to lake,
A long lament, as for the dead,
　In sadness make.

Of all we loved and honored, naught
　Save power remains, —
A fallen angel's pride of thought,
　Still strong in chains.

All else is gone ; from those great eyes
　The soul has fled :
When faith is lost, when honor dies,
　The man is dead !

Then pay the reverence of old days
　To his dead fame ;
Walk backward, with averted gaze,
　And hide the shame !
　　　　　　　JOHN GREENLEAF WHITTIER.

———◆———

THE DEAD CZAR NICHOLAS.

LAY him beneath his snows,
The great Norse giant who in these last days
Troubled the nations.　Gather decently
The imperial robes about him.　'T is but man, —

This demi-god.   Or rather it *was* man,
And is — a little dust, that will corrupt
As fast as any nameless dust which sleeps
'Neath Alma's grass or Balaklava's vines.

No vineyard grave for him.   No quiet tomb
By river margin, where across the seas
Children's fond thoughts and women's memories
    come,
Like angels, to sit by the sepulchre,
Saying : "All these were men who knew to count,
Front-faced, the cost of honor, nor did shrink
From its full payment ; coming here to die,
They died — like men."

                    But this man ? Ah ! for him
Funereal state, and ceremonial grand,
The stone-engraved sarcophagus, and then
Oblivion.

        Nay, oblivion were as bliss
To that fierce howl which rolls from land to land
Exulting, — "Art thou fallen, Lucifer,
Son of the morning ?" or condemning, — "Thus
Perish the wicked !" or blaspheming, — "Here
Lies our Belshazzar, our Sennacherib,
Our Pharaoh, — he whose heart God hardenèd,
So that he would not let the people go."

Self-glorifying sinners !   Why, this man
Was but like other men, — you, Levite small,
Who shut your saintly ears, and prate of hell
And heretics, because outside church-doors,
Your church-doors, congregations poor and small
Praise Heaven in their own way ; you, autocrat
Of all the hamlets, who add field to field
And house to house, whose slavish children cower
Before your tyrant footstep ; you, foul-tongued
Fanatic or ambitious egotist,
Who think God stoops from his high majesty
To lay his finger on your puny head,
And crown it, that you henceforth may parade
Your maggotship throughout the wondering
    world, —
"I am the Lord's anointed !"

                    Fools and blind !
This czar, this emperor, this disthronèd corpse,
Lying so straightly in an icy calm
Grander than sovereignty, was but as ye, —
No better and no worse : Heaven mend us all !

Carry him forth and bury him.   Death's peace
Rest on his memory !   Mercy by his bier
Sits silent, or says only these few words, —
"Let him who is without sin 'mongst ye all
Cast the first stone."
                    DINAH MARIA MULOCK CRAIK.

ABRAHAM LINCOLN.

FROM THE "COMMEMORATION ODE."

LIFE may be given in many ways,
    And loyalty to Truth be sealed
As bravely in the closet as the field,
    So bountiful is Fate ;
    But then to stand beside her,
    When craven churls deride her,
To front a lie in arms and not to yield,
    This shows, methinks, God's plan
    And measure of a stalwart man,
    Limbed like the old heroic breeds,
    Who stand self-poised on manhood's solid
        earth,
Not forced to frame excuses for his birth,
Fed from within with all the strength he needs.

Such was he, our Martyr-Chief,
    Whom late the Nation he had led,
    With ashes on her head,
Wept with the passion of an angry grief :
Forgive me, if from present things I turn
To speak what in my heart will beat and burn,
And hang my wreath on his world-honored urn.
    Nature, they say, doth dote,
    And cannot make a man
    Save on some worn-out plan,
    Repeating us by rote :
For him her Old-World moulds aside he threw,
    And, choosing sweet clay from the breast
    Of the unexhausted West,
With stuff untainted shaped a hero new,
Wise, steadfast in the strength of God, and true.
    How beautiful to see
Once more a shepherd of mankind indeed,
Who loved his charge, but never loved to lead ;
One whose meek flock the people joyed to be,
    Not lured by any cheat of birth,
    But by his clear-grained human worth,
And brave old wisdom of sincerity !
    They knew that outward grace is dust ;
    They could not choose but trust
In that sure-footed mind's unfaltering skill,
    And supple-tempered will
That bent like perfect steel to spring again and
        thrust.
    His was no lonely mountain-peak of mind,
    Thrusting to thin air o'er our cloudy bars,
    A sea-mark now, now lost in vapors blind ;
    Broad prairie rather, genial, level-lined,
Fruitful and friendly for all human kind,
Yet also nigh to heaven and loved of loftiest stars.
    Nothing of Europe here,
Or, then, of Europe fronting mornward still,
    Ere any names of Serf and Peer
    Could Nature's equal scheme deface ;

ON THE LIFE-MASK OF ABRAHAM LINCOLN.

THIS bronze doth keep the very form and mould
  Of our great martyr's face. Yes, this is he:
  That brow all wisdom, all benignity;
  That human, humorous mouth; those cheeks that hold
Like some harsh landscape all the summer's gold;
  That spirit fit for sorrow, as the sea
  For storms to beat on; the lone agony
 .Those silent, patient lips too well foretold.
Yes, this is he who ruled a world of men
  As might some prophet of the elder day,—
  Brooding above the tempest and the fray
With deep-eyed thought and more than mortal ken.
  A power was his beyond the touch of art
  Of armèd strength: his pure and mighty heart.

RICHARD WATSON GILDER.

After an Engraving by Wm. J. Linton.

OUT FROM BEHIND THIS MASK.

To confront his Portrait for " The Wound Dresser" in "Leaves of Grass."

OUT from behind this bending, rough-cut mask,
These lights and shades, this drama of the whole,
This common curtain of the face, contain'd in me for me, in you for you, in each for each.
(Tragedies. sorrows, laughter, tears — O heaven !
The passionate teeming plays this curtain hid !)
This glaze of God's serenest, purest sky,
This film of Satan's seething pit,
This heart's geography's map, this limitless small continent, this soundless sea ;
Out from the convolutions of this globe,
This subtler astronomic orb than sun or moon, than Jupiter, Venus. Mars,
This condensation of the universe (nay, here the only universe,
Here the idea, all in this mystic handful wrapt);

These burin'd eyes, flashing to you, to pass to future time,
To launch and spin through space, revolving, sideling, from these to emanate
To you — whoe'er you are — a look.

A traveler of thoughts and years, of peace and war,
Of youth long sped and middling age declining
(As the first volume of a tale perused and laid away, and this the second,
Songs, ventures, speculations, presently to close),
Lingering a moment here and now, to you I opposite turn,
As on the road, or at some crevice door by chance, or open'd window,
Pausing, inclining, baring my head, you specially I greet,
To draw and clinch your soul for once inseparably with mine,
Then travel, travel on.

WALT WHITMAN.

Here was a type of the true elder race,
And one of Plutarch's men talked with us face
    to face.
  I praise him not ; it were too late ;
And some innative weakness there must be
  In him who condescends to victory
Such as the Present gives, and cannot wait,
  Safe in himself as in a fate.
    So always firmly he :
    He knew to bide his time,
    And can his fame abide,
Still patient in his simple faith sublime,
    Till the wise years decide.
  Great captains, with their guns and drums,
    Disturb our judgment for the hour,
    But at last silence comes ;
These all are gone, and, standing like a tower,
  Our children shall behold his fame,
  The kindly-earnest, brave, foreseeing man,
Sagacious, patient, dreading praise, not blame,
New birth of our new soil, the first American.
                        JAMES RUSSELL LOWELL.

ABRAHAM LINCOLN.*

FOULLY ASSASSINATED APRIL 14, 1865.

You lay a wreath on murdered Lincoln's bier,
  You, who with mocking pencil wont to trace,
Broad for the self-complacent British sneer,
  His length of shambling limb, his furrowed face,

His gaunt, gnarled hands, his unkempt, brist-
    ling hair,
  His garb uncouth, his bearing ill at ease,
His lack of all we prize as debonair,
  Of power or will to shine, of art to please ;

You, whose smart pen backed up the pencil's
    laugh,
  Judging each step as though the way were
    plain,
Reckless, so it could point its paragraph
  Of chief's perplexity, or people's pain :

Beside this corpse, that bears for winding-sheet
  The Stars and Stripes he lived to rear anew,
Between the mourners at his head and feet,
  Say, scurrile jester, is there room for you ?

Yes : he had lived to shame me from my sneer,
  To lame my pencil, and confute my pen ;
To make me own this hind of princes peer,
  This rail-splitter a true-born king of men.

* This tribute appeared in the London *Punch*, which, up to
the time of the assassination of Mr. Lincoln, had ridiculed and
maligned him with all its well-known powers of pen and pencil.

My shallow judgment I had learned to rue,
  Noting how to occasion's height he rose ;
How his quaint wit made home-truth seem more
    true ;
  How, iron-like, his temper grew by blows.

How humble, yet how hopeful, he could be ;
  How, in good fortune and in ill, the same ;
Nor bitter in success, nor boastful he,
  Thirsty for gold, nor feverish for fame.

He went about his work, — such work as few
  Ever had laid on head and heart and hand, —
As one who knows, where there's a task to do,
  Man's honest will must Heaven's good grace
    command ;

Who trusts the strength will with the burden
    grow,
  That God makes instruments to work his will,
If but that will we can arrive to know,
  Nor tamper with the weights of good and ill.

So he went forth to battle, on the side
  That he felt clear was Liberty's and Right's,
As in his peasant boyhood he had plied
  His warfare with rude Nature's thwarting
    mights ;

The uncleared forest, the unbroken soil,
  The iron-bark, that turns the lumberer's axe,
The rapid, that o'erbears the boatman's toil,
  The prairie, hiding the mazed wanderer's tracks,

The ambushed Indian, and the prowling bear,—
  Such were the deeds that helped his youth to
    train :
Rough culture, but such trees large fruit may
    bear,
  If but their stocks be of right girth and grain.

So he grew up, a destined work to do,
  And lived to do it : four long-suffering years'
Ill-fate, ill-feeling, ill-report, lived through,
  And then he heard the hisses change to cheers,

The taunts to tribute, the abuse to praise,
  And took both with the same unwavering mood ;
Till, as he came on light, from darkling days,
  And seemed to touch the goal from where he
    stood,

A felon hand, between the goal and him,
  Reached from behind his back, a trigger prest,
And those perplexed and patient eyes were dim,
  Those gaunt, long-laboring limbs were laid to
    rest !

The words of mercy were upon his lips,
    Forgiveness in his heart and on his pen,
When this vile murderer brought swift eclipse
    To thoughts of peace on earth, good-will to men.

The Old World and the New, from sea to sea,
    Utter one voice of sympathy and shame :
Sore heart, so stopped when it at last beat high ;
    Sad life, cut short just as its triumph came !

A deed accurst ! Strokes have been struck before
    By the assassin's hand, whereof men doubt
If more of horror or disgrace they bore ;
    But thy foul crime, like Cain's, stands darkly
        out.

Vile hand, that brandest murder on a strife,
    Whate'er its grounds, stoutly and nobly striven ;
And with the martyr's crown crownest a life
    With much to praise, little to be forgiven.
                                TOM TAYLOR.

WILLIAM LLOYD GARRISON.

"Some time afterward, it was reported to me by the city officers that they had ferreted out the paper and its editor ; that his office was an obscure hole, his only visible auxiliary a negro boy, and his supporters a few very insignificant persons of all colors."— *Letter of* H. G. OTIS.

IN a small chamber, friendless and unseen,
    Toiled o'er his types one poor, unlearned young
        man ;
The place was dark, unfurnitured, and mean :
    Yet there the freedom of a race began.

Help came but slowly ; surely no man yet
    Put lever to the heavy world with less :
What need of help? He knew how types were set,
    He had a dauntless spirit, and a press.

Such earnest natures are the fiery pith,
    The compact nucleus, round which systems
        grow :
Mass after mass becomes inspired therewith,
    And whirls impregnate with the central glow.

O Truth ! O Freedom ! how are ye still born
    In the rude stable, in the manger nursed !
What humble hands unbar those gates of morn
    Through which the splendors of the New Day
        burst !

What ! shall one monk, scarce known beyond his
        cell,
    Front Rome's far-reaching bolts, and scorn her
        frown ?
Brave Luther answered Yes ; that thunder's swell
    Rocked Europe, and discharmed the triple
        crown.

Whatever can be known of earth we know,
    Sneered Europe's wise men, in their snail
        shells curled ;
No ! said one man in Genoa, and that No
    Out of the dark created this New World.

Who is it will not dare himself to trust ?
    Who is it hath not strength to stand alone ?
Who is it thwarts and bilks the inward Must ?
    He and his works, like sand, from earth are
        blown.

Men of a thousand shifts and wiles, look here !
    See one straightforward conscience put in paw
To win a world ; see the obedient sphere
    By bravery's simple gravitation drawn !

Shall we not heed the lesson taught of old,
    And by the Present's lips repeated still,
In our own single manhood to be bold,
    Fortressed in conscience and impregnable will ?

We stride the river daily at its spring,
    Nor, in our childish thoughtlessness, foresee
What myriad vassal streams shall tribute bring,
    How like an equal it shall greet the sea.

O small beginnings, ye are great and strong,
    Based on a faithful heart and weariless brain !
Ye build the future fair, ye conquer wrong,
    Ye earn the crown, and wear it not in vain.
                        JAMES RUSSELL LOWELL.

THE OLD ADMIRAL.

ADMIRAL STEWART, U. S. NAVY.

GONE at last,
    That brave old hero of the past !
His spirit has a second birth,
    An unknown, grander life ;
All of him that was earth
    Lies mute and cold,
    Like a wrinkled sheath and old,
Thrown off forever from the shimmering blade
That has good entrance made
    Upon some distant, glorious strife.

From another generation,
    A simpler age, to ours Old Ironsides came ;
The morn and noontide of the nation
    Alike he knew, nor yet outlived his fame, —
        O, not outlived his fame !
The dauntless men whose service guards our shore
    Lengthen still their glory-roll
    With his name to lead the scroll,
As a flagship at her fore
    Carries the Union, with its azure and the stars,
Symbol of times that are no more
    And the old heroic wars.

He was the one
Whom Death had spared alone
Of all the captains of that lusty age,
Who sought the foeman where he lay,
On sea or sheltering bay,
  Nor till the prize was theirs repressed their
    rage.
They are gone, — all gone :
  They rest with glory and the undying Powers ;
  Only their name and fame, and what they
    saved, are ours !

It was fifty years ago,
  Upon the Gallic Sea,
  He bore the banner of the free,
And fought the fight whereof our children
    know, —
  The deathful, desperate fight !
  Under the fair moon's light
The frigate squared, and yawed to left and right.
  Every broadside swept to death a score !
Roundly played her guns and well, till their
    fiery ensigns fell,
  Neither foe replying more.
All in silence, when the night-breeze cleared the
    air,
  Old Ironsides rested there,
Locked in between the twain, and drenched with
    blood.
  Then homeward, like an eagle with her prey !
  O, it was a gallant fray, —
  That fight in Biscay Bay !
Fearless the captain stood, in his youthful hardi-
    hood :
  He was the boldest of them all,
  Our brave old Admiral !

And still our heroes bleed,
Taught by that olden deed.
  Whether of iron or of oak
The ships we marshal at our country's need,
  Still speak their cannon now as then they
    spoke ;
Still floats our unstruck banner from the mast
  As in the stormy past.

Lay him in the ground :
  Let him rest where the ancient river rolls ;
Let him sleep beneath the shadow and the sound
  Of the bell whose proclamation, as it tolls,
Is of Freedom and the gift our fathers gave.
  Lay him gently down :
  The clamor of the town
Will not break the slumbers deep, the beautiful,
    ripe sleep,
  Of this lion of the wave,
  Will not trouble the old Admiral in his grave.

Earth to earth his dust is laid.
Methinks his stately shade
  On the shadow of a great ship leaves the shore ;
Over cloudless western seas
Seeks the far Hesperides,
  The islands of the blest,
Where no turbulent billows roar, —
  Where is rest.
His ghost upon the shadowy quarter stands
Nearing the deathless lands.
  There all his martial mates, renewed and
    strong,
  Await his coming long.
  I see the happy Heroes rise
  With gratulation in their eyes :
"Welcome, old comrade," Lawrence cries ;
"Ah, Stewart, tell us of the wars !
Who win the glory and the scars ?
  How floats the skyey flag, — how many
    stars ?
  Still speak they of Decatur's name ?
  Of Bainbridge's and Perry's fame ?
  Of me, who earliest came ?
Make ready, all :
Room for the Admiral !
  Come, Stewart, tell us of the wars ! "
                    EDMUND CLARENCE STEDMAN.

KANE.

DIED FEBRUARY 16, 1857.

ALOFT upon an old basaltic crag,
  Which, scalped by keen winds that defend
    the Pole,
  Gazes with dead face on the seas that roll
Around the secret of the mystic zone,
A mighty nation's star-bespangled flag
    Flutters alone,
And underneath, upon the lifeless front
  Of that drear cliff, a simple name is traced ;
Fit type of him who, famishing and gaunt,
  But with a rocky purpose in his soul,
    Breasted the gathering snows,
    Clung to the drifting floes,
  By want beleaguered, and by winter chased,
Seeking the brother lost amid that frozen waste.

Not many months ago we greeted him,
  Crowned with the icy honors of the North,
  Across the land his hard-won fame went forth,
And Maine's deep woods were shaken limb by
    limb.
His own mild Keystone State, sedate and prim,
  Burst from decorous quiet, as he came.
  Hot Southern lips, with eloquence aflame,
Sounded his triumph.   Texas, wild and grim,.

Proffered its horny hand. The large-lunged West,
 From out his giant breast,
Yelled its frank welcome. And from main to main
 Jubilant to the sky,
 Thundered the mighty cry,
  HONOR TO KANE !

In vain, — in vain beneath his feet we flung
 The reddening roses !   All in vain we poured
 The golden wine, and round the shining board
Sent the toast circling, till the rafters rung
 With the thrice-tripled honors of the feast !
Scarce the buds wilted and the voices ceased
Ere the pure light that sparkled in his eyes,
Bright as auroral fires in Southern skies,
 Faded and faded !   And the brave young heart
That the relentless Arctic winds had robbed
Of all its vital heat, in that long quest
For the lost captain, now within his breast
 More and more faintly throbbed.
His was the victory ; but as his grasp
Closed on the laurel crown with eager clasp,
 Death launched a whistling dart ;
And ere the thunders of applause were done
His bright eyes closed forever on the sun !
Too late, — too late the splendid prize he won
In the Olympic race of Science and of Art !
Like to some shattered berg that, pale and lone,
Drifts from the white North to a Tropic zone,
 And in the burning day
 Wastes peak by peak away,
 Till on some rosy even
It dies with sunlight blessing it ; so he
Tranquilly floated to a Southern sea,
 And melted into heaven !

He needs no tears who lived a noble life !
 We will not weep for him who died so well ;
 But we will gather round the hearth, and tell
  The story of his strife ;
  Such homage suits him well,
Better than funeral pomp or passing bell !

What tale of peril and self-sacrifice !
Prisoned amid the fastnesses of ice,
 With hunger howling o'er the wastes of snow !
 Night lengthening into months ; the ravenous
  floe
Crunching the massive ships, as the white bear
Crunches his prey.   The insufficient share
 Of loathsome food ;
The lethargy of famine ; the despair
 Urging to labor, nervelessly pursued :
 Toil done with skinny arms, and faces hued
Like pallid masks, while dolefully behind
Glimmered the fading embers of a mind !
That awful hour, when through the prostrate band
Delirium stalked, laying his burning hand

Upon the ghastly foreheads of the crew ;
The whispers of rebellion, faint and few
 At first, but deepening ever till they grew
Into black thoughts of murder, — such the throng
Of horrors bound the hero.   High the song
Should be that hymns the noble part he played
Sinking himself, yet ministering aid
 To all around him.   By a mighty will
 Living defiant of the wants that kill,
Because his death would seal his comrades' fate ;
Cheering with ceaseless and inventive skill
Those polar waters, dark and desolate.
Equal to every trial, every fate,
 He stands, until spring, tardy with relief,
  Unlocks the icy gate,
And the pale prisoners thread the world once
  more,
To the steep cliffs of Greenland's pastoral shore
  Bearing their dying chief !

Time was when he should gain his spurs of gold
 From royal hands, who wooed the knightly
  state ;
The knell of old formalities is tolled,
 And the world's knights are now self-conse-
  crate.
No grander episode doth chivalry hold
 In all its annals, back to Charlemagne,
 Than that lone vigil of unceasing pain,
Faithfully kept through hunger and through cold,
 By the good Christian knight, Elisha Kane !
    FITZ-JAMES O'BRIEN.

MAZZINI.

A LIGHT is out in Italy,
 A golden tongue of purest flame.
We watched it burning, long and lone,
 And every watcher knew its name,
 And knew from whence its fervor came :
 That one rare light of Italy,
Which put self-seeking souls to shame !

This light which burnt for Italy,
 Through all the blackness of her night,
She doubted, once upon a time,
 Because it took away her sight.
She looked and said, ' There is no light ! "
 It was thine eyes, poor Italy !
That knew not dark apart from bright.

This flame which burnt for Italy,
 It would not let her haters sleep.
They blew at it with angry breath,
 And only fed its upward leap,
 And only made it hot and deep.

Its burning showed us Italy,
And all the hopes she had to keep.

This light is out in Italy,
  Her eyes shall seek for it in vain !
For her sweet sake it spent itself,
  Too early flickering to its wane, —
Too long blown over by her pain.
  Bow down and weep, O Italy,
Thou canst not kindle it again !

LAURA C. REDDEN (*Howard Glyndon*).

JOHN CHARLES FREMONT.

THY error, Fremont, simply was to act
A brave man's part, without the statesman's tact,
And, taking counsel but of common sense,
To strike at cause as well as consequence.
O, never yet since Roland wound his horn
At Roncesvalles has a blast been blown
Far-heard, wide-echoed, startling as thine own,
Heard from the van of freedom's hope forlorn !
It had been safer, doubtless, for the time,
To flatter treason, and avoid offence
To that Dark Power whose underlying crime
Heaves upward its perpetual turbulence.
But, if thine be the fate of all who break
The ground for truth's seed, or forerun their
    years
Till lost in distance, or with stout hearts make
A lane for freedom through the level spears,
Still take thou courage ! God has spoken through
    thee,
Irrevocable, the mighty words, Be free !
The land shakes with them, and the slave's dull
    ear
Turns from the rice-swamp stealthily to hear.
Who would recall them now must first arrest
The winds that blow down from the free North-
    west,
Ruffling the Gulf ; or like a scroll roll back
The Mississippi to its upper springs.
Such words fulfil their prophecy, and lack
But the full time to harden into things.

JOHN GREENLEAF WHITTIER.

TO THE MEMORY OF FLETCHER HARPER.

No soldier, statesman, hierophant, or king ;
None of the heroes that you poets sing ;
A toiler ever since his days began,
Simple, though shrewd, just-judging, man to
    man ;

God-fearing, learnèd in life's hard-taught school ;
By long obedience lessoned how to rule ;
Through many an early struggle led to find
That crown of prosperous fortune, — to be kind.
Lay on his breast these English daisies sweet !
Good rest to the gray head and the tired feet
That walked this world for seventy steadfast
    years !
Bury him with fond blessings and few tears,
Or only of remembrance, not regret.
On his full life the eternal seal is set,
Unbroken till the resurrection day.
So let his children's children go their way,
Go and do likewise, leaving 'neath this sod
An honest man, " the noblest work of God."

DINAH MARIA MULOCK CRAIK.

THE FIFTIETH BIRTHDAY OF AGASSIZ.

MAY 28, 1857.

IT was fifty years ago,
  In the pleasant month of May,
In the beautiful Pays de Vaud,
  A child in its cradle lay.

And Nature, the old nurse, took
  The child upon her knee,
Saying, "Here is a story-book
  Thy Father has written for thee."

"Come, wander with me," she said,
  "Into regions yet untrod,
And read what is still unread
  In the manuscripts of God."

And he wandered away and away
  With Nature, the dear old nurse,
Who sang to him night and day
  The rhymes of the universe.

And whenever the way seemed long,
  Or his heart began to fail,
She would sing a more wonderful song,
  Or tell a more marvellous tale.

So she keeps him still a child,
  And will not let him go,
Though at times his heart beats wild
  For the beautiful Pays de Vaud ;

Though at times he hears in his dreams
  The Ranz des Vaches of old,
And the rush of mountain streams
  From glaciers clear and cold ;

And the mother at home says, "Hark!
  For his voice I listen and yearn :
It is growing late and dark,
  And my boy does not return ! "
                    HENRY WADSWORTH LONGFELLOW.

THE PRAYER OF AGASSIZ.

ON the isle of Penikese,
Ringed about by sapphire seas,
Fanned by breezes salt and cool,
Stood the Master with his school.
Over sails that not in vain
Wooed the west-wind's steady strain,
Line of coast that low and far
Stretched its undulating bar,
Wings aslant along the rim
Of the waves they stooped to skim,
Rock and isle and glistening bay,
Fell the beautiful white day.

Said the Master to the youth :
" We have come in search of truth,
Trying with uncertain key
Door by door of mystery ;
We are reaching, through His laws,
To the garment-hem of Cause,
Him, the endless, unbegun,
The Unnameable, the One,
Light of all our light the Source,
Life of life, and Force of force.
As with fingers of the blind,
We are groping here to find
What the hieroglyphics mean
Of the Unseen in the seen,
What the Thought which underlies
Nature's masking and disguise,
What it is that hides beneath
Blight and bloom and birth and death.
By past efforts unavailing,
Doubt and error, loss and failing,
Of our weakness made aware,
On the threshold of our task
Let us light and guidance ask,
Let us pause in silent prayer ! "

Then the Master in his place
Bowed his head a little space,
And the leaves by soft airs stirred,
Lapse of wave and cry of bird,
Left the solemn hush unbroken
Of that wordless prayer unspoken,
While its wish, on earth unsaid,
Rose to heaven interpreted.
As in life's best hours we hear
By the spirit's finer ear
His low voice within us, thus

The All-Father heareth us ;
And his holy ear we pain
With our noisy words and vain.
Not for him our violence,
Storming at the gates of sense,
His the primal language, his
The eternal silences !
Even the careless heart was moved,
And the doubting gave assent,
With a gesture reverent,
To the Master well-beloved.
As thin mists are glorified
By the light they cannot hide,
All who gazed upon him saw,
Through its veil of tender awe,
How his face was still uplit
By the old sweet look of it,
Hopeful, trustful, full of cheer,
And the love that casts out fear.
Who the secret may declare
Of that brief, unuttered prayer ?
Did the shade before him come
Of the inevitable doom,
Of the end of earth so near,
And Eternity's new year ?

In the lap of sheltering seas
Rests the isle of Penikese ;
But the lord of the domain
Comes not to his own again :
Where the eyes that follow fail,
On a vaster sea his sail
Drifts beyond our beck and hail !
Other lips within its bound
Shall the laws of life expound ;
Other eyes from rock and shell
Read the world's old riddles well ;
But when breezes light and bland
Blow from Summer's blossomed land,
When the air is glad with wings,
And the blithe song-sparrow sings,
Many an eye with his still face
Shall the living ones displace,
Many an ear the word shall seek
He alone could fitly speak.
And one name forevermore
Shall be uttered o'er and o'er
By the waves that kiss the shore,
By the curlew's whistle, sent
Down the cool, sea-scented air ;
In all voices known to her
Nature own her worshipper,
Half in triumph, half lament.
Thither love shall tearful turn,
Friendship pause uncovered there,
And the wisest reverence learn
From the Master's silent prayer.
                    JOHN GREENLEAF WHITTIER.

TO HENRY WADSWORTH LONGFELLOW,

ON HIS BIRTHDAY, 27TH FEBRUARY, 1867.

NEED not praise the sweetness of his song,
  Where limpid verse to limpid verse succeeds
Smooth as our Charles, when, fearing lest he
    wrong
The new moon's mirrored skiff, he slides along,
  Full without noise, and whispers in his reeds.

With loving breath of all the winds his name
  Is blown about the world, but to his friends
A sweeter secret hides behind his fame,
And Love steals shyly through the loud acclaim
  To murmur a *God bless you!* and there ends.

As I muse backward up the checkered years,
  Wherein so much was given, so much was lost,
Blessings in both kinds, such as cheapen tears —
But hush! this is not for profaner ears;
  Let them drink molten pearls nor dream the
    cost.

Some suck up poison from a sorrow's core,
  As naught but nightshade grew upon earth's
    ground;
Love turned all his to heart's-ease, and the more
Fate tried his bastions, she but forced a door,
  Leading to sweeter manhood and more sound.

Even as a wind-waved fountain's swaying shade
  Seems of mixed race, a gray wraith shot with sun,
So through his trial faith translucent rayed,
Till darkness, half disnatured so, betrayed
  A heart of sunshine that would fain o'errun.

Surely if skill in song the shears may stay,
  And of its purpose cheat the charmed abyss,
If our poor life be lengthened by a lay,
He shall not go, although his presence may,
  And the next age in praise shall double this.

Long days be his, and each as lusty-sweet
  As gracious natures find his song to be;
May Age steal on with softly cadenced feet
Falling in music, as for him were meet
  Whose choicest verse is harsher-toned than he!
                        JAMES RUSSELL LOWELL.

———◆———

JOSEPH RODMAN DRAKE.

DIED IN NEW YORK, SEPTEMBER, 1820.

GREEN be the turf above thee,
  Friend of my better days!
None knew thee but to love thee,
  Nor named thee but to praise.

Tears fell, when thou wert dying,
  From eyes unused to weep,
And long, where thou art lying,
  Will tears the cold turf steep.

When hearts, whose truth was proven,
  Like thine, are laid in earth,
There should a wreath be woven
  To tell the world their worth;

And I, who woke each morrow
  To clasp thy hand in mine,
Who shared thy joy and sorrow,
  Whose weal and woe were thine,

It should be mine to braid it
  Around thy faded brow,
But I 've in vain essayed it,
  And feel I cannot now.

While memory bids me weep thee,
  Nor thoughts nor words are free,
The grief is fixed too deeply
  That mourns a man like thee.
                        FITZ-GREENE HALLECK.

———◆———

FITZ-GREENE HALLECK.

READ AT THE UNVEILING OF HIS STATUE IN CENTRAL PARK, MAY, 1877.

AMONG their graven shapes to whom
  Thy civic wreaths belong,
O city of his love! make room
  For one whose gift was song.

Not his the soldier's sword to wield,
  Nor his the helm of state,
Nor glory of the stricken field,
  Nor triumph of debate.

In common ways, with common men,
  He served his race and time
As well as if his clerkly pen
  Had never danced to rhyme.

If, in the thronged and noisy mart,
  The Muses found their son,
Could any say his tuneful art
  A duty left undone?

He toiled and sang; and year by year
  Men found their homes more sweet,
And through a tenderer atmosphere
  Looked down the brick-walled street.

The Greek's wild onset Wall Street knew,
  The Red King walked Broadway;
And Alnwick Castle's roses blew
  From Palisades to Bay.

Fair City by the Sea ! upraise
  His veil with reverent hands ;
And mingle with thy own the praise
  And pride of other lands.

Let Greece his fiery lyric breathe
  Above her hero-urns ;
And Scotland, with her holly, wreathe
  The flower he culled for Burns.

O, stately stand thy palace walls,
  Thy tall ships ride the seas ;
To-day thy poet's name recalls
  A prouder thought than these.

Not less thy pulse of trade shall beat,
  Nor less thy tall fleets swim,
That shaded square and dusty street
  Are classic ground through him.

Alive, he loved, like all who sing,
  The echoes of his song ;
Too late the tardy meed we bring,
  The praise delayed so long.

Too late, alas ! — Of all who knew
  The living man, to-day
Before his unveiled face, how few
  Make bare their locks of gray !

Our lips of praise must soon be dumb,
  Our grateful eyes be dim ;
O, brothers of the days to come,
  Take tender charge of him !

New hands the wires of song may sweep,
  New voices challenge fame ;
But let no moss of years o'ercreep
  The lines of Halleck's name.

          JOHN GREENLEAF WHITTIER.

FRAGMENTS.

CHAUCER.

As that renownèd poet them compyled
 With warlike numbers and heroicke sound,
Dan Chaucer, well of English undefyled,
On Fame's eternall beadroll worthie to be fyled.
 Faerie Queene, Book iv. Cant. ii.   SPENSER.

THE EARL OF WARWICK.

Peace, impudent and shameless Warwick !
Proud setter-up and puller-down of kings.
 King Henry VI., Part III. Act iii. Sc. 3. SHAKESPEARE.

THE DUKE OF GLOSTER.

I, that am rudely stamped and want love's
    majesty
To strut before a wanton ambling nymph ;
I, that am curtailed of this fair proportion,
Cheated of feature by dissembling nature,
Deformed, unfinished, sent before my time
Into this breathing world, scarce half made up,
And that so lamely and unfashionable
That dogs bark at me as I halt by them, —
Why, I, in this weak piping time of peace,
Have no delight to pass away the time,
Unless to see my shadow in the sun.
 King Richard III., Act i. Sc. 1.   SHAKESPEARE.

GALILEO.

The starry Galileo, with his woes.
 Childe Harold, Cant. iv.   BYRON.

SIR PHILIP SIDNEY.

The admired mirror, glory of our isle,
Thou far, far more than mortal man, whose style
Struck more men dumb to hearken to thy song
Than Orpheus' harp, or Tully's golden tongue.
To him, as right, for wit's deep quintessence,
For honor, valor, virtue, excellence,
Be all the garlands, crown his tomb with bay,
Who spake as much as e'er our tongue can say.
 Britannia's Pastorals, Book ii. Song 2.   W. BROWNE.

EDMUND SPENSER.

Divinest Spenser, heaven-bred, happy Muse !
Would any power into my brain infuse
Thy worth, or all that poets had before,
I could not praise till thou deserv'st no more.
 Britannia's Pastorals, Book ii. Song 1.   W. BROWNE.

I was promised on a time
To have reason for my rhyme ;
From that time unto this season,
I received nor rhyme nor reason.
 Lines on his promised Pension.   SPENSER

CHRISTOPHER MARLOWE.

For that fine madness still he did retain,
Which rightly should possess a poet's brain.
 To Henry Reynolds : Of Poets and Poesy. M. DRAYTON.

LORD BACON.

If parts allure thee, think how Bacon shined,
The wisest, brightest, meanest of mankind !
 Essay on Man, Epistle IV.   POPE.

BEN JONSON.

O rare Ben Jonson !
Epitaph. SIR J. YOUNG.

What things have we seen
Done at the Mermaid ! heard words that have
    been
So nimble, and so full of subtle flame,
As if that every one from whence they came
Had meant to put his whole wit in a jest,
And had resolved to live a fool the rest
Of his dull life : then when there hath been
    thrown
Wit able enough to justify the town
For three days past ; wit that might warrant be
For the whole city to talk foolishly
Till that were cancelled; and when that was gone,
We left an air behind us, which alone
Was able to make the two next companies
(Right witty, though but downright fools) more
    wise.
Letter to Ben Jonson. F. BEAUMONT.

WILLIAM SHAKESPEARE.

Far from the sun and summer gale,
In thy green lap was Nature's darling laid,
What time, where lucid Avon strayed,
    To him the mighty mother did unveil
Her awful face : the dauntless child
Stretched forth his little arms and smiled.
"This pencil take," she said, " whose colors clear
Richly paint the vernal year :
Thine too these golden keys, immortal boy !
This can unlock the gates of joy ;
Of horror that, and thrilling fears,
Or ope the sacred source of sympathetic tears."
Progress of Poesy. T. GRAY.

Renownèd Spenser, lie a thought more nigh
To learnèd Chaucer, and rare Beaumont lie
A little nearer Spenser, to make room
For Shakespeare in your threefold, fourfold tomb.
On Shakespeare. W. BASSE.

ABRAHAM COWLEY.

Old mother-wit and nature gave
Shakespeare and Fletcher all they have ;
In Spenser and in Jonson art
Of slower nature got the start ;
But both in him so equal are,
None knows which bears the happiest share ;
To him no author was unknown,
Yet what he wrote was all his own.
Elegy on Cowley. SIR J. DENHAM.

EARL OF MARLBOROUGH.

[Lord-President of the Council to King James I. Parliament was
dissolved March 10, and he died March 14, 1628.]

Till the sad breaking of that Parliament
    Broke him. . . .
Killed with report that old man eloquent.
To the Lady Margaret Ley. MILTON.

JOHN WICKLIFFE.

As thou these ashes, little Brook ! wilt bear
Into the Avon, Avon to the tide
Of Severn, Severn to the narrow seas,
Into main ocean they, this deed accursed
An emblem yields to friends and enemies,
How the bold Teacher's doctrine, sanctified
By truth, shall spread, throughout the world
    dispersed.
Eccles. Sonnets, Part II. xvii. : *To Wickliffe.* WORDSWORTH.

[Bartlett quotes, in this connection, the following:]
" Some prophet of that day said :
  ' The Avon to the Severn runs,
    The Severn to the sea ;
  And Wickliffe's dust shall spread abroad,
    Wide as the waters be.' "
From Address before the " Sons of New Hampshire " (1849).
DANIEL WEBSTER.

JOHN MILTON.

Nor second he, that rode sublime
Upon the seraph-wings of ecstasy,
The secrets of the abyss to spy.
He passed the flaming bounds of place and time
The living throne, the sapphire blaze,
Where angels tremble while they gaze,
He saw ; but, blasted with excess of light,
Closed his eyes in endless night.
Progress of Poesy. T. GRAY.

OLIVER CROMWELL.

How shall I then begin, or where conclude,
  To draw a fame so truly circular ?
For in a round what order can be showed,
  Where all the parts so equal perfect are ?

His grandeur he derived from Heaven alone ;
  For he was great, ere fortune made him so :
And wars, like mists that rise against the sun,
  Made him but greater seem, not greater grow.
Oliver Cromwell. J. DRYDEN.

Or, ravished with the whistling of a name,
See Cromwell, damned to everlasting fame !
Essay on Man, Epistle IV. POPE.

KING CHARLES II.

Here lies our sovereign lord the king,
  Whose word no man relies on ;
He never says a foolish thing,
  Nor ever does a wise one.
Written on the Bedchamber Door of Charles II.
                       EARL OF ROCHESTER.

JAMES THOMSON.

A bard here dwelt, more fat than bard beseems
Who, void of envy, guile, and lust of gain,
On virtue still, and nature's pleasing themes,
Poured forth his unpremeditated strain :
The world forsaking with a calm disdain,
Here laughed he careless in his easy seat ;
Here quaffed, encircled with the joyous train,
Oft moralizing sage : his ditty sweet
He loathèd much to write, ne carèd to repeat.
Stanza introduced into Thomson's " Castle of Indolence," Cant. i.
                       LORD LYTTELTON.

In yonder grave a Druid lies,
  Where slowly winds the stealing wave ;
The year's best sweets shall duteous rise
  To deck its poet's sylvan grave.

    .   .   .

And see, the fairy valleys fade ;
  Dun night has veiled the solemn view !
Yet once again, dear parted shade,
  Meek Nature's child, again adieu !
Ode on the Death of Thomson.   W. COLLINS.

WILLIAM HOGARTH.

The hand of him here torpid lies
  That drew the essential form of grace ;
Here closed in death the attentive eyes
  That saw the manners in the face.
Epitaph.   DR. S. JOHNSON.

WILLIAM WORDSWORTH.

Thine is a strain to read among the hills,
  The old and full of voices ; — by the source
Of some free stream, whose gladdening presence
    fills
The solitude with sound ; for in its course
Even such is thy deep song, that seems a part
Of those high scenes, a fountain from their heart.
Wordsworth.   F. D. HEMANS.

RICHARD BRINSLEY SHERIDAN.

Whose humor, as gay as the firefly's light,
  Played round every subject, and shone as it
    played ; —
Whose wit, in the combat, as gentle as bright,
  Ne'er carried a heart-stain away on its blade ; —

Whose eloquence — brightening whatever it
    tried,
  Whether reason or fancy, the gay or the grave —
Was as rapid, as deep, and as brilliant a tide,
  As ever bore freedom aloft on its wave !
Lines on the Death of Sheridan.   T. MOORE.

Ye men of wit and social eloquence !
He was your brother, — bear his ashes hence !
While powers of mind almost of boundless range,
Complete in kind, as various in their change, —
While eloquence, wit, poesy, and mirth,
That humbler harmonist of care on earth,
Survive within our souls, — while lives our sense
Of pride in merit's proud pre-eminence,
Long shall we seek his likeness, — long in vain,
And turn to all of him which may remain,
Sighing that Nature formed but one such man,
And broke the die — in moulding Sheridan !
Monody on the Death of Sheridan.   BYRON.

AMOS COTTLE.

Oh ! Amos Cottle ! *— Phœbus ! what a name
To fill the speaking trump of future fame ! —
Oh ! Amos Cottle ! for a moment think
What meagre profits spring from pen and ink !
English Bards and Scotch Reviewers.   BYRON.

THE DUKE OF WELLINGTON.

O good gray head which all men knew,
O voice from which their omens all men drew,
O iron nerve to true occasion true,
O fallen at length that tower of strength
Which stood four-square to all the winds that
    blew !
Such was he whom we deplore.
The long self-sacrifice of life is o'er.
The great World-victor's victor will be seen no
    more.
On the Death of the Duke of Wellington.   TENNYSON.

NATHANIEL HAWTHORNE.

There in seclusion and remote from men
  The wizard hand lies cold,
Which at its topmost speed let fall the pen,
  And left the tale half told.

Ah ! who shall lift that wand of magic power,
  And the lost clew regain ?
The unfinished window in Aladdin's tower
  Unfinished must remain !
Hawthorne, May 23, 1864.   LONGFELLOW.

  * " Mr. Cottle, Amos or Joseph, I don't know which, but one or
both, once sellers of books they did not write, but now writers of
books that do not sell, have published a pair of epics." — THE
AUTHOR.

THE OLD MANSE.

EARLY HOME OF EMERSON, AND, LATER, OF HAWTHORNE.

Because I . . . found a home in haunts by others scorned,
The partial wood-gods overpaid my love, . . .
And through my rock-like, solitary wont
Shot million rays of thought and tenderness.

HAWTHORNE

HARP of New England Song,
That even in slumber trembled with the touch
　Of poets who like the four winds from thee waken
All harmonies that to thy strings belong,—
Say, wilt thou blame the younger hands too much
　Which from thy laureled resting place have taken
Thee crowned one in their hold ?　There is a name
　Should quicken thee !　No carol Hawthorne sang,
Yet his articulate spirit, like thine own,
　　　　　　Made answer, quick as flame,
To each breath of the shore from which he sprang,
And prose like his was poesy's high tone.

．　　．　　　．　　　．　　　．　　　．　　　．　　　．

　　　　　　But he whose quickened eye
Saw through New England's life her inmost spirit,—
　Her heart, and all the stays on which it leant,—
Returns not, since he laid the pencil by
Whose mystic touch none other shall inherit !
　What though its work unfinished lies ?　Half-bent
The rainbow's arch fades out in upper air ;
　The shining cataract half-way down the height
Breaks into mist ; the haunting strain, that fell
　　　　　　On listeners unaware,
Ends incomplete, but through the starry night
The ear still waits for what it did not tell.

EDMUND CLARENCE STEDMAN

Publishers: Houghton, Mifflin & Co., Boston

HUMOROUS POEMS

Such a paragon is woman
That, you see, it must be true
She is always exactly better
Than the best that you can do!"

Chas. G. Sage.

Let's cups' up quite undrawn
An' hushed in them the window
An' there let shabby all alone
With no one nigh to hushl.

S. H. Lawrence

Let us live, Uncle Dan;
Let us live and love, Biddy;
What's the world to a man
When his wife is a widdy?

R. H. Stoddard.

HUMOROUS POEMS.

KING JOHN AND THE ABBOT OF CANTERBURY.

FROM "PERCY'S RELIQUES."

AN ancient story I 'll tell you anon
Of a notable prince that was called King John ;
And he ruled England with main and with might,
For he did great wrong, and maintained little
    right.

And I 'll tell you a story, a story so merry,
Concerning the Abbot of Canterbury ;
How for his house-keeping and high renown,
They rode poste for him to fair London towne.

An hundred men the king did heare say,
The abbot kept in his house every day ;
And fifty golde chaynes without any doubt,
In velvet coates waited the abbot about.

"How now, father abbot, I heare it of thee,
Thou keepest a farre better house than mee ;
And for thy house-keeping and high renowne,
I feare thou work'st treason against my crown."

"My liege," quo the abbot, "I would it were
    knowne
I never spend nothing, but what is my owne ;
And I trust your grace will doe me no deere,
For spending of my owne true-gotten geere."

"Yes, yes, father abbot, thy fault it is highe,
And now for the same thou needest must dye ;
For except thou canst answer me questions three,
Thy head shall be smitten from thy bodie.

"And first," quo' the king, "when I 'm in this
    stead,
With my crowne of golde so faire on my head,
Among all my liege-men so noble of birthe,
Thou must tell me to one penny what I am
    worthe.

"Secondly, tell me, without any doubt,
How soone I may ride the whole world about ;
And at the third question thou must not shrink,
But tell me here truly what I do think."

"O these are hard questions for my shallow witt,
Nor I cannot answer your grace as yet :
But if you will give me but three weeks' space,
Ile do my endeavor to answer your grace."

"Now three weeks' space to thee will I give,
And that is the longest time thou hast to live ;
For if thou dost not answer my questions three,
Thy lands and thy livings are forfeit to mee."

Away rode the abbot all sad at that word,
And he rode to Cambridge, and Oxenford ;
But never a doctor there was so wise,
That could with his learning an answer devise.

Then home rode the abbot of comfort so cold,
And he met his shepheard a-going to fold :
"How now, my lord abbot, you are welcome
    home ;
What newes do you bring us from good King
    John ? "

"Sad news, sad news, shepheard, l must give,
That I have but three days more to live ;
For if I do not answer him questions three,
My head will be smitten from my bodie.

"The first is to tell him, there in that stead,
With his crowne of golde so fair on his head,
Among all his liege-men so noble of birth,
To within one penny of what he is worth.

"The seconde, to tell him without any doubt,
How soone he may ride this whole world about ;
And at the third question I must not shrinke,
But tell him there truly what he does thinke."

"Now cheare up, sire abbot, did you never hear
    yet,
That a fool he may learne a wise man witt ?
Lend me horse, and serving-men, and your ap-
    parel,
And Ile ride to London to answere your quarrel.

"Nay, frowne not, if it hath bin told unto me,
I am like your lordship, as ever may be ;

And if you will but lend me your gowne,
There is none shall know us at fair London towne."

" Now horses and serving-men thou shalt have,
With sumptuous array most gallant and brave,
With crozier, and mitre, and rochet, and cope,
Fit to appear 'fore our fader the pope."

" Now welcome, sire abbot," the king he did say,
" 'T is well thou 'rt come back to keepe thy day :
For and if thou canst answer my questions three,
Thy life and thy living both saved shall be.

" And first, when thou seest me here in this stead,
With my crowne of golde so fair on my head,
Among all my liege-men so noble of birthe,
Tell me to one penny what I am worth."

" For thirty pence our Saviour was sold
Among the false Jewes, as I have bin told,
And twenty-nine is the worth of thee,
For I thinke thou art one penny worser than he."

The king he laughed, and swore by St. Bittel,
" I did not think I had been worth so littel !
— Now secondly tell me, without any doubt,
How soone I may ride this whole world about."

" You must rise with the sun, and ride with the
        same
Until the next morning he riseth againe ;
And then your grace need not make any doubt
But in twenty-four hours you 'll ride it about."

The king he laughed, and swore by St. Jone,
" I did not think it could be gone so soone !
— Now from the third question thou must not
        shrinke,
But tell me here truly what I do thinke."

" Yea, that shall I do, and make your grace
        merry ;
You thinke I 'm the Abbot of Canterbury ;
But I 'm his poor shepheard, as plain you may
        see,
That am come to beg pardon for him and for me."

The king he laughed, and swore by the Masse,
" Ile make thee lord abbot this day in his place !"
" Now naye, my liege, be not in such speede,
For alacke I can neither write ne reade."

" Four nobles a week then I will give thee,
For this merry jest thou hast showne unto me ;
And tell the old abbot when thou comest home,
Thou hast brought him a pardon from good King
        John."

                                ANONYMOUS.

JOHN BARLEYCORN.*

THERE was three kings into the East,
    Three kings both great and high,
And they hae sworn a solemn oath
    John Barleycorn should die.

They took a plough and ploughed him down,
    Put clods upon his head,
And they hae sworn a solemn oath,
    John Barleycorn was dead.

But the cheerful spring came kindly on,
    And showers began to fall ;
John Barleycorn got up again,
    And sore surprised them all.

The sultry suns of summer came,
    And he grew thick and strong,
His head well armed wi' pointed spears,
    That no one should him wrong.

The sober autumn entered mild,
    When he grew wan and pale ;
His bending joints and drooping head
    Showed he began to fail.

His color sickened more and more,
    He faded into age ;
And then his enemies began
    To show their deadly rage.

They 've ta'en a weapon long and sharp,
    And cut him by the knee ;
And tied him fast upon the cart,
    Like a rogue for forgerie.

They laid him down upon his back,
    And cudgelled him full sore ;
They hung him up before the storm,
    And turned him o'er and o'er.

They fillèd up a darksome pit
    With water to the brim,
They heavèd in John Barleycorn,
    There let him sink or swim.

They laid him out upon the floor,
    To work him further woe,
And still, as signs of life appeared,
    They tossed him to and fro.

They wasted, o'er a scorching flame,
    The marrow of his bones ;
But a miller used him worst of all,
    For he crushed him between two stones.

* An improvement on a very old ballad found in a black-letter
volume in the Pepys library, Cambridge University

And they hae ta'en his very heart's blood,
　And drank it round and round ;
And still the more and more they drank,
　Their joy did more abound.

John Barleycorn was a hero bold,
　Of noble enterprise ;
For if you do but taste his blood,
　'T will make your courage rise.

Then let us toast John Barleycorn,
　Each man a glass in hand ;
And may his great posterity
　Ne'er fail in old Scotland !

ROBERT BURNS.

OF A CERTAINE MAN.

THERE was (not certaine when) a certaine
　　preacher,
That never learned, and yet became a teacher,
Who having read in Latine thus a text
Of *erat quidam homo*, much perplext,
He seemed the same with studie great to scan,
In English thus, *There was a certaine man.*
But now (quoth he), good people, note you this,
He saith there was, he doth not say there is ;
For in these daies of ours it is most plaine
Of promise, oath, word, deed, no man's certaine ;
Yet by my text you see it comes to passe
That surely once a certaine man there was :
　But yet, I think, in all your Bible no man
　Can finde this text, *There was a certaine
　　woman.*

SIR JOHN HARRINGTON.

LOGIC OF HUDIBRAS.

FROM "HUDIBRAS," PART I. CANTO I.

HE was in logic a great critic,
Profoundly skilled in analytic ;
He could distinguish and divide
A hair, 'twixt south and southwest side ;
On either which he would dispute,
Confute, change hands, and still confute ;
He'd undertake to prove, by force
Of argument, a man's no horse ;
He'd prove a buzzard is no fowl,
And that a lord may be an owl,
A calf an alderman, a goose a justice,
And rooks committee-men and trustees.
He'd run in debt by disputation,
And pay with ratiocination :
All this by syllogism true,
In mood and figure he would do.

DR. SAMUEL BUTLER.

THE VICAR OF BRAY.

["The Vicar of Bray in Berkshire, England, was Simon Alleyn,
or Allen, and held his place from 1540 to 1588. He was a Papist
under the reign of Henry the Eighth, and a Protestant under Edward the Sixth. He was a Papist again under Mary, and once more
became a Protestant in the reign of Elizabeth. When this scandal
to the gown was reproached for his versatility of religious creeds,
and taxed for being a turn-coat and an inconstant changeling, as
Fuller expresses it, he replied : 'Not so neither ; for if I changed
my religion, I am sure I kept true to my principle, which is to live
and die the Vicar of Bray.'" — DISRAELI.]

IN good King Charles's golden days,
　When loyalty no harm meant,
A zealous high-churchman was I,
　And so I got preferment.
To teach my flock I never missed :
　Kings were by God appointed,
And lost are those that dare resist
　Or touch the Lord's anointed.
　　And this is law that I'll maintain
　　　Until my dying day, sir,
　　That whatsoever king shall reign,
　　　Still I'll be the Vicar of Bray, sir

When royal James possessed the crown,
　And popery came in fashion,
The penal laws I hooted down,
　And read the Declaration ;
The Church of Rome I found would fit
　Full well my constitution ;
And I had been a Jesuit
　But for the Revolution.
　　And this is law, etc.

When William was our king declared,
　To ease the nation's grievance ;
With this new wind about I steered,
　And swore to him allegiance ;
Old principles I did revoke,
　Set conscience at a distance ;
Passive obedience was a joke,
　A jest was non-resistance.
　　And this is law, etc.

When royal Anne became our queen,
　The Church of England's glory,
Another face of things was seen,
　And I became a Tory ;
Occasional conformists base,
　I blamed their moderation ;
And thought the Church in danger was,
　By such prevarication.
　　And this is law, etc.

When George in pudding-time came o'er,
　And moderate men looked big, sir,
My principles I changed once more,
　And so became a Whig, sir ;

And thus preferment I procured
　From our new faith's-defender,
And almost every day abjured
　The Pope and the Pretender.
　　And this is law, etc.

The illustrious house of Hanover,
　And Protestant succession,
To these I do allegiance swear—
　While they can keep possession :
For in my faith and loyalty
　I nevermore will falter,
And George my lawful king shall be—
　Until the times do alter.
　　And this is law, etc.

ANONYMOUS.

GOOD ALE.

I CANNOT eat but little meat, —
　My stomach is not good ;
But, sure, I think that I can drink
　With him that wears a hood.
Though I go bare, take ye no care ;
　I nothing am a-cold, —
I stuff my skin so full within
　Of jolly good ale and old.
　　Back and side go bare, go bare ;
　　　Both foot and hand go cold :
　　But, belly, God send thee good ale enough,
　　　Whether it be new or old !

I love no roast but a nut-brown toast,
　And a crab laid in the fire ;
A little bread shall do me stead, —
　Much bread I not desire.
No frost, nor snow, nor wind, I trow,
　Can hurt me if I wold, —
I am so wrapt, and thorowly lapt
　Of jolly good ale and old.
　　Back and side, etc.

And Tyb, my wife, that as her life
　Loveth well good ale to seek,
Full oft drinks she, till you may see
　The tears run down her cheek ;
Then doth she trowl to me the bowl,
　Even as a malt-worm should ;
And saith, "Sweetheart, I took my part
　Of this jolly good ale and old."
　　Back and side, etc.

Now let them drink till they nod and wink,
　Even as good fellows should do ;
They shall not miss to have the bliss
　Good ale doth bring men to ;

And all poor souls that have scoured bowls,
　Or have them lustily trowled,
God save the lives of them and their wives,
　Whether they be young or old !
　　Back and side, etc.

JOHN STILL.

GLUGGITY GLUG.
FROM "THE MYRTLE AND THE VINE."

A JOLLY fat friar loved liquor good store,
　And he had drunk stoutly at supper ;
He mounted his horse in the night at the door,
　And sat with his face to the crupper :
"Some rogue," quoth the friar, " quite dead to
　　remorse,
　Some thief, whom a halter will throttle,
Some scoundrel has cut off the head of my horse,
　While I was engaged at the bottle,
　　Which went gluggity, gluggity — glug
　　　— glug — glug."

The tail of the steed pointed south on the dale,
　'T was the friar's road home, straight and level;
But, when spurred, a horse follows his nose, not
　　his tail,
　So he scampered due north, like a devil :
"This new mode of docking," the friar then said,
　" I perceive does n't make a horse trot ill ;
And 't is cheap, — for he never can eat off his head
　While I am engaged at the bottle,
　　Which goes gluggity, gluggity — glug
　　　— glug — glug."

The steed made a stop, — in a pond he had got,
　He was rather for drinking than grazing ;
Quoth the friar, "'T is strange headless horses
　　should trot,
　But to drink with their tails is amazing !"
Turning round to see whence this phenomenon
　　rose,
　In the pond fell this son of a pottle ;
Quoth he, "The head 's found, for I 'm under
　　his nose, —
　I wish I were over a bottle,
　　Which goes gluggity, gluggity — glug
　　　— glug — glug !"

GEORGE COLMAN, THE YOUNGER.

THE VIRTUOSO.*
　　　　　"Videmus
　Nugari solitos."— PERSIUS.

WHILOM by silver Thames's gentle stream,
　In London town there dwelt a subtle wight, —
A wight of mickle wealth, and mickle fame,
　Book-learned and quaint : a Virtuoso hight.

---

* In imitation of Spenser's style and stanza.

Uncommon things, and rare, were his delight ;
  From musings deep his brain ne'er gotten
    ease,
Nor ceasèd he from study, day or night,
  Until (advancing onward by degrees)
He knew whatever breeds on earth or air or
    seas.

He many a creature did anatomize,
  Almost unpeopling water, air, and land ;
Beasts, fishes, birds, snails, caterpillars, flies,
  Were laid full low by his relentless hand,
That oft with gory crimson was distained ;
  He many a dog destroyed, and many a cat ;
Of fleas his bed, of frogs the marshes drained,
  Could tellen if a mite were lean or fat,
And read a lecture o'er the entrails of a
    gnat.

He knew the various modes of ancient times,
  Their arts and fashions of each different guise,
Their weddings, funerals, punishments for
    crimes,
  Their strength, their learning eke, and rarities ;
Of old habiliments, each sort and size,
  Male, female, high and low, to him were known;
Each gladiator dress, and stage disguise ;
  With learnèd, clerkly phrase he could have
    shown
How the Greek tunic differed from the Roman
    gown.

A curious medallist, I wot, he was,
  And boasted many a course of ancient coin ;
Well as his wife's he knewen every face,
  From Julius Cæsar down to Constantine :
For some rare sculpture he would oft ypine,
  (As green-sick damosels for husbands do ;)
And when obtainèd, with enraptured eyne,
  He'd run it o'er and o'er with greedy view,
And look, and look again, as he would look it
    through.

His rich museum, of dimensions fair,
  With goods that spoke the owner's mind was
    fraught :
Things ancient, curious, value-worth, and rare,
  From sea and land, from Greece and Rome,
    were brought,
Which he with mighty sums of gold had bought :
  On these all tides with joyous eyes he pored ;
And, sooth to say, himself he greater thought,
  When he beheld his cabinets thus stored,
Than if he'd been of Albion's wealthy cities lord.

MARK AKENSIDE.

THE SPLENDID SHILLING.*

" Sing, heavenly Muse.
Things unattempted yet in prose or rhyme ; "
A shilling, breeches, and chimeras dire.

HAPPY the man, who, void of cares and strife,
In silken or in leathern purse retains
A Splendid Shilling : he nor hears with pain
New oysters cried, nor sighs for cheerful ale ;
But with his friends, when nightly mists arise,
To Juniper's Magpie, or Town Hall repairs ;
Where, mindful of the nymph, whose wanton eye
Transfixed his soul, and kindled amorous flames,
Chloe or Phyllis, he each circling glass
Wisheth her health and joy and equal love.
Meanwhile he smokes, and laughs at merry tale,
Or pun ambiguous or conundrum quaint.
But I, whom griping penury surrounds,
And hunger, sure attendant upon want,
With scanty offals, and small acid tiff
(Wretched repast !) my meagre corpse sustain :
Then solitary walk, or doze at home
In garret vile, and with a warming puff
Regale chilled fingers ; or from tube as black
As winter-chimney or well-polished jet,
Exhale mundungus, ill-perfuming scent.
Not blacker tube, nor of a shorter size,
Smokes Cambro-Briton (versed in pedigree,
Sprung from Cadwallador and Arthur, kings
Full famous in romantic tale) when he
O'er many a craggy hill and barren cliff,
Upon a cargo of famed Cestrian cheese,
High overshadowing rides, with a design
To wend his wares at the Arvonian mart,
Or Maridunum, or the ancient town
Ycleped Brechinia, or where Vaga's stream
Encircles Ariconium, fruitful soil !
Whence flow nectareous wines, that well may vie
With Massic, Setin, or renowned Falern.
  Thus, while my joyless minutes tedious flow,
With looks demure, and silent pace, a Dun,
Horrible monster ! hated by gods and men,
To my aerial citadel ascends.†
With vocal heel thrice thundering at my gate,
With hideous accent thrice he calls ; I know
The voice ill-boding, and the solemn sound,
What should I do ? or whither turn ? Amazed,
Confounded, to the dark recess I fly
Of wood-hole ; straight my bristling hairs erect
Through sudden fear ; a chilly sweat bedews
My shuddering limbs, and (wonderful to tell !)
My tongue forgets her faculty of speech ;
So horrible he seems ! His faded brow
Intrenched with many a frown, and conic beard,
And spreading band, admired by modern saints,
Disastrous acts forebode ; in his right hand

---

  * A burlesque imitation of Milton's style.
  † To wit, his garret.

Long scrolls of paper solemnly he waves,
With characters and figures dire inscribed,
Grievous to mortal eyes, (ye gods, avert
Such plagues from righteous men !) Behind him
 stalks
Another monster, not unlike itself,
Sullen of aspect, by the vulgar called
A Catchpole, whose polluted hands the gods
With force incredible, and magic charms,
First have endued : if he his ample palm
Should haply on ill-fated shoulder lay
Of debtor, straight his body to the touch
Obsequious (as whilom knights were wont)
To some enchanted castle is conveyed,
Where gates impregnable, and coercive chains,
In durance strict detain him, till, in form
Of money, Pallas sets the captive free.

 Beware, ye debtors ! when ye walk, beware,
Be circumspect ; oft with insidious ken
The caitiff eyes your steps aloof, and oft
Lies perdue in a nook or gloomy cave,
Prompt to enchant some inadvertent wretch
With his unhallowed touch. So (poets sing)
Grimalkin to domestic vermin sworn
An everlasting foe, with watchful eye
Lies nightly brooding o'er a chinky gap,
Portending her fell claws, to thoughtless mice
Sure ruin. So her disembowelled web
Arachne, in a hall or kitchen, spreads
Obvious to vagrant flies : she secret stands
Within her woven cell ; the humming prey,
Regardless of their fate, rush on the toils
Inextricable, nor will aught avail
Their arts, or arms, or shapes of lovely hue.
The wasp insidious, and the buzzing drone,
And butterfly proud of expanded wings
Distinct with gold, entangled in her snares,
Useless resistance make ; with eager strides,
She towering flies to her expected spoils :
Then with envenomed jaws the vital blood
Drinks of reluctant foes, and to her cave
Their bulky carcasses triumphant drags.

 So pass my days. But when nocturnal shades
This world envelop, and the inclement air
Persuades men to repel benumbing frosts
With pleasant wines and crackling blaze of wood,
Me, lonely sitting, nor the glimmering light
Of make-weight candle, nor the joyous talk
Of loving friend, delights ; distressed, forlorn,
Amidst the horrors of the tedious night,
Darkling I sigh, and feed with dismal thoughts
My anxious mind ; or sometimes mournful verse
Indite, and sing of groves and myrtle shades,
Or desperate lady near a purling stream,
Or lover pendent on a willow-tree.
Meanwhile I labor with eternal drought,
And restless wish, and rave ; my parchèd throat

Finds no relief, nor heavy eyes repose :
But if a slumber haply does invade
My weary limbs, my fancy, still awake,
Thoughtful of drink, and eager, in a dream,
Tipples imaginary pots of ale ;
In vain ; — awake I find the settled thirst
Still gnawing, and the pleasant phantom curse.

 Thus do I live, from pleasure quite debarred,
Nor taste the fruits that the sun's genial rays
Mature, john-apple, nor the downy peach,
Nor walnut in rough-furrowed coat secure,
Nor medlar fruit delicious in decay ;
Afflictions great ! yet greater still remain.
My galligaskins, that have long withstood
The winter's fury and encroaching frosts,
By time subdued, (what will not time subdue !)
An horrid chasm disclose with orifice
Wide, discontinuous ; at which the winds
Eurus and Auster and the dreadful force
Of Boreas, that congeals the Cronian waves,
Tumultuous enter with dire chilling blasts,
Portending agues. Thus a well-fraught ship,
Long sails secure, or through the Ægean deep,
Or the Ionian, till cruising near
The Lilybean shore, with hideous crush
On Scylla or Charybdis (dangerous rocks)
She strikes rebounding ; whence the shattered
 oak,
So fierce a shock unable to withstand,
Admits the sea. In at the gaping side
The crowding waves gush with impetuous rage,
Resistless, overwhelming ; horrors seize
The mariners ; Death in their eyes appears,
They stare, they lave, they pump, they swear,
 they pray :
(Vain efforts !) still the battering waves rush in,
Implacable, till, deluged by the foam,
The ship sinks foundering in the vast abyss.

John Philips

————◆————

ELEGY ON THE DEATH OF A MAD DOG.

 Good people all, of every sort,
  Give ear unto my song ;
 And if you find it wondrous short,
  It cannot hold you long.

 In Islington there was a man
  Of whom the world might say,
 That still a godly race he ran —
  Whene'er he went to pray.

 A kind and gentle heart he had,
  To comfort friends and foes :
 The naked every day he clad —
  When he put on his clothes.

And in that town a dog was found,
  As many dogs there be,
Both mongrel, puppy, whelp, and hound,
  And curs of low degree.

This dog and man at first were friends ;
  But when a pique began,
The dog, to gain his private ends,
  Went mad, and bit the man.

Around from all the neighboring streets
  The wondering neighbors ran,
And swore the dog had lost his wits,
  To bite so good a man !

The wound it seemed both sore and sad
  To every Christian eye :
And while they swore the dog was mad,
  They swore the man would die.

But soon a wonder came to light,
  That showed the rogues they lied : —
The man recovered of the bite,
  The dog it was that died !
                          OLIVER GOLDSMITH.

———◆———

ELEGY ON MADAM BLAIZE.

GOOD people all, with one accord,
  Lament for Madam Blaize ;
Who never wanted a good word —
  From those who spoke her praise.

The needy seldom passed her door,
  And always found her kind ;
She freely lent to all the poor —
  Who left a pledge behind.

She strove the neighborhood to please,
  With manner wondrous winning ;
She never followed wicked ways —
  Unless when she was sinning.

At church, in silk and satins new,
  With hoop of monstrous size,
She never slumbered in her pew —
  But when she shut her eyes.

Her love was sought, I do aver,
  By twenty beaux, or more ;
The king himself has followed her —
  When she has walked before.

But now, her wealth and finery fled,
  Her hangers-on cut short all,
Her doctors found, when she was dead —
  Her last disorder mortal.

Let us lament, in sorrow sore ;
  For Kent Street well may say,
That, had she lived a twelvemonth more —
  She had not died to-day.
                          OLIVER GOLDSMITH.

———◆———

THE DEVIL'S WALK.

FROM his brimstone bed at break of day
  A walking the Devil has gone,
To look at his little, snug farm of the world,
  And see how his stock went on.

Over the hill and over the dale,
  And he went over the plain,
And backward and forward he swished his tail,
  As a gentleman swishes a cane.

How then was the Devil dressed ?
  O, he was in his Sunday's best ;
His coat was red, and his breeches were blue,
  And there was a hole where his tail came through.

A lady drove by in her pride,
  In whose face an expression he spied,
    For which he could have kissed her ;
Such a flourishing, fine, clever creature was she,
With an eye as wicked as wicked can be :
  "I should take her for my aunt," thought he ;
    " If my dam had had a sister."

    He met a lord of high degree, —
    No matter what was his name, —
Whose face with his own when he came to com-
    pare
    The expression, the look, and the air,
  And the character too, as it seemed to a hair, —
  Such a twin-likeness there was in the pair,
    That it made the Devil start and stare ;
For he thought there was surely a looking-glass
    there
    But he could not see the frame.

He saw a lawyer killing a viper
  On a dunghill beside his stable ;
" Ho !" quoth he, " thou put'st me in mind
  Of the story of Cain and Abel."

An apothecary on a white horse
  Rode by on his vocation ;
And the Devil thought of his old friend
  Death in the Revelation.

He passed a cottage with a double coach-house,
  A cottage of gentility ;
And he owned with a grin
That his favorite sin
  Is pride that apes humility.

He saw a pig rapidly
  Down a river float ;
The pig swam well, but every stroke
  Was cutting his own throat ;

And Satan gave thereat his tail
  A twirl of admiration ;
For he thought of his daughter War
  And her suckling babe Taxation.

Well enough, in sooth, he liked that truth,
  And nothing the worse for the jest ;
But this was only a first thought ;
  And in this he did not rest :
Another came presently into his head ;
And here it proved, as has often been said,
  That second thoughts are best.

For as piggy plied, with wind and tide,
  His way with such celerity,
And at every stroke the water dyed
With his own red blood, the Devil cried,
" Behold a swinish nation's pride
  In cotton-spun prosperity ! "

He walked into London leisurely ;
  The streets were dirty and dim ;
But there he saw Brothers the prophet,
  And Brothers the prophet saw him.*

He entered a thriving bookseller's shop ;
  Quoth he, " We are both of one college,
For I myself sate like a cormorant once
  Upon the tree of knowledge."

As he passed through Cold-Bath Fields, he looked
  At a solitary cell ;
And he was well pleased, for it gave him a hint
  For improving the prisons of hell.

He saw a turnkey tie a thief's hands
  With a cordial tug and jerk ;
" Nimbly," quoth he, " a man's fingers move
  When his heart is in his work."

He saw the same turnkey unfettering a man
  With little expedition ;
And he chuckled to think of his dear slave-trade,
And the long debates and delays that were made
  Concerning its abolition.
    .   .

At this good news, so great
  The Devil's pleasure grew,
That with a joyful swish he rent
  The hole where his tail came through.

* " After this I was in a vision, having the angel of God near me,
and saw Satan walking leisurely into London." — BROTHERS'
Prophecies, Part I. p. 41.

His countenance fell for a moment
  When he felt the stitches go ;
" Ah ! " thought he, " there's a job now
  That I 've made for my tailor below."

" Great news ! bloody news ! " cried a newsman ;
  The Devil said, " Stop, let me see !
Great news ? bloody news ? " thought the Devil,
  " The bloodier the better for me."

So he bought the newspaper, and no news
  At all for his money he had.
" Lying varlet," thought he, " thus to take in
    Old Nick !
But it 's some satisfaction, my lad,
To know thou art paid beforehand for the trick,
  For the sixpence I gave thee is bad."

And then it came into his head,
  By oracular inspiration,
That what he had seen and what he had said,
  In the course of this visitation,
Would be published in the Morning Post
  For all this reading nation.

Therewith in second-sight he saw
  The place and the manner and time,
In which this mortal story
  Would be put in immortal rhyme.

That it would happen when two poets
  Should on a time be met
In the town of Nether Stowey,
  In the shire of Somerset.

There, while the one was shaving,
  Would he the song begin ;
And the other, when he heard it at breakfast,
  In ready accord join in.

So each would help the other,
  Two heads being better than one ;
  And the phrase and conceit
  Would in unison meet,
And so with glee the verse flow free
  In ding-dong chime of sing-song rhyme,
  Till the whole were merrily done.

And because it was set to the razor,
  Not to the lute or harp,
Therefore it was that the fancy
Should be bright, and the wit be sharp

" But then," said Satan to himself,
  " As for that said beginner,
Against my infernal Majesty
  There is no greater sinner.

"He hath put me in ugly ballads
  With libellous pictures for sale ;
He hath scoffed at my hoofs and my horns,
  And has made very free with my tail.

"But this Mister Poet shall find
  I am not a safe subject for whim ;
For I 'll set up a school of my own,
  And my poets shall set upon him."

As he went along the Strand
  Between three in the morning and four,
He observed a queer-looking person *
  Who staggered from Perry's door.

And he thought that all the world over
  In vain for a man you might seek,
Who could drink more like a Trojan,
  Or talk more like a Greek.

The Devil then he prophesied
  It would one day be matter of talk,
That with wine when smitten,
And with wit moreover being happily bitten,
This erudite bibber was he who had written
  The story of this walk.

"A pretty mistake," quoth the Devil ;
  "A pretty mistake, I opine !
I have put many ill thoughts in his mouth ;
  He will never put good ones in mine."

Now the morning air was cold for him,
  Who was used to a warm abode ;
And yet he did not immediately wish
  To set out on his homeward road.

For he had some morning calls to make
  Before he went back to hell ;
"So," thought he, "I 'll step into a gaming-
      house,
  And that will do as well ; "
But just before he could get to the door
  A wonderful chance befell.

For all on a sudden, in a dark place,
He came upon General ——'s burning face ;
  And it struck him with such consternation,
That home in a hurry his way did he take,
Because he thought by a slight mistake
  'T was the general conflagration.
                    ROBERT SOUTHEY.

* Porson, the Greek scholar.

THE DEVIL AT HOME.

FROM "THE DEVIL'S PROGRESS."

The Devil sits in his easy-chair,
  Sipping his sulphur tea,
And gazing out, with a pensive air,
O'er the broad bitumen sea ;
Lulled into sentimental mood
By the spirits' far-off wail,
That sweetly, o'er the burning flood,
Floats on the brimstone gale ! —
The Devil, who can be sad at times,
In spite of all his mummery,
And grave, — though not so prosy quite
As drawn by his friend Montgomery, —
The Devil to-day has a dreaming air,
And his eye is raised, and his throat is bare.
His musings are of many things,
That — good or ill — befell,
Since Adam's sons macadamized
The highways into hell : —
And the Devil — whose mirth is *never* loud —
Laughs with a quiet mirth,
As he thinks how well his serpent-tricks
Have been mimicked upon earth ;
Of Eden and of England, soiled
And darkened by the foot
Of those who preach with adder-tongues,
And those who eat the fruit ;
Of creeping things, that drag their slime
Into God's chosen places,
And knowledge leading into crime,
Before the angels' faces ;
Of lands — from Nineveh to Spain —
That have bowed beneath his sway,
And men who did his work, — from Cain
To Viscount Castlereagh !
              THOMAS KIBBLE HERVEY.

———◆———

THE NOSE AND THE EYES.

BETWEEN Nose and Eyes a strange contest arose ;
  The spectacles set them, unhappily, wrong ;
The point in dispute was, as all the world knows,
  To whom the said spectacles ought to belong.

So Tongue was the lawyer, and argued the cause,
  With a great deal of skill, and a wig full of
        learning,
While chief baron Ear sat to balance the laws, —
  So famed for his talent in nicely discerning.

"In behalf of the Nose, it will quickly appear
  (And your lordship," he said, "will undoubt-
      edly find)

That the Nose has the spectacles always to wear,
  Which amounts to possession, time out of
    mind."

Then, holding the spectacles up to the court,
  "Your lordship observes, they are made with
    a straddle,
As wide as the ridge of the Nose is ; in short,
  Designed to sit close to it, just like a saddle.

"Again, would your lordship a moment suppose
  ('T is a case that has happened, and may hap-
    pen again)
That the visage or countenance had *not* a Nose,
  Pray, who *would*, or who *could*, wear spectacles
    then ?

"On the whole, it appears, and my argument
    shows,
  With a reasoning the court will never condemn,
That the spectacles, plainly, were made for the
    Nose,
  And the Nose was, as plainly, intended for
    them."

Then shifting his side (as a lawyer knows how),
  He pleaded again in behalf of the Eyes :
But what were his arguments, few people know,
  For the court did not think them equally wise.

So his lordship decreed, with a grave, solemn
    tone,
  Decisive and clear, without one *if* or *but*,
That whenever the Nose put his spectacles on,
  By daylight or candlelight, — Eyes should be
    shut.
                    WILLIAM COWPER.

ADDRESS TO THE TOOTHACHE.

My curse upon thy venomed stang,
That shoots my tortured gums alang ;
An' through my lugs gies mony a twang,
    Wi' gnawing vengeance !
Tearing my nerves wi' bitter pang,
    Like racking engines.

When fevers burn, or ague freezes,
Rheumatics gnaw, or cholic squeezes ;
Our neighbor's sympathy may ease us,
    Wi' pitying moan ;
But thee, — thou hell o' a' diseases,
    Aye mocks our groan.

Adown my beard the slavers trickle ;
I throw the wee stools o'er the mickle,
As round the fire the giglets keckle
    To see me loup ;
While, raving mad, I wish a heckle
    Were in their doup.

O' a' the numerous human dools,
Ill har'sts, daft bargains, cutty-stools,
Or worthy friends raked i' the mools,
    Sad sight to see !
The tricks o' knaves or fash o' fools,
    Thou bear'st the gree.

Where'er that place be priests ca' hell,
Whence a' the tones o' mis'ry yell,
And rankèd plagues their numbers tell,
    In dreadfu' raw,
Thou, Toothache, surely bear'st the bell,
    Among them a' ;

O thou grim mischief-making chiel,
That gars the notes of discord squeal,
  Till daft mankind aft dance a reel
    In gore a shoe-thick ! —
Gie a' the faes o' Scotland's weal
    A fowmond's Toothache !
                  ROBERT BURNS.

THE FRIEND OF HUMANITY AND THE KNIFE-GRINDER.*

FRIEND OF HUMANITY.

Needy knife-grinder ! whither are you going ?
Rough is the road ; your wheel is out of order.
Bleak blows the blast ; — your hat has got a hole
    in 't ;
    So have your breeches !

Weary knife-grinder! little think the proud ones,
Who in their coaches roll along the turnpike-
Road, what hard work 't is crying all day,
    ' Knives and
    Scissors to grind O ! '

Tell me, knife-grinder, how came you to grind
    knives ?
Did some rich man tyrannically use you ?
Was it the squire ? or parson of the parish ?
    Or the attorney ?

Was it the squire for killing of his game ? or
Covetous parson for his tithes distraining ?
Or roguish lawyer made you lose your little
    All in a lawsuit ?

(Have you not read the Rights of Man, by Tom
    Paine ?)
Drops of compassion tremble on my eyelids,
Ready to fall as soon as you have told your
    Pitiful story.

* A burlesque upon the humanitarian sentiments of Southey in his younger days, as well as of the Sapphic stanzas in which he sometimes embodied them.

KNIFE-GRINDER.

Story! God bless you! I have none to tell, sir;
Only, last night, a-drinking at the Chequers,
This poor old hat and breeches, as you see, were
 Torn in a scuffle.

Constables came up for to take me into
Custody; they took me before the justice;
Justice Oldmixon put me into the parish
 Stocks for a vagrant.

I should be glad to drink your honor's health in
A pot of beer, if you will give me sixpence;
But for my part, I never love to meddle
 With politics, sir.

FRIEND OF HUMANITY.

I give thee sixpence! I will see thee damned
 first, —
Wretch! whom no sense of wrongs can rouse to
 vengeance, —
Sordid, unfeeling, reprobate, degraded,
 Spiritless outcast!

(*Kicks the knife-grinder, overturns his wheel, and
exit in a transport of republican enthusiasm
and universal philanthropy.*)
GEORGE CANNING.

EPITAPH

FOR THE TOMBSTONE ERECTED OVER THE MAR-
QUIS OF ANGLESEA'S LEG, LOST AT THE BATTLE
OF WATERLOO.

HERE rests, and let no saucy knave
 Presume to sneer and laugh,
To learn that mouldering in the grave
 Is laid a British Calf.

For he who writes these lines is sure,
 That those who read the whole
Will find such laugh was premature,
 For here, too, lies a sole.

And here five little ones repose,
 Twin born with other five,
Unheeded by their brother toes,
 Who all are now alive.

A leg and foot, to speak more plain,
 Rests here of one commanding;
Who, though his wits he might retain,
 Lost half his understanding.

And when the guns, with thunder fraught,
 Poured bullets thick as hail,
Could only in this way be taught
 To give the foe leg-bail.

And now in England, just as gay
 As in the battle brave,
Goes to a rout, review, or play,
 With one foot in the grave.

Fortune in vain here showed her spite,
 For he will still be found,
Should England's sons engage in fight,
 Resolved to stand his ground.

But Fortune's pardon I must beg;
 She meant not to disarm,
For when she lopped the hero's leg,
 She did not seek his harm,

And but indulged a harmless whim;
 Since he could walk with one,
She saw two legs were lost on him,
 Who never meant to run.
GEORGE CANNING.

THE PILGRIMS AND THE PEAS.

A BRACE of sinners, for no good,
 Were ordered to the Virgin Mary's shrine,
Who at Loretto dwelt, in wax, stone, wood,
 And in a fair white wig looked wondrous fine
Fifty long miles had those sad rogues to travel
With something in their shoes much worse than
 gravel;
In short, their toes so gentle to amuse,
The priest had ordered peas into their shoes:
A nostrum famous in old popish times
For purifying souls that stunk of crimes:
 A sort of apostolic salt,
 Which popish parsons for its powers exalt,
For keeping souls of sinners sweet,
Just as our kitchen salt keeps meat.

The knaves set off on the same day,
Peas in their shoes, to go and pray;
 But very different was their speed, I wot:
One of the sinners galloped on,
Swift as a bullet from a gun;
 The other limped, as if he had been shot.
One saw the Virgin soon, Peccavi cried,
 Had his soul whitewashed all so clever;
Then home again he nimbly hied,
 Made fit with saints above to live forever.

In coming back, however, let me say,
He met his brother rogue about half-way, —
Hobbling, with outstretched arms and bended
 knees,
Cursing the souls and bodies of the peas;
His eyes in tears, his cheeks and brow in sweat,
Deep sympathizing with his groaning feet.

" How now," the light-toed, whitewashed pil-
    grim broke,
    " You lazy lubber !"
"Ods curse it !" cried the other, " 't is no joke ;
My feet, once hard as any rock,
    Are now as soft as blubber.

" Excuse me, Virgin Mary, that I swear,
As for Loretto, I shall not get there ;
No, to the devil my sinful soul must go,
For damme if I ha'n't lost every toe.
But, brother sinner, pray explain
How 't is that you are not in pain.
    What power hath worked a wonder for your
        toes,
Whilst I just like a snail am crawling,
Now swearing, now on saints devoutly bawling,
    Whilst not a rascal comes to ease my woes ?

" How is 't that you can like a greyhound go,
    Merry as if that naught had happened, burn
        ye !"
" Why," cried the other, grinning, " you must
        know,
    That just before I ventured on my journey,
        To walk a little more at ease,
    I took the liberty to *boil my peas.*"

DR. JOHN WOLCOTT (*Peter Pindar*).

THE RAZOR-SELLER.

A FELLOW in a market-town,
Most musical, cried razors up and down,
    And offered twelve for eighteen pence ;
Which certainly seemed wondrous cheap,
And, for the money, quite a heap,
    As every man would buy, with cash and sense.

A country bumpkin the great offer heard, —
Poor Hodge, who suffered by a broad black beard,
    That seemed a shoe-brush stuck beneath his
        nose :
With cheerfulness the eighteen pence he paid,
And proudly to himself in whispers said,
    " This rascal stole the razors, I suppose.

" No matter if the fellow *be* a knave,
Provided that the razors *shave* ;
    It certainly will be a monstrous prize."
So home the clown, with his good fortune, went,
Smiling, in heart and soul content,
    And quickly soaped himself to ears and eyes.

Being well lathered from a dish or tub,
Hodge now began with grinning pain to grub,
    Just like a hedger cutting furze ;

'T was a vile razor !—then the rest he tried, —
All were impostors. " Ah !" Hodge sighed,
    "I wish my eighteen pence within my purse."

In vain to chase his beard, and bring the graces,
    He cut, and dug, and winced, and stamped,
        and swore ;
Brought blood, and danced, blasphemed, and
        made wry faces,
    And cursed each razor's body o'er and o'er :

His muzzle formed of *opposition* stuff,
Firm as a Foxite, would not lose its ruff ;
    So kept it, — laughing at the steel and suds.
Hodge, in a passion, stretched his angry jaws,
Vowing the direst vengeance with clenched claws,
    On the vile cheat that sold the goods.
" Razors ! a mean, confounded dog,
Not fit to scrape a hog !"

Hodge sought the fellow, — found him, — and
        begun :
" P'rhaps, Master Razor-rogue, to you 't is fun,
    That people flay themselves out of their lives.
You rascal ! for an hour have I been grubbing,
Giving my crying whiskers here a scrubbing,
    With razors just like oyster-knives.
Sirrah ! I tell you you 're a knave,
To cry up razors that can't shave !"

" Friend," quoth the razor-man, " I 'm not a
        knave,
        As for the razors you have bought,
        Upon my soul, I never thought
That they would *shave.*"
" Not think they 'd *shave !*" quoth Hodge, with
        wondering eyes,
    And voice not much unlike an Indian yell ;
" What were they made for, then, you dog ?"
        he cries.
    " *Made,*" quoth the fellow with a smile, —
    " *to sell.*"

DR. JOHN WOLCOTT (*Peter Pindar*).

EPIGRAMS BY S. T. COLERIDGE.

COLOGNE.

IN Köln, a town of monks and bones,
And pavements fanged with murderous stones,
And rags, and hags, and hideous wenches, —
I counted two-and-seventy stenches,
All well-defined and several stinks !
Ye nymphs that reign o'er sewers and sinks,
The river Rhine, it is well known,
Doth wash your city of Cologne ;
But tell me, nymphs ! what power divine
Shall henceforth wash the river Rhine ?

SLY Beelzebub took all occasions
To try Job's constancy and patience.
He took his honor, took his health ;
He took his children, took his wealth,
His servants, oxen, horses, cows —
But cunning Satan did *not* take his spouse.

But Heaven, that brings out good from evil,
And loves to disappoint the devil,
Had predetermined to restore
Twofold all he had before ;
His servants, horses, oxen, cows —
Short-sighted devil, not to take his spouse !

HOARSE Mævius reads his hobbling verse
    To all, and at all times,
And finds them both divinely smooth,
    His voice as well as rhymes.

Yet folks say Mævius is no ass ;
    But Mævius makes it clear
That he 's a monster of an ass, —
    An ass without an ear !

SWANS sing before they die, — 'twere no bad thing
Did certain persons die before they sing.

THE WELL OF ST. KEYNE.

"In the parish of St. Neots, Cornwall, is a well arched over with the robes of four kinds of trees, — withy, oak, elm, and ash, — and dedicated to St. Keyne. The reported virtue of the water is this, that, whether husband or wife first drink thereof, they get the mastery thereby." — FULLER.

A WELL there is in the West country,
    And a clearer one never was seen ;
There is not a wife in the West country
    But has heard of the Well of St. Keyne.

An oak and an elm tree stand beside,
    And behind does an ash-tree grow,
And a willow from the bank above
    Droops to the water below.

A traveller came to the Well of St. Keyne ;
    Pleasant it was to his eye,
For from cock-crow he had been travelling,
    And there was not a cloud in the sky.

He drank of the water so cool and clear,
    For thirsty and hot was he,
And he sat down upon the bank,
    Under the willow-tree.

There came a man from the neighboring town
    At the well to fill his pail,
On the well-side he rested it,
    And bade the stranger hail.

"Now art thou a bachelor, stranger ?" quoth he,
    "For an if thou hast a wife,
The happiest draught thou hast drank this day
    That ever thou didst in thy life.

"Or has your good woman, if one you have,
    In Cornwall ever been ?
For an if she have, I 'll venture my life
    She has drunk of the Well of St. Keyne."

"I have left a good woman who never was here,"
    The stranger he made reply ;
"But that my draught should be better for that,
    "I pray you answer me why."

"St. Keyne," quoth the countryman, "many a time
    Drank of this crystal well,
And before the angel summoned her
    She laid on the water a spell.

"If the husband of this gifted well
    Shall drink before his wife,
A happy man thenceforth is he,
    For he shall be master for life.

"But if the wife should drink of it first,
    Heaven help the husband then !"
The stranger stooped to the Well of St. Keyne,
    And drank of the waters again.

"You drank of the well, I warrant, betimes ?"
    He to the countryman said.
But the countryman smiled as the stranger spake,
    And sheepishly shook his head.

"I hastened, as soon as the wedding was done,
    And left my wife in the porch.
But i' faith, she had been wiser than me,
    For she took a bottle to church."
                          ROBERT SOUTHEY.

THE EGGS AND THE HORSES.

A MATRIMONIAL EPIC.

JOHN DOBBINS was so captivated
By Mary Trueman's fortune, face, and cap,
(With near two thousand pounds the hook was
            baited,)
That in he popped to matrimony's trap.

One small ingredient towards happiness,
It seems, ne'er occupied a single thought ;
    For his accomplished bride
    Appearing well supplied
With the three charms of riches, beauty, dress,
    He did not, as he ought,
    Think of aught else ; so no inquiry made he
    As to the temper of the lady.

And here was certainly a great omission ;
None should accept of Hymen's gentle fetter,
  "For worse or better,"
Whatever be their prospect or condition,
Without acquaintance with each other's nature ;
  For many a mild and quiet creature
    Of charming disposition,
Alas ! by thoughtless marriage has destroyed it.
So take advice ; let girls dress e'er so tastily,
  Don't enter into wedlock hastily
    Unless you can't avoid it.

Week followed week, and, it must be confest,
The bridegroom and the bride had both been
  blest ;
Month after month had languidly transpired,
  Both parties became tired :
    Year after year dragged on ;
    Their happiness was gone.

Ah ! foolish pair !
  "Bear and forbear"
Should be the rule for married folks to take.
But blind mankind (poor discontented elves !)
  Too often make
  The misery of themselves.

At length the husband said, " This will not do !
Mary, I never will be ruled by you ;
  So, wife, d' ye see ?
To live together as we can't agree,
    Suppose we part ! "
    With woman's pride,
    Mary replied,
    "With all my heart ! "

John Dobbins then to Mary's father goes,
And gives the list of his imagined woes.

"Dear son-in-law !" the father said, "I see
All is quite true that you 've been telling me ;
Yet there in marriage is such strange fatality,
  That when as much of life
    You shall have seen
    As it has been
My lot to see, I think you 'll own your wife
As good or better than the generality.

"An interest in your case I really take,
And therefore gladly this agreement make :
An hundred eggs within this basket lie,
With which your luck, to-morrow, you shall try ;
Also my five best horses, with my cart ;
And from the farm at dawn you shall depart.
  All round the country go,
    And be particular, I beg ;
  Where husbands rule, a horse bestow,
    But where the wives, an egg.

And if the horses go before the eggs,
I 'll ease you of your wife, — I will, — I' fegs ! "

Away the married man departed,
  Brisk and light-hearted :
  Not doubting that, of course,
The first five houses each would take a horse.
  At the first house he knocked,
  He felt a little shocked
To hear a female voice, with angry roar,
  Scream out, — " Hullo !
  Who 's there below ?
Why, husband, are you deaf ? go to the door,
  See who it is, I beg."
    Our poor friend John
    Trudged quickly on,
But first laid at the door an egg.

  I will not all his journey through
  The discontented traveller pursue ;
    Suffice it here to say
That when his first day's task was nearly done,
He 'd seen an hundred husbands, minus one,
And eggs just ninety-nine had given away.
"Ha ! there 's a house where he I seek must
    dwell,"
At length cried John ; " I 'll go and ring the
    bell."

The servant came, — John asked him,
    " Pray,
Friend, is your master in the way ? "
  " No," said the man, with smiling phiz,
  " My master is not, but my mistress is ;
Walk in that parlor, sir, my lady 's in it :
Master will be himself there — in a minute."
The lady said her husband then was dressing,
And, if his business was not very pressing,
She would prefer that he should wait until
  His toilet was completed ;
  Adding, " Pray, sir, be seated."
    " Madam, I will,"
Said John, with great politeness ; " but I own
    That you alone
  Can tell me all I wish to know ;
    Will you do so ?
    Pardon my rudeness,
    And just have the goodness
  (A wager to decide) to tell me — do —
Who governs in this house, — your spouse or
    you ? "

  " Sir," said the lady, with a doubting nod,
    " Your question 's very odd ;
  But as I think none ought to be
  Ashamed to do their duty (do you see ?)
  On that account I scruple not to say
  It always is my pleasure to obey.

But here's my husband (always sad without
 me);
Take not my word, but ask him, if you doubt
 me."

"Sir," said the husband, "'t is most true;
 I promise you,
A more obedient, kind, and gentle woman
  Does not exist."
  "Give us your fist,"
Said John, "and, as the case is something more
  than common,
 Allow me to present you with a beast
 Worth fifty guineas at the very least.

"There's Smiler, sir, a beauty, you must own,
 There's Prince, that handsome black,
Ball the gray mare, and Saladin the roan,
  Besides old Dunn;
  Come, sir, choose one;
  But take advice from me,
  Let Prince be he;
 Why, sir, you'll look the hero on his back."

I'll take the black, and thank you too."
 "Nay, husband, that will never do;
 You know, you've often heard me say
 How much I long to have a gray;
 And this one will exactly do for me."
  "No, no," said he,
 "Friend, take the four others back,
  And only leave the black."
 "Nay, husband, I declare
 I must have the gray mare;"
  Adding (with gentle force),
"The gray mare is, I'm sure, the better horse."

"Well, if it must be so, — good sir,
 The gray mare we prefer;
So we accept your gift." John made a leg:
"Allow me to present you with an egg;
 'T is my last egg remaining,
 The cause of my regaining,
I trust, the fond affection of my wife,
Whom I will love the better all my life.

"Home to content has her kind father brought
 me;
I thank him for the lesson he has taught me."
        ANONYMOUS.

    ——◆——

THE MILKMAID.

A MILKMAID, who poised a full pail on her head,
Thus mused on her prospects in life, it is said:
"Let me see, — I should think that this milk
 will procure
One hundred good eggs, or fourscore, to be sure.

"Well then, — stop a bit, — it must not be forgotten,
Some of these may be broken, and some may be
 rotten;
But if twenty for accident should be detached,
It will leave me just sixty sound eggs to be
 hatched.

"Well, sixty sound eggs, — no, sound chickens,
 I mean:
Of these some may die, — we'll suppose seventeen,
Seventeen! not so many, — say ten at the most,
Which will leave fifty chickens to boil or to roast.

"But then there's their barley: how much will
 they need?
Why, they take but one grain at a time when
 they feed, —
So that's a mere trifle; now then, let us see,
At a fair market price how much money there'll
 be.

"Six shillings a pair — five — four — three-and-
 six,
To prevent all mistakes, that low price I will fix;
Now what will that make? fifty chickens, I said, —
Fifty times three-and-sixpence — I'll ask Brother
 Ned.

"O, but stop, — three-and-sixpence a pair I must
 sell 'em;
Well, a pair is a couple, — now then let us tell
 'em;
A couple in fifty will go (my poor brain!)
Why, just a score times, and five pair will remain.

"Twenty-five pair of fowls — now how tiresome
 it is
That I can't reckon up so much money as this!
Well, there's no use in trying, so let's give a
 guess, —
I'll say twenty pounds, and it can't be no less.

"Twenty pounds, I am certain, will buy me a cow,
Thirty geese, and two turkeys, — eight pigs and
 a sow;
Now if these turn out well, at the end of the year,
I shall fill both my pockets with guineas, 't is
 clear."

Forgetting her burden, when this she had said,
The maid superciliously tossed up her head;
When, alas for her prospects! her milk-pail de-
 scended,
And so all her schemes for the future were ended.

This moral, I think, may be safely attached, —
"Reckon not on your chickens before they are
 hatched."
        JEFFREYS TAYLOR.

WHERE ARE YOU GOING, MY PRETTY MAID?

"WHERE are you going, my pretty maid?"
"I am going a-milking, sir," she said.
"May I go with you, my pretty maid?"
"You're kindly welcome, sir," she said.
"What is your father, my pretty maid?"
"My father's a farmer, sir," she said.
"What is your fortune, my pretty maid?"
"My face is my fortune, sir," she said.
"Then I won't marry you, my pretty maid?"
"Nobody asked you, sir," she said.
                                        ANONYMOUS.

TOBY TOSSPOT.

ALAS! what pity 't is that regularity,
    Like Isaac Shove's, is such a rarity!
But there are swilling wights in London town,
    Termed jolly dogs, choice spirits, alias swine,
Who pour, in midnight revel, bumpers down,
    Making their throats a thoroughfare for wine.

These spendthrifts, who life's pleasures thus run on,
    Dozing with headaches till the afternoon,
Lose half men's regular estate of sun,
    By borrowing too largely of the moon.

One of this kidney — Toby Tosspot hight —
Was coming from the Bedford late at night;
    And being *Bacchi plenus*, full of wine,
        Although he had a tolerable notion
        Of aiming at progressive motion,
'T was n't direct, — 't was serpentine.
He worked with sinuosities, along,
Like Monsieur Corkscrew, worming through a
        cork,
Not straight, like Corkscrew's proxy, stiff Don
        Prong, — a fork.

At length, with near four bottles in his pate,
He saw the moon shining on Shove's brass plate,
When reading, " Please to ring the bell,"
    And being civil beyond measure,
"Ring it!" says Toby, — "very well;
    I'll ring it with a deal of pleasure."
Toby, the kindest soul in all the town,
Gave it a jerk that almost jerked it down.

He waited full two minutes, — no one came;
    He waited full two minutes more; — and then
Says Toby, "If he's deaf, I'm not to blame;
    I'll pull it for the gentleman again."

But the first peal woke Isaac in a fright,
    Who, quick as lightning, popping up his head,
    Sat on his head's antipodes, in bed,
Pale as a parsnip, — bolt upright.

At length he wisely to himself doth say, calming
        his fears, —
"Tush! 't is some fool has rung and run away;"
When peal the second rattled in his ears.

Shove jumped into the middle of the floor;
    And, trembling at each breath of air that
        stirred,
He groped down stairs, and opened the street
        door,
    While Toby was performing peal the third.

Isaac eyed Toby, fearfully askant,
    And saw he was a strapper, stout and tall;
Then put this question, "Pray, sir, what d' ye
        want?"
    Says Toby, "I want nothing, sir, at all."

"Want nothing! Sir, you've pulled my bell, I
        vow,
    As if you'd jerk it off the wire."
Quoth Toby, gravely making him a bow,
    "I pulled it, sir, at your desire."

"At mine?" "Yes, yours; I hope I've done
        it well.
    High time for bed, sir; I was hastening to it;
But if you write up, 'Please to ring the bell,'
    Common politeness makes me stop and do it."
                        GEORGE COLMAN THE YOUNGER.

SIR MARMADUKE.

SIR MARMADUKE was a hearty knight, —
        Good man! old man!
He's painted standing bolt upright,
        With his hose rolled over his knee;
His periwig's as white as chalk,
And on his fist he holds a hawk;
        And he looks like the head
            Of an ancient family.

His dining-room was long and wide, —
        Good man! old man!
His spaniels lay by the fireside;
        And in other parts, d' ye see,
Cross-bows, tobacco-pipes, old hats,
A saddle, his wife, and a litter of cats;
        And he looked like the head
            Of an ancient family.

He never turned the poor from the gate, —
        Good man! old man!
But was always ready to break the pate
        Of his country's enemy.

What knight could do a better thing
Than serve the poor and fight for his king ?
And so may every head
Of an ancient family.
GEORGE COLMAN THE YOUNGER.

THE FINE OLD ENGLISH GENTLEMAN.*

I 'LL sing you a good old song,
Made by a good old pate,
Of a fine old English gentleman
Who had an old estate,
And who kept up his old mansion
At a bountiful old rate ;
With a good old porter to relieve
The old poor at his gate,
Like a fine old English gentleman
All of the olden time.

His hall so old was hung around
With pikes and guns and bows,
And swords, and good old bucklers,
That had stood some tough old blows ;
'T was there "his worship" held his state
In doublet and trunk hose,
And quaffed his cup of good old sack,
To warm his good old nose,
Like a fine, etc.

When winter's cold brought frost and snow,
He opened house to all ;
And though threescore and ten his years,
He featly led the ball ;
Nor was the houseless wanderer
E'er driven from his hall ;
For while he feasted all the great,
He ne'er forgot the small ;
Like a fine, etc.

But time, though old, is strong in flight,
And years rolled swiftly by ;
And Autumn's falling leaves proclaimed
This good old man must die !
He laid him down right tranquilly,
Gave up life's latest sigh ;
And mournful stillness reigned around,
And tears bedewed each eye,
For this good, etc.

Now surely this is better far
Than all the new parade
Of theatres and fancy balls,
"At home" and masquerade :

* Modelled upon an old black-letter song, called "The Old and Young Courtier."

And much more economical,
For all his bills were paid.
Then leave your new vagaries quite,
And take up the old trade
Of a fine old English gentleman,
All of the olden time.
ANONYMOUS.

THE DIVERTING HISTORY OF JOHN GILPIN.

SHOWING HOW HE WENT FARTHER THAN HE INTENDED, AND CAME SAFE HOME AGAIN.

JOHN GILPIN was a citizen
Of credit and renown,
A trainband captain eke was he
Of famous London town.

John Gilpin's spouse said to her dear —
"Though wedded we have been
These twice ten tedious years, yet we
No holiday have seen.

"To-morrow is our wedding-day,
And we will then repair
Unto the Bell at Edmonton
All in a chaise and pair.

"My sister and my sister's child,
Myself and children three,
Will fill the chaise ; so you must ride
On horseback after we."

He soon replied, "I do admire
Of womankind but one,
And you are she, my dearest dear :
Therefore it shall be done.

"I am a linendraper bold,
As all the world doth know,
And my good friend the calender
Will lend his horse to go."

Quoth Mrs. Gilpin, "That 's well said ;
And for that wine is dear,
We will be furnished with our own,
Which is both bright and clear."

John Gilpin kissed his loving wife ;
O'erjoyed was he to find,
That, though on pleasure she was bent,
She had a frugal mind.

The morning came, the chaise was brought,
But yet was not allowed
To drive up to the door, lest all
Should say that she was proud.

So three doors off the chaise was stayed,
  Where they did all get in ;
Six precious souls, and all agog
  To dash through thick and thin.

Smack went the whip, round went the wheels,
  Were never folks so glad ;
The stones did rattle underneath,
  As if Cheapside were mad.

John Gilpin at his horse's side
  Seized fast the flowing mane,
And up he got, in haste to ride,
  But soon came down again ;

For saddle-tree scarce reached had he,
  His journey to begin,
When, turning round his head, he saw
  Three customers come in.

So down he came ; for loss of time,
  Although it grieved him sore,
Yet loss of pence, full well he knew,
  Would trouble him much more.

'T was long before the customers
  Were suited to their mind,
When Betty screaming came down stairs,
  " The wine is left behind ! "

" Good lack ! " quoth he, " yet bring it me,
  My leathern belt likewise,
In which I bear my trusty sword
  When I do exercise."

Now Mistress Gilpin (careful soul !)
  Had two stone bottles found,
To hold the liquor that she loved,
  And keep it safe and sound.

Each bottle had a curling ear,
  Through which the belt he drew,
And hung a bottle on each side,
  To make his balance true.

Then over all, that he might be
  Equipped from top to toe,
His long red cloak, well brushed and neat,
  He manfully did throw.

Now see him mounted once again
  Upon his nimble steed,
Full slowly pacing o'er the stones,
  With caution and good heed.

But finding soon a smoother road
  Beneath his well-shod feet,
The snorting beast began to trot,
  Which galled him in his seat.

" So, fair and softly," John he cried,
  But John he cried in vain ;
That trot became a gallop soon,
  In spite of curb and rein.

So stooping down, as needs he must
  Who cannot sit upright,
He grasped the mane with both his hands,
  And eke with all his might.

His horse, who never in that sort
  Had handled been before,
What thing upon his back had got
  Did wonder more and more.

Away went Gilpin, neck or naught ;
  Away went hat and wig ;
He little dreamt, when he set out,
  Of running such a rig.

The wind did blow, the cloak did fly,
  Like streamer long and gay,
Till, loop and button failing both,
  At last it flew away.

Then might all people well discern
  The bottles he had slung ;
A bottle swinging at each side,
  As hath been said or sung.

The dogs did bark, the children screamed,
  Up flew the windows all ;
And every soul cried out, " Well done ! "
  As loud as he could bawl.

Away went Gilpin, — who but he ?
  His fame soon spread around,
" He carries weight ! he rides a race !
  'T is for a thousand pound ! "

And still as fast as he drew near,
  'T was wonderful to view,
How in a trice the turnpike men
  Their gates wide open threw.

And now, as he went bowing down
  His reeking head full low,
The bottles twain behind his back
  Were shattered at a blow.

Down ran the wine into the road,
  Most piteous to be seen,
Which made his horse's flanks to smoke
  As they had basted been.

But still he seemed to carry weight,
  With leathern girdle braced ;
For all might see the bottle necks
  Still dangling at his waist.

Thus all through merry Islington
  These gambols did he play,
Until he came unto the Wash
  Of Edmonton so gay ;

And there he threw the wash about
  On both sides of the way,
Just like unto a trundling mop,
  Or a wild goose at play.

At Edmonton his loving wife
  From the balcony spied
Her tender husband, wondering much
  To see how he did ride.

"Stop, stop, John Gilpin ! — Here 's the house,"
  They all at once did cry ;
"The dinner waits, and we are tired."
  Said Gilpin, "So am I ! "

But yet his horse was not a whit
  Inclined to tarry there ;
For why ? — his owner had a house
  Full ten miles off, at Ware.

So like an arrow swift he flew,
  Shot by an archer strong ;
So did he fly — which brings me to
  The middle of my song.

Away went Gilpin out of breath,
  And sore against his will,
Till at his friend the calender's
  His horse at last stood still.

The calender, amazed to see
  His neighbor in such trim,
Laid down his pipe, flew to the gate,
  And thus accosted him :

" What news ? what news ? your tidings tell ;
  Tell me you must and shall, —
Say why bareheaded you are come,
  Or why you come at all ? "

Now Gilpin had a pleasant wit,
  And loved a timely joke ;
And thus unto the calender
  In merry guise he spoke :

"I came because your horse would come ;
  And, if I well forebode,
My hat and wig will soon be here,
  They are upon the road."

The calender, right glad to find
  His friend in merry pin,
Returned him not a single word,
  But to the house went in ;

Whence straight he came with hat and wig ;
  A wig that flowed behind,
A hat not much the worse for wear,
  Each comely in its kind.

He held them up, and in his turn
  Thus showed his ready wit,
"My head is twice as big as yours,
  They therefore needs must fit.

" But let me scrape the dirt away
  That hangs upon your face ;
And stop and eat, for well you may
  Be in a hungry case."

Said John, " It is my wedding-day,
  And all the world would stare,
If wife should dine at Edmonton,
  And I should dine at Ware."

So turning to his horse, he said,
  " I am in haste to dine ;
'T was for your pleasure you came here,
  You shall go back for mine."

Ah, luckless speech, and bootless boast !
  For which he paid full dear ;
For, while he spake, a braying ass
  Did sing most loud and clear ;

Whereat his horse did snort, as he
  Had heard a lion roar,
And galloped off with all his might,
  As he had done before.

Away went Gilpin, and away
  Went Gilpin's hat and wig :
He lost them sooner than at first,
  For why ? — they were too big.

Now Mistress Gilpin, when she saw
  Her husband posting down
Into the country far away,
  She pulled out half a crown ;

And thus unto the youth she said,
  That drove them to the Bell,
"This shall be yours when you bring back
  My husband safe and well."

The youth did ride, and soon did meet
  John coming back amain ;
Whom in a trice he tried to stop
  By catching at his rein ;

But not performing what he meant,
  And gladly would have done,
The frighted steed he frighted more,
  And made him faster run.

Away went Gilpin, and away
    Went postboy at his heels,
The postboy's horse right glad to miss
    The lumbering of the wheels.

Six gentlemen upon the road,
    Thus seeing Gilpin fly,
With postboy scampering in the rear,
    They raised the hue and cry : —

"Stop thief ! stop thief ! — a highwayman !"
    Not one of them was mute ;
And all and each that passed that way
    Did join in the pursuit.

And now the turnpike-gates again
    Flew open in short space ;
The toll-men thinking, as before,
    That Gilpin rode a race.

And so he did, and won it too,
    For he got first to town ;
Nor stopped till where he had got up
    He did again get down.

Now let us sing, " Long live the king,
    And Gilpin, long live he ;
And when he next doth ride abroad,
    May I be there to see ! "
                  WILLIAM COWPER.

THE GOUTY MERCHANT AND THE STRANGER.

IN Broad Street building (on a winter night),
Snug by his parlor-fire, a gouty wight
Sat all alone, with one hand rubbing
His feet, rolled up in fleecy hose :
With t' other he 'd beneath his nose
The Public Ledger, in whose columns grubbing,
    He noted all the sales of hops,
    Ships, shops, and slops ;
Gum, galls, and groceries ; ginger, gin,
Tar, tallow, turmeric, turpentine, and tin ;
When lo ! a decent personage in black
Entered and most politely said, —
" Your footman, sir, has gone his nightly
    track
    To the King's Head,
And left your door ajar ; which I
Observed in passing by,
    And thought it neighborly to give you notice."
" Ten thousand thanks ; how very few get,
In time of danger,
Such kind attentions from a stranger !
Assuredly, that fellow's throat is
Doomed to a final drop at Newgate ;

He knows, too, (the unconscionable elf !)
That there 's no soul at home except myself."
    " Indeed," replied the stranger (looking grave),
    " Then he 's a double knave ;
He knows that rogues and thieves by scores
Nightly beset unguarded doors :
And see, how easily might one
    Of these domestic foes,
    Even beneath your very nose,
Perform his knavish tricks ;
Enter your room, as I have done,
Blow out your candles — thus — and thus —
Pocket your silver candlesticks,
And — walk off — thus " —
So said, so done ; he made no more remark
    Nor waited for replies,
    But marched off with his prize,
Leaving the gouty merchant in the dark.
                  HORACE SMITH.

ORATOR PUFF.

MR. ORATOR PUFF had two tones in his voice,
    The one squeaking *thus*, and the other down *so;*
In each sentence he uttered he gave you your
        choice,
    For one half was B alt, and the rest G below.
        O ! O ! Orator Puff,
        One voice for an orator 's surely enough.

But he still talked away, spite of coughs and of
        frowns,
    So distracting all ears with his ups and his
        downs,
That a wag once, on hearing the orator say,
    " My voice is for war ! " asked, " Which of
        them, pray ? "
        O ! O ! Orator Puff, etc.

Reeling homewards one evening, top-heavy with
        gin,
    And rehearsing his speech on the weight of
        the crown,
He tripped near a saw-pit, and tumbled right in,
    " Sinking fund " the last words as his noddle
        came down.
        O ! O ! Orator Puff, etc.

" Good Lord ! " he exclaimed, in his he-and-she
        tones,
    " HELP ME OUT ! *Help me out !* I have broken
        my bones ! "
" Help you out ? " said a Paddy who passed,
        " what a bother !
    Why, there 's two of you there — can't you help
        one another ? "
        O ! O ! Orator Puff,
        One voice for an orator 's surely enough.
                  THOMAS MOORE.

MORNING MEDITATIONS.

LET Taylor preach, upon a morning breezy,
How well to rise while nights and larks are flying,—
For my part, getting up seems not so easy
        By half as *lying*.

What if the lark does carol in the sky,
Soaring beyond the sight to find him out,—
Wherefore am I to rise at such a fly?
        I 'm not a trout.

Talk not to me of bees and such-like hums,
The smell of sweet herbs at the morning prime,—
Only lie long enough, and bed becomes
        A bed of *time*.

To me Dan Phœbus and his car are naught,
His steeds that paw impatiently about, —
Let them enjoy, say I, as horses ought,
        The first turn-out !

Right beautiful the dewy meads appear
Besprinkled by the rosy-fingered girl ;
What then, — if I prefer my pillow-beer
        To early pearl ?

My stomach is not ruled by other men's,
And, grumbling for a reason, quaintly begs
Wherefore should master rise before the hens
        Have laid their eggs ?

Why from a comfortable pillow start
To see faint flushes in the east awaken ?
A fig, say I, for any streaky part,
        Excepting bacon.

An early riser Mr. Gray has drawn,
Who used to haste the dewy grass among,
"To meet the sun upon the upland lawn,"—
        Well, — he died young.

With charwomen such early hours agree,
And sweeps that earn betimes their bit and sup ;
But I 'm no climbing boy, and need not be
        All up, — all up !

So here I lie, my morning calls deferring,
Till something nearer to the stroke of noon ; —
A man that 's fond precociously of *stirring*
        Must be a spoon.
                        THOMAS HOOD.

FAITHLESS SALLY BROWN.

YOUNG Ben he was a nice young man,
    A carpenter by trade ;
And he fell in love with Sally Brown,
    That was a lady's maid.

But as they fetched a walk one day,
    They met a press-gang crew ;
And Sally she did faint away,
    Whilst Ben he was brought to.

The boatswain swore with wicked words
    Enough to shock a saint,
That, though she did seem in a fit,
    'T was nothing but a feint.

"Come, girl," said he, "hold up your head,
    He 'll be as good as me ;
For when your swain is in our boat
    A boatswain he will be."

So when they 'd made their game of her,
    And taken off her elf,
She roused, and found she only was
    A coming to herself.

"And is he gone, and is he gone ?"
    She cried and wept outright ;
"Then I will to the water-side,
    And see him out of sight."

A waterman came up to her ;
    "Now, young woman," said he,
"If you weep on so, you will make
    Eye-water in the sea."

"Alas ! they 've taken my beau, Ben,
    To sail with old Benbow ;"
And her woe began to run afresh,
    As if she 'd said, Gee woe !

Says he, "They 've only taken him
    To the tender-ship, you see."
"The tender-ship," cried Sally Brown,
    "What a hard-ship that must be !"

"O, would I were a mermaid now,
    For then I 'd follow him !
But O, I 'm not a fish-woman,
    And so I cannot swim.

"Alas ! I was not born beneath
    The Virgin and the Scales,
So I must curse my cruel stars,
    And walk about in Wales."

Now Ben had sailed to many a place
    That 's underneath the world ;
But in two years the ship came home,
    And all her sails were furled.

But when he called on Sally Brown,
    To see how she got on,
He found she 'd got another Ben,
    Whose Christian-name was John.

"O Sally Brown ! O Sally Brown !
　How could you serve me so ?
I 've met with many a breeze before,
　But never such a blow ! "

Then, reading on his 'bacco box,
　He heaved a heavy sigh,
And then began to eye his pipe,
　And then to pipe his eye.

And then he tried to sing, " All 's Well ! "
　But could not, though he tried ;
His head was turned, — and so he chewed
　His pigtail till he died.

His death, which happened in his berth,
　At forty-odd befel ;
They went and told the sexton, and
　The sexton tolled the bell.
　　　　　　　　　　　　THOMAS HOOD.

FAITHLESS NELLY GRAY.

A PATHETIC BALLAD.

BEN BATTLE was a soldier bold,
　And used to war's alarms ;
But a cannon-ball took off his legs,
　So he laid down his arms.

Now as they bore him off the field,
　Said he, " Let others shoot ;
For here I leave my second leg,
　And the Forty-second Foot."

The army-surgeons made him limbs :
　Said he, " They 're only pegs ;
But there 's as wooden members quite,
　As represent my legs."

Now Ben he loved a pretty maid, —
　Her name was Nelly Gray ;
So he went to pay her his devours,
　When he devoured his pay.

But when he called on Nelly Gray,
　She made him quite a scoff ;
And when she saw his wooden legs,
　Began to take them off.

"O Nelly Gray ! O Nelly Gray !
　Is this your love so warm ?
The love that loves a scarlet coat
　Should be more uniform."

Said she, " I loved a soldier once,
　For he was blithe and brave ;
But I will never have a man
　With both legs in the grave.

"Before you had those timber toes
　Your love I did allow ;
But then, you know, you stand upon
　Another footing now."

"O Nelly Gray ! O Nelly Gray !
　For all your jeering speeches,
At duty's call I left my legs
　In Badajos's breaches."

" Why, then," said she, " you 've lost the feet
　Of legs in war's alarms,
And now you cannot wear your shoes
　Upon your feats of arms ! "

"O false and fickle Nelly Gray !
　I know why you refuse :
Though I 've no feet, some other man
　Is standing in my shoes.

" I wish I ne'er had seen your face ;
　But, now, a long farewell !
For you will be my death ; — alas !
　You will not be my Nell ! "

Now when he went from Nelly Gray
　His heart so heavy got,
And life was such a burden grown,
　It made him take a knot.

So round his melancholy neck
　A rope he did intwine,
And, for his second time in life,
　Enlisted in the Line.

One end he tied around a beam,
　And then removed his pegs ;
And, as his legs were off, — of course
　He soon was off his legs.

And there he hung till he was dead
　As any nail in town ;
For, though distress had cut him up,
　It could not cut him down.

A dozen men sat on his corpse,
　To find out why he died, —
And they buried Ben in four cross-roads,
　With a stake in his inside.
　　　　　　　　　　　　THOMAS HOOD

I AM A FRIAR OF ORDERS GRAY.

FROM THE OPERA OF " ROBIN HOOD."

I AM a friar of orders gray,
　And down in the valleys I take my way ;
I pull not blackberry, haw, or hip, —
　Good store of venison fills my scrip ;

My long bead-roll I merrily chant ;
Where'er I walk no money I want ;
And why I 'm so plump the reason I tell, —
Who leads a good life is sure to live well.
    What baron or squire,
    Or knight of the shire,
    Lives half so well as a holy friar ?

After supper of heaven I dream,
But that is a pullet and clouted cream ;
Myself, by denial, I mortify —
With a dainty bit of a warden-pie ;
I 'm clothed in sackcloth for my sin, —
With old sack wine I 'm lined within ;
A chirping cup is my matin song,
And the vesper's bell is my bowl, ding dong.
    What baron or squire,
    Or knight of the shire,
    Lives half so well as a holy friar ?
                  JOHN O'KEEFE.

THE JACKDAW OF RHEIMS.

THE Jackdaw sat on the Cardinal's chair !
Bishop and abbot and prior were there ;
    Many a monk, and many a friar,
    Many a knight, and many a squire,
With a great many more of lesser degree, —
In sooth, a goodly company ;
And they served the Lord Primate on bended
      knee.
    Never, I ween,
    Was a prouder seen,
Read of in books, or dreamt of in dreams,
Than the Cardinal Lord Archbishop of Rheims !
    In and out,
    Through the motley rout,
That little Jackdaw kept hopping about :
    Here and there,
    Like a dog in a fair,
    Over comfits and cates,
    And dishes and plates,
Cowl and cope, and rochet and pall,
Mitre and crosier, he hopped upon all.
    With a saucy air,
    He perched on the chair
Where, in state, the great Lord Cardinal sat,
In the great Lord Cardinal's great red hat ;
    And he peered in the face
    Of his Lordship's Grace,
With a satisfied look, as if he would say,
" WE TWO are the greatest folks here to-day ! "
    And the priests, with awe,
    As such freaks they saw,
Said, " The Devil must be in that little Jack-
    daw ! "

The feast was over, the board was cleared,
The flawns and the custards had all disappeared,
And six little Singing-boys, — dear little souls
In nice clean faces, and nice white stoles, —
    Came, in order due,
    Two by two,
Marching that grand refectory through !
A nice little boy held a golden ewer,
Embossed and filled with water, as pure
As any that flows between Rheims and Namur.
Which a nice little boy stood ready to catch
In a fine golden hand-basin made to match.
Two nice little boys, rather more grown,
Carried lavender-water and eau-de-Cologne ;
And a nice little boy had a nice cake of soap,
Worthy of washing the hands of the Pope !
    One little boy more
    A napkin bore,
Of the best white diaper, fringed with pink,
And a cardinal's hat marked in " permanent
    ink."

The great Lord Cardinal turns at the sight
Of these nice little boys dressed all in white ;
    From his finger he draws
    His costly turquoise :
And, not thinking at all about little Jackdaws
    Deposits it straight
    By the side of his plate,
While the nice little boys on his Eminence wait,
Till, when nobody 's dreaming of any such thing,
That little Jackdaw hops off with the ring !

    .   .   .   .

    There 's a cry and a shout,
    And a deuce of a rout,
And nobody seems to know what they 're about,
But the monks have their pockets all turned in-
    side out ;
    The friars are kneeling,
    And hunting and feeling
The carpet, the floor, and the walls, and the ceiling.
    The Cardinal drew
    Off each plum-colored shoe,
And left his red stockings exposed to the view ;
    He peeps, and he feels
    In the toes and the heels.
They turn up the dishes, — they turn up the
    plates, —
They take up the poker and poke out the grates,
    — They turn up the rugs,
    They examine the mugs ;
    But, no ! — no such thing, —
    They can't find THE RING !
And the Abbot declared that " when nobody
    twigged it,
Some rascal or other had popped in and prigged
    it ! "

The Cardinal rose with a dignified look,
He called for his candle, his bell, and his book !
    In holy anger and pious grief
    He solemnly cursed that rascally thief !
He cursed him at board, he cursed him in bed ;
From the sole of his foot to the crown of his
        head ;
He cursed him in sleeping, that every night
He should dream of the Devil, and wake in a
        fright.
He cursed him in eating, he cursed him in
        drinking,
He cursed him in coughing, in sneezing, in
        winking ;
He cursed him in sitting, in standing, in lying ;
He cursed him in walking, in riding, in flying ;
He cursed him living, he cursed him dying ! —
Never was heard such a terrible curse !
        But what gave rise
        To no little surprise,
Nobody seemed one penny the worse !

        The day was gone,
        The night came on,
The monks and the friars they searched till dawn ;
        When the sacristan saw,
        On crumpled claw,
Come limping a poor little lame Jackdaw !
        No longer gay,
        As on yesterday ;
His feathers all seemed to be turned the wrong
        way ; —
His pinions drooped, — he could hardly stand, —
His head was as bald as the palm of your hand ;
        His eye so dim,
        So wasted each limb,
That, heedless of grammar, they all cried,
        "THAT 'S HIM ! —
That 's the scamp that has done this scandalous
        thing,
That 's the thief that has got my Lord Cardinal's
        Ring ! "
        The poor little Jackdaw,
        When the monks he saw,
Feebly gave vent to the ghost of a caw ;
And turned his bald head as much as to say,
" Pray be so good as to walk this way ! "
        Slower and slower
        He limped on before,
Till they came to the back of the belfry-door,
        Where the first thing they saw,
        Midst the sticks and the straw,
Was the RING, in the nest of that little Jackdaw !

Then the great Lord Cardinal called for his book,
And off that terrible curse he took :
        The mute expression
        Served in lieu of confession,

And, being thus coupled with full restitution,
The Jackdaw got plenary absolution !
        — When those words were heard,
        That poor little bird
Was so changed in a moment, 't was really ab-
        surd :
        He grew sleek and fat ;
        In addition to that,
A fresh crop of feathers came thick as a mat !
        His tail waggled more
        Even than before ;
But no longer it wagged with an impudent air,
No longer he perched on the Cardinal's chair :
        He hopped now about
        With a gait devout ;
At Matins, at Vespers, he never was out ;
And, so far from any more pilfering deeds,
He always seemed telling the Confessor's beads.
If any one lied, or if any one swore,
Or slumbered in prayer-time and happened to
        snore,
        That good Jackdaw
        Would give a great " Caw ! "
As much as to say, " Don't do so any more ! "
While many remarked, as his manners they saw,
That they "never had known such a pious Jack-
        daw ! "
        He long lived the pride
        Of that country side,
And at last in the odor of sanctity died ;
        When, as words were too faint
        His merits to paint,
The Conclave determined to make him a Saint.
And on newly made Saints and Popes, as you
        know,
It 's the custom of Rome new names to bestow,
So they canonized him by the name of Jem Crow !
                    RICHARD HARRIS BARHAM
                        (*Thomas Ingoldsby, Esq.*).

MISADVENTURES AT MARGATE.

MR. SIMPKINSON (*loquitur*).

I WAS in Margate last July, I walked upon the
        pier,
I saw a little vulgar Boy, — I said, " What make
        you here ?
The gloom upon your youthful cheek speaks any-
        thing but joy ; "
Again I said, " What make you here, you little
        vulgar Boy ? "

He frowned, that little vulgar Boy, — he deemed
        I meant to scoff, —
And when the little heart is big, a little " sets
        it off."

He put his finger in his mouth, his little bosom
  rose, —
He had no little handkerchief to wipe his little
  nose !

"Hark ! don't you hear, my little man ? — it's
  striking Nine," I said,
"An hour when all good little boys and girls
  should be in bed.
Run home and get your supper, else your Ma
  will scold, — O fie !
It's very wrong indeed for little boys to stand
  and cry !"

The tear-drop in his little eye again began to
  spring,
His bosom throbbed with agony, — he cried like
  anything !
I stooped, and thus amidst his sobs I heard him
  murmur, — "Ah !
I have n't got no supper ! and I have n't got no
  Ma !

"My father, he is on the seas, — my mother's
  dead and gone !
And I am here, on this here pier, to roam the
  world alone ;
I have not had, this livelong day, one drop to
  cheer my heart,
Nor 'brown' to buy a bit of bread with, — let
  alone a tart.

"If there's a soul will give me food, or find me
  in employ,
By day or night, then blow me tight !" (he was
  a vulgar Boy ;)
"And now I'm here, from this here pier it is my
  fixed intent
To jump as Mister Levi did from off the Monument !"

"Cheer up ! cheer up ! my little man, — cheer
  up !" I kindly said,
"You are a naughty boy to take such things
  into your head ;
If you should jump from off the pier, you'd surely
  break your legs,
Perhaps your neck, — then Bogey'd have you,
  sure as eggs are eggs !

"Come home with me, my little man, come home
  with me and sup !
My landlady is Mrs. Jones, — we must not keep
  her up, —
There's roast potatoes at the fire, — enough for
  me and you, —
Come home, you little vulgar Boy, — I lodge at
  Number 2."

I took him home to Number 2, the house beside
  "The Foy,"
I bade him wipe his dirty shoes, — that little
  vulgar Boy, —
And then I said to Mistress Jones, the kindest of
  her sex,
"Pray be so good as go and fetch a pint of
  double X !"

But Mrs. Jones was rather cross, she made a little
  noise,
She said she "did not like to wait on little vulgar Boys."
She with her apron wiped the plates, and, as she
  rubbed the delf,
Said I might "go to Jericho, and fetch my beer
  myself !"

I did not go to Jericho, — I went to Mr. Cobb, —
I changed a shilling (which in town the people
  call a Bob), —
It was not so much for myself as for that vulgar
  child, —
And I said, "A pint of double X, and please to
  draw it mild !"

When I came back I gazed about, — I gazed on
  stool and chair, —
I could not see my little friend, because he was
  not there !
I peeped beneath the table-cloth, beneath the
  sofa, too, —
I said, "You little vulgar Boy ! why, what's
  become of you !"

I could not see my table-spoons. — I looked, but
  could not see
The little fiddle-patterned ones I use when I'm
  at tea ;
I could not see my sugar-tongs, my silver watch,
  — O, dear !
I know 't was on the mantel-piece when I went
  out for beer.

I could not see my Macintosh, — it was not to
  be seen !
Nor yet my best white beaver hat, broad-brimmed
  and lined with green ;
My carpet-bag, — my cruet-stand, that holds my
  sauce and soy, —
My roast potatoes ! — all are gone ! — and so's
  that vulgar Boy !

I rang the bell for Mrs. Jones, for she was down
  below,
"O Mrs. Jones, what do you think ? — ain't this
  a pretty go ?

That horrid little vulgar Boy whom I brought
  here to-night
He 's stolen my things and run away!" Says
  she, "And sarve you right!"

Next morning I was up betimes, — I sent the
  Crier round,
All with his bell and gold-laced hat, to say I 'd
  give a pound
To find that little vulgar Boy, who 'd gone and
  used me so ;
But when the Crier cried, "O Yes!" the people
  cried, "O No!"

I went to "Jarvis' Landing-place," the glory of
  the town,
There was a common sailor-man a walking up
  and down,
I told my tale, — he seemed to think I 'd not
  been treated well,
And called me "Poor old Buffer!" — what that
  means I cannot tell.

That Sailor-man, he said he 'd seen that morning
  on the shore
A son of — something — 't was a name I 'd never
  heard before, —
A little "gallows-looking chap," — dear me,
  what could he mean ? —
With a "carpet-swab" and "mucking-togs,"
  and a hat turned up with green.

He spoke about his "precious eyes," and said
  he 'd seen him "sheer," —
It 's very odd that Sailor-men should talk so very
  queer ;
And then he hitched his trousers up, as is, I 'm
  told, their use, —
It 's very odd that Sailor-men should wear those
  things so loose.

I did not understand him well, but think he
  meant to say
He 'd seen that little vulgar Boy, that morning,
  swim away
In Captain Large's Royal George, about an hour
  before,
And they were now, as he supposed, "some-
  wheres" about the Nore.

A landsman said, "I *twig* the chap, he 's been
  upon the Mill, —
And 'cause he *gammons* so the *flats*, ve calls him
  Veeping Bill !"
He said "he 'd done me werry brown, and nicely
  stowed the *swag*," —
That 's French, I fancy, for a hat, or else a car-
  pet-bag.

I went and told the constable my property to
  track ;
He asked me if "I did not wish that I might get
  it back."
I answered, "To be sure I do ! — it 's what I 'm
  come about."
He smiled and said, " Sir, does your mother know
  that you are out ?"

Not knowing what to do, I thought I 'd hasten
  back to town,
And beg our own Lord Mayor to catch the boy
  who 'd "done me brown,"
His Lordship very kindly said he 'd try and find
  him out,
But he "rather thought that there were several
  vulgar boys about."

He sent for Mr. Whithair then, and I described
  " the swag,"
My Macintosh, my sugar-tongs, my spoons, and
  carpet-bag ;
He promised that the New Police should all
  their powers employ,
But never to this hour have I beheld that vulgar
  Boy !

MORAL.

Remember, then, that when a boy I 've heard my
  Grandma tell,
" BE WARNED IN TIME BY OTHERS' HARM, AND
  YOU SHALL DO FULL WELL !"
Don't link yourself with vulgar folks, who 've
  got no fixed abode,
Tell lies, use naughty words, and say they "wish
  they may be blowed !"

Don't take too much of double X ! — and don'
  at night go out
To fetch your beer yourself, but make the pot
  boy bring your stout !
And when you go to Margate next, just stop
  and ring the bell,
Give my respects to Mrs. Jones, and say I 'm
  pretty well !

RICHARD HARRIS BARHAM.
(Thomas Ingoldsby, Esq.)

THE YARN OF THE "NANCY BELL."

FROM "THE BAB BALLADS."

'T WAS on the shores that round our coast
  From Deal to Ramsgate span,
That I found alone, on a piece of stone,
  An elderly naval man.

His hair was weedy, his beard was long,
   And weedy and long was he ;
And I heard this wight on the shore recite,
   In a singular minor key : —

" O, I am a cook and a captain bold,
   And the mate of the Nancy brig,
And a bo'sun tight, and a midshipmite,
   And the crew of the captain's gig."

And he shook his fists and he tore his hair,
   Till I really felt afraid,
For I could n't help thinking the man had been
     drinking,
   And so I simply said : —

" O elderly man, it 's little I know
   Of the duties of men of the sea,
And I 'll eat my hand if I understand
   How you can possibly be

" At once a cook and a captain bold,
   And the mate of the Nancy brig,
And a bo'sun tight, and a midshipmite,
   And the crew of the captain's gig !"

Then he gave a hitch to his trousers, which
   Is a trick all seamen larn,
And having got rid of a thumping quid
   He spun this painful yarn : —

" 'T was in the good ship Nancy Bell
   That we sailed to the Indian sea,
And there on a reef we come to grief,
   Which has often occurred to me.

" And pretty nigh all o' the crew was drowned
   (There was seventy-seven o' soul) ;
And only ten of the Nancy's men
   Said ' Here ' to the muster-roll.

" There was me, and the cook, and the captain
     bold,
   And the mate of the Nancy brig,
And the bo'sun tight, and a midshipmite,
   And the crew of the captain's gig.

" For a month we 'd neither wittles nor drink,
   Till a-hungry we did feel,
So we drawed a lot, and, accordin', shot
   The captain for our meal.

" The next lot fell to the Nancy's mate,
   And a delicate dish he made ;
Then our appetite with the midshipmite
   We seven survivors stayed.

" And then we murdered the bo'sun tight,
   And he much resembled pig ;
Then we wittled free, did the cook and me,
   On the crew of the captain's gig.

" Then only the cook and me was left,
   And the delicate question, ' Which
Of us two goes to the kettle ? ' arose,
   And we argued it out as sich.

" For I loved that cook as a brother, I did,
   And the cook he worshipped me ;
But we 'd both be blowed if we 'd either be stowed
   In the other chap's hold, you see.

" ' I 'll be eat if you dines off me,' says Tom.
   ' Yes, that,' says I, ' you 'll be.
I 'm boiled if I die, my friend,' quoth I ;
   And ' Exactly so,' quoth he.

" Says he : ' Dear James, to murder me
   Were a foolish thing to do,
For don't you see that you can't cook me,
   While I can — and will — cook you ?'

" So he boils the water, and takes the salt
   And the pepper in portions true
(Which he never forgot), and some chopped sha-
     lot,
   And some sage and parsley too.

" ' Come here,' says he, with a proper pride,
   Which his smiling features tell ;
' 'T will soothing be if I let you see
   How extremely nice you 'll smell.'

" And he stirred it round, and round, and round,
   And he sniffed at the foaming froth ;
When I ups with his heels, and smothers his
     squeals
   In the scum of the boiling broth.

" And I eat that cook in a week or less,
   And as I eating be
The last of his chops, why I almost drops,
   For a wessel in sight I see.

    *   *   *   *   *

" And I never larf, and I never smile,
   And I never lark nor play ;
But I sit and croak, and a single joke
   I have — which is to say :

" O, I am a cook and a captain bold
   And the mate of the Nancy brig,
And a bo'sun tight, and a midshipmite,
   And the crew of the captain's gig !"

             WILLIAM SCHWENCK GILBERT

CAPTAIN REECE.*

OF all the ships upon the blue,
No ship contained a better crew
Than that of worthy Captain Reece,
Commanding of The Mantelpiece.

He was adored by all his men,
For worthy Captain Reece, R. N.,
Did all that lay within him to
Promote the comfort of his crew.

If ever they were dull or sad,
Their captain danced to them like mad,
Or told, to make the time pass by,
Droll legends of his infancy.

A feather-bed had every man,
Warm slippers and hot-water can,
Brown windsor from the captain's store,
A valet, too, to every four.

Did they with thirst in summer burn,
Lo, seltzogenes at every turn,
And on all very sultry days
Cream ices handed round on trays.

Then currant wine and ginger pops
Stood handily on all the " tops : "
And, also, with amusement rife,
A " Zoetrope, or Wheel of Life."

New volumes came across the sea
From Mister Mudie's libraree ;
The Times and Saturday Review
Beguiled the leisure of the crew.

Kind-hearted Captain Reece, R. N.,
Was quite devoted to his men ;
In point of fact, good Captain Reece
Beatified The Mantelpiece.

One summer eve, at half past ten,
He said (addressing all his men),
"Come, tell me, please, what I can do,
To please and gratify my crew.

" By any reasonable plan
I 'll make you happy if I can ;
My own convenience count as *nil ;*
It is my duty, and I will."

Then up and answered William Lee
(The kindly captain's coxswain he,
A nervous, shy, low-spoken man);
He cleared his throat, and thus began :

* In this delicious piece of absurdity will be found the germs of
Gilbert's two famous comic operas, — " *H. M. S. Pinafore,*" with its
amiable captain, cheerful crew, and the " sisters and the cousins
and the aunts," and " *The Pirates of Penzance, or The Slave of
Duty.*"

" You have a daughter, Captain Reece,
Ten female cousins and a niece,
A ma, if what I 'm told is true,
Six sisters, and an aunt or two.

" Now, somehow, sir, it seems to me,
More friendly-like we all should be,
If you united of 'em to
Unmarried members of the crew.

" If you 'd ameliorate our life,
Let each select from them a wife ;
And as for nervous me, old pal,
Give me your own enchanting gal ! "

Good Captain Reece, that worthy man,
Debated on his coxswain's plan :
" I quite agree," he said, " O Bill ;
It is my duty, and I will.

" My daughter, that enchanting gurl,
Has just been promised to an earl,
And all my other familee
To peers of various degree.

" But what are dukes and viscounts to
The happiness of all my crew ?
The word I gave you I 'll fulfil ;
It is my duty, and I will.

" As you desire it shall befall,
I 'll settle thousands on you all,
And I shall be, despite my hoard,
The only bachelor on board."

The boatswain of The Mantelpiece,
He blushed and spoke to Captain Reece :
" I beg your honor's leave," he said,
" If you would wish to go and wed,

" I have a widowed mother who
Would be the very thing for you —
She long has loved you from afar,
She washes for you, Captain R."

The captain saw the dame that day —
Addressed her in his playful way —
" And did it want a wedding-ring ?
It was a tempting ickle sing !

" Well, well, the chaplain I will seek,
We 'll all be married this day week
At yonder church upon the hill ;
It is my duty, and I will ! "

The sisters, cousins, aunts, and niece,
And widowed ma of Captain Reece,
Attended there as they were bid ;
It was their duty, and they did.

WILLIAM SCHWENCK GILBERT

LITTLE BILLEE.

THERE were three sailors of Bristol City
  Who took a boat and went to sea,
But first with beef and captain's biscuits
  And pickled pork they loaded she.

There was gorging Jack, and guzzling Jimmy,
  And the youngest he was little Billee ;
Now when they 'd got as far as the Equator,
  They 'd nothing left but one split pea.

Says gorging Jack to guzzling Jimmy,
  "I am extremely hungaree."
To gorging Jack says guzzling Jimmy,
  "We 've nothing left, us must eat we."

Says gorging Jack to guzzling Jimmy,
  "With one another we should n't agree !
There 's little Bill, he 's young and tender,
  We 're old and tough, so let 's eat he."

"O Billy ! we 're going to kill and eat you,
  So undo the button of your chemie."
When Bill received this information,
  He used his pocket-handkerchie.

"First let me say my catechism
  Which my poor mother taught to me."
"Make haste ! make haste !" says guzzling Jimmy,
  While Jack pulled out his snickersnee.

Billy went up to the main-top-gallant mast,
  And down he fell on his bended knee,
He scarce had come to the Twelfth Commandment
  When up he jumps — "There 's land I see !

"Jerusalem and Madagascar
  And North and South Amerikee,
There 's the British flag a riding at anchor,
  With Admiral Napier, K. C. B."

So when they got aboard of the Admiral's,
  He hanged fat Jack and flogged Jimmee,
But as for little Bill he made him
  The Captain of a Seventy-three.
                WILLIAM MAKEPEACE THACKERAY.

---◆---

THE BELLE OF THE BALL.

YEARS, years ago, ere yet my dreams
  Had been of being wise or witty,
Ere I had done with writing themes,
  Or yawned o'er this infernal Chitty, —
Years, years ago, while all my joys
  Were in my fowling-piece and filly ;
In short, while I was yet a boy,
  I fell in love with Laura Lilly.

I saw her at the county ball ;
  There, when the sounds of flute and fiddle
Gave signal sweet in that old hall
  Of hands across and down the middle,
Hers was the subtlest spell by far
  Of all that sets young hearts romancing :
She was our queen, our rose, our star ;
  And then she danced, — O Heaven ! her dancing.

Dark was her hair ; her hand was white ;
  Her voice was exquisitely tender ;
Her eyes were full of liquid light ;
  I never saw a waist so slender ;
Her every look, her every smile,
  Shot right and left a score of arrows :
I thought 't was Venus from her isle,
  And wondered where she 'd left her sparrows.

She talked of politics or prayers,
  Of Southey's prose or Wordsworth's sonnets,
Of danglers or of dancing bears,
  Of battles or the last new bonnets ;
By candle-light, at twelve o'clock, —
  To me it mattered not a tittle, —
If those bright lips had quoted Locke,
  I might have thought they murmured Little.

Through sunny May, through sultry June,
  I loved her with a love eternal ;
I spoke her praises to the moon,
  I wrote them to the Sunday Journal.
My mother laughed ; I soon found out
  That ancient ladies have no feeling :
My father frowned ; but how should gout
  See any happiness in kneeling ?

She was the daughter of a dean, —
  Rich, fat, and rather apoplectic ;
She had one brother just thirteen,
  Whose color was extremely hectic ;
Her grandmother for many a year
  Had fed the parish with her bounty ;
Her second cousin was a peer,
  And lord-lieutenant of the county.

But titles and the three-per-cents,
  And mortgages, and great relations,
And India bonds, and tithes and rents,
  O, what are they to love's sensations ?
Black eyes, fair forehead, clustering locks, —
  Such wealth, such honors Cupid chooses ;
He cares as little for the stocks
  As Baron Rothschild for the muses.

She sketched ; the vale, the wood, the beach,
  Grew lovelier from her pencil's shading :
She botanized ; I envied each
  Young blossom in her boudoir fading :

She warbled Handel ; it was grand, —
  She made the Catilina jealous :
She touched the organ ; I could stand
  For hours and hours to blow the bellows.

She kept an album too, at home,
  Well filled with all an album's glories, —
Paintings of butterflies and Rome,
  Patterns for trimmings, Persian stories,
Soft songs to Julia's cockatoo,
  Fierce odes to famine and to slaughter,
And autographs of Prince Leeboo,
  And recipes for elder-water.

And she was flattered, worshipped, bored ;
  Her steps were watched, her dress was noted ;
Her poodle-dog was quite adored ;
  Her sayings were extremely quoted.
She laughed, — and every heart was glad,
  As if the taxes were abolished ;
She frowned, — and every look was sad,
  As if the opera were demolished.

She smiled on many just for fun, —
  I knew that there was nothing in it ;
I was the first, the only one,
  Her heart had thought of for a minute.
I knew it, for she told me so,
  In phrase which was divinely moulded ;
She wrote a charming hand, — and O,
  How sweetly all her notes were folded !

Our love was most like other loves, —
  A little glow, a little shiver,
A rosebud and a pair of gloves,
  And " Fly Not Yet," upon the river ;
Some jealousy of some one's heir,
  Some hopes of dying broken-hearted ;
A miniature, a lock of hair,
  The usual vows, — and then we parted.

We parted : months and years rolled by ;
  We met again four summers after.
Our parting was all sob and sigh,
  Our meeting was all mirth and laughter !
For in my heart's most secret cell
  There had been many other lodgers ;
And she was not the ball-room's belle,
  But only Mrs. — Something — Rogers !
          WINTHROP MACKWORTH PRAED.

SORROWS OF WERTHER.

WERTHER had a love for Charlotte
  Such as words could never utter ;
Would you know how first he met her ?
  She was cutting bread and butter.

Charlotte was a married lady,
  And a moral man was Werther,
And for all the wealth of Indies
  Would do nothing for to hurt her.

So he sighed and pined and ogled,
  And his passion boiled and bubbled,
Till he blew his silly brains out,
  And no more was by it troubled.

Charlotte, having seen his body
  Borne before her on a shutter,
Like a well-conducted person,
  Went on cutting bread and butter.
        WILLIAM MAKEPEACE THACKERAY.

A LIFE'S LOVE.

I LOVED him in my dawning years —
  Far years, divinely dim ;
My blithest smiles, my saddest tears,
  Were evermore for him.
My dreaming when the day began,
  The latest thought I had,
Was still some little loving plan
  To make my darling glad.

They deemed he lacked the conquering wiles,
  That other children wear ;
To me his face, in frowns or smiles,
  Was never aught but fair.
They said that self was all his goal,
  He knew no thought beyond ;
To me, I know, no living soul
  Was half so true and fond.

In love's eclipse, in friendship's dearth,
  In grief and feud and bale,
My heart has learnt the sacred worth
  Of one that cannot fail ;
And come what must, and come what may,
  Nor power, nor praise, nor pelf,
Shall lure my faith from thee to stray.
  My sweet, my own — *Myself.*
        ANONYMOUS.

ON AN OLD MUFF.

TIME has a magic wand !
  What is this meets my hand,
  Moth-eaten, mouldy, and
    Covered with fluff,
Faded and stiff and scant ?
Can it be ? no, it can't,
Yes, — I declare 't is Aunt
    Prudence's Muff !

Years ago — twenty-three !
Old Uncle Barnaby
Gave it to Aunty P.,
    Laughing and teasing, —
" Pru. of the breezy curls,
Whisper these solemn churls,
What holds a pretty girl's
    Hand without squeezing ? "

Uncle was then a lad,
Gay, but, I grieve to add,
Gone to what 's called " the bad," —
    Smoking, — and worse !
Sleek sable then was this
Muff, lined with *pinkiness,* —
Bloom to which beauty is
    Seldom averse.

I see in retrospect
Aunt, in her best bedecked,
Gliding, with mien erect,
    Gravely to meeting :
Psalm-book, and kerchief new,
Peeped from the Muff of Pru.,
Young men — and pious, too —
    Giving her greeting.

Pure was the life she led
Then : from her Muff, 't is said,
Tracts she distributed ; —
    Scapegraces many,
Seeing the grace they lacked,
Followed her ; one attacked
Prudence, and got his tract
    Oftener than any !

Love has a potent spell !
Soon this bold ne'er-do-well,
Aunt's sweet susceptible
    Heart undermining,
Slipped, so the scandal runs,
Notes in the pretty nun's
Muff, — triple-cornered ones, —
    Pink as its lining !

Worse, even, soon the jade
Fled (to oblige her blade !)
Whilst her friends thought that they 'd
    Locked her up tightly :
After such shocking games,
Aunt is of wedded dames
Gayest, — and now her name 's
    Mrs. Golightly.

In female conduct flaw
Sadder I never saw,
Still I 've faith in the **law**
    Of compensation.

Once uncle went astray, —
Smoked, joked, and swore away ;
Sworn by, he 's now, by a
    Large congregation !

Changed is the child of sin ;
Now he 's (he once was thin)
Grave, with a double chin, —
    Blest be his fat form !
Changed is the garb he wore :
Preacher was never more
Prized than is uncle for
    Pulpit or platform.

If all 's as best befits
Mortals of slender wits,
Then beg this Muff, and its
    Fair owner pardon ;
All 's for the best, — indeed,
Such is my simple creed ;
Still I must go and weed
    Hard in my garden.

                FREDERICK LOCKER.

JACK HORNER.

ROM " MOTHER GOOSE FOR GROWN FOLKS."

> " Little Jack Horner
>   Sat in a corner
>   Eating a Christmas Pie ;
>   He put in his thumb,
>   And pulled out a plum,
>   And said, ' What a great boy am I ! ' "

AH, the world hath many a Horner,
  Who, seated in his corner,
Finds a Christmas Pie provided for his thumb ;
  And cries out with exultation,
  When successful exploration
Doth discover the predestinated plum !

Little Jack outgrows his 'tire,
  And becometh John, Esquire ;
And he finds a monstrous pasty ready made,
  Stuffed with stocks and bonds and bales,
  Gold, currencies, and sales,
And all the mixed ingredients of Trade.

And again it is his luck
  To be just in time to pluck,
By a clever " operation," from the pie
  An unexpected " plum ; "
  So he glorifies his thumb,
And says proudly, " What a mighty man am I !"

Or, perchance to science turning,
  And with weary labor learning
All the formulas and phrases that oppress her, —
  For the fruit of others' baking
  So a fresh diploma taking,
Comes he forth, a full accredited Professor !

Or he's not too nice to mix
In the dish of politics ;
And the dignity of office he puts on ;
And he feels as big again
As a dozen nobler men,
While he writes himself the Honorable John !

Ah me, for the poor nation !
In her hour of desperation,
Her worst foe is that unsparing Horner thumb !
To which War and Death and Hate,
Right, Policy, and State,
Are but pies wherefrom his greed may grasp a
plum !

O, the work was fair and true,
But 't is riddled through and through,
And plundered of its glories everywhere ;
And before men's cheated eyes
Doth the robber triumph rise
And magnify itself in all the air.

Why, if even a good man dies,
And is welcomed to the skies
In the glorious resurrection of the just,
They must ruffle it below
With some vain and wretched show,
To make each his little mud-pie of the dust !

Shall we hint at Lady Horners,
Who, in their exclusive corners,
Think the world is only made of upper-crust ?
Who in the queer mince-pie
That we call Society,
Do their dainty fingers delicately thrust ;

Till, if it come to pass,
In the spiced and sugared mass,
One should compass — don't they call it so ? —
a catch,
By the gratulation given
It would seem the very heaven
Had outdone itself in making such a match !

Or the Woman Horner, now,
Who is raising such a row
To prove that Jack's no bigger boy than Jill ;
And that she won't sit by,
With her little saucer pie,
While he from the Great Pastry picks his fill.

Jealous-wild to be a sharer
In the fruit she thinks the fairer,
Flings by all for the swift gaining of her wish ;
Not discerning in her blindness,
How a tender Loving Kindness
Hid the best things in her own rejected dish !

O, the world keeps Christmas Day
In a queer, perpetual way ;
Shouting always, "What a great big boy am I !"
Yet how many of the crowd
Thus vociferating loud,
And their honors or pretensions lifting high,
Have really, *more than Jack,*
With their boldness or their knack,
Had a finger in the *making* of the Pie ?

ADELINE D. T. WHITNEY.

COMFORT.

WHO would care to pass his life away
Of the Lotos-land a dreamful denizen, —
Lotos-islands in a waveless bay,
Sung by Alfred Tennyson ?

Who would care to be a dull new-comer
Far across the wild sea's wide abysses,
Where, about the earth's three thousandth sum-
mer,
Passed divine Ulysses ?

Rather give me coffee, art, a book,
From my windows a delicious sea-view,
Southdown mutton, somebody to cook, —
"Music ?" — I believe you.

Strawberry icebergs in the summer time, —
But of elm-wood many a massive splinter,
Good ghost stories, and a classic rhyme,
For the nights of winter.

Now and then a friend and some Sauterne,
Now and then a haunch of Highland venison,
And for Lotos-land I 'll never yearn,
Malgré Alfred Tennyson.

MORTIMER COLLINS.

THE WOMEN FO'K.*

O, SAIRLY may I rue the day
I fancied first the womenkind ;
For aye sinsyne I ne'er can hae
Ae quiet thought or peace o' mind !
They hae plagued my heart an' pleased my e'e,
An' teased an' flattered me at will,
But aye for a' their witcherye,
The pawky things I lo'e them still.

* The air of this song is my own. It was first set to music by
Heather, and most beautifully set too. It was afterwards set by
Dewar, whether with the same accompaniments or not, I have forgot. It is my own favorite humorous song, when forced to sing by
ladies against my will, which too frequently happens ; and, notwithstanding my wood-notes wild, it will never be sung by any so well
again. — THE AUTHOR.

THE V-A-S-E.

FROM the madding crowd they stand apart,
The maidens four and the Work of Art;

And none might tell from sight alone
In which had culture ripest grown,—

The Gotham Millions fair to see,
The Philadelphia Pedigree,

The Boston Mind of azure hue,
Or the soulful Soul from Kalamazoo,—

For all loved Art in a seemly way,
With an earnest soul and a capital A.

. . . .

Long they worshipped; but no one broke
The sacred stillness, until up spoke

The Western one from the nameless place,
Who blushing said: "What a lovely vace!"

Over three faces a sad smile flew,
And they edged away from Kalamazoo.

But Gotham's haughty soul was stirred
To crush the stranger with one small word

Deftly hiding reproof in praise,
She cries: "'Tis, indeed, a lovely vaze!"

But brief her unworthy triumph when
The lofty one from the home of Penn,

With the consciousness of two grand papas,
Exclaims: "It is quite a lovely vahs!"

And glances round with an anxious thrill,
Awaiting the word of Beacon Hill.

But the Boston maid smiles courteouslee,
And gently murmurs: "Oh pardon me!

"I did not catch your remark, because
J was so entranced with that charming vaws!"

THE BRYANT VASE.
Designed by Jas. M. Whitehouse, of
Tiffany & Co.

>   *Dies erit prægelida*
>   *Sinistra quum Bostonia.*

>   JAMES JEFFREY ROCHE.

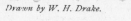

Drawn by W. H. Drake.

NEBUCHADNEZZAR.

You, Nebuchadnezzah, whoa, sah!
Whar is you tryin' to go, sah?
I'd hab you fur to know, sah,
I's a-holdin' ob de lines.
You better stop dat prancin',
You's paw'ful fond ob dancin',
But I'll bet my yeah's advancin'
Dat I'll cure you ob yo' shines.

Look heah, mule! Better min' out;
Fus' t'ing you know you'll fin' out
How quick I'll wear dis line out
On your ugly, stubbo'n back.
You needn't try to steal up;
An' lif' dat precious heel up;
You's got to plough dis fiel' up,
You has, sah, fur a fac'.

Dar, *dat's* de way to do it!
He's comin' right down to it;
Jes watch him ploughin' troo it!
Dis nigger ain't no fool.
Some folks dey would 'a' beat him;
Now, dat would only heat him—
I know jes how to treat him:
You mus' *reason* wid a mule.

He minds me like a nigger.
If he wuz only bigger
He'd fotch a mighty figger,
He would, I *tell* you! Yes, sah!
See how he keeps a-clickin'!
He's as gentle as a chicken,
And nebber thinks o' kickin'—
Whoa dar! Nebuchadnezzah!

Is this heah me, or not me?
Or is de debbil got me?
Wuz dat a cannon shot me?
Hab I laid heah more'n a week?
Dat mule do kick amazin'!
De beast was sp'iled in raisin';
But now I spect he's grazin'
On de oder side de creek.

IRWIN RUSSELL.

O the women fo'k ! O the women fo'k !
　But they hae been the wreck o' me ;
O weary fa' the women fo'k,
　For they winna let a body be !

I hae thought an' thought, but darena tell,
　I 've studied them wi' a' my skill,
I 've lo'd them better than mysell,
　I 've tried again to like them ill.
Wha sairest strives, will sairest rue,
　To comprehend what nae man can ;
When he has done what man can do,
　He 'll end at last where he began.
　　O the women fo'k, etc.

That they hae gentle forms an' meet,
　A man wi' half a look may see ;
An gracefu' airs, an' faces sweet,
　An' waving curls aboon the bree ;
An' smiles as soft as the young rosebud,
　And een sae pawky, bright, an' rare,
Wad lure the laverock frae the cludd, —
　But, laddie, seek to ken nae mair !
　　O the women fo'k, etc.

Even but this night nae farther gane,
　The date is neither lost nor lang,
I tak ye witness ilka ane,
　How fell they fought, and fairly dang.
Their point they 've carried right or wrang,
　Without a reason, rhyme, or law,
An' forced a man to sing a sang,
　That ne'er could sing a verse ava.
　　O the women fo'k ! O the women fo'k !
　　But they hae been the wreck o' me ;
　O weary fa' the women fo'k,
　　For they winna let a body be !
　　　　　　　　　　JAMES HOGG.

WOMAN.

WHEN Eve brought *woe* to all mankind
Old Adam called her *wo-man ;*
But when she *woo*ed with love so kind,
He then pronounced her *woo-man.*
But now, with folly and with pride,
Their husbands' pockets trimming,
The women are so full of *whims*
That men pronounce them *wimmen !*
　　　　　　　　　ANONYMOUS.

PAPER.

A CONVERSATIONAL PLEASANTRY.

SOME wit of old — such wits of old there were,
Whose hints showed meaning, whose allusions
　　care —
By one brave stroke to mark all human kind,
Called clear, blank paper every infant mind ;

Where still, as opening sense her dictates wrote,
Fair virtue put a seal, or vice a blot.

The thought was happy, pertinent, and true ;
Methinks a genius might the plan pursue.
I (can you pardon my presumption ?) — I,
No wit, no genius, yet for once will try.

Various the paper various wants produce, —
The wants of fashion, elegance, and use.
Men are as various ; and, if right I scan,
Each sort of paper represents some man.

Pray note the fop, half powder and half lace ;
Nice, as a bandbox were his dwelling-place ;
He 's the *gilt-paper*, which apart you store,
And lock from vulgar hands in the 'scrutoire.

Mechanics, servants, farmers, and so forth,
Are *copy-paper*, of inferior worth ;
Less prized, more useful, for your desk decreed ;
Free to all pens, and prompt at every need.

The wretch whom avarice bids to pinch and spare,
Starve, cheat, and pilfer, to enrich an heir,
Is *coarse brown paper*, such as pedlers choose
To wrap up wares, which better men will use.

Take next the miser's contrast, who destroys
Health, fame, and fortune in a round of joys ;
Will any paper match him ? Yes, throughout ;
He 's a true *sinking-paper*, past all doubt.

The retail politician's anxious thought
Deems this side always right, and that stark
　　naught ;
He foams with censure ; with applause he raves ;
A dupe to rumors, and a tool of knaves ;
He 'll want no type, his weakness to proclaim,
While such a thing as *foolscap* has a name.

The hasty gentleman, whose blood runs high,
Who picks a quarrel, if you step awry,
Who can't a jest, a hint, or look endure, —
What is he ? — what ? *Touch-paper*, to be sure.

What are our poets, take them as they fall,
Good, bad, rich, poor, much read, not read at all ?
They and their works in the same class you 'll
　　find ;
They are the mere *waste-paper* of mankind.

Observe the maiden, innocently sweet !
She 's fair, *white paper*, an unsullied sheet :
On which the happy man whom fate ordains
May write his name, and take her for his pains.

One instance more, and only one I 'll bring ;
'T is the great man who scorns a little thing ;

Whose thoughts, whose deeds, whose maxims,
      are his own,
Formed on the feelings of his heart alone,
True, genuine, *royal paper* is his breast ;
Of all the kinds most precious, purest, best.
                              BENJAMIN FRANKLIN.

OLD GRIMES.

OLD Grimes is dead, that good old man, —
    We ne'er shall see him more ;
He used to wear a long black coat,
    All buttoned down before.

His heart was open as the day,
    His feelings all were true ;
His hair was some inclined to gray, —
    He wore it in a queue.

Whene'er he heard the voice of pain,
    His breast with pity burned ;
The large round head upon his cane
    From ivory was turned.

Kind words he ever had for all ;
    He knew no base design ;
His eyes were dark and rather small,
    His nose was aquiline.

He lived at peace with all mankind,
    In friendship he was true ;
His coat had pocket-holes behind,
    His pantaloons were blue.

Unharmed, the sin which earth pollutes
    He passed securely o'er, —
And never wore a pair of boots
    For thirty years or more.

But good Old Grimes is now at rest,
    Nor fears misfortune's frown ;
He wore a double-breasted vest, —
    The stripes ran up and down.

He modest merit sought to find,
    And pay it its desert ;
He had no malice in his mind,
    No ruffles on his shirt.

His neighbors he did not abuse, —
    Was sociable and gay ;
He wore large buckles on his shoes,
    And changed them every day.

His knowledge, hid from public gaze,
    He did not bring to view,
Nor make a noise, town-meeting days,
    As many people do.

His worldly goods he never threw
    In trust to fortune's chances,
But lived (as all his brothers do)
    In easy circumstances.

Thus undisturbed by anxious cares
    His peaceful moments ran ;
And everybody said he was
    A fine old gentleman.
                            ALBERT G. GREENE.

THE HEIGHT OF THE RIDICULOUS.

I WROTE some lines once on a time
    In wondrous merry mood,
And thought, as usual, men would say
    They were exceeding good.

They were so queer, so very queer,
    I laughed as I would die ;
Albeit, in the general way,
    A sober man am I.

I called my servant, and he came ;
    How kind it was of him,
To mind a slender man like me,
    He of the mighty limb !

" These to the printer," I exclaimed,
    And, in my humorous way,
I added (as a trifling jest),
    " There 'll be the devil to pay."

He took the paper, and I watched,
    And saw him peep within ;
At the first line he read, his face
    Was all upon the grin.

He read the next ; the grin grew broad,
    And shot from ear to ear ;
He read the third ; a chuckling noise
    I now began to hear.

The fourth ; he broke into a roar ;
    The fifth ; his waistband split ;
The sixth ; he burst five buttons off,
    And tumbled in a fit.

Ten days and nights, with sleepless eye,
    I watched that wretched man,
And since, I never dare to write
    As funny as I can.
                        OLIVER WENDELL HOLMES.

Oliver Wendell Holmes

THE ONE-HOSS SHAY ;

OR, THE DEACON'S MASTERPIECE.

A LOGICAL STORY.

HAVE you heard of the wonderful one-hoss shay,
That was built in such a logical way
It ran a hundred years to a day,
And then of a sudden, it — ah, but stay,
I 'll tell you what happened without delay,
Scaring the parson into fits,
Frightening people out of their wits, —
Have you ever heard of that. I say ?

Seventeen hundred and fifty-five.
Georgius Secundus was then alive, —
Snuffy old drone from the German hive.
That was the year when Lisbon-town
Saw the earth open and gulp her down,
And Braddock's army was done so brown,
Left without a scalp to its crown.
It was on the terrible Earthquake-day
That the Deacon finished the one-hoss shay.

Now in building of chaises, I tell you what,
There is always *somewhere* a weakest spot, —
In hub, tire, felloe, in spring or thill,
In panel, or crossbar, or floor, or sill,
In screw, bolt, thoroughbrace, — lurking still,
Find it somewhere you must and will, —
Above or below, or within or without, —
And that 's the reason, beyond a doubt,
A chaise *breaks down*, but does n't *wear out*.

But the Deacon swore (as Deacons do,
With an "I dew vum," or an " I tell *yeou*,")
He would build one shay to beat the taown
'n' the keounty 'n' all the kentry raoun' ;
It should be so built that it *could n'* break daown ;
— " Fur," said the Deacon, " 't 's mighty plain
Thut the weakes' place mus' stan' the strain ;
'n' the way t' fix it, uz I maintain,
          Is only jest
T' make that place uz strong uz the rest."

So the Deacon inquired of the village folk
Where he could find the strongest oak,
That could n't be split nor bent nor broke, —
That was for spokes and floor and sills ;
He sent for lancewood to make the thills ;
The crossbars were ash, from the straightest trees ;
The panels of whitewood, that cuts like cheese,
But lasts like iron for things like these ;
The hubs of logs from the " Settler's ellum," —
Last of its timber, — they could n't sell 'em,
Never an axe had seen their chips,
And the wedges flew from between their lips,
Their blunt ends frizzled like celery-tips ;

Step and prop-iron, bolt and screw,
Spring, tire, axle, and linchpin too,
Steel of the finest, bright and blue ;
Thoroughbrace bison-skin, thick and wide ;
Boot, top, dasher, from tough old hide
Found in the pit when the tanner died.
That was the way he " put her through."
" There ! " said the Deacon, " naow she 'll dew ! "

Do ! I tell you, I rather guess
She was a wonder, and nothing less !
Colts grew horses, beards turned gray,
Deacon and deaconess dropped away,
Children and grandchildren, — where were they !
But there stood the stout old one-hoss shay
As fresh as on Lisbon-earthquake-day !

EIGHTEEN HUNDRED ; — it came and found
The Deacon's masterpiece strong and sound.
Eighteen hundred increased by ten ; —
" Hahnsum kerridge " they called it then.
Eighteen hundred and twenty came ; —
Running as usual ; much the same.
Thirty and forty at last arrive,
And then came fifty, and FIFTY-FIVE.

Little of all we value here
Wakes on the morn of its hundredth year
Without both feeling and looking queer.
In fact, there 's nothing that keeps its youth,
So far as I know, but a tree and truth.
(This is a moral that runs at large ;
Take it. — You 're welcome. — No extra charge.]

FIRST OF NOVEMBER, — the Earthquake-day. —
There are traces of age in the one-hoss shay,
A general flavor of mild decay,
But nothing local as one may say.
There could n't be, — for the Deacon's art
Had made it so like in every part
That there was n't a chance for one to start.
For the wheels were just as strong as the thills,
And the floor was just as strong as the sills,
And the panels just as strong as the floor,
And the whippletree neither less nor more,
And the back-crossbar as strong as the fore,
And spring and axle and hub *encore*.
And yet, *as a whole*, it is past a doubt
In another hour it will be *worn out* !

First of November, 'Fifty-five !
This morning the parson takes a drive.
Now, small boys, get out of the way !
Here comes the wonderful one-hoss shay,
Drawn by a rat-tailed, ewe-necked bay.
" Huddup ! " said the parson. — Off went they
The parson was working his Sunday's text, —
Had got to *fifthly*, and stopped perplexed

At what the — Moses — was coming next.
All at once the horse stood still,
Close by the meet'n'-house on the hill.
— First a shiver, and then a thrill,
Then something decidedly like a spill, —
And the parson was sitting upon a rock,
At half past nine by the meet'n'-house clock, —
Just the hour of the Earthquake shock !
— What do you think the parson found,
When he got up and stared around ?
The poor old chaise in a heap or mound,
As if it had been to the mill and ground !
You see, of course, if you 're not a dunce,
How it went to pieces all at once, —
All at once, and nothing first, —
Just as bubbles do when they burst.

End of the wonderful one-hoss shay.
Logic is logic.   That 's all I say.
OLIVER WENDELL HOLMES.

RUDOLPH THE HEADSMAN.

RUDOLPH, professor of the headsman's trade,
Alike was famous for his arm and blade.
One day a prisoner Justice had to kill
Knelt at the block to test the artist's skill.
Bare-armed, swart-visaged, gaunt, and shaggy-
    browed,
Rudolph the headsman rose above the crowd.
His falchion lightened with a sudden gleam,
As the pike's armor flashes in the stream.
He sheathed his blade ; he turned as if to go ;
The victim knelt, still waiting for the blow.
"Why strikest not ?   Perform thy murderous
    act,"
The prisoner said.   (His voice was slightly
    cracked.)
"Friend, I *have* struck," the artist straight re-
    plied ;
"Wait but one moment, and yourself decide."
He held his snuff-box, — "Now then, if you
    please !"
The prisoner sniffed, and, with a crashing sneeze,
Off his head tumbled, bowled along the floor,
Bounced down the steps ; — the prisoner said no
    more !
OLIVER WENDELL HOLMES.

THE BOYS.

HAS there any old fellow got mixed with the
    boys ?
If there has, take him out, without making a
    noise.

Hang the Almanac's cheat and the Catalogue's
    spite !
Old Time is a liar !   We 're twenty to-night !

We 're twenty !   We 're twenty !   Who says we
    are more ?
He 's tipsy, — young jackanapes ! — show him the
    door !
"Gray temples at twenty ?" — Yes !   *white*, if we
    please ;
Where the snow-flakes fall thickest there 's noth-
    ing can freeze !

Was it snowing I spoke of ?   Excuse the mis-
    take !
Look close, — you will see not a sign of a flake !
We want some new garlands for those we have
    shed, —
And these are white roses in place of the red.

We 've a trick, we young fellows, you may have
    been told,
Of talking (in public) as if we were old :
That boy we call "Doctor," and this we call
    "Judge ;" —
It 's a neat little fiction, — of course it 's all
    fudge.

That fellow 's the "Speaker," — the one on the
    right ;
"Mr. Mayor," my young one, how are you to-
    night ?
That 's our "Member of Congress," we say when
    we chaff ;
There 's the "Reverend"   What 's his name ? —
    don't make me laugh !

That boy with the grave mathematical look
Made believe he had written a wonderful book,
And the ROYAL SOCIETY thought it was *true !*
So they chose him right in, — a good joke it was
    too !

There 's a boy, we pretend, with a three-decker
    brain,
That could harness a team with a logical chain ;
When he spoke for our manhood in syllabled
    fire,
We called him "The Justice," but now he 's
    "The Squire."

And there 's a nice youngster of excellent pith, —
Fate tried to conceal him by naming him Smith,
But he shouted a song for the brave and the
    free, —
Just read on his medal, "My country," "of
    thee !"

You hear that boy laughing ? — You think he 's
   all fun ;
But the angels laugh, too, at the good he has
   done ;
The children laugh loud as they troop to his call,
And the poor man that knows him laughs loudest
   of all !

Yes, we 're boys, — always playing with tongue
   or with pen ;
And I sometimes have asked, Shall we ever be
   men ?
Shall we always be youthful, and laughing, and
   gay,
Till the last dear companion drop smiling away ?

Then here 's to our boyhood, its gold and its
   gray !
The stars of its winter, the dews of its May !
And when we have done with our life-lasting
   toys,
Dear Father, take care of thy children, THE
   BOYS.
OLIVER WENDELL HOLMES.

THE OLD MAN DREAMS.

O FOR one hour of youthful joy !
   Give back my twentieth spring !
I 'd rather laugh a bright-haired boy
   Than reign a gray-beard king !

Off with the spoils of wrinkled age !
   Away with learning's crown !
Tear out life's wisdom-written page,
   And dash its trophies down !

One moment let my life-blood stream
   From boyhood's fount of flame !
Give me one giddy, reeling dream
   Of life all love and fame !

My listening angel heard the prayer,
   And, calmly smiling, said,
" If I but touch thy silvered hair,
   Thy hasty wish hath sped.

" But is there nothing in thy track
   To bid thee fondly stay,
While the swift seasons hurry back
   To find the wished-for day ? "

Ah ! truest soul of womankind !
   Without thee what were life ?
One bliss I cannot leave behind :
   I 'll take — my — precious — wife !

The angel took a sapphire pen
   And wrote in rainbow dew,
" The man would be a boy again,
   And be a husband, too ! "

" And is there nothing yet unsaid
   Before the change appears ?
Remember, all their gifts have fled
   With those dissolving years ! "

" Why, yes ; for memory would recall
   My fond paternal joys ;
I could not bear to leave them all :
   I 'll take — my — girl — and — boys ! "

The smiling angel dropped his pen —
   " Why, this will never do ;
The man would be a boy again,
   And be a father, too ! "

And so I laughed — my laughter woke
   The household with its noise —
And wrote my dream, when morning broke,
   To please the gray-haired boys.
OLIVER WENDELL HOLMES

WHITTLING.

A "NATIONAL PORTRAIT."

THE Yankee boy, before he 's sent to school,
Well knows the mysteries of that magic tool,
The pocket-knife.   To that his wistful eye
Turns, while he hears his mother's lullaby ;
His hoarded cents he gladly gives to get it,
Then leaves no stone unturned till he can whet it :
And in the education of the lad
No little part that implement hath had.
His pocket-knife to the young whittler brings
A growing knowledge of material things.

Projectiles, music, and the sculptor's art,
His chestnut whistle and his shingle dart,
His elder popgun with its hickory rod,
Its sharp explosion and rebounding wad,
His cornstalk fiddle, and the deeper tone
That murmurs from his pumpkin-stalk trombone,
Conspire to teach the boy.   To these succeed
His bow, his arrow of a feathered seed,
His windmill, raised the passing breeze to win,
His water-wheel, that turns upon a pin ;
Or, if his father lives upon the shore,
You 'll see his ship, " beam ends upon the floor,"
Full rigged with raking masts, and timbers
   stanch,
And waiting near the wash-tub for a launch.

Thus by his genius and his jack-knife driven,
Erelong he 'll solve you any problem given ;
Make any gimcrack musical or mute,
A plough, a couch, an organ or a flute ;
Make you a locomotive or a clock,
Cut a canal, or build a floating-dock,
Or lead forth Beauty from a marble block ; —
Make anything in short, for sea or shore,
From a child's rattle to a seventy-four ; —
Make it, said I ? — Ay, when he undertakes it,
He 'll make the thing and the machine that
     makes it.

And when the thing is made, — whether it be
To move on earth, in air, or on the sea ;
Whether on water, o'er the waves to glide,
Or upon land to roll, revolve, or slide ;
Whether to whirl or jar, to strike or ring,
Whether it be a piston or a spring,
Wheel, pulley, tube sonorous, wood or brass,
The thing designed shall surely come to pass ;
For, when his hand 's upon it, you may know
That there 's go in it, and he 'll make it go.
JOHN PIERPONT.

RAILROAD RHYME.

SINGING through the forests,
    Rattling over ridges ;
Shooting under arches,
    Rumbling over bridges ;
Whizzing through the mountains,
    Buzzing o'er the vale, —
Bless me ! this is pleasant,
    Riding on the rail !

Men of different " stations "
    In the eye of fame,
Here are very quickly
    Coming to the same ;
High and lowly people,
    Birds of every feather,
On a common level,
    Travelling together.

Gentleman in shorts,
    Looming very tall ;
Gentleman at large
    Talking very small ;
Gentleman in tights,
    With a loose-ish mien ;
Gentleman in gray,
    Looking rather green ;

Gentleman quite old,
    Asking for the news .

Gentleman in black,
    In a fit of blues ;
Gentleman in claret,
    Sober as a vicar ;
Gentleman in tweed,
    Dreadfully in liquor !

Stranger on the right
    Looking very sunny,
Obviously reading
    Something rather funny.
Now the smiles are thicker, —
    Wonder what they mean !
Faith, he 's got the Knicker-
    Bocker Magazine !

Stranger on the left
    Closing up his peepers ;
Now he snores amain,
    Like the Seven Sleepers ;
At his feet a volume
    Gives the explanation,
How the man grew stupid
    From " Association " !

Ancient maiden lady
    Anxiously remarks,
That there must be peril
    'Mong so many sparks ;
Roguish-looking fellow,
    Turning to the stranger,
Says it 's his opinion
    She is out of danger !

Woman with her baby,
    Sitting *vis-à-vis* ;
Baby keeps a-squalling,
    Woman looks at me ;
Asks about the distance,
    Says it 's tiresome talking,
Noises of the cars
    Are so very shocking !

Market-woman, careful
    Of the precious casket,
Knowing eggs are eggs,
    Tightly holds her basket ;
Feeling that a smash,
    If it came, would surely
Send her eggs to pot,
    Rather prematurely.

Singing through the forests,
    Rattling over ridges ;
Shooting under arches,
    Rumbling over bridges ;

Whizzing through the mountains,
Buzzing o'er the vale, —
Bless me ! this is pleasant,
Riding on the rail !
JOHN GODFREY SAXE.

WOMAN'S WILL.

AN EPIGRAM.

MEN, dying, make their wills, but wives
Escape a work so sad ;
Why should they make what all their lives
The gentle dames have had ?
JOHN GODFREY SAXE.

"NOTHING TO WEAR."

MISS FLORA MCFLIMSEY, of Madison Square,
Has made three separate journeys to Paris,
And her father assures me, each time she was
there,
That she and her friend Mrs. Harris
(Not the lady whose name is so famous in his-
tory,
But plain Mrs. H., without romance or mystery)
Spent six consecutive weeks without stopping
In one continuous round of shopping, —
Shopping alone, and shopping together,
At all hours of the day, and in all sorts of
weather, —
For all manner of things that a woman can put
On the crown of her head or the sole of her foot,
Or wrap round her shoulders, or fit round her
waist,
Or that can be sewed on, or pinned on, or laced,
Or tied on with a string, or stitched on with a
bow,
In front or behind, above or below ;
For bonnets, mantillas, capes, collars, and shawls;
Dresses for breakfasts and dinners and balls ;
Dresses to sit in and stand in and walk in ;
Dresses to dance in and flirt in and talk in ;
Dresses in which to do nothing at all ;
Dresses for winter, spring, summer, and fall ;
All of them different in color and pattern,
Silk, muslin, and lace, crape, velvet, and satin,
Brocade, and broadcloth, and other material,
Quite as expensive and much more ethereal ;
In short, for all things that could ever be thought
of,
Or milliner, *modiste*, or tradesmen be bought of,
From ten-thousand-francs robes to twenty-
sous frills ;

In all quarters of Paris, and to every store,
While McFlimsey in vain stormed, scolded, an
swore,
They footed the streets, and he footed the bills.

The last trip, their goods shipped by the steamer
Arago,
Formed, McFlimsey declares, the bulk of her
cargo,
Not to mention a quantity kept from the rest,
Sufficient to fill the largest-sized chest,
Which did not appear on the ship's manifest,
But for which the ladies themselves manifested
Such particular interest, that they invested
Their own proper persons in layers and rows
Of muslins, embroideries, workedunder-clothes,
Gloves, handkerchiefs, scarfs, and such trifles as
those ;
Then, wrapped in great shawls, like Circassian
beauties,
Gave *good-by* to the ship, and *go-by* to the duties.
Her relations at home all marvelled, no doubt,
Miss Flora had grown so enormously stout
For an actual belle and a possible bride ;
But the miracle ceased when she turned inside
out,
And the truth came to light, and the dry-goods
beside,
Which, in spite of collector and custom-house
sentry,
Had entered the port without any entry.
And yet, though scarce three months have passed
since the day
This merchandise went, on twelve carts, up
Broadway,
This same Miss McFlimsey, of Madison Square,
The last time we met was in utter despair,
Because she had nothing whatever to wear !

NOTHING TO WEAR ! Now, as this is a true ditty,
I do not assert — this, you know, is between
us —
That she's in a state of absolute nudity,
Like Powers' Greek Slave, or the Medici Venus;
But I do mean to say, I have heard her declare,
When, at the same moment, she had on a dress
Which cost five hundred dollars, and not a cent
less,
And jewelry worth ten times more, I should
guess,
That she had not a thing in the wide world to
wear !
I should mention just here, that out of Miss
Flora's
Two hundred and fifty or sixty adorers,
I had just been selected as he who should throw all
The rest in the shade, by the gracious bestowal

On myself, after twenty or thirty rejections,
Of those fossil remains which she called her
 "affections,"
And that rather decayed, but well-known work
 of art,
Which Miss Flora persisted in styling "her
 heart."
So we were engaged. Our troth had been plighted,
Not by moonbeam or starbeam, by fountain or
 grove,
But in a front parlor, most brilliantly lighted,
Beneath the gas-fixtures we whispered our love,
Without any romance or raptures or sighs,
Without any tears in Miss Flora's blue eyes,
Or blushes, or transports, or such silly actions,
It was one of the quietest business transactions,
With a very small sprinkling of sentiment, if any,
And a very large diamond imported by Tiffany.
On her virginal lips while I printed a kiss,
She exclaimed, as a sort of parenthesis,
And by way of putting me quite at my ease,
"You know, I'm to polka as much as I please,
And flirt when I like, — now, stop, don't you
 speak,
And you must not come here more than twice in
 the week,
Or talk to me either at party or ball,
But always be ready to come when I call ;
So don't prose to me about duty and stuff,
If we don't break this off, there will be time
 enough
For that sort of thing ; but the bargain must be
That, as long as I choose, I am perfectly free,
For this is a sort of engagement, you see,
Which is binding on you but not binding on me."

Well, having thus wooed Miss McFlimsey and
 gained her,
With the silks, crinolines, and hoops that con-
 tained her,
I had, as I thought, a contingent remainder
At least in the property, and the best right
To appear as its escort by day and by night ;
And it being the week of the Stuckups' grand
 ball, —
 Their cards had been out a fortnight or so,
 And set all the Avenue on the tiptoe, —
I considered it only my duty to call,
And see if Miss Flora intended to go.
I found her, — as ladies are apt to be found,
When the time intervening between the first
 sound
Of the bell and the visitor's entry is shorter
Than usual, — I found — I won't say, I caught
 her, —
Intent on the pier-glass, undoubtedly meaning
To see if perhaps it didn't need cleaning.

She turned as I entered, — "Why, Harry, you
 sinner,
I thought that you went to the Flashers' to din-
 ner !"
"So I did," I replied ; "but the dinner is swal-
 lowed
 And digested, I trust, for 't is now nine and
 more,
So being relieved from that duty, I followed
 Inclination, which led me, you see, to your
 door ;
And now will your ladyship so condescend
As just to inform me if you intend
Your beauty and graces and presence to lend
(All of which, when I own, I hope no one will
 borrow)
To the Stuckups, whose party, you know, is to-
 morrow ?"

The fair Flora looked up with a pitiful air,
And answered quite promptly, "Why, Harry,
 mon cher,
I should like above all things to go with you
 there ;
But really and truly — I've nothing to wear."
"Nothing to wear ! go just as you are ;
Wear the dress you have on, and you'll be by
 far,
I engage, the most bright and particular star
 On the Stuckup horizon" — I stopped — for
 her eye,
Notwithstanding this delicate onset of flattery,
Opened on me at once a most terrible battery
 Of scorn and amazement. She made no reply,
But gave a slight turn to the end of her nose
(That pure Grecian feature), as much as to say,
"How absurd that any sane man should suppose
That a lady would go to a ball in the clothes,
 No matter how fine, that she wears every day !"

So I ventured again : "Wear your crimson bro-
 cade"
(Second turn-up of nose) — "That's too dark by
 a shade."
"Your blue silk"— "That's too heavy." "Your
 pink"—"That's too light."
"Wear tulle over satin" — "I can't endure
 white."
"Your rose-colored, then, the best of the
 batch"—
"I haven't a thread of point lace to match."
"Your brown *moire antique*" — "Yes, and look
 like a Quaker."
"The pearl-colored" — "I would, but that
 plaguy dressmaker
Has had it a week." "Then that exquisite lilac
In which you would melt the heart of a Shylock,"

(Here the nose took again the same elevation) —
"I would n't wear that for the whole of creation."
  "Why not? It's my fancy, there's nothing
    could strike it
As more *comme il faut*"—"Yes, but, dear me!
    that lean
  Sophronia Stuckup has got one just like it,
And I won't appear dressed like a chit of sixteen."
"Then that splendid purple, that sweet Maza-
    rine,
That superb *point d'aiguille*, that imperial green,
That zephyr-like tarlatan, that rich *grenadine*"—
"Not one of all which is fit to be seen,"
Said the lady, becoming excited and flushed.
"Then wear," I exclaimed, in a tone which quite
    crushed
  Opposition, "that gorgeous *toilette* which you
    sported
In Paris last spring, at the grand presentation,
When you quite turned the head of the head of
    the nation;
  And by all the grand court were so very much
    courted."
The end of the nose was portentously tipped up,
And both the bright eyes shot forth indignation,
As she burst upon me with the fierce exclamation,
"I have worn it three times at the least calcula-
    tion,
  And that and most of my dresses are ripped
    up!"
Here I *ripped out* something, perhaps rather rash,
  Quite innocent, though; but, to use an ex-
    pression
More striking than classic, it "settled my hash,"
  And proved very soon the last act of our ses-
    sion.
"Fiddlesticks, is it, sir? I wonder the ceiling
Does n't fall down and crush you — oh! you men
    have no feeling;
You selfish, unnatural, illiberal creatures,
Who set yourselves up as patterns and preachers,
Your silly pretence, — why, what a mere guess
    it is!
Pray, what do you know of a woman's necessities?
I have told you and showed you I've nothing to
    wear,
And it's perfectly plain you not only don't care,
But you do not believe me" (here the nose went
    still higher),
"I suppose, if you dared, you would call me a
    liar.
Our engagement is ended, sir — yes, on the spot;
You're a brute, and a monster, and — I don't
    know what."
I mildly suggested the words — Hottentot,
Pickpocket, and cannibal, Tartar, and thief,
As gentle expletives which might give relief;

But this only proved as a spark to the powder,
And the storm I had raised came faster and
    louder;
It blew and it rained, thundered, lightened, and
    hailed
Interjections, verbs, pronouns, till language quite
    failed
To express the abusive, and then its arrears
Were brought up all at once by a torrent of tears,
And my last faint, despairing attempt at an obs-
Ervation was lost in a tempest of sobs.

Well, I felt for the lady, and felt for my hat,
    too,
Improvised on the crown of the latter a tattoo,
In lieu of expressing the feelings which lay
Quite too deep for words, as Wordsworth would
    say;
Then, without going through the form of a bow,
Found myself in the entry — I hardly knew
    how, —
On doorstep and sidewalk, past lamp-post and
    square,
At home and up stairs, in my own easy-chair;
  Poked my feet into slippers, my fire into blaze,
And said to myself, as I lit my cigar,
Supposing a man had the wealth of the Czar
  Of the Russias to boot, for the rest of his days,
On the whole, do you think he would have much
    to spare,
If he married a woman with nothing to wear?

Since that night, taking pains that it should not
    be bruited
Abroad in society, I've instituted
A course of inquiry, extensive and thorough,
On this vital subject, and find, to my horror,
That the fair Flora's case is by no means sur-
    prising,
  But that there exists the greatest distress
In our female community, solely arising
  From this unsupplied destitution of dress,
Whose unfortunate victims are filling the air
With the pitiful wail of "Nothing to wear."
Researches in some of the "Upper Ten" districts
Reveal the most painful and startling statistics,
Of which let me mention only a few:
In one single house, on Fifth Avenue,
Three young ladies were found, all below twenty-
    two,
Who have been three whole weeks without any-
    thing new
In the way of flounced silks, and thus left in the
    lurch
Are unable to go to ball, concert, or church.
In another large mansion, near the same place,
Was found a deplorable, heartrending case

Of entire destitution of Brussels point lace.
In a neighboring block there was found, in three
  calls,
Total want, long continued, of camel's-hair
  shawls ;
And a suffering family, whose case exhibits
The most pressing need of real ermine tippets ;
One deserving young lady almost unable
To survive for the want of a new Russian sable ;
Another confined to the house, when it 's windier
Than usual, because her shawl is n't India.
Still another, whose tortures have been most
  terrific
Ever since the sad loss of the steamer Pacific,
In which were engulfed, not friend or relation
(For whose fate she perhaps might have found
  consolation,
Or borne it, at least, with serene resignation),
But the choicest assortment of French sleeves
  and collars
Ever sent out from Paris, worth thousands of
  dollars,
And all as to style most *recherché* and rare,
The want of which leaves her with nothing to
  wear,
And renders her life so drear and dyspeptic
That she 's quite a recluse, and almost a scep-
  tic ;
For she touchingly says that this sort of grief
Cannot find in Religion the slightest relief,
And Philosophy has not a maxim to spare
For the victim of such overwhelming despair.
But the saddest by far of all these sad features
Is the cruelty practised upon the poor creatures
By husbands and fathers, real Bluebeards and
  Timons,
Who resist the most touching appeals made for
  diamonds
By their wives and their daughters, and leave
  them for days
Unsupplied with new jewelry, fans, or bouquets,
Even laugh at their miseries whenever they have
  a chance,
And deride their demands as useless extrava-
  gance ;
One case of a bride was brought to my view,
Too sad for belief, but, alas ! 't was too true,
Whose husband refused, as savage as Charon,
To permit her to take more than ten trunks to
  Sharon.
The consequence was, that when she got there,
At the end of three weeks she had nothing to
  wear,
And when she proposed to finish the season
At Newport, the monster refused out and out,
For his infamous conduct alleging no reason,
Except that the waters were good for his gout.

Such treatment as this was too shocking, of course,
And proceedings are now going on for divorce.

But why harrow the feelings by lifting the cur-
  tain
From these scenes of woe ?   Enough, it is certain,
Has here been disclosed to stir up the pity
Of every benevolent heart in the city,
And spur up Humanity into a canter
To rush and relieve these sad cases instanter.
Won't somebody, moved by this touching de-
  scription,
Come forward to-morrow and head a subscription ?
Won't some kind philanthropist, seeing that
  aid is
So needed at once by these indigent ladies,
Take charge of the matter ?   Or won't Peter
  Cooper
The corner-stone lay of some splendid super-
Structure, like that which to-day links his name
In the Union unending of honor and fame ;
And found a new charity just for the care
Of these unhappy women with nothing to wear,
Which, in view of the cash which would daily
  be claimed,
The *Laying-out* Hospital well might be named ?
Won't Stewart, or some of our dry-goods im-
  porters,
Take a contract for clothing our wives and our
  daughters ?
Or, to furnish the cash to supply these distresses,
And life's pathway strew with shawls, collars,
  and dresses,
Ere the want of them makes it much rougher and
  thornier,
Won't some one discover a new California ?

O ladies, dear ladies, the next sunny day
Please trundle your hoops just out of Broadway
From its whirl and its bustle, its fashion and
  pride,
And temples of trade which tower on each side,
To the alleys and lanes, where Misfortune and
  Guilt
Their children have gathered, their city have
  built ;
Where Hunger and Vice, like twin beasts of prey,
  Have hunted their victims to gloom and de-
  spair ;
Raise the rich, dainty dress, and the fine broi-
  dered skirt,
Pick your delicate way through dampness and
  dirt,
  Grope through the dark dens, climb the
  rickety stair
To the garret, where wretches, the young and
  the old,

Half starved and half naked, lie crouched from
    the cold.
Se those skeleton limbs, those frost-bitten feet,
All bleeding and bruised by the stones of the
    street ;
Hear the sharp cry of childhood, the deep groans
    that swell
    From the poor dying creature who writhes on
      the floor,
Hear the curses that sound like the echoes of
    Hell,
    As you sicken and shudder and fly from the
      door ;
Then home to your wardrobes, and say, if you
    dare, —
Spoiled children of Fashion, — you 've nothing to
    wear !

And O, if perchance there should be a sphere
Where all is made right which so puzzles us
    here,
Where the glare and the glitter and tinsel of Time
Fade and die in the light of that region sublime,
Where the soul, disenchanted of flesh and of
    sense,
Unscreened by its trappings and shows and
    pretence,
Must be clothed for the life and the service above,
With purity, truth, faith, meekness, and love ;
O daughters of Earth ! foolish virgins, beware !
Lest in that upper realm you have nothing to
    wear !
                WILLIAM ALLEN BUTLER.

THE PROUD MISS MACBRIDE.

A LEGEND OF GOTHAM.

O, TERRIBLY proud was Miss MacBride,
The very personification of pride,
As she minced along in fashion's tide,
Adown Broadway — on the proper side —
    When the golden sun was setting ;
There was pride in the head she carried so high,
Pride in her lip, and pride in her eye,
And a world of pride in the very sigh
    That her stately bosom was fretting !

O, terribly proud was Miss MacBride,
Proud of her beauty, and proud of her pride,
And proud of fifty matters beside —
    That would n't have borne dissection ;
Proud of her wit, and proud of her walk,
Proud of her teeth, and proud of her talk,
Proud of "knowing cheese from chalk,"
    On a very slight inspection !

Proud abroad, and proud at home,
Proud wherever she chanced to come —
When she was glad, and when she was glum ;
    Proud as the head of a Saracen
Over the door of a tippling-shop ! —
Proud as a duchess, proud as a fop,
"Proud as a boy with a brand-new top,"
    Proud beyond comparison !

It seems a singular thing to say,
But her very senses led her astray
    Respecting all humility ;
In sooth, her dull auricular drum
Could find in *humble* only a "hum,"
And heard no sound of " gentle " come,
    In talking about gentility.

What *lowly* meant she did n't know,
For she always avoided " everything low,"
    With care the most punctilious ;
And, queerer still, the audible sound
Of "super-silly" she never had found
    In the adjective supercilious !

The meaning of *meek* she never knew,
But imagined the phrase had something to do
With " Moses," a peddling German Jew,
Who, like all hawkers, the country through,
    Was " a person of no position ; "
And it seemed to her exceedingly plain,
If the word was really known to pertain
To a vulgar German, it was n't germane
    To a lady of high condition !

Even her graces — not her grace —
For that was in the " vocative case " —
Chilled with the touch of her icy face,
    Sat very stiffly upon her !
She never confessed a favor aloud,
Like one of the simple, common crowd —
But coldly smiled, and faintly bowed,
As who should say, " You do me proud,
    And do yourself an honor ! "

And yet the pride of Miss MacBride,
Although it had fifty hobbies to ride,
    Had really no foundation ;
But, like the fabrics that gossips devise —
Those single stories that often arise
And grow till they reach a four-story size —
    Was merely a fancy creation !

Her birth, indeed, was uncommonly high —
For Miss MacBride first opened her eye
Through a skylight dim, on the light of the sky ;

But pride is a curious passion —
And in talking about her wealth and worth,
She always forgot to mention her birth
    To people of rank and fashion !

Of all the notable things on earth,
The queerest one is pride of birth
        Among our "fierce democracie ! "
A bridge across a hundred years,
Without a prop to save it from sneers, —
Not even a couple of rotten *peers*, —
A thing for laughter, fleers, and jeers,
    Is American aristocracy !

English and Irish, French and Spanish,
German, Italian, Dutch and Danish,
Crossing their veins until they vanish
        In one conglomeration !
So subtle a tangle of blood, indeed,
No Heraldry Harvey will ever succeed
    In finding the circulation.

Depend upon it, my snobbish friend,
Your family thread you can't ascend,
Without good reason to apprehend
    You may find it waxed, at the farther end,
        By some plebeian vocation !
Or, worse than that, your boasted line
May end in a loop of *stronger* twine,
    That plagued some worthy relation !

But Miss MacBride had something beside
Her lofty birth to nourish her pride —
For rich was the old paternal MacBride,
    According to public rumor ;
And he lived "up town," in a splendid square,
And kept his daughter on dainty fare,
And gave her gems that were rich and rare,
And the finest rings and things to wear,
    And feathers enough to plume her.

A thriving tailor begged her hand,
But she gave "the fellow" to understand,
    By a violent manual action,
She perfectly scorned the best of his clan,
And reckoned the ninth of any man
    An exceedingly vulgar fraction !

Another, whose sign was a golden boot,
Was mortified with a bootless suit,
    In a way that was quite appalling ;
For, though a regular *sutor* by trade,
He wasn't a suitor to suit the maid,
Who cut him off with a saw — and bade
    "The cobbler keep to his calling ! "

A rich tobacconist comes and sues,
And, thinking the lady would scarce refuse
A man of his wealth, and liberal views,
Began, at once, with "If you *choose* —
        And could you really love him —"
But the lady spoiled his speech in a huff,
With an answer rough and ready enough,
To let him know she was up to snuff,
    And altogether above him !

A young attorney, of winning grace,
Was scarce allowed to "open his face,"
Ere Miss MacBride had closed his case
    With true judicial celerity ;
For the lawyer was poor, and "seedy" to boot,
And to say the lady discarded his *suit*,
    Is merely a double verity !

The last of those who came to court,
Was a lively beau, of the dapper sort,
"Without any visible means of support,"
    A crime by no means flagrant
In one who wears an elegant coat,
But the very point on which they vote
    A ragged fellow "a vagrant ! "

Now dapper Jim his courtship plied
(I wish the fact could be denied)
With an eye to the purse of the old MacBride,
    And really "nothing shorter ! "
For he said to himself, in his greedy lust,
"Whenever he dies — as die he must —
And yields to Heaven his vital trust,
He 's very sure to 'come down with his dust,'
    In behalf of his only daughter."

And the very magnificent Miss MacBride,
Half in love, and half in pride,
    Quite graciously relented ;
And, tossing her head, and turning her back,
No token of proper pride to lack —
To be a bride, without the "Mac,"
    With much disdain, consented !

Old John MacBride, one fatal day,
Became the unresisting prey
    Of fortune's undertakers ;
And staking all on a single die,
His foundered bark went high and dry
    Among the brokers and breakers !

But, alas, for the haughty Miss MacBride,
'T was such a shock to her precious pride !
She could n't recover, although she tried
    Her jaded spirits to rally ;

'T was a dreadful change in human affairs,
From a place " up town " to a nook " up stairs,"
   From an avenue down to an alley !

'T was little condolence she had, God wot,
From her " troops of friends," who had n't forgot
   The airs she used to borrow !
They had civil phrases enough, but yet
'T was plain to see that their " deepest regret "
   Was a different thing from sorrow !

And one of those chaps who make a pun,
As if it were quite legitimate fun
To be blazing away at every one
With a regular, double-loaded gun —
   Remarked that moral transgression
Always brings retributive stings
To candle-makers as well as kings ;
For " making light of *cereous* things "
   Was a very *wick*-ed profession !

And vulgar people — the saucy churls —
Inquired about " the price of pearls,"
   And mocked at her situation :
" She was n't ruined — they ventured to hope —
Because she was poor, she need n't mope ;
Few people were better off for *soap*,
   And that was a consolation ! "

And to make her cup of woe run over,
Her elegant, ardent plighted lover
   Was the very first to forsake her ;
" He quite regretted the step, 't was true —
The lady had pride enough ' for two,'
But that alone would never do
   To quiet the butcher and baker ! "

And now the unhappy Miss MacBride —
The merest ghost of her early pride —
   Bewails her lonely position ;
Cramped in the very narrowest niche,
Above the poor, and below the rich —
   Was ever a worse condition !

MORAL.

Because you flourish in worldly affairs,
Don't be haughty, and put on airs,
   With insolent pride of station !
Don't be proud, and turn up your nose
At poorer people in plainer clothes,
But learn, for the sake of your mind's repose,
That wealth 's a bubble that comes — and goes !
And that all proud flesh, wherever it grows,
   Is subject to irritation !

           JOHN GODFREY SAXE.

PLAIN LANGUAGE FROM TRUTHFUL JAMES.

POPULARLY KNOWN AS THE " HEATHEN CHINEE."

WHICH I wish to remark —
   And my language is plain —
That for ways that are dark
   And for tricks that are vain,
The heathen Chinee is peculiar :
   Which the same I would rise to explain.

Ah Sin was his name ;
   And I shall not deny
In regard to the same
   What that name might imply ;
But his smile it was pensive and childlike,
   As I frequent remarked to Bill Nye.

It was August the third,
   And quite soft was the skies,
Which it might be inferred
   That Ah Sin was likewise ;
Yet he played it that day upon William
   And me in a way I despise.

Which we had a small game,
   And Ah Sin took a hand :
It was euchre.   The same
   He did not understand,
But he smiled, as he sat by the table,
   With the smile that was childlike and bland

Yet the cards they were stocked
   In a way that I grieve,
And my feelings were shocked
   At the state of Nye's sleeve,
Which was stuffed full of aces and bowers,
   And the same with intent to deceive.

But the hands that were played
   By that heathen Chinee,
And the points that he made,
   Were quite frightful to see, —
Till at last he put down a right bower,
   Which the same Nye had dealt unto me.

Then I looked up at Nye,
   And he gazed upon me ;
And he rose with a sigh,
   And said, " Can this be ?
We are ruined by Chinese cheap labor,' —
   And he went for that heathen Chinee.

In the scene that ensued
   I did not take a hand,
But the floor it was strewed,
   Like the leaves on the strand,
With the cards that Ah Sin had been hiding
   In the game " he did not understand."

In his sleeves, which were long,
 He had twenty-four jacks, —
Which was coming it strong,
 Yet I state but the facts.
And we found on his nails, which were taper, —
 What is frequent in tapers, — that 's wax.

Which is why I remark,
 And my language is plain,
That for ways that are dark,
 And for tricks that are vain,
The heathen Chinee is peculiar, —
 Which the same I am free to maintain.
BRET HARTE.

THE SOCIETY UPON THE STANISLAUS.

I RESIDE at Table Mountain, and my name is
 Truthful James :
I am not up to small deceit or any sinful games ;
 And I 'll tell in simple language what I know
  about the row
That broke up our Society upon the Stanislow.

But first I would remark, that 't is not a proper
  plan
For any scientific gent to whale his fellow-man ;
 And, if a member don't agree with his peculiar
  whim,
 To lay for that same member for to " put a
  head " on him.

Now, nothing could be finer, or more beautiful
  to see,
Than the first six months' proceedings of that
  same society ;
 Till Brown of Calaveras brought a lot of fossil
  bones
 That he found within a tunnel near the tenement of Jones.

Then Brown he read a paper, and he recon-
  structed there,
From those same bones, an animal that was
  extremely rare ;
 And Jones then asked the Chair for a suspen-
  sion of the rules,
 Till he could prove that those same bones was
  one of his lost mules.

Then Brown he smiled a bitter smile, and said
  he was at fault ;
It seemed he had been trespassing on Jones's
  family vault ;
 He was a most sarcastic man, this quiet Mr.
  Brown,
 And on several occasions he had cleaned out
  the town,

Now I hold it is not decent for a scientific gent
To say another is an ass, — at least, to all intent ;
 Nor should the individual who happens to be
  meant
 Reply by heaving rocks at him to any great
  extent.

Then Abner Dean of Angel's raised a point of
  order, when
A chunk of old red sandstone took him in the
  abdomen ;
 And he smiled a kind of sickly smile, and
  curled up on the floor,
 And the subsequent proceedings interested him
  no more.

For in less time than I write it, every member
  did engage
In a warfare with the remnants of a palæozoic
  age ;
 And the way they heaved those fossils in their
  anger was a sin,
 Till the skull of an old mammoth caved the
  head of Thompson in.

And this is all I have to say of these improper
  games,
For I live at Table Mountain and my name is
  Truthful James,
 And I 've told in simple language what I know
  about the row
 That broke up our Society upon the Stanislow.
BRET HARTE.

THE NANTUCKET SKIPPER.

MANY a long, long year ago,
 Nantucket skippers had a plan
Of finding out, though "lying low,"
 How near New York their schooners ran.

They greased the lead before it fell,
 And then by sounding, through the night,
Knowing the soil that stuck so well,
 They always guessed their reckoning right.

A skipper gray, whose eyes were dim,
 Could tell, by tasting, just the spot,
And so below he 'd "douse the glim," —
 After, of course, his "something hot."

Snug in his birth, at eight o'clock,
 This ancient skipper might be found ;
No matter how his craft would rock,
 He slept, — for skippers' naps are sound.

The watch on deck would now and then
 Run down and wake him, with the lead ;
He 'd up, and taste, and tell the men
 How many miles they went ahead.

One night 't was Jotham Marden's watch,
 A curious wag, — the pedler's son ;
And so he mused, (the wanton wretch !)
 "To-night I 'll have a grain of fun.

"We 're all a set of stupid fools,
 To think the skipper knows, by tasting,
What ground he 's on ; Nantucket schools
 Don't teach such stuff, with all their basting!"

And so he took the well-greased lead,
 And rubbed it o'er a box of earth
That stood on deck, — a parsnip-bed, —
 And then he sought the skipper's berth.

"Where are we now, sir ? Please to taste."
 The skipper yawned, put out his tongue,
Opened his eyes in wondrous haste,
 And then upon the floor he sprung !

The skipper stormed, and tore his hair,
 Hauled on his boots, and roared to Marden,
"Nantucket 's sunk, and here we are
 Right over old Marm Hackett's garden !"
       JAMES THOMAS FIELDS.

———◆———

THE ART OF BOOK-KEEPING.

How hard, when those who do not wish
 To lend, thus lose, their books,
Are snared by anglers — folks that fish
 With literary hooks —
Who call and take some favorite tome,
 But never read it through ;
They thus complete their set at home
 By making one at you.

I, of my "Spenser" quite bereft,
 Last winter sore was shaken ;
Of "Lamb" I 've but a quarter left,
 Nor could I save my "Bacon ;"
And then I saw my "Crabbe" at last,
 Like Hamlet, backward go,
And, as the tide was ebbing fast,
 Of course I lost my "Rowe."

My "Mallet" served to knock me down,
 Which makes me thus a talker,
And once, when I was out of town,
 My "Johnson" proved a "Walker."
While studying o'er the fire one day
 My "Hobbes" amidst the smoke,
They bore my "Colman" clean away,
 And carried off my "Coke."

They picked my "Locke," to me far more
 Than Bramah's patent worth,
And now my losses I deplore,
 Without a "Home" on earth.

If once a book you let them lift,
 Another they conceal,
For though I caught them stealing "Swift,"
 As swiftly went my "Steele."

"Hope" is not now upon my shelf,
 Where late he stood elated,
But, what is strange, my "Pope" himself
 Is excommunicated.
My little "Suckling" in the grave
 Is sunk to swell the ravage,
And what was Crusoe's fate to save,
 'T was mine to lose — a "Savage."

Even "Glover's" works I cannot put
 My frozen hands upon,
Though ever since I lost my "Foote"
 My "Bunyan" has been gone.
My "Hoyle" with "Cotton" went oppressed,
 My "Taylor," too, must fail,
To save my "Goldsmith" from arrest,
 In vain I offered "Bayle."

I "Prior" sought, but could not see
 The "Hood" so late in front,
And when I turned to hunt for "Lee,"
 O, where was my "Leigh Hunt" ?
I tried to laugh, old Care to tickle,
 Yet could not "Tickell" touch,
And then, alack ! I missed my "Mickle,"
 And surely mickle 's much.

'T is quite enough my griefs to feed,
 My sorrows to excuse,
To think I cannot read my "Reid,"
 Nor even use my "Hughes."
My classics would not quiet lie, —
 A thing so fondly hoped ;
Like Dr. Primrose, I may cry,
 My "Livy" has eloped.

My life is ebbing fast away ;
 I suffer from these shocks ;
And though I fixed a lock on "Gray,"
 There 's gray upon my locks.
I 'm far from "Young," am growing pale,
 I see my "Butler" fly,
And when they ask about my ail,
 'T is "Burton" I reply.

They still have made me slight returns,
 And thus my griefs divide ;
For O, they cured me of my "Burns,"
 And eased my "Akenside."
But all I think I shall not say,
 Nor let my anger burn,
For, as they never found me "Gay,"
 They have not left me "Sterne."
       THOMAS HOOD.

ODE TO TOBACCO.

Thou who, when fears attack,
Bid'st them avaunt, and Black
Care, at the horseman's back
   Perching, unseatest ;
Sweet when the morn is gray ;
Sweet, when they 've cleared away
Lunch ; and at close of day
   Possibly sweetest :

I have a liking old
For thee, though manifold
Stories, I know, are told,
   Not to thy credit ;
How one (or two at most)
Drops make a cat a ghost —
Useless, except to roast —
   Doctors have said it :

How they who use fusees
All grow by slow degrees
Brainless as chimpanzees,
   Meagre as lizards ;
Go mad, and beat their wives ;
Plunge (after shocking lives)
Razors and carving-knives
   Into their gizzards.

Confound such knavish tricks !
Yet know I five or six
Smokers who freely mix
   Still with their neighbors ;
Jones — (who, I 'm glad to say,
Asked leave of Mrs. J.) —
Daily absorbs a clay
   After his labors.

Cats may have had their goose
Cooked by tobacco-juice ;
Still why deny its use
   Thoughtfully taken ?
We 're not as tabbies are :
Smith, take a fresh cigar !
Jones, the tobacco-jar !
   Here 's to thee, Bacon !
                CHARLES S. CALVERLEY.

DISASTER.

T was ever thus from childhood's hour
   My fondest hopes would not decay :
I never loved a tree or flower
   Which was the first to fade away !
The garden, where I used to delve
   Short-frocked, still yields me pinks in plenty;
The pear-tree that I climbed at twelve,
   I see still blossoming, at twenty.

I never nursed a dear gazelle.
   But I was given a paroquet —
How I did nurse him if unwell !
   He 's imbecile, but lingers yet.
He 's green, with an enchanting tuft ;
   He melts me with his small black eye :
He 'd look inimitable stuffed,
   And knows it — but he will not die !

I had a kitten — I was rich
   In pets — but all too soon my kitten
Became a full-sized cat, by which
   I 've more than once been scratched and bitten
And when for sleep her limbs she curled
   One day beside her untouched plateful,
And glided calmly from the world,
   I freely own that I was grateful.

And then I bought a dog — a queen !
   Ah, Tiny, dear departing pug !
She lives, but she is past sixteen,
   And scarce can crawl across the rug.
I loved her beautiful and kind ;
   Delighted in her pert Bow-wow :
But now she snaps if you don't mind ;
   'T were lunacy to love her now.

I used to think, should e'er mishap
   Betide my crumple-visaged Ti,
In shape of prowling thief, or trap,
   Or coarse bull-terrier — I should die.
But ah ! disasters have their use ;
   And life might e'en be too sunshiny :
Nor would I make myself a goose,
   If some big dog should swallow Tiny.
                CHARLES S. CALVERLEY.

MOTHERHOOD.

She laid it where the sunbeams fall
Unscanned upon the broken wall.
Without a tear, without a groan,
She laid it near a mighty stone,
Which some rude swain had haply cast
Thither in sport, long ages past,
And Time with mosses had o'erlaid,
And fenced with many a tall grass-blade,
And all about bid roses bloom
And violets shed their soft perfume.
There, in its cool and quiet bed,
She set her burden down and fled :
Nor flung, all eager to escape,
One glance upon the perfect shape,
That lay, still warm and fresh and fair,
But motionless and soundless there.

No human eye had marked her pass
Across the linden-shadowed grass
Ere yet the minster clock chimed seven :
Only the innocent birds of heaven —
The magpie, and the rook whose nest
Swings as the elm-tree waves his crest—
And the lithe cricket, and the hoar
And huge-limbed hound that guards the door,
Looked on when, as a summer wind
That, passing, leaves no trace behind,
All unapparelled, barefoot all,
She ran to that old ruined wall,
To leave upon the chill dank earth
(For ah ! she never knew its worth),
Mid hemlock rank, and fern and ling,
And dews of night, that precious thing !
And then it might have lain forlorn
From morn to eve, from eve to morn :
But that, by some wild impulse led,
The mother, ere she turned and fled,
One moment stood erect and high ;
Then poured into the silent sky
A cry so jubilant, so strange,
That Alice — as she strove to range
Her rebel ringlets at her glass —
Sprang up and gazed across the grass ;
Shook back those curls so fair to see,
Clapped her soft hands in childish glee ;
And shrieked — her sweet face all aglow,
 Her very limbs with rapture shaking —
" My hen has laid an egg, I know ;
 And only hear the noise she 's making ! "

CHARLES S. CALVERLEY.

THE HEN.

A FAMOUS hen 's my story's theme,
 Which ne'er was known to tire
Of laying eggs, but then she 'd scream
So loud o'er every egg, 't would seem
 The house must be on fire.
A turkey-cock, who ruled the walk,
 A wiser bird and older,
Could bear 't no more, so off did stalk
Right to the hen, and told her :
" Madam, that scream, I apprehend,
Adds nothing to the matter ;
It surely helps the egg no whit ;
Then lay your egg, and done with it !
I pray you, madam, as a friend,
 Cease that superfluous clatter !
You know not how 't goes through my head."
" Humph ! very likely ! " madam said,
Then, proudly putting forth a leg, —
" Uneducated barnyard fowl !
You know, no more than any owl,

The noble privilege and praise
Of authorship in modern days —
 I 'll tell you why I do it :
First, you perceive, I lay the egg,
 And then — review it."

From the German of CLAUDIUS.

THE COSMIC EGG.

UPON a rock yet uncreate,
Amid a chaos inchoate,
An uncreated being sate ;
Beneath him, rock,
Above him, cloud.
And the cloud was rock,
And the rock was cloud.
The rock then growing soft and warm,
The cloud began to take a form,
A form chaotic, vast, and vague,
Which issued in the cosmic egg.
Then the Being uncreate
On the egg did incubate,
And thus became the incubator ;
And of the egg did allegate,
And thus became the alligator ;
And the incubator was potentate,
But the alligator was potentator.

ANONYMOUS.

DARWIN.

THERE was an ape in the days that were earlier ;
Centuries passed, and his hair grew curlier ;
Centuries more gave a thumb to his wrist,
Then he was a Man and a Positivist.

MORTIMER COLLINS.

TO THE PLIOCENE SKULL.

A GEOLOGICAL ADDRESS.

" A human skull has been found in California, in the pliocene
formation. This skull is the remnant, not only of the earliest pioneer of this State, but the oldest known human being. . . . The
skull was found in a shaft one hundred and fifty feet deep, two
miles from Angel's, in Calaveras County, by a miner named James
Matson, who gave it to Mr. Scribner, a merchant, and he gave it to
Dr. Jones, who sent it to the State Geological Survey. . . . The
published volume of the State Survey on the Geology of California
states that man existed contemporaneously with the mastodon, but
this fossil proves that he was here before the mastodon was known
to exist." — Daily Paper.

"SPEAK, O man, less recent ! Fragmentary fossil !
Primal pioneer of pliocene formation,
Hid in lowest drifts below the earliest stratum
 Of Volcanic tufa !

" Older than the beasts, the oldest Palæotherium ;
Older than the trees, the oldest Cryptogamia ;
Older than the hills, those infantile eruptions
 Of earth's epidermis !

" Eo — Mio — Plio — whatsoe'er the ' cene ' was
That those vacant sockets filled with awe and
        wonder, —
Whether shores Devonian or Silurian beaches, —
    Tell us thy strange story !

" Or has the Professor slightly antedated
By some thousand years thy advent on this planet,
Giving thee an air that 's somewhat better fitted
    For cold-blooded creatures ?

" Wert thou true spectator of that mighty forest,
When above thy head the stately Sigillaria
Reared its columned trunks in that remote and
        distant
        Carboniferous epoch ?

" Tell us of that scene, — the dim and watery
        woodland,
Songless, silent, hushed, with never bird or in-
        sect,
Veiled with spreading fronds and screened with
        tall club-mosses,
        Lycopodiacea —

" When beside thee walked the solemn Plesio-
        saurus,
And around thee crept the festive Ichthyosaurus,
While from time to time above thee flew and
        circled
        Cheerful Pterodactyls.

" Tell us of thy food, — those half-marine refec-
        tions,
Crinoids on the shell, and Brachipods *au natu-
        rel,* —
Cuttle-fish to which the *pieuvre* of Victor Hugo
        Seems a periwinkle.

" Speak, thou awful vestige of the earth's crea-
        tion, —
Solitary fragment of remains organic !
Tell the wondrous secrets of thy past existence, —
        Speak ! thou oldest primate ! "

Even as I gazed, a thrill of the maxilla
And a lateral movement of the condyloid process,
With post-pliocene sounds of healthy mastica-
        tion,
        Ground the teeth together ;

And from that imperfect dental exhibition,
Stained with expressed juices of the weed Nico-
        tian,
Came these hollow accents, blent with softer
        murmurs
        Of expectoration :

" Which my name is Bowers, and my crust was
        busted
Falling down a shaft, in Calaveras County,
But I 'd take it kindly if you 'd send the pieces
        Home to old Missouri ! "

                                        BRET HARTE.

———◆———

PHYSICS.

[THE UNCONSCIOUS POETIZING OF A PHILOSOPHER.]

THERE is no force however great
    Can stretch a cord however fine
    Into a horizontal line
That shall be accurately straight.

                                WILLIAM WHEWELL.

———◆———

THE COLLEGIAN TO HIS BRIDE :

BEING A MATHEMATICAL MADRIGAL IN THE SIMPLEST FORM

CHARMER, on a given straight line,
And which we will call B C,
Meeting at a common point A,
Draw the lines A C, A B.
But, my sweetest, so arrange it
That they 're equal, all the three ;
Then you 'll find that, in the sequel,
All their angles, too, are equal.

Equal angles, so to term them,
Each one opposite its brother !
Equal joys and equal sorrows,
Equal hopes, 't were sin to smother,
Equal, — O, divine ecstatics, —
Based on Hutton's mathematics !

                                        PUNCH.

———◆———

THE LAWYER'S INVOCATION TO
SPRING.

WHEREAS, on certain boughs and sprays
    Now divers birds are heard to sing,
And sundry flowers their heads upraise,
    Hail to the coming on of spring !

The songs of those said birds arouse
    The memory of our youthful hours,
As green as those said sprays and boughs,
    As fresh and sweet as those said flowers.

The birds aforesaid, — happy pairs, —
    Love, mid the aforesaid boughs, inshrines
In freehold nests ; themselves, their heirs,
    Administrators, and assigns.

O busiest term of Cupid's Court,
  Where tender plaintiffs actions bring, —
Season of frolic and of sport,
  Hail, as aforesaid, coming Spring !
                    HENRY HOWARD BROWNELL.

TONIS AD RESTO MARE.

AIR : *"O Mary, heave a sigh for me."*

O MARE æva si forme ;
  Forme ure tonitru ;
Iambicum as amandum,
  Olet Hymen promptu ;
Mihi is vetas an ne se,
  As humano erebi ;
Olet mecum marito te,
  Or *eta beta pi.*

Alas, plano more meretrix,
  Mi ardor vel uno ;
Inferiam ure artis base,
  Tolerat me urebo.
Ah me ve ara silicet,
  Vi laudu vimin thus ?
Hiatu as arandum sex —
  Illuc Ionicus.

Heu sed heu vix en imago,
  My missis mare sta ;
O cantu redit in mihi
  Hibernas arida ?
A veri vafer heri si,
  Mihi resolves indu :
Totius olet Hymen cum —
  Accepta tonitru.
                    JONATHAN SWIFT.

NURSERY RHYMES.

"JOHN, JOHN, THE PIPER'S SON."

JOHANNES, Johannes, tibicine natus
Fugit perniciter porcum furatus,
Sed porcus voratus, Johannes delatus,
Et plorans per vias est fur flagellatus.

"TWINKLE, TWINKLE, LITTLE STAR."

MICA, mica, parva stella ;
Miror, quænam si tam bella !
Splendens eminus in illo,
Alba velut gemma, cœlo.

"BOYS AND GIRLS, COME OUT TO PLAY."

GARÇONS et filles venez toujours,
La lune est brillante comme le jour,
Venez au bruit d'un joyeux éclat
Venez du bons cœurs, ou ne venez pas.

"THREE WISE MEN OF GOTHAM."

TRES Philosophi de Tusculo
Mare navigarunt vasculo :
Si vas id esset tutius
Tibi canerem diutius.

"DING DONG BELL, THE CAT'S IN THE WELL."

ΑΙΛΝΟΝ αἴλινον εἰπε· φρέαρ λάβεν, οὖλον ἄβυσσον,
  Τὴν γαλέην· τίσ τησδ' αἴτιος ἀμπλακίης;
Τυτθὸς Ἰωάννης, χλωρὸν γάνος, αἴσυλα εἰδως·
  Τοῦ γαλέην βυθίσαι νήπιον ὦδ' ἄκακον.

THE COURTIN'.

GOD makes sech nights, all white an' still
  Fur 'z you can look or listen ;
Moonshine an' snow on field an' hill,
  All silence an' all glisten.

Zekle crep' up quite unbeknown
  An' peeked in thru' the winder,
An' there sot Huldy all alone,
  'Ith no one nigh to hender.

A fireplace filled the room's one side,
  With half a cord o' wood in —
There warn't no stoves (tell comfort died)
  To bake ye to a puddin'.

The wa'nut logs shot sparkles out
  Towards the pootiest, bless her !
An' leetle flames danced all about
  The chiny on the dresser.

Agin the chimbley crook-necks hung,
  An' in amongst 'em rusted
The ole queen's arm thet gran'ther Young
  Fetched back from Concord busted.

The very room, coz she was in,
  Seemed warm from floor to ceilin',
An' she looked full ez rosy agin
  Ez the apples she was peelin'.

'T was kin o' kingdom-come to look
  On sech a blessèd cretur,
A dogrose blushin' to a brook
  Ain't modester nor sweeter.

He was six foot o' man, A 1,
  Clean grit an' human natur' ;
None could n't quicker pitch a ton,
  Nor dror a furrer straighter.

He 'd sparked it with full twenty gals,
  Hed squired 'em, danced 'em, druv 'em,
Fust this one, an' then thet, by spells —
  All is, he could n't love 'em.

But long o' her his veins 'ould run
  All crinkly like curled maple,
The side she breshed felt full o' sun
  Ez a south slope in Ap'il.

She thought no v'ice hed such a swing
  Ez hisn in the choir ;
My ! when he made Ole Hundred ring,
  She *knowed* the Lord was nigher.

An' she 'd blush scarlit, right in prayer,
  When her new meetin'-bunnet
Felt somehow thru' its crown a pair
  O' blue eyes sot upon it.

Thet night, I tell ye, she looked *some !*
  She seemed to 've gut a new soul,
For she felt sartin-sure he 'd come,
  Down to her very shoe-sole.

She heered a foot, an' knowed it tu,
  A-raspin' on the scraper, —
All ways to once her feelin's flew
  Like sparks in burnt-up paper.

He kin' o' l'itered on the mat,
  Some doubtfle o' the sekle,
His heart kep' goin' pitty-pat,
  But hern went pity Zekle.

An' yit she gin her cheer a jerk
  Ez though she wished him furder,
An' on her apples kep' to work,
  Parin' away like murder.

"You want to see my Pa, I s'pose ?"
  "Wal . . . no . . . I come dasignin' " —
"To see my Ma ? She 's sprinklin' clo'es
  Agin to-morrer's i'nin'."

To say why gals acts so or so,
  Or don't, 'ould be presumin' ;
Mebby to mean *yes* an' say *no*
  Comes nateral to women.

He stood a spell on one foot fust,
  Then stood a spell on t' other,
An' on which one he felt the wust
  He couldn't ha' told ye nuther.

Says he, "I 'd better call agin ;"
  Says she, "Think likely, Mister ;"
Thet last word pricked him like a pin,
  An' . . . Wal, he up an' kist her.

When Ma bimeby upon 'em slips,
  Huldy sot pale ez ashes,
All kin' o' smily roun' the lips
  An' teary roun' the lashes.

For she was jes' the quiet kind
  Whose naturs never vary,
Like streams that keep a summer mind
  Snow-hid in Jenooary.

The blood clost roun' her heart felt glued
  Too tight for all expressin',
Tell mother see how metters stood,
  And gin 'em both her blessin'.

Then her red come back like the tide
  Down to the Bay o' Fundy,
An' all I know is they was cried
  In meetin' come nex' Sunday.

JAMES RUSSELL LOWELL.

———◆———

WHAT MR. ROBINSON THINKS.*

FROM "THE BIGLOW PAPERS," NO. III.

GUVENER B. is a sensible man ;
  He stays to his home an' looks arter his folks ;
He draws his furrer ez straight ez he can,
  An' into nobody's tater-patch pokes ; —
      But John P.
      Robinson he
  Sez he wunt vote fer Guvener B.

My ! ain't it terrible ? Wut shall we du ?
  We can't never choose him o' course, — thet 's
      flat ;
Guess we shall hev to come round, (don't you ?)
  An' go in fer thunder an' guns, an' all that ;
      Fer John P.
      Robinson he
  Sez he wunt vote fer Guvener B.

Gineral C. is a dreffle smart man :
  He 's ben on all sides thet give places or pelf ;
But consistency still wuz a part of his plan, —
  He 's ben true to *one* party, — an' thet is him-
      self ; —
      So John P.
      Robinson he
  Sez he shall vote fer Gineral C.

Gineral C. he goes in fer the war ; †
  He don't vally principle more 'n an old cud ;
Wut did God make us raytional creeturs fer,
  But glory an' gunpowder, plunder an' blood ?

* Preserved here because the essential humor of the satire has
outlived its local and temporary application.
† Written at the time of the Mexican war, which was strongly
opposed by the Antislavery party as being unnecessary and wrong.

So John P.
Robinson he
Sez he shall vote fer Gineral C.

We were gittin' on nicely up here to our village,
  With good old idees o' wut's right an' wut
    ain't,
We kind o' thought Christ went agin war an'
    pillage,
  An' thet eppyletts worn't the best mark of a
    saint ;
    But John P.
    Robinson he
  Sez this kind o' thing 's an exploded idee.

The side of our country must ollers be took,
  An' Presidunt Polk, you know, he is our coun-
    try ;
An' the angel thet writes all our sins in a book
  Puts the *debit* to him, an' to us the *per contry ;*
    An' John P.
    Robinson he
  Sez this is his view o' the thing to a T.

Parson Wilbur he calls all these argimunts lies ;
  Sez they 're nothin' on airth but jest *fee, faw,*
    fum :
And thet all this big talk of our destinies
  Is half ov it ign'ance, an' t' other half rum ;
    But John P.
    Robinson he
  Sez it ain't no sech thing ; an', of course, so
    must we.

Parson Wilbur sez *he* never heerd in his life
  Thet th' Apostles rigged out in their swaller-
    tail coats,
An' marched round in front of a drum an' a fife,
  To git some on 'em office, an' some on 'em
    votes ;
    But John P.
    Robinson he
  Sez they did n't know everythin' down in
    Judee.

Wal, it 's a marcy we 've gut folks to tell us
  The rights an' the wrongs o' these matters, I
    vow, —
God sends country lawyers, an' other wise fellers,
  To drive the world's team wen it gits in a
    slough ;
    Fer John P.
    Robinson he
  Sez the world 'll go right, ef he hollers out
    Gee !
             JAMES RUSSELL LOWELL.

WIDOW BEDOTT TO ELDER SNIFFLES.

FROM "THE WIDOW BEDOTT PAPERS."

O REVEREND sir, I do declare
  It drives me most to frenzy,
To think of you a lying there
  Down sick with influenzy.

A body 'd thought it was enough
  To mourn your wive's departer,
Without sich trouble as this ere
  To come a follerin' arter.

But sickness and affliction
  Are sent by a wise creation,
And always ought to be underwent
  By patience and resignation.

O, I could to your bedside fly,
  And wipe your weeping eyes,
And do my best to cure you up,
  If 't would n't create surprise.

It 's a world of trouble we tarry in,
  But, Elder, don't despair ;
That you may soon be movin' again
  Is constantly my prayer.

Both sick and well, you may depend
  You 'll never be forgot
By your faithful and affectionate friend,
  PRISCILLA POOL BEDOTT.
        FRANCES MIRIAM WHITCHER.

THE NEW CHURCH ORGAN.

THEY 've got a bran new organ, Sue,
  For all their fuss and search ;
They 've done just as they said they 'd do,
  And fetched it into church.
They 're bound the critter shall be seen,
  And on the preacher's right,
They 've hoisted up their new machine
  In everybody's sight.
They 've got a chorister and choir,
  Ag'in *my* voice and vote ;
For it was never *my* desire
  To praise the Lord by note !

I 've been a sister good an' true,
  For five an' thirty year ;
I 've done what seemed my part to do,
  An' prayed my duty clear ;
I 've sung the hymns both slow and quick,
  Just as the preacher read ;
And twice, when Deacon Tubbs was sick,
  I took the fork an' led !

An' now, their bold, new-fangled ways
　　Is comin' all about ;
And I, right in my latter days,
　　Am fairly crowded out !

To-day, the preacher, good old dear,
　　With tears all in his eyes,
Read — "I can read my title clear
　　To mansions in the skies."—
I al'ays liked that blessed hymn —
　　I s'pose I al'ays will ;
It somehow gratifies *my* whim,
　　In good old Ortonville ;
But when that choir got up to sing,
　　I could n't catch a word ;
They sung the most dog-gonedest thing
　　A body ever heard !

Some worldly chaps was standin' near,
　　An' when I see them grin,
I bid farewell to every fear,
　　And boldly waded in.
I thought I 'd chase the tune along,
　　An' tried with all my might ;
But though my voice is good an' strong,
　　I could n't steer it right.
When they was high, then I was low,
　　An' also contra'wise ;
And I too fast, or they too slow,
　　To "mansions in the skies."

An' after every verse, you know,
　　They played a little tune ;
I did n't understand, an' so
　　I started in too soon.
I pitched it purty middlin' high,
　　And fetched a lusty tone,
But O, alas ! I found that I
　　Was singin' there alone !
They laughed a little, I am told ;
　　But I had done my best ;
And not a wave of trouble rolled
　　Across my peaceful breast.

And Sister Brown, — I could but look, —
　　She sits right front of me ;
She never was no singin' book,
　　An' never went to be ;
But then she al'ays tried to do
　　The best she could, she said ;
She understood the time, right through,
　　An' kep' it with her head ;
But when she tried this mornin', O,
　　I had to laugh, or cough !
It kep' her head a bobbin' so,
　　It e'en a'most come off !

An' Deacon Tubbs, — he all broke down,
　　As one might well suppose ;
He took one look at Sister Brown,
　　And meekly scratched his nose.
He looked his hymn-book through and through,
　　And laid it on the seat,
And then a pensive sigh he drew,
　　And looked completely beat.
An' when they took another bout,
　　He did n't even rise ;
But drawed his red bandanner out,
　　An' wiped his weeping eyes.

I 've been a sister, good an' true,
　　For five an' thirty year ;
I 've done what seemed my part to do,
　　An' prayed my duty clear ;
But death will stop my voice, I know,
　　For he is on my track ;
And some day, I 'll to meetin' go,
　　And nevermore come back.
And when the folks get up to sing —
　　Whene'er that time shall be —
I do not want no *patent* thing
　　A squealin' over me !

　　　　　　　　　　WILL M. CARLETON.

THE RETORT.

OLD BIRCH, who taught the village school,
　　Wedded a maid of homespun habit ;
He was as stubborn as a mule,
　　And she as playful as a rabbit.
Poor Kate had scarce become a wife
　　Before her husband sought to make her
The pink of country polished life,
　　And prim and formal as a Quaker.

One day the tutor went abroad,
　　And simple Katie sadly missed him ,
When he returned, behind her lord
　　She shyly stole, and fondly kissed him.
The husband's anger rose, and red
　　And white his face alternate grew :
"Less freedom, ma'am !" Kate sighed and said,
　"O, dear ! I *did n't know 't was you !*"
　　　　　　　　GEORGE PERKINS MORRIS.

DOW'S FLAT.

1856.

Dow's Flat.　That 's its name.
　　And I reckon that you
　　Are a stranger ?　The same ?
　　Well, I thought it was true,
For thar is n't a man on the river as can't spot
　　the place at first view.

It was called after Dow, —
    Which the same was an ass ;
And as to the how
    Thet the thing kem to pass, —
Just tie up your hoss to that buckeye, and sit ye
    down here in the grass.

You see this yer Dow
    Hed the worst kind of luck ;
He slipped up somehow
    On each thing thet he struck.
Why, ef he 'd a' straddled thet fence-rail the
    derned thing 'ed get up and buck.

He mined on the bar
    Till he could n't pay rates ;
He was smashed by a car
    When he tunnelled with Bates ;
And right on the top of his trouble kem his wife
    and five kids from the States.

It was rough, — mighty rough ;
    But the boys they stood by,
And they brought him the stuff
    For a house, on the sly ;
And the old woman, — well, she did washing, and
    took on when no one was nigh.

But this yer luck of Dow's
    Was so powerful mean
That the spring near his house
    Dried right up on the green ;
And he sunk forty feet down for water, but nary
    a drop to be seen.

Then the bar petered out,
    And the boys would n't stay ;
And the chills got about,
    And his wife fell away ;
But Dow, in his well, kept a peggin' in his usual
    ridikilous way.

One day, — it was June, —
    And a year ago, jest, —
This Dow kem at noon
    To his work like the rest,
With a shovel and pick on his shoulder, and a
    derringer hid in his breast.

He goes to the well,
    And he stands on the brink,
And stops for a spell
    Jest to listen and think :
For the sun in his eyes, (jest like this, sir !) you
    see, kinder made the cuss blink.

His two ragged gals
    In the gulch were at play,
And a gownd that was Sal's

Kinder flapped on a bay :
Not much for a man to be leavin', but his all, —
    as I 've heer'd the folks say.

And — that 's a peart hoss
    Thet you 've got — ain't it now ?
What might be her cost ?
    Eh ? Oh ! — Well then, Dow —
Let 's see, — well, that forty-foot grave was n't
    his, sir, that day, anyhow.

For a blow of his pick
    Sorter caved in the side,
And he looked and turned sick,
    Then he trembled and cried.
For you see the dern cuss had struck — "Wa-
    ter ?" — beg your parding, young man,
    there you lied !

It was *gold*, — in the quartz,
    And it ran all alike ;
And I reckon five oughts
    Was the worth of that strike ;
And that house with the coopilow 's his'n, —
    which the same is n't bad for a Pike.

Thet 's why it 's Dow's Flat ;
    And the thing of it is
That he kinder got that
    Through sheer contrairiness :
For 't was *water* the derned cuss was seekin', and
    his luck made him certain to miss.

Thet 's so. Thar 's your way
    To the left of yon tree ;
But — a — look h'yur, say,
    Won't you come up to tea ?
No ? Well, then the next time you 're passin' ;
    and ask after Dow, — and thet 's *me*.
                 BRET HARTE.

JIM.

SAY there ! P'r'aps
    Some on you chaps
    Might know Jim Wild ?
Well, — no offence :
Thar ain't no sense
    In gittin' riled !

Jim was my chum
    Up on the Bar :
That 's why I come
    Down from up thar,
Lookin' for Jim.
Thank ye, sir ! *you*
Ain't of that crew, —
    Blest if you are !

Money ? — Not much :
  That ain't my kind ;
I ain't no such.
Rum ? — I don't mind,
  Seein' it 's you.

Well, this yer Jim,
Did you know him ? —
Jess 'bout your size ;
Same kind of eyes ? —
Well, that is strange :
  Why, it 's two year
  Since he come here,
Sick, for a change.

Well, here 's to us ;
  Eh ?
The *deuce* you say !
  Dead ? —
That little cuss ?

What makes you star, —
You over thar ?
Can't a man drop
's glass in yer shop
But you must rar' ?
  It would n't take
  Derned much to break
You and your bar.

  Dead !
Poor — little — Jim !
— Why, there was me,
Jones, and Bob Lee,
Harry and Ben, —
No-account men :
Then to take *him !*

Well, thar — Good-by, —
No more, sir, — I —
  Eh ?
What 's that you say ? —
Why, dern it ! — sho ! —
No ? Yes ! By Jo !
  Sold !
Sold ! Why you limb,
You ornery,
  Derned old
Long-leggèd Jim !
              BRET HARTE.

          ◆

BANTY TIM.

[Remarks of Sergeant Tilmon Joy to the White Man's Committee of Spunky Point, Illinois.]

I RECKON I git your drift, gents —
  You 'low the boy sha'n't stay ;
This is a white man's country :
  You 're Dimocrats, you say :

And whereas, and seein', and wherefore,
  The times bein' all out o' jint,
The nigger has got to mosey
  From the limits o' Spunky P'int !

Let 's reason the thing a minute ;
  I 'm an old-fashioned Dimocrat, too,
Though I laid my politics out o' the way
  For to keep till the war was through.
But I come back here allowin'
  To vote as I used to do,
Though it gravels me like the devil to train
  Along o' sich fools as you.

Now dog my cats ef I kin see,
  In all the light of the day,
What you 've got to do with the question
  Ef Tim shall go or stay.
And furder than that I give notice,
  Ef one of you tetches the boy,
He kin check his trunks to a warmer clime
  Than he 'll find in Illanoy.

Why, blame your hearts, jist hear me !
  You know that ungodly day
When our left struck Vicksburg Heights, how
    ripped
  And torn and tattered we lay.
When the rest retreated, I stayed behind,
  Fur reasons sufficient to me, —
With a rib caved in, and a leg on a strike,
  I sprawled on that cursed glacee.

Lord ! how the hot sun went for us,
  And br'iled and blistered and burned !
How the rebel bullets whizzed round us
  When a cuss in his death-grip turned !
Till along toward dusk I seen a thing
  I could n't believe for a spell :
That nigger — that Tim — was a-crawlin' to me
  Through that fire-proof, gilt-edged hell !

The rebels seen him as quick as me,
  And the bullets buzzed like bees ;
But he jumped for me, and shouldered me,
  Though a shot brought him once to his knees ;
But he staggered up, and packed me off,
  With a dozen stumbles and falls,
Till safe in our lines he drapped us both,
  His black hide riddled with balls.

So, my gentle gazelles, thar 's my answer,
  And here stays Banty Tim :
He trumped Death's ace for me that day,
  And I 'm not goin' back on him !
You may rezoloot till the cows come home,
  But ef one of you tetches the boy,
He 'll wrastle his hash to-night in hell,
  Or my name 's not Tilmon Joy !
              JOHN HAY.

LITTLE BREECHES.

A PIKE COUNTY VIEW OF SPECIAL PROVIDENCE.

I DON'T go much on religion,
  I never ain't had no show ;
But I 've got a middlin' tight grip, sir,
  On the handful o' things I know.
I don't pan out on the prophets
  And free-will, and that sort of thing, —
But I b'lieve in God and the angels,
  Ever sence one night last spring.

I come into town with some turnips,
  And my little Gabe come along, —
No four-year-old in the county
  Could beat him for pretty and strong,
Peart and chipper and sassy,
  Always ready to swear and fight, —
And I 'd larnt him ter chaw terbacker,
  Jest to keep his milk-teeth white.

The snow come down like a blanket
  As I passed by Taggart's store ;
I went in for a jug of molasses
  And left the team at the door.
They scared at something and started, —
  I heard one little squall,
And hell-to-split over the prairie
  Went team, Little Breeches and all.

Hell-to-split over the prairie !
  I was almost froze with skeer ;
But we rousted up some torches,
  And sarched for 'em far and near.
At last we struck hosses and wagon,
  Snowed under a soft white mound,
Upsot, dead beat, — but of little Gabe
  No hide nor hair was found.

And here all hope soured on me
  Of my fellow-critter's aid, —
I jest flopped down on my marrow-bones,
  Crotch-deep in the snow, and prayed.
        *   *   *   *   *
By this, the torches was played out,
  And me and Isrul Parr
Went off for some wood to a sheepfold
  That he said was somewhar thar.

We found it at last, and a little shed
  Where they shut up the lambs at night.
We looked in, and seen them huddled thar,
  So warm and sleepy and white ;
And THAR sot Little Breeches and chirped,
  As peart as ever you see,
" I want a chaw of terbacker,
  And that 's what 's the matter of me."

How did he git thar ? Angels.
  He could never have walked in that storm
They jest scooped down and toted him
  To whar it was safe and warm.
And I think that saving a little child,
  And bringing him to his own,
Is a derned sight better business
  Than loafing around The Throne.
                              JOHN HAY.

HANS BREITMANN'S PARTY.

HANS BREITMANN gife a barty,
  Dey had biano-blayin ;
I felled in lofe mit a Merican frau,
  Her name was Madilda Yane.
She had haar as prown ash a pretzel,
  Her eyes vas himmel-plue,
Und ven dey looket indo mine,
  Dey shplit mine heart in two.

Hans Breitmann gife a barty,
  I vent dere you 'll pe pound.
I valtzet mit Madilda Yane
  Und vent shpinnen round und round.
De pootiest Fraulein in de House,
  She vayed 'pout dwo hoondred pound,
Und efery dime she gife a shoomp
  She make de vindows sound.

Hans Breitmann gife a barty,
  I dells you it cost him dear.
Dey rolled in more as sefen kecks
  Of foost-rate Lager Beer.
Und venefer dey knocks de shpicket in
  De Deutschers gifes a cheer.
I dinks dat so vine a barty
  Nefer coom to a het dis year.

Hans Breitmann gife a barty ;
  Dere all vas Souse und Brouse.
Ven de sooper comed in, de gompany
  Did make demselfs to house ;
Dey ate das Brot und Gensy broost,
  De Bratwurst und Braten fine,
Und vash der Abendessen down
  Mit four parrels of Neckarwein.

Hans Breitmann gife a barty ;
  We all cot troonk ash bigs.
I poot mine mout to a parrel of bier,
  Und emptied it oop mit a schwigs.
Und denn I gissed Madilda Yane
  Und she shlog me on de kop,
Und de gompany fited mit daple-lecks
  Dill de coonshtable made oos shtop.

Hans Breitmann gife a barty —
  Where ish dat barty now ?
Wheie ish de lofely golden cloud
  Dat float on de moundain's prow ?
Where ish de himmelstrahlende Stern —
  De shtar of de shpirit's light ?
All goned afay mit de Lager Beer —
  Afay in de Ewigkeit !
CHARLES G. LELAND.

RITTER HUGO.

DER noble Ritter Hugo
  Von Schwillensanfenstein
Rode out mit shpeer und helmet,
  Und he coom to de panks of de Rhine.

Und oop dere rose a meermaid,
  Vot had n't got nodings on,
Und she say, "O, Ritter Hugo,
  Vare you goes mit yourself alone ?"

Und he says, "I ride in de creen-wood,
  Mit helmet and mit shpeer,
Till I cooms into ein Gasthaus,
  Und dere I drinks some peer."

Und den outshpoke de maiden,
  Vot had n't got nodings on,
"I ton't dink mooch of beebles
  Dat goes mit demselfs alone.

"You 'd petter coom down in de wasser,
  Vare dere 's heaps of dings to see,
Und hafe a shplendid dinner,
  Und trafel along mit me.

"Dare you sees de fish a schwimmin,
  Und you catches dem efery one."
So sang dis wasser maiden,
  Vat had n't got nodings on.

"Dare is drunks all full mit money,
  In ships dat vent down of old ;
Und you helpsh yourself, by dunder !
  To shimmerin crowns of gold.

"Snoost look at dese shpoons und vatches !
  Shoost look at dese diamond rings !
Come down und fill your bockets,
  Und I 'll kiss you like eferydings '

"Vat you vantsh mit your schnapps und your
    lager ?
  Coom down into der Rhine !
Dere ish pottles der Kaiser Charlemagne,
  Vonce filled mit gold-red wine ! "

Dat fetched him, — he shtood all shpell-pound,
  She pulled his coat-tails down,
She drawed him under de wasser,
  Dis maiden mit nodings on.
CHARLES G. LELAND.

COLLUSION BETWEEN A ALEGAITER AND A WATER-SNAIK.

TRIUMPH OF THE WATER-SNAIK : DETH OF THE ALEGAITER.

THERE is a niland on a river lying,
Which runs into Gautimaly, a warm country,
Lying near the Tropicks, covered with sand ;
Hear and their a symptum of a Wilow,
Hanging of its umberagious limbs & branches
Over the clear streme meandering far below.
This was the home of the now silent Alegaiter,
When not in his other element confine'd :
Here he wood set upon his eggs asleep
With 1 ey observart of flis and other passing
Objects : a while it kept a going on so :
Fereles of danger was the happy Alegaiter !
But a las ! in a nevil our he was fourced to
Wake ! that dreme of Blis was two sweet for
    him.
1 morning the sun arose with unusool splender
Whitch allso did our Alegaiter, coming from tne
    water,
His scails a flinging of the rais of the son back,
To the fountain-head which tha originly sprung,
But having not had nothing to eat for some time,
    he
Was slepy and gap'd, in a short time, widely.
Unfoalding soon a welth of perl-white teth,
The rais of the son soon shet his sinister ey
Because of their mutool splendor and warmth.
The evil Our (which I sed) was now come ;
Evidently a good chans for a water snaik
Of the large specie, which soon appeared
Into the horison, near the bank where repos'd
Calmly in slepe the Alegaiter before spoken of,
About 60 feet was his Length (not the 'gaiter)
And he was aperiently a well-proportioned snaik.
When he was all ashore he glared upon
The iland with approval, but was soon
"Astonished with the view and lost to wonder '
    (from Wats)
(For jest then he began to see the Alegaiter)
Being a nateral enemy of his'n, he worked his-
    self
Into a fury, also a ni position.
Before the Alegaiter well could ope
His eye (in other words perceive his danger)
The Snaik had enveloped his body just 19
Times with "foalds voluminous and vast" (from
    Milton)

And had tore off several scails in the confusion,
Besides squeazing him awfully into his stomoc.
Just then, by a fortinate turn in his affairs,
He ceazed into his mouth the careless tale
Of the unreflecting water-snaik ! Grown des-
      perate
He, finding that his tale was fast squesed
Terrible while they roaled all over the iland.

        *   *   *   *

It was a well-conduckted Affair ; no noise
Disturbed the harmony of the seen, ecsept
Onct when a Wilow was snaped into by the
      roaling.
Eeach of the combatence had n't a minit for
      holering.
So the conflick was naterally tremenjous !
But soon by grate force the tale was bit complete-
Ly of ; but the eggzeration was too much
For his delicate Constitootion : he felt a com-
      pression
Onto his chest and generally over his body ;
When he ecspress'd his breathing, it was with
Grate difficulty that he felt inspired again onct
      more.
Of course this State must suffer a revoolootion.
So the Alegaiter give but one yel, and egspired.
The waiter-snaik realed hisself off, & survay'd
For say 10 minits, the condition of
His fo : then wondering what made his tail hurt,
He sloly went off for to cool.
                                    J. W. MORRIS.

        ———◆———

SWELL'S SOLILOQUY.

1 DON'T appwove this hawid waw ;
    Those dweadful bannahs hawt my eyes ;
And guns and dwums are such a baw, —
    Why don't the pawties compwamise ?

Of cawce, the twoilet has its chawms ;
    But why must all the vulgah cwowd
Pawsist in spawting unifawms,
    In cullahs so extwemely loud ?

And then the ladies, pwecious deahs ! —
    I mawk the change on ev'wy bwow ;
Bai Jove ! I weally have my feahs
    They wathah like the hawid wow !

To heah the chawming cweatures talk,
    Like patwons of the bloody wing,
Of waw and all its dawty wawk, —
    It does n't seem a pwappah thing !

I called at Mrs. Gweene's last night,
    To see her niece, Miss Mawy Hertz,
And found her making — cwushing sight ! —
    The weddest kind of flannel shirts !

Of cawce, I wose, and sought the daw,
    With fawyah flashing from my eyes !
I can't appwove this hawid waw ; —
    Why don't the pawties compwamise ?
                                    ANONYMOUS.

        ———◆———

TO THE "SEXTANT."

O SEXTANT of the meetin house, wich sweeps
And dusts, or is supposed to ! and makes fires,
And lites the gass, and sumtimes leaves a screw
      loose,
in wich case it smells orful, worse than lamp ile ;
And wrings the Bel and toles it when men dyes,
to the grief of survivin pardners, and sweeps paths
And for the servusses gets $ 100 per annum,
Wich them that thinks deer, let 'em try it ;
Gettin up before starlite in all wethers and
Kindlin fires when the wether is as cold
As zero, and like as not green wood for kindlin
i would n't be hired to do it for no sum,
But O Sextant ! there are 1 kermoddity
Wich 's more than gold, wich doant cost nothin,
Worth more than anything except the sole of man!
i mean pewer *Are*, Sextant, i mean pewer are !
O it is plenty out of doors, so plenty it doant no
What on airth to dew with itself, but flys about
Scatterin leaves and bloin off men's hatts !
in short, it 's jest as " fre as are " out dores,
But O Sextant, in our church its scarce as buty,
Scarce as bank bills, when agints begs for misch-
      uns,
Wich some say is purty offten (taint nothin to
      me, wat I give aint nothin to nobody) but
      O Sextant
U shet 500 men, wimmin, and children,
Speshally the latter, up in a tite place,
And every 1 on em brethes in and out, and out
      and in,
Say 50 times a minnit, or 1 million and a half
      breths an our.
Now how long will a church ful of are last at
      that rate,
I ask you — say 15 minits — and then wats to be
      did ?
Why then they must brethe it all over agin,
And then agin, and so on till each has took it
      down
At least 10 times, and let it up agin, and wats
      more
The same individoal don't have the priviledge
of brethin his own are, and no ones else,
Each one must take whatever comes to him.
O Sextant, doant you no our lungs is bellusses,
To blo the fier of life, and keep it from goin out;
and how can bellusses blo without wind
And aint wind *are* ? i put it to your conschens

Are is the same to us as milk to babies,
　Or water is to fish, or pendlums to clox,
　Or roots and airbs unto an injun doctor,
　Or little p.lls unto an omepath,
　Or boys to gurls.　Are is for us to brethe,
What signifies who preaches if i cant brethe?
Wats Pol?　Wats Pollus to sinners who are
　ded?
Ded for want of breth, why Sextant, when we dy
Its oniy coz we cant brethe no more, thats all.
And now O Sextant, let me beg of you
To let a little are into our church.
(Pewer are is sertain proper for the pews)
And do it weak days, and Sundays tew,
It aint much trouble, only make a hole
And the are will come of itself;
(It luvs to come in where it can git warm)
And O how it will rouze the people up,
And sperrit up the preacher, and stop garps,
And yawns and figgits, as effectooal
As wind on the dry boans the Profit tells of.

　　　　　　　　ARABELLA M. WILLSON.

MR. MOLONY'S ACCOUNT OF THE BALL.

GIVEN TO THE NEPAULESE AMBASSADOR BY THE PENIN-
SULAR AND ORIENTAL COMPANY.

O, WILL ye choose to hear the news?
　Bedad, I cannot pass it o'er:
I 'll tell you all about the ball
　To the Naypaulase Ambassador.
Begor! this fête all balls does bate,
　At which I worn a pump, and I
Must here relate the splendthor great
　Of th' Oriental Company.

These men of sinse disposed expinse,
　To fête these black Achilleses.
"We 'll show the blacks," says they, "Almack's,
　And take the rooms at Willis's."
With flags and shawls, for these Nepauls,
　They hung the rooms of Willis up,
And decked the walls and stairs and halls
　With roses and with lilies up.

And Jullien's band it tuck its stand
　So sweetly in the middle there,
And soft bassoons played heavenly chunes,
　And violins did fiddle there.
And when the Coort was tired of spoort,
　I 'd lave you, boys, to think there was
A nate buffet before them set,
　Where lashins of good dhrink there was!

At ten before the ball-room door,
　His moighty Excelléncy was;

He smoiled and bowed to all the crowd,
　So gorgeous and immense he was,
His dusky shuit, sublime and mute,
　Into the doorway followed him;
And O the noise of the blackguard boys,
　As they hurrood and hollowed him!

The noble Chair stud at the stair,
　And bade the dthrums to thump; and he
Did thus evince to that Black Prince
　The welcome of his Company.
O fair the girls, and rich the curls,
　And bright the oys, you saw there, was;
And fixed each oye, ye there could spoi,
　On Gineral Jung Bahawther was!

This Gineral great then tuck his sate,
　With all the other ginerals
(Bedad, his troat, his belt, his coat,
　All bleezed with precious minerals);
And as he there, with princely air,
　Recloinin on his cushion was,
All round about his royal chair,
　The squeezin and the pushin was.

O Pat, such girls, such Jukes and Earls,
　Such fashion and nobilitee!
Just think of Tim, and fancy him
　Amidst the hoigh gentility!
There was Lord De L'Huys, and the Portygeese
　Ministher and his lady there,
And I reckonized, with much surprise,
　Our messmate, Bob O'Grady, there;

There was Baroness Brunow, that looked like
　Juno,
　And Baroness Rehausen there,
And Countess Roullier, that looked peculiar
　Well, in her robes of gauze in there.
There was Lord Crowhurst (I knew him first
　When only Mr. Pips he was),
And Mick O'Toole, the great big fool,
　That after supper tipsy was.

There was Lord Fingall and his ladies all,
　And Lords Killeen and Dufferin,
And Paddy Fife, with his fat wife, —
　I wondther how he could stuff her in.
There was Lord Belfast, that by me past,
　And seemed to ask how should I go there?
And the Widow Macræ, and Lord A. Hay.
　And the Marchioness of Sligo there.

Yes, Jukes and Earls, and diamonds and pearls,
　And pretty girls, was spoorting there;
And some beside (the rogues!) I spied,
　Behind the windies, coorting there.

O, there's one I know, bedad, would show
  As beautiful as any there ;
And I'd like to hear the pipers blow,
  And shake a fut with Fanny there !
        WILLIAM MAKEPEACE THACKERAY.

WIDOW MALONE.

DID you hear of the Widow Malone,
      Ohone !
Who lived in the town of Athlone,
      Alone !
  O, she melted the hearts
  Of the swains in them parts :
So lovely the Widow Malone,
      Ohone !
So lovely the Widow Malone.

Of lovers she had a full score,
      Or more,
And fortunes they all had galore,
      In store ;
  From the minister down
  To the clerk of the Crown
All were courting the Widow Malone,
      Ohone !
All were courting the Widow Malone.

But so modest was Mistress Malone,
      'T was known
That no one could see her alone,
      Ohone !
  Let them ogle and sigh,
  They could ne'er catch her eye,
So bashful the Widow Malone,
      Ohone !
So bashful the Widow Malone.

Till one Misther O'Brien, from Clare
      (How quare !
It's little for blushing they care
      Down there),
  Put his arm round her waist, —
  Gave ten kisses at laste, —
"O," says he, "you're my Molly Malone,
      My own !
O," says he, "you're my Molly Malone !"

And the widow they all thought so shy,
      My eye !
Ne'er thought of a simper or sigh, —
      For why ?
  But, "Lucius," says she,
  "Since you've now made so free,
You may marry your Mary Malone,
      Ohone !
You may marry your Mary Malone."

There's a moral contained in my song,
      Not wrong ;
And one comfort, it's not very long,
      But strong, —
  If for widows you die,
  Learn to kiss, not to sigh ;
For they're all like sweet Mistress Malone,
      Ohone !
O, they're all like sweet Mistress Malone !
        CHARLES LEVER.

BACHELOR'S HALL.

BACHELOR'S HALL, what a quare-lookin' place
  it is !
Kape me from such all the days of my life !
Sure but I think what a burnin' disgrace it is,
  Niver at all to be gettin' a wife.

Pots, dishes, pans, an' such grasy commodities,
  Ashes and praty-skins, kiver the floor ;
His cupboard's a storehouse of comical oddities,
  Things that had niver been neighbors before.

Say the old bachelor, gloomy an' sad enough,
  Placin' his tay-kettle over the fire ;
Soon it tips over — Saint Patrick ! he's mad
  enough,
  If he were prisent, to fight with the squire !

He looks for the platter — Grimalkin is scourin'
  it !
Sure, at a baste like that, swearin' 's no sin ;
His dishcloth is missing ; the pigs are devourin'
  it —
  Tunder and turf ! what a pickle he's in !

When his male's over, the table's left sittin'
  so ;
Dishes, take care of yourselves if you can ;
Divil a drop of hot water will visit ye, —
  Och, let him alone for a baste of a man !

Now, like a pig in a mortar-bed wallowin',
  Say the old bachelor kneading his dough ;
Troth, if his bread he could ate without swal-
  lowin',
  How it would favor his palate, ye know !

Late in the night, when he goes to bed shiverin',
  Niver a bit is the bed made at all ;
He crapes like a terrapin under the kiverin' ; —
  Bad luck to the pictur of Bachelor's Hall !
        JOHN FINLEY.

ST. PATRICK WAS A GENTLEMAN.

O, ST. PATRICK was a gentleman,
    Who came of decent people ;
He built a church in Dublin town,
    And on it put a steeple.
His father was a Gallagher ;
    His mother was a Brady ;
His aunt was an O'Shaughnessy,
    His uncle an O'Grady.
      So, success attend St. Patrick's fist,
        For he 's a Saint so clever ;
      O, he gave the snakes and toads a twist,
        And bothered them forever !

The Wicklow hills are very high,
    And so 's the Hill of Howth, sir ;
But there 's a hill, much bigger still,
    Much higher nor them both, sir.
'T was on the top of this high hill
    St. Patrick preached his sarmint
That drove the frogs into the bogs,
    And banished all the varmint.
      So, success attend St. Patrick's fist, etc.

There 's not a mile in Ireland's isle
    Where dirty varmin musters,
But there he put his dear fore-foot,
    And murdered them in clusters.
The toads went pop, the frogs went hop,
    Slap-dash into the water ;
And the snakes committed suicide
    To save themselves from slaughter.
      So, success attend St. Patrick's fist, etc.

Nine hundred thousand reptiles blue
    He charmed with sweet discourses,
And dined on them at Killaloe
    In soups and second courses.
Where blind worms crawling in the grass
    Disgusted all the nation,
He gave them a rise, which opened their eyes
    To a sense of their situation.
      So, success attend St. Patrick's fist, etc.

No wonder that those Irish lads
    Should be so gay and frisky,
For sure St. Pat he taught them that,
    As well as making whiskey ;
No wonder that the saint himself
    Should understand distilling,
Since his mother kept a shebeen shop
    In the town of Enniskillen.
      So, success attend St. Patrick's fist, etc.

O, was I but so fortunate
    As to be back in Munster,
'T is I 'd be bound that from that ground
    I nevermore would once stir.

For there St. Patrick planted turf,
    And plenty of the praties,
With pigs galore, ma gra, ma 'store,
    And cabbages — and ladies !
      Then my blessing on St. Patrick's fist,
        For he 's the darling Saint O !
      O, he gave the snakes and toads a twist ;
        He 's a beauty without paint, O !
                  HENRY BENNETT.

THE BIRTH OF ST. PATRICK.

ON the eighth day of March it was, some people
    say,
That Saint Pathrick at midnight he first saw the
    day ;
While others declare 't was the ninth he was
    born,
And 't was all a mistake between midnight and
    morn ;
For mistakes will occur in a hurry and shock,
And some blamed the babby — and some blamed
    the clock —
Till with all their cross-questions sure no one
    could know
If the child was too fast, or the clock was too
    slow.

Now the first faction-fight in owld Ireland, they
    say,
Was all on account of Saint Pathrick's birthday :
Some fought for the eighth — for the ninth more
    would die,
And who would n't see right, sure they blackened
    his eye !
At last, both the factions so positive grew,
That each kept a birthday, so Pat then had two,
Till Father Mulcahy, who showed them their
    sins,
Said, " No one could have two birthdays, but a
    twins."

Says he, " Boys, don't be fightin' for eight or for
    nine,
Don't be always dividin' — but sometimes com-
    bine ;
Combine eight with nine, and seventeen is the
    mark,
So let that be his birthday," — " Amen," says
    the clerk.
" If he was n't a twins, sure our hist'ry will show
That, at least, he 's worthy any two saints that
    we know ! "
Then they all got blind dhrunk — which com
    plated their bliss,
And we keep up the practice from that day to
    this.
                  SAMUEL LOVER.

THE LOVERS.

SALLY SALTER, she was a young teacher who
    taught,
And her friend, Charley Church, was a preacher
    who praught,
Though his enemies called him a screecher who
    scraught.

His heart, when he saw her, kept sinking and
    sunk,
And his eye, meeting hers, began winking, and
    wunk ;
While she, in her turn, kept thinking, and
    thunk.

He hastened to woo her, and sweetly he wooed,
For his love grew until to a mountain it grewed,
And what he was longing to do then he doed

In secret he wanted to speak, and he spoke,
To seek with his lips what his heart long had
    soke ;
So he managed to let the truth leak, and it loke.

He asked her to ride to the church, and they
    rode ;
They so sweetly did glide that they both thought
    they glode,
And they came to the place to be tied, and were
    toed.

Then homeward, he said, let us drive, and they
    drove,
And as soon as they wished to arrive, they
    arrove,
For whatever he could n't contrive, she controve.

The kiss he was dying to steal, then he stole ;
At the feet where he wanted to kneel then he
    knole ;
And he said, "I feel better than ever I fole."

So they to each other kept clinging, and clung,
While Time his swift circuit was winging, and
    wung ;
And this was the thing he was bringing, and
    brung :

The man Sally wanted to catch, and had caught ;
That she wanted from others to snatch, and had
    snaught ;
Was the one she now liked to scratch, and she
    scraught.

And Charley's warm love began freezing, and
    froze,
While he took to teazing, and cruelly toze
The girl he had wished to be squeezing, and
    squoze.

"Wretch !" he cried, when she threatened to
    leave him, and left,
"How could you deceive me, as you have de-
    ceft ?"
And she answered, "I promised to cleave, and
    I 've cleft."

PHŒBE CARY.

DEBORAH LEE.*

'T IS a dozen or so of years ago,
    Somewhere in the West countree,
That a nice girl lived, as ye Hoosiers know
    By the name of Deborah Lee ;
Her sister was loved by Edgar Poe,
    But Deborah by me.

Now I was green, and she was green,
    As a summer's squash might be ;
And we loved as warmly as other folks, —
    I and my Deborah Lee, —
With a love that the lasses of Hoosierdom
    Coveted her and me.

But somehow it happened a long time ago
    In the aguish West countree,
That a chill March morning gave the *shakes*
    To my beautiful Deborah Lee ;
And the grim steam-doctor (drat him !) came,
    And bore her away from me, —
The doctor and death, old partners they, —
    In the aguish West countree.

The angels wanted her in heaven
    (But they never asked for me),
And that is the reason, I rather guess,
    In the aguish West countree,
That the cold March wind, and the doctor, and
    death,
    Took off my Deborah Lee —
    My beautiful Deborah Lee —
From the warm sunshine and the opening flower,
    And bore her away from me.

Our love was as strong as a six-horse team,
    Or the love of folks older than we,
    Or possibly wiser than we ;
But death, with the aid of doctor and steam,
    Was rather too many for me ;
He closed the peepers and silenced the breath
    Of my sweetheart Deborah Lee,
And her form lies cold in the prairie mould,
    Silent and cold, — ah me !

The foot of the hunter shall press her grave,
    And the prairie's sweet wild flowers
In their odorous beauty around it wave
    Through all the sunny hours, —

* See page 285.

The still, bright summer hours ;
And the birds shall sing in the tufted grass
And the nectar-laden bee,
With his dreamy hum, on his gauze wings pass, —
She wakes no more to me ;
Ah, nevermore to me !
Though the wild birds sing and the wild flowers
    spring,
She wakes no more to me.

Yet oft in the hush of the dim, still night,
A vision of beauty I see
Gliding soft to my bedside, —a phantom of light,
Dear, beautiful Deborah Lee, —
My bride that was to be ;
And I wake to mourn that the doctor, and
    death,
And the cold March wind, should stop the breath
Of my darling Deborah Lee, —
Adorable Deborah Lee, —
That angels should want her up in heaven
Before they wanted me.

WILLIAM H. BURLEIGH.

ONLY SEVEN.*

A PASTORAL STORY, AFTER WORDSWORTH.

I MARVELLED why a simple child,
    That lightly draws its breath,
Should utter groans so very wild
    And look as pale as Death.

Adopting a parental tone,
    I asked her why she cried.
The damsel answered, with a groan,
    " I 've got a pain inside !

" I thought it would have sent me mad
    Last night about eleven."
Said I, " What is it makes you bad ?
How many apples have you had ? "
    She answered, " Only seven ! "

" And are you sure you took no more,
    My little maid ? " quoth I.
" O, please, sir, mother gave me four,
    But they were in a pie ! "

" If that 's the case," I stammered out,
    " Of course you 've had eleven."
The maiden answered with a pout,
    " I ain't had more nor seven ! "

I wondered hugely what she meant,
    And said, " I 'm bad at riddles,
But I know where little girls are sent
    For telling taradiddles.

* See page 87.

" Now if you don't reform," said I,
    " You 'll never go to heaven ! "
But all in vain ; each time I try
The little idiot makes reply,
    " I ain't had more nor seven ! "

POSTSCRIPT.

To borrow Wordsworth's name was wrong,
    Or slightly misapplied ;
And so I 'd better call my song,
    " Lines after Ache-inside."

H. S. LEIGH.

A TALE OF DRURY LANE.*

FROM "REJECTED ADDRESSES."

" Thus he went on, stringing one extravagance upon another, in
the style his books of chivalry had taught him, and imitating, as
near as he could, their very phrase.' — DON QUIXOTE.

*To be spoken by Mr. Kemble, in a suit of the Black
    Prince's armor, borrowed from the Tower.*

REST there awhile, my bearded lance,
While from green curtain I advance
To yon foot-lights, no trivial dance,
And tell the town what sad mischance
    Did Drury Lane befall.

As Chaos, which, by heavenly doom,
Had slept in everlasting gloom,
Started with terror and surprise
When light first flashed upon her eyes, —
So London's sons in nightcap woke,
    In bedgown woke her dames ;
For shouts were heard mid fire and smoke,
And twice ten hundred voices spoke, —
    "The playhouse is in flames ! "
And, lo ! where Catherine Street extends,
A fiery tail its lustre lends
    To every window-pane ;
Blushes each spout in Martlet Court,
And Barbican, moth-eaten fort,
And Covent Garden kennels sport,
    A bright ensanguined drain ;
Meux's new Brewhouse shows the light,
Rowland Hill's Chapel, and the height
    Where Patent Shot they sell ;
The Tennis Court, so fair and tall,
Partakes the ray, with Surgeons' Hall,
The Ticket-Porters' House of Call,
Old Bedlam, close by London Wall,
Wright's shrimp and oyster shop withal,
    And Richardson's Hotel.
Nor these alone, but far and wide,
Across red Thames's gleaming tide,
To distant fields the blaze was borne,
And daisy white and hoary thorn

* An imitation of Sir Walter Scott.

In borrowed lustre seemed to sham
The rose, or red Sweet Wil-li-am.
To those who on the hills around
Beheld the flames from Drury's mound,
    As from a lofty altar rise,
It seemed that nations did conspire
To offer to the god of fire
    Some vast, stupendous sacrifice !
The summoned firemen woke at call,
And hied them to their stations all:
Starting from short and broken snooze,
Each sought his ponderous hob-nailed shoes,
But first his worsted hosen plied ;
Plush breeches next, in crimson dyed,
    His nether bulk embraced ;
Then jacket thick, of red or blue,
Whose massy shoulder gave to view
The badge of each respective crew,
    In tin or copper traced.
The engines thundered through the street,
Fire-hook, pipe, bucket, all complete,
And torches glared, and clattering feet
    Along the pavement paced.
And one, the leader of the band,
From Charing Cross along the Strand,
Like stag by beagles hunted hard,
Ran till he stopped at Vin'gar Yard.
The burning badge his shoulder bore,
The belt and oil-skin hat he wore,
The cane he had, his men to bang,
Showed foreman of the British gang, —
His name was Higginbottom. Now
'T is meet that I should tell you how
    The others came in view :
The Hand-in-Hand the race begun,
Then came the Phœnix and the Sun,
The Exchange, where old insurers run,
    The Eagle, where the new ;
With these came Rumford, Bumford, Cole,
Robins from Hockley in the Hole,
Lawson and Dawson, cheek by jowl,
    Crump from St. Giles's Pound :
Whitford and Mitford joined the train,
Huggins and Muggins from Chick Lane,
And Clutterbuck, who got a sprain
    Before the plug was found.
Hobson and Jobson did not sleep,
But ah ! no trophy could they reap,
For both were in the Donjon Keep
    Of Bridewell's gloomy mound !
E'en Higginbottom now was posed,
For sadder scene was ne'er disclosed ;
Without, within, in hideous show,
Devouring flames resistless glow,
And blazing rafters downward go,
And never halloo " Heads below ! "
    Nor notice give at all.

The firemen terrified are slow
To bid the pumping torrent now,
    For fear the roof should fall.
Back, Robins, back ! Crump, stand aloof !
Whitford, keep near the walls !
Huggins, regard your own behoof,
For, lo ! the blazing, rocking roof
Down, down in thunder falls !
An awful pause succeeds the stroke,
And o'er the ruins volumed smoke,
Rolling around its pitchy shroud,
Concealed them from the astonished crowd.
At length the mist awhile was cleared,
When, lo ! amid the wreck upreared,
Gradual a moving head appeared,
    And Eagle firemen knew
'T was Joseph Muggins, name revered,
    The foreman of their crew.
Loud shouted all in signs of woe,
" A Muggins ! to the rescue, ho ! "
    And poured the hissing tide :
Meanwhile the Muggins fought amain,
And strove and struggled all in vain,
For, rallying but to fall again,
    He tottered, sunk, and died !

Did none attempt, before he fell,
To succor one they loved so well ?
Yes, Higginbottom did aspire
(His fireman's soul was all on fire)
    His brother chief to save ;
But ah ! his reckless generous ire
    Served but to share his grave !
Mid blazing beams and scalding streams,
Through fire and smoke he dauntless broke,
    Where Muggins broke before.
But sulphury stench and boiling drench,
Destroying sight, o'erwhelmed him quite,
    He sunk to rise no more.
Still o'er his head, while Fate he braved,
His whizzing water-pipe he waved :
" Whitford and Mitford, ply your pumps !
You, Clutterbuck, come, stir your stumps !
Why are you in such doleful dumps ?
A fireman, and afraid of bumps ! —
What are they feared on ? fools ! 'od rot 'em ! "
Were the last words of Higginbottom.
              HORACE SMITH.

POEMS

RECEIVED IN RESPONSE TO AN ADVERTISED CALL FOR A
NATIONAL ANTHEM.

NATIONAL ANTHEM.

BY DR. OLIVER WENDELL H——

A DIAGNOSIS of our history proves
Our native land a land its native loves ;

Its birth a deed obstetric without peer,
Its growth a source of wonder far and near.

To love it more, behold how foreign shores
Sink into nothingness beside its stores.
Hyde Park at best — though counted ultra
    grand —
The " Boston Common " of Victoria's land —

The committee must not be blamed for rejecting the above after
reading thus far, for such an " anthem " could only be sung by a
college of surgeons or a Beacon Street tea-party.
Turn we now to a

NATIONAL ANTHEM.

BY WILLIAM CULLEN B——.

THE sun sinks softly to his evening post,
    The sun swells grandly to his morning crown ;
Yet not a star our flag of heaven has lost,
    And not a sunset stripe with him goes down.

So thrones may fall ; and from the dust of those
    New thrones may rise, to totter like the last ;
But still our country's nobler planet glows,
    While the eternal stars of Heaven are fast.

Upon finding that this does not go well to the air of "Yankee
Doodle," the committee feel justified in declining it ; it being further-
more prejudiced against it by a suspicion that the poet has crowded
an advertisement of a paper which he edits into the first line.
Next we quote from a

NATIONAL ANTHEM.

BY GENERAL GEORGE P. M——.

IN the days that tried our fathers,
    Many years ago,
Our fair land achieved her freedom
    Blood-bought, you know,
Shall we not defend her ever,
    As we 'd defend
That fair maiden, kind and tender,
    Calling us friend ?

Yes !   Let all the echoes answer,
    From hill and vale ;
Yes !   Let other nations hearing,
    Joy in the tale.
Our Columbia is a lady,
    High-born and fair,
We have sworn allegiance to her, —
    Touch her who dare.

The tone of this " anthem " not being devotional enough to suit
the committee, it should be printed on an edition of linen-cambric
handkerchiefs for ladies especially.
Observe this

NATIONAL ANTHEM.

BY N. P. W——.

ONE hue of our flag is taken
    From the cheeks of my blushing pet,
And its stars beat time and sparkle
    Like the studs on her chemisette.

Its blue is the ocean shadow
    That hides in her dreamy eyes,
And it conquers all men, like her,
    And still for a Union flies.

Several members of the committee find that this "anthem" has
too much of the Anacreon spice to suit them.
We next peruse a

NATIONAL ANTHEM.

BY THOMAS BAILEY A——.

THE little brown squirrel hops in the corn,
    The cricket quaintly sings ;
The emerald pigeon nods his head,
    And the shad in the river springs ;
The dainty sunflower hangs its head
    On the shore of the summer sea ;
And better far that I were dead,
    If Maud did not love me.

I love the squirrel that hops in the corn,
    And the cricket that quaintly sings ;
And the emerald pigeon that nods his head,
    And the shad that gayly springs.
I love the dainty sunflower, too,
    And Maud with her snowy breast ;
I love them all ; but I love — I love —
    I love my country best.

This is certainly very beautiful, and sounds somewhat like Tennyson. Though it may be rejected by the committee, it can never
lose its value as a piece of excellent reading for children. It is
calculated to fill the youthful mind with patriotism and natural history, beside touching the youthful heart with an emotion palpitating
for all.
            ROBERT H. NEWELL (Orpheus C. Kerr).

———◆———

THE COCK AND THE BULL.*

YOU see this pebble-stone? It's a thing I bought
Of a bit of a chit of a boy i' the mid o' the day —
I like to dock the smaller parts-o'-speech,
As we curtail the already cur-tailed cur
(You catch the paronomasia, play o' words ?) —
Did, rather, i' the pre-Landseerian days.
Well, to my muttons.   I purchased the concern,
And clapt it i' my poke, and gave for same
By way, to-wit, of barter or exchange —
"Chop" was my snickering dandiprat's own
    term —
One shilling and fourpence, current coin o' the
    realm.
O-n-e one and f-o-u-r four
Pence, one and fourpence — you are with me,
    Sir ? —
What hour it skills not: ten or eleven o' the clock,
One day (and what a roaring day it was !)

* In imitation of Robert Browning.

In February, eighteen sixty-nine,
Alexandrina Victoria, Fidei
Hm — hm — how runs the jargon? — being on
    throne.

Such, sir, are all the facts, succinctly put,
The basis or substratum — what you will —
Of the impending eighty thousand lines.
" Not much in 'em either," quoth perhaps simple
    Hodge.
But there 's a superstructure.   Wait a bit.

Mark first the rationale of the thing :
Hear logic rival and levigate the deed.
That shilling — and for matter o' that, the
    pence —
I had o' course upo' me — wi' me, say —
(Mecum's the Latin, make a note o' that)
When I popped pen i' stand, blew snout,
    scratched ear,
Sniffed — tch ! — at snuff-box ; tumbled up, he-
    heed,
Haw-hawed (not hee-hawed, that 's another guess
    thing :)
Then fumbled at, and stumbled out of, door,
I shoved the door ope wi' my omoplat ;
And in vestibulo, i' the entrance-hall,
Donned galligaskins, antigropeloes,
And so forth ; and, complete with hat and gloves,
One on and one a-dangle i' my hand.
And ombrifuge, (Lord love you !) case o' rain,
I flopped forth, 's buddikins ! on my own ten toes,
(I do assure you there be ten of them,)
And went clump-clumping up hill and down dale
To find myself o' the sudden i' front o' the boy.
Put case I had n't 'em on me, could I ha' bought
This sort-o'-kind-o'-what-you-might-call toy,
This pebble-thing, o' the boy-thing? Q. E. D.
That 's proven without aid from mumping Pope,
Sleek porporate or bloated Cardinal,
(Is n't it, old Fatchaps? You 're in Euclid now.)
So, having the shilling — having i' fact a lot —
And pence and halfpence, ever so many o' them,
I purchased, as I think I said before,
The pebble (lapis, lapidis, — di, — dem, — de, —
What nouns 'crease short i' the genitive, Fat-
    chaps, eh ?)
O' the boy, a bare-legged beggarly son of a gun,
For one and fourpence.   Here we are again.

Now Law steps in, big-wigged, voluminous-
    jawed ;
Investigates and re-investigates.
Was the transaction illegal?   Law shakes head.
Perpend, sir, all the bearings of the case.

At first the coin was mine, the chattel his.
But now (by virtue of the said exchange
And barter) vice versa all the coin,

Per juris operationem, vests
I' the boy and his assigns till ding o' doom ;
(In sæcula sæculo-o-o-orum ;
I think I hear the Abbate mouth out that.)
To have and hold the same to him and them . . .
Confer some idiot on Conveyancing,
Whereas the pebble and every part thereof,
And all that appertaineth thereunto,
Or shall, will, may, might, can, could, would, or
    should,
(Subandi cœtera — clap me to the close —
For what 's the good of law in a case o' the kind ?)
Is mine to all intents and purposes.
This settled, I resume the thread o' the tale.

Now for a touch o' the vendor's quality.
He says a gen'lman bought a pebble of him,
(This pebble i' sooth, sir, which I hold i' my
    hand) —
And paid for 't, like a gen'lman, on the nail.
" Did I o'ercharge him a ha'penny ? Devil a bit.
Fiddlestick's end ! Get out, you blazing ass !
Gabble o' the goose.   Don't bugaboo-baby me !
Go double or quits ? Yah ! tittup ! what 's the
    odds ?"
— There 's the transaction viewed, i' the vendor's
    light.

Next ask that dumpled hag, stood snuffling by,
With her three frowsy-browsy brats o' babes,
The scum o' the kennel, cream o' the filth-heap
    — Faugh ?
Aie, aie, aie, aie ! ὀτοτοτοτοτοῖ,
('Stead which we blurt out Hoighty-toighty
    now) —
And the baker and candlestick-maker, and Jack
    and Gill,
Bleared Goody this and queasy Gaffer that.
Ask the schoolmaster.   Take schoolmaster first.

He saw a gentleman purchase of a lad
A stone, and pay for it rite, on the square,
And carry it off per saltum, jauntily,
Propria quæ maribus, gentleman's property now
(Agreeably to the law explained above),
In proprium usum, for his private ends.
The boy he chucked a brown i' the air, and bit
I' the face the shilling : heaved a thumping stone
At a lean hen that ran cluck-clucking by,
(And hit her, dead as nail i' post o' door,)
Then abiit — what 's the Ciceronian phrase ? —
Excessit, evasit, erupit, — off slogs boy ;
Off in three flea-skips. Hactenus, so far,
So good, tam bene. Bene, satis, male, —
Where was I ? who said what of one in a quag ?
I did once hitch the syntax into verse :
Verbum personale, a verb personal,
Concordat. — ay, " agrees," old Fatchaps — cum

Nominativo, with its nominative,
Genere, i' point o' gender, *numero*,
O' number, *et persona*, and person.   *Ut*,
Instance : *Sol ruit*, down flops sun, *et*, and,
Montes umbrantur, snuffs out mountains.   Pah !
Excuse me, sir, I think I 'm going mad.
You see the trick on 't though, and can yourself
Continue the discourse *ad libitum*.
It takes up about eighty thousand lines,
A thing imagination boggles at :
And might, odds-bobs, sir ! in judicious hands,
Extend from here to Mesopotamy.

CHARLES S. CALVERLEY.

LOVERS, AND A REFLECTION.*

IN moss-prankt dells which the sunbeams flatter
    (And heaven it knoweth what that may mean ;
Meaning, however, is no great matter)
    Where woods are a-tremble, with rifts atween ;

Through God's own heather we wonned together,
    I and my Willie (O love my love) :
I need hardly remark it was glorious weather,
    And flitterbats wavered alow, above :

Boats were curtseying, rising, bowing
    (Boats in that climate are so polite),
And sands were a ribbon of green endowing,
    And O the sun-dazzle on bark and bight !

Through the rare red heather we danced together,
    (O love my Willie !) and smelt for flowers :
I must mention again it was glorious weather,
    Rhymes are so scarce in this world of ours : —

By rises that flushed with their purple favors,
    Through becks that brattled o'er grasses sheen,
We walked or waded, we two young shavers,
    Thanking our stars we were both so green.

We journeyed in parallels, I and Willie,
    In "fortunate parallels !"   Butterflies,
Hid in weltering shadows of daffodilly
    Or marjoram, kept making peacock's eyes :

Song-birds darted about, some inky
    As coal, some snowy (I ween) as curds ;
Or rosy as pinks, or as roses pinky —
    They reck of no eerie To-come, those birds !

But they skim over bents which the mill-stream
        washes,
    Or hang in the lift 'neath a white cloud's hem ;
They need no parasols, no galoshes ;
    And good Mrs. Trimmer she feedeth them.

* In imitation of Jean Ingelow.

Then we thrid God's cowslips (as erst his heather)
    That endowed the wan grass with their golden
        blooms ;
And snapt— (it was perfectly charming weather)—
    Our fingers at Fate and her goddess-glooms :

And Willie 'gan sing — (O, his notes were fluty ;
    Wafts fluttered them out to the white-winged
        sea) —
Something made up of rhymes that have done
        much duty,
    Rhymes (better to put it) of "ancientry :"

Bowers of flowers encountered showers
    In William's carol (O love my Willie !)
When he bade sorrow borrow from blithe To-
        morrow
    I quite forget what — say a daffodilly :

A nest in a hollow, "with buds to follow,"
    I think occurred next in his nimble strain ;
And clay that was "kneaden" of course in Eden —
    A rhyme most novel, I do maintain :

Mists, bones, the singer himself, love-stories,
    And all least furlable things got "furled ;"
Not with any design to conceal their glories,
    But simply and solely to rhyme with "world."

.   .   .   .   .

O, if billows and pillows and hours and flowers,
    And all the brave rhymes of an elder day,
Could be furled together this genial weather,
    And carted, or carried on wafts away,
Nor ever again trotted out — ay me !
How much fewer volumes of verse there 'd be !

CHARLES S. CALVERLEY.

THE ARAB.

ON, on, my brown Arab, away, away !
Thou hast trotted o'er many a mile to-day,
And I trow right meagre hath been thy fare
Since they roused thee at dawn from thy straw-
        piled lair,
To tread with those echoless, unshod feet
Yon weltering flats in the noontide heat,
Where no palm-tree proffers a kindly shade,
And the eye never rests on a cool grass blade ;
And lank is thy flank, and thy frequent cough,
O, it goes to my heart — but away, friend, off !

And yet, ah ! what sculptor who saw thee stand,
As thou standest now, on thy native strand,
With the wild wind ruffling thine uncombed hair,
And thy nostril upturned to the odorous air,
Would not woo thee to pause, till his skill might
        trace
At leisure the lines of that eager face ;

The collarless neck and the coal-black paws
And the bit grasped tight in the massive jaws ;
The delicate curve of the legs, that seem
Too slight for their burden — and, O, the gleam
Of that eye, so sombre and yet so gay !
Still away, my lithe Arab, once more away !

Nay, tempt me not, Arab, again to stay ;
Since I crave neither *Echo* nor *Fun* to-day.
For thy *hand* is not Echoless — there they are,
Fun, Glowworm, and *Echo,* and *Evening Star,*
And thou hintest withal that thou fain wouldst
shine,
As I read them, these bulgy old boots of mine.
But I shrink from thee, Arab ! Thou eatest
eel-pie,
Thou evermore hast at least one black eye ;
There is brass on thy brow, and thy swarthy hues
Are due not to nature, but handling shoes ;
And the bit in thy mouth, I regret to see,
Is a bit of tobacco-pipe — Flee, child, flee !
CHARLES S. CALVERLEY.

THE MODERN HOUSE THAT JACK BUILT.

BEHOLD the mansion reared by dædal Jack.

See the malt, stored in many a plethoric sack,
In the proud cirque of Ivan's bivouac.

Mark how the rat's felonious fangs invade
The golden stores in John's pavilion laid.

Anon, with velvet foot and Tarquin strides,
Subtle grimalkin to his quarry glides, —
Grimalkin grim, that slew the fierce *rodent*
Whose tooth insidious Johann's sackcloth rent.

Lo ! now the deep-mouthed canine foe's assault,
That vexed the avenger of the stolen malt ;
Stored in the hallowed precincts of the hall
That rose complete at Jack's creative call.

Here stalks the impetuous cow, with crumpled
horn,
Whereon the exacerbating hound was torn,
Who bayed the feline slaughter-beast, that slew
The rat predacious, whose keen fangs ran through
The textile fibres that involved the grain
That lay in Hans' inviolate domain.

Here walks forlorn the damsel crowned with rue,
Lactiferous spoils from vaccine dugs who drew,
Of that corniculate beast whose tortuous horn
Tossed to the clouds, in fierce vindictive scorn,

The harrowing hound, whose braggart bark and
stir
Arched the lithe spine and reared the indignant fur
Of puss, that with verminicidal claw
Struck the weird rat, in whose insatiate maw
Lay reeking malt, that erst in Ivan's courts we
saw.

Robed in senescent garb, that seemed, in sooth,
Too long a prey to Chronos' iron tooth,
Behold the man whose amorous lips incline,
Full with young Eros' osculative sign,
To the lorn maiden, whose lac-albic hands
Drew albu-lactic wealth from lacteal glands
Of the immortal bovine, by whose horn,
Distort, to realm ethereal was borne
The beast catulean, vexer of that sly
Ulysses quadrupedal who made die
The old mordacious rat, that dared devour
Antecedaneous ale in John's domestic bower.

Lo ! here, with hirsute honors doffed, succinct
Of saponaceous locks, the priest who linked
In Hymen's golden bands the torn unthrift,
Whose means exiguous stared from many a rift,
Even as he kissed the virgin all forlorn,
Who milked the cow with implicated horn,
Who in fine wrath the canine torturer skied,
That dared to vex the insidious muricide,
Who let auroral effluence through the pelt
Of the sly rat that robbed the palace Jack had
built.

The loud cantankerous Shanghai comes at last,
Whose shouts aroused the shorn ecclesiast,
Who sealed the vows of Hymen's sacrament
To him who, robed in garments indigent,
Exosculates the damsel lachrymose,
The emulgator of that hornèd brute morose
That tossed the dog that worried the cat that *kilt*
The rat that ate the malt that lay in the house
that Jack built.
ANONYMOUS.

JONES AT THE BARBER'S SHOP.

SCENE, *a Barber's Shop. Barber's man engaged
in cutting hair, making wigs, and other bar-
beresque operations.*

Enter JONES, *meeting* OILY *the barber.*

JONES. I wish my hair cut.
OILY.   Pray, sir, take a seat.

(OILY *puts a chair for* JONES, *who sits. During
the following dialogue* OILY *continues cutting*
JONES's *hair.*)

OILY. We've had much wet, sir.
JONES.   Very much indeed.

OILY. And yet November's days were fine.
JONES. They were.
OILY. I hoped fair weather might have lasted us
Until the end.
JONES. At one time — so did I.
OILY. But we have had it very wet.
JONES. We have.

(*A pause of some ten minutes.*)

OILY. I know not, sir, who cut your hair last
time ;
But this I say, sir, it was badly cut :
No doubt 't was in the country.
JONES. No ! in town !
OILY. Indeed ! I should have fancied other-
wise.
JONES. 'T was cut in town and in this very
room.
OILY. Amazement ! — but I now remember
well —
We had an awkward, new provincial hand,
A fellow from the country. Sir, he did
More damage to my business in a week
Than all my skill can in a year repair.
He must have cut your hair.
JONES (*looking at him*). No, 't was yourself.
OILY. Myself ? Impossible ! You must mis-
take.
JONES. I don't mistake — 't was you that cut
my hair.

{*A long pause, interrupted only by the clipping
of the scissors.*}

OILY. Your hair is very dry, sir.
JONES. Oh ! indeed.
OILY. Our Vegetable Extract moistens it.
JONES. I like it dry.
OILY. But, sir, the hair when dry
Turns quickly gray.
JONES. That color I prefer.
OILY. But hair, when gray, will rapidly fall
off,
And baldness will ensue.
JONES. I would be bald.
OILY. Perhaps you mean to say you 'd like a
wig, —
We 've wigs so natural they can't be told
From real hair.
JONES. Deception I detest.

(*Another pause ensues, during which* OILY *blows
down* JONES'S *neck, and relieves him from the
linen wrapper in which he has been enveloped
during the process of hair-cutting.*)

OILY. We 've brushes, soaps, and scent of
every kind.
JONES. I see you have. (*Pays* 6 *d.*) I think
you 'll find that right.

OILY. If there is nothing I can show you, sir.
JONES. No ; nothing. Yet — there may be
something, too,
That you may show me.
OILY. Name it, sir.
JONES. The door.
OILY (*to his man*). That 's a rum customer
at any rate.
Had I cut him as short as he cut me,
How little hair upon his head would be !
But if kind friends will all our pains requite,
We 'll hope for better luck another night.
[*Shop bell rings, and curtain falls.*
PUNCH.

TO THE TERRESTRIAL GLOBE.

BY A MISERABLE WRETCH.

ROLL on, thou ball, roll on !
Through pathless realms of space
Roll on !
What though I 'm in a sorry case ?
What though I cannot meet my bills ?
What though I suffer toothache's ills ?
What though I swallow countless pills ?
Never *you* mind !
Roll on !

Roll on, thou ball, roll on !
Through seas of inky air
Roll on !
It 's true I 've got no shirts to wear,
It 's true my butcher's bill is due,
It 's true my prospects all look blue, —
But don't let that unsettle you !
Never *you* mind !
Roll on !
[*It rolls on.*
WILLIAM SCHWENCK GILBERT.

MY LOVE.*

I ONLY knew she came and went   *Powell.*
    Like troutlets in a pool ;   *Hood.*
She was a phantom of delight,   *Wordsworth.*
    And I was like a fool.   *Eastman.*

One kiss, dear maid, I said, and sighed, *Coleridge.*
    Out of those lips unshorn :   *Longfellow.*
She shook her ringlets round her head, *Stoddard.*
    And laughed in merry scorn.   *Tennyson.*

Ring out, wild bells, to the wild sky, *Tennyson.*
    You heard them, O my heart ;   *Alice Cary.*
'T is twelve at night by the castle clock, *Coleridge.*
    Beloved, we must part.   *Alice Cary.*

* A specimen of what are called "Cento Verses :" patchwork.

"Come back, come back ! " she cried in grief,
                                        Campbell.
"My eyes are dim with tears, —*Bayard Taylor.*
How shall I live through all the days ? *Osgood.*
All through a hundred years ? "   *T. S. Perry.*

'T was in the prime of summer time   *Hood.*
She blessed me with her hand ;   *Hoyt.*
We strayed together, deeply blest,   *Edwards.*
Into the dreaming land.   *Cornwall.*

The laughing bridal roses blow,   *Patmore.*
To dress her dark-brown hair ; *Bayard Taylor.*
My heart is breaking with my woe,   *Tennyson.*
Most beautiful ! most rare !   *Read.*

I clasped it on her sweet, cold hand, *Browning.*
The precious golden link !   *Smith.*
I calmed her fears, and she was calm, *Coleridge.*
"Drink, pretty creature, drink." *Wordsworth.*

And so I won my Genevieve,   *Coleridge.*
And walked in Paradise ;   *Hervey.*
The fairest thing that ever grew   *Wordsworth.*
Atween me and the skies.   *Osgood.*
                                        ANONYMOUS.

RECIPES.

ROASTED SUCKING-PIG.

AIR, — Scots wha hae," etc.

COOKS who 'd roast a sucking-pig,
Purchase one not over big ;
Coarse ones are not worth a fig ;
        So a young one buy.
See that he is scalded well
(That is done by those who sell),
Therefore on that point to dwell
        Were absurdity.

Sage and bread, mix just enough,
Salt and pepper *quantum suff.*,
And the pig's interior stuff,
        With the whole combined.
To a fire that 's rather high,
Lay it till completely dry ;
Then to every part apply
        Cloth, with butter lined.

Dredge with flour o'er and o'er,
Till the pig will hold no more ;
Then do nothing else before
        'T is for serving fit.
Then scrape off the flour with care ;
Then a buttered cloth prepare ;
Rub it well ; then cut — not tear —
        Off the head of it.

Then take out and mix the brains
With the gravy it contains ;
While it on the spit remains,
        Cut the pig in two.
Chop the sage and chop the bread
Fine as very finest shred ;
O'er it melted butter spread, —
        Stinginess won't do.

When it in the dish appears,
Garnish with the jaws and ears ;
And when dinner-hour nears,
        Ready let it be.
Who can offer such a dish
May dispense with fowl and fish ;
And if he a guest should wish,
        Let him send for me !
              PUNCH'S *Poetical Cookery Book*.

A RECIPE FOR SALAD.

To make this condiment your poet begs
The pounded yellow of two hard-boiled eggs ;
Two boiled potatoes, passed through kitchen
        sieve,
Smoothness and softness to the salad give ;
Let onion atoms lurk within the bowl,
And, half suspected, animate the whole ;
Of mordant mustard add a single spoon,
Distrust the condiment that bites so soon ;
But deem it not, thou man of herbs, a fault
To add a double quantity of salt ;
Four times the spoon with oil from Lucca
        crown,
And twice with vinegar, procured from town ;
And lastly, o'er the flavored compound toss
A magic *soupçon* of anchovy sauce.
O green and glorious ! O herbaceous treat !
'T would tempt the dying anchorite to eat ;
Back to the world he 'd turn his fleeting soul,
And plunge his fingers in the salad-bowl ;
Serenely full, the epicure would say,
"Fate cannot harm me, — I have dined to-day."
              SYDNEY SMITH.

SIEGE OF BELGRADE.

AN Austrian army, awfully arrayed,
Boldly by battery besieged Belgrade.
Cossack commanders cannonading come,
Dealing destruction's devastating doom.
Every endeavor engineers essay,
For fame, for fortune fighting, — furious fray !
Generals 'gainst generals grapple — gracious God !
How honors Heaven heroic hardihood !

Infuriate, indiscriminate in ill,
Kindred kill kinsmen, kinsmen kindred kill.
Labor low levels longest loftiest lines ;
Men march mid mounds, mid moles, mid mur-
　　derous mines ;
Now noxious, noisy numbers nothing, naught
Of outward obstacles, opposing ought ;
Poor patriots, partly purchased, partly pressed,
Quite quaking, quickly "Quarter ! Quarter !"
　　quest.
Reason returns, religious right redounds,
Suwarrow stops such sanguinary sounds.
Truce to thee, Turkey !　Triumph to thy train,
Unwise, unjust, unmerciful Ukraine !
Vanish, vain victory ! vanish, victory vain !
Why wish we warfare ?　Wherefore welcome
　　were
Xerxes, Ximenes, Xanthus, Xavier ?
Yield, yield, ye youths ! ye yeomen, yield your
　　yell !
Zeus's, Zarpater's, Zoroaster's zeal,
Attracting all, arms against acts appeal !
　　　　　　　　　　　　　　ANONYMOUS.

ECHO AND THE LOVER.

Lover.　Echo ! mysterious nymph, declare
　　　Of what you 're made, and what you are.
Echo.　　　　　　　　　　　　　Air !
Lover.　Mid airy cliffs and places high,
　　　Sweet Echo ! listening love, you lie.
Echo.　　　　　　　　　　　　You lie !
Lover.　Thou dost resuscitate dead sounds, —
　　　Hark ! how my voice revives, resounds !
Echo.　　　　　　　　　　　　Zounds !
Lover.　I 'll question thee before I go, —
　　　Come, answer me more apropos !
Echo.　　　　　　　　　　　　Poh ! poh !
Lover.　Tell me, fair nymph, if e'er you saw
　　　So sweet a girl as Phœbe Shaw.
Echo.　　　　　　　　　　　　Pshaw !
Lover.　Say, what will turn that frisking coney
　　　Into the toils of matrimony ?
Echo.　　　　　　　　　　　　Money !
Lover.　Has Phœbe not a heavenly brow ?
　　　Is not her bosom white as snow ?
Echo.　　　　　　　　　　　　Ass ! No !
Lover.　Her eyes ! was ever such a pair ?
　　　Are the stars brighter than they are ?
Echo.　　　　　　　　　　　　They are !
Lover.　Echo, thou liest, but can't deceive me.
Echo.　　　　　　　　　　　　Leave me !
Lover.　But come, thou saucy, pert romancer,
　　　Who is as fair as Phœbe ?　Answer !
Echo.　　　　　　　　　　　　Ann, sir.
　　　　　　　　　　　　　　ANONYMOUS.

ECHO.

I ASKED of Echo, t' other day,
　(Whose words are few and often funny,)
What to a novice she could say
　Of courtship, love, and matrimony.
Quoth Echo, plainly, — "Matter-o'-money !"

Whom should I marry ? — should it be
　A dashing damsel, gay and pert,
A pattern of inconstancy ;
　Or selfish, mercenary flirt ?
Quoth Echo, sharply, — "Nary flirt !"

What if, aweary of the strife
　That long has lured the dear deceiver,
She promise to amend her life,
　And sin no more ; can I believe her ?
Quoth Echo, very promptly, — "Leave her !"

But if some maiden with a heart
　On me should venture to bestow it,
Pray, should I act the wiser part
　To take the treasure or forego it ?
Quoth Echo, with decision, — "Go it !"

But what if, seemingly afraid
　To bind her fate in Hymen's fetter,
She vow she means to die a maid,
　In answer to my loving letter ?
Quoth Echo, rather coolly, — "Let her !"

What if, in spite of her disdain,
　I find my heart intwined about
With Cupid's dear delicious chain
　So closely that I can't get out ?
Quoth Echo, laughingly, — "Get out !"

But if some maid with beauty blest,
　As pure and fair as Heaven can make her,
Will share my labor and my rest
　Till envious Death shall overtake her ?
Quoth Echo (*sotto voce*), — "Take her !"
　　　　　　　　　　　JOHN GODFREY SAXE.

NOCTURNAL SKETCH.

BLANK VERSE IN RHYME.

EVEN is come ; and from the dark Park, hark,
The signal of the setting sun — one gun !
And six is sounding from the chime, prime time
To go and see the Drury-Lane Dane slain, —
Or hear Othello's jealous doubt spout out, —
Or Macbeth raving at that shade-made blade,
Denying to his frantic clutch much touch ;
Or else to see Ducrow with wide stride ride
Four horses as no other man can span ;
Or in the small Olympic pit sit split
Laughing at Liston, while you quiz his phiz.

Anon Night comes, and with her wings brings
   things
Such as, with his poetic tongue, Young sung ;
The gas upblazes with its bright white light,
And paralytic watchmen prowl, howl, growl
About the streets, and take up Pall-Mall Sal,
Who, hasting to her nightly jobs, robs fobs.

Now thieves to enter for your cash, smash, crash,
Past drowsy Charley, in a deep sleep, creep,
But, frightened by Policeman B. 3, flee,
And while they 're going, whisper low, "No go !"

Now puss, when folks are in their beds, treads
   leads,
And sleepers, waking, grumble, "Drat that cat!"
Who in the gutter caterwauls, squalls, mauls
Some feline foe, and screams in shrill ill-will.

Now Bulls of Bashan, of a prize size, rise
In childish dreams, and with a roar gore poor
Georgy, or Charley, or Billy, willy-nilly ; —
But Nursemaid in a nightmare rest, chest-pressed,
Dreameth of one of her old flames, James Games,
And that she hears — what faith is man's ! —
   Ann's banns
And his, from Reverend Mr. Rice, twice, thrice ;
White ribbons flourish, and a stout shout out,
That upward goes, shows Rose knows those bows'
   woes !
                    THOMAS HOOD.

ODE FOR A SOCIAL MEETING ;

WITH SLIGHT ALTERATIONS BY A TEETOTALER.

COME ! fill a fresh bumper, — for why should
   we go
      logwood
While the ~~nectar~~ still reddens our cups as they
   flow ?
     decoction
Pour out the ~~rich juices~~ still bright with the sun,
         dye-stuff
Till o'er the brimmed crystal the ~~rubies~~ shall run.
  half-ripened apples
The ~~purple-globed clusters~~ their life-dews have
   bled ;
    taste   *sugar of lead*
How sweet is the ~~breath~~ of the ~~fragrance they shed~~!
   rank poisons   *wines !!!*
For summer's ~~last roses~~ lie hid in the ~~wines~~
       stable-boys smoking long-nines
That were garnered by ~~maidens who laughed
   through the vines.~~
  scowl   *howl*   *scoff*   *sneer*
Then a ~~smile~~, and a ~~glass~~, and a ~~toast~~, and a ~~cheer~~,
  strychnine and whiskey, and ratsbane and beer
For ~~all the good wine, and we 've some of it here~~ !
In cellar, in pantry, in attic, in hall,
  Down, down with the tyrant that masters us all !
~~Long live the gay servant that laughs for us all~~ !
          OLIVER WENDELL HOLMES.

LINES WRITTEN IN AN ALBUM.

[A farmer's daughter, during the rage for albums, handed to the author an old account-book ruled for pounds, shillings, and pence, and requested a contribution.]

	£.	s.	d.
THIS world 's a scene as dark as Styx,			
Where hope is scarce worth		2	6
Our joys are borne so fleeting hence			
That they are dear at			18
And yet to stay here most are willing,			
Although they may not have	]		

            WILLIS GAYLORD.

METRICAL FEET.

TROCHEE trips from long to short ;
From long to long in solemn sort
Slow Spondee stalks ; strong foot ! yet ill able
Ever to come up with dactyl trisyllable.
Iambics march from short to long ; —
With a leap and a bound the swift Anapæsts
   throng ;
One syllable long, with one short at each side,
Amphibrachys hastes with a stately stride ; —
First and last being long, middle short, Amphi
   macer
Strikes his thundering hoofs like a proud high
   bred racer.
       SAMUEL TAYLOR COLERIDGE.

SNEEZING.

WHAT a moment, what a doubt !
All my nose is inside out, —
All my thrilling, tickling caustic,
Pyramid rhinocerostic,
  Wants to sneeze and cannot do it !
How it yearns me, thrills me, stings me,
How with rapturous torment wrings me !
  Now says, "Sneeze, you fool, — get through
   it."
Shee — shee — oh ! 't is most del-ishi —
Ishi — ishi — most del-ishi !
(Hang it, I shall sneeze till spring !)
Snuff is a delicious thing.
            LEIGH HUNT

TO MY NOSE.

KNOWS he that never took a pinch,
Nosey, the pleasure thence which flows?
Knows he the titillating joys
   Which my nose knows ?
O nose, I am as proud of thee
As any mountain of its snows ;
I gaze on thee, and feel that pride
   A Roman knows !
    ALFRED A. FORRESTER (*Alfred Crowquill*).

BELAGCHOLLY DAYS.

CHILLY Dovebber with its boadigg blast
  Dow cubs add strips the beddow add the lawd,
Eved October's suddy days are past —
    Add Subber's gawd !

I kdow dot what it is to which I cligg
  That stirs to sogg add sorrow, yet I trust
That still I sigg, but as the liddets sigg —
    Because I bust.

Dear leaves that rustle sadly 'death by feet —
  By liggerigg feet — add fill by eyes with tears,
Ye bake be sad, add, oh ! it gars be greet
    That ye are sear !

The sud id sulled skies too early sigks ;
  Do trees are greed but evergreeds add ferds ;
Gawd are the orioles add boboligks —
    Those Robert Burds !

Add dow, farewell to roses add to birds,
  To larded fields and tigkligg streablets eke ;
Farewell to all articulated words
    I faid would speak.

Farewell, by cherished strolliggs od the sward,
  Greed glades add forest shades, farewell to you ;
With sorrowigg heart I, wretched add forlord,
    Bid you — achew ! ! !

ANONYMOUS.

INDEX OF TITLES.

INDEX OF TITLES.

INDEX OF FIRST LINES.

INDEX OF FIRST LINES.

INDEX OF FAMOUS QUOTATIONS.

ANALYTICAL INDEX

OF FAMOUS AND APT POETICAL QUOTATIONS.

The Poetical Quotations referred to in this Index will be found — as indicated by the page-number following the line or phrase indexed — either in the body of some poem, or as a brief or "fragment' in its appropriate Division. The key-words, under which these are indexed, will ordinarily be the *nouns* of the quotation, although there is many a " bold expressive phrase," the essential peculiarities of which are indexed, whatever they may be. Take two familiar instances, the key-words being here italicised :

<blockquote>" Truth crushed to earth shall rise again "</blockquote>

is found in Wm. Cullen Bryant's poem entitled " The Battle-Field," on page 534; while

<blockquote>" Sighed and looked unutterable things "</blockquote>

on page 204 is found to be a fragment from " The Seasons: Summer," by James Thomson. Thus the reader may ascertain the position in this volume, the original source or poem, the name of the author, and the correct reading of the thousands of poetical quotations given in the book.

AARON'S serpent, like. 799.
Abandon, all hope, ye who enter here, 396.
Abashed, the devil stood, 398.
Abdiel, the seraph, faithful found, 387.
Abode, draw his frailties from their dread, 307.
Abora, Mount, singing of, 834.
Abou Ben Adhem, may his tribe increase, 768.
Above the reach of ordinary men, 807.
Abridgment of all that was pleasant in man, 724.
Absence, every little, is an age, 248.
    I dote on his very, 248.
    increases love at second sight, 248.
    makes the heart grow fonder, 248
    of occupation is not rest, 815.
    short, hurt him more, 248.
    short, yields to, 814.
Absent, a sigh, the claims, 801.
    from him I roam, 389.
    or dead let a friend be dear, 801.
    thee from felicity awhile, 811.
    though, present in desires, 248.
Absolute rule, his eye sublime declared, 711.
Abstract, doth contain that large, 107.
Absurd, flattery never seems, 810.
Absurdity, passion for, so strong, 799.
Abyss, cares little into what, 271.
Abyssinian maid, it was an, 834.
Academe, olive grove of, 720.
Academes that nourish all the world, 133.
Accent, persuasive, 724.
Accents flow with artless ease, 807.
    of that unknown tongue, 777.
Access and passage to remorse, stop up, 900.
Accidents, moving, by flood and field, 145.
Accomplishment of verse, wanting the, 766.
Account, beggarly, of empty boxes, 809.
    sent to my, 310.
Accoutred as I was, I plunged in, 670.
Accursed by fate, 345.
Accuse not Nature, she hath done her part, 795.
Acorns, tall oaks from little, 107.
Acquaintance, should auld, be forgot, 118.
Acres, a few paternal, 225.
    o'er whose, walked blessèd feet, 397.
Across the walnuts and the wine, 814.
Act, kingliest, of freedom is the vote, 603.
    well your part, 781.
Acting of a dreadful thing, 900.
Action, faithful in, 120.
    in the tented field, their dearest, 145.
    lose the name of, 297.
    no worthy, done, 398.
    of the tiger, imitate the, 503.
    pious, sugar o'er with, 396.

Actions of the just, only the, 301.
    speaker of my living, 84.
    virtuous, are but born and die, 811.
Actors, these our, 867.
Acts being seven ages, his, 711.
    graceful, those thousand decencies, 209.
    little nameless unremembered, 404.
    our, our angels are, or good or ill, 797.
    the best, he most lives who, 743.
Ad infinitum, and so proceed, 496.
Adage, like the poor cat i' the, 800.
Adam could find no solid peace, 232.
    dolve and Eve span, 559.
    goodliest man of men, 712.
    waked, so customed, 490.
    whipped the offending, out of him, 395.
Adam's fall, we sinnèd all, in, 397.
Added pudding, 803.
Adds a precious seeing to the eye, 203.
Adieu, dear amiable youth, 796.
    my native shore, 238.
    she cried and waved her lily hand, 235.
    so sweetly she bade me, 241.
Admiration, greatest works of, 348.
Admire, useless to excel where none, 133.
Admirer, the nice, 723.
Admit impediments, 208.
Admitted to that equal sky, 399.
Adoption, their, tried, 121.
Adore, deify the things that we, 232.
    the hand that gives the blow, 312.
Adores and burns, rapt seraph that, 394.
Adorn a tale, point a moral or, 909.
    her modest looks the cottage might, 690.
Adorned the most, when unadorned, 795.
Adorning thee with so much art, 795.
Adorns and cheers the way, 800.
Adulteries of art, 713.
Advantage, nailed for our, on the bitter cross, 397.
Adventure of the diver, 801.
Adventuring both, I oft found both by, 802.
Adversaries do in law, do as, 121.
    souls of fearful, 541.
Adversity, autumn of, 120.
    bruisèd with, 345.
    crossed with, 345.
    uses of, sweet are the, 348.
    works of admiration wrought by, 348.
Advices, lengthened sage, 847.
Aerial tumult swells, 631.
Aery-light, his sleep was, 490.
Affairs of men, tide in the, 802.
    office and, of love, 121.
Affect, study what you most, 804.
Affection cannot hold the bent, 215.
Affections dark as Erebus, 776.
    mild, of, 724.

Affects to nod, 771.
Affliction, of all, taught the lover yet, 248.
    try me with, 725.
Affliction's heaviest shower, 398.
    violence, 348.
Affront, fear is, and jealousy injustice, 795.
    well-bred man will not, me, 780.
Afloat on such a full sea, 802.
Afraid to strike, 910.
Afric's sunny fountains, 395.
After-loss, drop in for an, 271.
Agate-stone, in shape no bigger than an, 836.
Age, accompany old, that which should, 794.
    ache, penury, and imprisonment, 347.
    cannot wither her, 712.
    comfort to my, be, 394.
    decrepit, childhood manhood and, 792.
    exempt from scorn or crime, 794.
    gaping, holds its warped mirror to a, 804.
    grow dim with, the sun, 759.
    in every, in every clime adored, 370.
    labor of an, in pilèd stones, 906.
    make the, to come mine own, 811.
    not of an, but for all time, 905.
    of ease, 687.
    old, serene and bright, 311.
    root of, a worm is at the, 308.
    scarce expect one of my, 107.
    soul of the, 905.
    talking, and whispering lovers, 686.
    that melts with unperceived decay, 794.
    'twixt boy and youth, 108.
Ages, alike all, 232.
    flight of past, 308.
    heir of all the, 258.
    his acts being seven, 711.
    on ages thy splendors unfold, 588.
    slumbering, wakens the, 812.
    three poets in three, 907.
    through the, one increasing purpose runs, 257.
    ye unborn, crowd not on my soul, 868.
Agitation, endless, heart of, 631.
Agonies, despairing, destroy, 800.
Agony, all we know of, 583.
    deep and utter, 800.
    distrest, oft to, 203.
    of prayer, by thine, 358.
    strong swimmer in his, 632.
Agree as angels do above, 399.
    though all things differ, all, 815.
Ague, famine and the, eat them up, 540.
Aid, apt alliteration's artful, 807.
    foreign, of ornament, 795.
Aim, hunter's, ta'en a hurt from the, 496.
Air, a chartered libertine, 723.
    a diviner, an ampler ether, 399.
    a solemn stillness holds, 305.

Concord, firm, holds, 815.
heart with heart in, beats, 206.
of sweet sounds, 776.
Concur to general use, extremes in man, 799.
Condemn the wrong and yet pursue, 395.
Condemned to have an itching palm, much, 797.
wretch, on hope relies, 347.
Condense thy soul, 726.
Condescend to take a bit, 810.
Condition, honor and shame from no, rise, 781.
Conduct, nice, of a clouded cane, 799.
Confabulate, if birds, or no, 495.
Confidence, filial, inspired with, 600.
of heaven's applause, 540.
of reason, 797.
Confine, hies to his, 868.
Confined, cabined cribbed, 800.
Confirm the tidings as they roll, 376.
Confirmations, strong as proofs of holy writ, 207.
Conflict, dire was the noise of, 500.
heat of, 540.
Confused, harmoniously, 815.
Confusion hath made his master-piece, 900.
worse confounded, 725.
Congenial to my heart, 689.
with the night, 491.
Conjectures, I am weary of, 759.
Conjugal petard, 215.
Conquer love, only they that run away, 250.
twenty worlds, 308.
we must our cause it is just, 593.
Conqueror, proud foot of a, 603.
Conquerors, lean fellow beats all, 308.
Conquest, carnage and his, cease, 541.
Conscience avaunt, 541.
does make cowards of us all, 297.
have vacation, why should not, 395.
of her worth, 209.
of the king, catch the, 804.
wakes despair, 396.
with injustice is corrupted, 796.
Conscious honor is to feel no sin, 796.
water saw its God and blushed, 352.
Consent, whispering I will ne'er, consented, 205.
Consequence, deepest, betray us in, 396.
trammel up the, 900.
Consideration like an angel came, 395.
Constancy in wind, hope, 806.
lives in realms above, 116.
Constant as gliding waters roll, 796.
as the northern star, 492.
at church and change, 803.
become more, as they cool, 795.
friendship is, save in love, 121.
to one thing, never, 138, 271.
Constellations, happy, 209.
Consume as they kiss, 815.
Consummation devoutly to be wished, 297.
Consumption's ghastly form, 582.
Contagion to this world, 491.
Contemplation and valor formed, for, 711.
Contemplative, fools so deep, 810.
Content, an elegant sufficiency, 214.
farewell, 722.
humble livers in, range with, 347.
in externals, 815.
thyself to be obscurely good, 601.
to dwell in decencies forever, 232.
Contentment from health springs, 559.
Contests, mighty, rise from trivial things, 815.
Conthraries, dhrames go by, 197.
Contiguity of shade, some boundless, 593.
Continual plodders small have ever won, 804.
Contingencies of pomp, 867.
Contortions of his face, shrugs and strange, 793.
Contradiction, woman's at best a, still, 795.
Contrive, let those, who need, 539.
Control stops with the shore, 607.
Controls them and subdues, 539.
Contumely, proud man's, 297.
Conversation coped withal, 111.
Conversation's burrs, 803.
Converse, formed by thy, 911.
high, with the mighty dead, 806.
if much, thee satiate, 814.
Conversing with thee, I forget all time, 206.
Conveyed the dismal tidings when he frowned, 688.
the opening bud to heaven, 107.
Convolutions of a smooth-lipped shell, 631.
Cooks, man cannot live without, 814.
Cool, become more constant as they, 795.
reason, 806.
sequestered vale of life, 306.
Copious Dryden wanted or forgot, 806.
Copy, leave the world no, 122.
of the father, whole matter and, 107.
Corages, nature in hir, 695.

Coral lip admires, 141.
of his bones are, made, 869.
stems, steadfast, 807.
Cordial, gold in phisik is a, 807.
hope like a, 800.
Core, in my heart's, 112.
Corn, flies o'er the unbending, 806.
Coronets, kind hearts are more than, 268.
what seemed, 868.
Corporal sufferance, finds a pang in, 310.
Corrupted, conscience with injustice is, 796.
Corruption, keep mine honor from, 811.
wins not more than honesty, 322.
Corse, slovenly unhandsome, 506.
Cortez, like stout, 805.
Costly thy habit as thy purse can buy, 722.
Cot beside the hill, mine be a, 225.
Cottage, modest looks the, might adorn, 690.
the soul's dark, 755.
Couch, drapery of his, 308.
frowzy, in sorrow steep, 346.
grassy, they to their, 413.
of war, flinty and steel, 539.
Couched with revenge, 396.
Counsel, sometimes, sometimes tea, 814.
Counsels, harmonic, sweet, 847.
maturest, perplex and dash, 724.
Count that day lost, 398.
time by heart-throbs, 242.
Counterfeit a gloom, teach light to, 787.
presentment, 721.
Country, die but once to save our, 601.
for his, he sighed, 578.
God made the, the man the town, 672.
his first best, ever is at home, 229.
messes, herbs and other, 785.
my bleeding, save, 583.
touch our, and their shackles fall, 594.
undiscovered, from whose bourn, 297.
Country's cause, bosom beats not in his, 602.
Countrymen, friends Romans, 875.
O what a fall was there my, 876.
Courage mounteth with occasion, 541.
never to submit or yield, 540.
screw your, to the sticking place, 802.
unbounded, and compassion, 539.
whistling to keep his, up, 107.
Course, fair, is not hindered, 493.
great Nature's second, 88
of empire, westward the [?].
of love, my whole, 145.
of nature is the art of G[?] 489.
of one revolving moon, 9
of true love never did run smooth, 250.
wheels her pale, the moon, 491.
Courses of my life do show, 812.
steer their, like ships, 807.
Court camp church, 795.
love rules the, the camp, 203.
the vapory god, 816.
Courted by all the winds, 631.
in your girls again be, 215.
Courtesy, pink of, I am the very, 724.
scant this breathing, 121.
Courts, other, o' th' nation, 395.
Cover friendless bodies of unburied men, 495.
Covert, in shadiest, hid, 407.
Covet honor, if it be a sin to, 811.
Covetous for gold, I am not, 811.
Cowards, all mankind is one of these two, 900.
and wicked livers, 899.
conscience does make, of us all, 297.
die many times, 310.
Cowslip's bell I lie, in a, 869.
Cowslips wan that hang the pensive head, 494.
Coy submission, yielded with, 711.
uncertain, and hard to please, 509.
Cozenage, strange, 793.
Crack of doom, 725.
your cheeks, blow winds and, 494.
Cradle, curst from his, 320.
Cradled into poetry by wrong, 806.
Cradles rock us nearer to the tomb, 308.
Crag, castled, of Drachenfels, 446.
Crags, the rattling, among, 686.
Crammed with observation, 803.
Cranks, quips and, and wanton wiles, 785.
Cranny, every, but the right, 802.
Crape, saint in, twice a saint in lawn, 812.
Crave my minde forbids to, 729.
Craves a kind of wit, 798.
Crazy sorrow, 310.
Create a soul under the ribs of death, 831.
Created half to rise and half to fall, 792.
Creation, amid its gay, 489.
a new, rescued from his reign, 632.
essential vesture of, 722.
fevers into false, 867.
a false, from the heat-oppressed brain, 882.
sweet, of some heart, Egeria, 869.

Creation's blot creation's blank, 797.
dawn, 607.
Creator, his great, drew his spirit, 309.
Creature, blank misgivings of a, 759.
not a, was stirring, 96.
not too bright or good, 128.
Creatures, call these delicate, ours, 207.
gay, of the element, 869.
millions of spiritual, 868.
Credit his own lie, 797.
of his book confounds, 805.
who breaketh his, 802.
Creditor, glory of a, determines the, 797.
Creed outworn, pagan suckled in a, 403.
Creeds, more faith in doubt than half the, 397.
Creep into his study of imagination, 801.
wit that can, 910.
Creeping like snail, 711.
where no life is seen, 466.
Creeps in this petty pace from day to day, 792.
Crest, snaky, fierce Repentance rears her, 799.
Crew, helpless, sunk in the roaring main, 632.
Cribbed, cabined, confined, 800.
Cricket chirrups on the hearth, 139.
on the hearth, 787.
Crime, forgive the, too late I stayed, 117.
madden to, 451.
numbers sanctified the, 541.
untold, price of many a, 802.
Crisis, mortal, doth portend, 309.
Cristès lore and his apostles twelve, 697.
Critic, in logic a great, 945.
Critic's eye, don't view me with a, 107.
Critical, I am nothing if not, 723.
Criticise, not o'en critics, 810.
Criticising elves, spite of all the, 804.
Critique, each day a, on the last, 798.
Cromwell damned to everlasting fame, 939.
guiltless of his country's blood, some, 306.
restless, could not cease, 539.
Crony, ancient trusty drouthy, 847.
Crook, by hook or, 671.
the pregnant hinges of the knee, 111.
Crops the flowery food, 496.
Cross, bitter, nailed for our advantage on the, 397.
e'en tho' it be a, that raiseth me, 373.
last at his, earliest at his grave, 795.
sparkling, in her white breast, 128.
Cross-bow, bolt from steel, 671.
Crossed with adversity, 345.
Crosses, losses and, 348.
relics crucifixes, 396.
Crow doth sing sweetly as the lark, 496.
like chanticleer, my lungs, 810.
that flies in heaven's sweetest air, 722.
Crowd, far from the madding, 306.
not on my soul, 868.
of common men, death calls ye to, 308.
the hum the shock of men, 415.
Crown, a sorrow's of, sorrow, 255.
fruitless, placed upon my head, 345.
head that wears, a uneasy lies the, 763.
old Winter's head with flowers, 193.
the god of sleep, 816.
thrice presented him a, 876.
Crowning good repressing ill, 599.
Crowns, bloody, of mothers' sons, 541.
twenty mortal murders on their, 868.
Crow-toe, tufted, 494.
Crucifixes crosses relics, 396.
Cruel as death, hungry as the grave, 310.
Crush of worlds, 759.
Crutch, shouldered his, 688.
Cry, bubbling, of some strong swimmer, 632.
for being born, 320.
Havock and let slip the dogs of war, 539.
is still: They come, 540.
mew, be a kitten and cry, 807.
no language but a, 392.
war is still the, 541.
Cud of sweet and bitter fancy, 813.
Cunning of the scene, struck by the very, 804.
stagers, old, 803.
Cup, leave a kiss but in the, 125.
o' kindness yet, tak a, 118.
of water, little thing to give a, 770.
to the dead already, 898.
Cupid, bolt of, 836.
painted blind, winged, 203.
Cupola or minaret, fantastically set with, 710.
Cups, flowing, pass swiftly round, 147.
that cheer but not inebriate, 810.
Curded by the frost from purest snow, 493.
Cure, cheap and universal, hope, 800.
for life's worst ills, 'tis an ill, 348.
on exercise depend for, the wise, 671.
sad, to be no more, 794.

Game, war's a, kings would not play at, 541.
Games confederate imitative of the chase, 672.
Gang aft a-gley, best-laid schemes, 468.
Gaping age, hold its warped mirror to a, 804.
Garden, come into the, Maud, 152.
  in her face, there is a, 123.
  paradise of God the, was, 719.
  rosebud, of girls, 153.
Garden's end, river at my, 121.
Gardener, grand old, 268.
Gardens trim, takes his pleasure in, 786.
Garden-state, happy, 813.
Garish sun, pay no worship to the, 134.
Garland, call him vile that was your, 813.
  sweetest, to the sweetest maid, 134.
  well beseene, on his head a, 492.
Garlands dead, 318.
Garments, trailing, of the night, 416.
  vacant, stuffs out his, 107.
Gars me greet, 847.
Garter, familiar as his, 723.
Gate, at heaven's, she claps her wings, 495.
Gates of light, unbarred the, 490.
  of hell, my heart detests him as the, 797.
  of mercy, shut the, 306.
Gather ye rosebuds while ye may, 754.
Gathering energies, toil of, 807.
Gaudy, rich not, 722.
Gawds, new-born, 811.
Gay, from grave to, 911.
  gilded scenes, 807.
  hope is theirs, by fancy fed, 793.
Gaze of other men, shuns the, 205.
Gazelle, I never nursed a dear, 251.
Gazing rustics ranged around, 688.
Gem of purest ray serene, 306.
Gems entangled in her hair, 721.
  illumination of all, 862.
  of heaven her starry train, 491.
  rich and rare were the, she wore, 721.
Generous and free, 142.
  friendship no cold medium knows, 120.
  race, lives to build a, 812.
Genial current of the soul, 306.
Genius commands thee, thy, 588.
  my, spreads her wing, 603.
Genteel in personage, 142.
Gentle airs, fresh gales and, 209.
  dulness ever loves a joke, 803.
  rain from heaven, droppeth as the, 798.
  Spring ethereal mildness, come, 492.
  yet not dull, 723.
Gentleman, a fine old English, 959.
  grand old name of, 797.
  of England, ye, 632.
  the first true, 723.
  who was then the, 559.
Gentlest beauty, 814.
Gently not smiting it, hand upon my heart, 794.
  scan your brother man, 784.
George, if his name be, 812.
Gestic lore, skilled in, 232.
Gesture, dignity and love in every, 209.
Get wealth and place by any means, 803.
Getting and spending, 403.
Ghost, like an ill-used, 396.
  vex not his, 346.
Giant, pang great as when a, dies, 310.
Giant's strength, excellent to have a, 813.
Gibbets keep the lifted hand in awe, 541.
Giddiness, nothing but noise and, 108.
Giddy and unfirm, our fancies are more, 215.
Gift by the all-gracious Giver sent, 795.
  heaven's last best, 215.
  love 's the, which God has given, 203.
  of heaven, good sense the only, 798.
Giftie, wad some power the, gie us, 486.
Gifts that make sweet the bitter draught, 672.
Gild refined gold, 726.
Gild'd scenes, gay, 807.
Gill shall dance, Jack shall pipe and, 816.
Gilpin long live he, 962.
Gilt, dust that is a little, 811.
  o'er dusted, more laud than, 811.
Girdled with the sky, round ocean, 491.
Girls, between two, 810.
  courted again in your, 215.
  golden lads and, 301.
  of all the, that are so smart, 198.
  rosebud garden of, 153.
Girt with golden wings, 830.
Give every man thine ear, 815.
  him a little earth for charity, 346.
  his little senate laws, 602, 910.
  it an understanding, 815.
  lettered pomp to teeth of time, 915.
  me a cigar, 814.
  me a look give me a face, 713.
  me another horse, 540.
  me excess of it, 808.
  not a windy night a rainy morrow, 271.
  sorrow words, 312.
  thee all I can no more, 795.

Give thee sixpence, I will see thee d—d first, 953.
  the world assurance of a man, 721.
  to God each moment as it flies, 794.
  what thou canst, 394.
Given unsought is better, love, 205.
Giver, all-gracious, gift sent by the, 795.
Gives, much receives but nothing, 797.
Glad him with its soft black eye, 251.
  waters of the dark blue sea, o'er the, 626.
Glade, unfathomable, 719.
Gladlier grew, touched by her fair tend-ance, 205.
Glance, intermingling, 206.
  of the mind, 739.
  sparkling, soon blown to fire, 670.
Glancing in the mellow light, 491.
Glare, lighted by, maidens like moths, 215.
  of false science, 737.
Glass of fashion and mould of form, 722.
  she 'll prove an excuse for the, 131.
Glasses itself in tempests, 607.
Glassy cool translucent wave, 869.
  essence, 813.
Gleam over this tufted grove, cast a, 491.
Gleams of joy intensely bright, 539.
  purpureal, fields invested with, 399.
  such, as from thy polished shield, 539.
Glee, counterfeited, laughed with, 688.
  forward and frolic, 670.
Glides in modest innocence away, 794.
  the smooth current, 807.
Glimmer on my mind, cease every joy to, 800.
Glimmering, mere, and decays, 274.
  square, casement grows a, 315.
  taper's light, hope like a, 800.
  tapers to the sun, hold their, 805.
  through the dream of things that were, 792.
Glistering grief, perked up in a, 347.
  with dew, 206, 490.
Globe, distracted, seat in this, 801.
Globe, our annual visit o'er the, 472.
  radiant line that girts the, beneath the, 631.
  the great, itself shall dissolve, 867.
Gloom, amid the encircling, 364.
  counterfeit a, teach light to, 787.
Glories of our blood and state, 301.
Glorious by my pen, I'll make thee, 150.
  in a pipe, 814.
  works, these are thy, 363.
Glory beyond all glory ever seen, 867.
  but the blaze of flame, 811.
  Columbia to, arise, 588.
  full meridian of my, 346.
  full-orbed, yonder moon divine in, 491.
  go where, waits thee, 237.
  into, peep, 274.
  jest and riddle of the world, 792.
  left him alone with his, 920.
  of a creditor, determines the, 797.
  of this world, vain pomp and, 321.
  or the grave, rush to, 513.
  paths of, lead but to the grave, 306.
  sea of, 321.
  set the stars of, there, 592.
  trailing clouds of, 758.
  uncertain, of an April day, 492.
  visions of, spare my aching sight, 868.
  walking in an air of, 274.
  ways of, once trod the, 322.
Glory's is o'er, 577.
Gloss of art, 689.
Glows in every heart, love of praise, 810.
  in the stars blossoms in the trees, 489.
  with one resentment, 120.
Glow-worm, her eyes the, lend thee, 134.
  shows the matin to be near, 490.
Glut your ire, eat ye Goths and, 681.
Gnarled oak, unwedgeable and, 813.
Go boldly forth my simple lay, 807.
  lovely rose, 125.
  where glory waits thee, 237.
Goal of ill, good the final, 392.
  the grave is not its, 769.
God alone was to be seen in heaven, 765.
  art of, course of nature the, 489.
  assumes the, affects to nod, 771.
  attribute to, himself, 798.
  bids us to do good for evil, tell them, 396.
  bosom of his Father and his, 307.
  built, a church, 396.
  builds a church to, and not to fame, 797.
  conscious water saw its, and blushed, 362.
  eternal years of, 534.
  fast by the oracle of, 399.
  for Harry England and St. George, 503.
  freedom to worship, 587.
  garden of, paradise, 719.
  hath made them so, 108.
  hath made this world so fair, 399.

God himself scarce seemèd there to be, 860.
  in him, she for, 711.
  in, is our trust, this be our motto, 593.
  is love, 394.
  love of, and love of man, 808.
  made the country man the town, 672.
  man in the bush with, may meet, 744.
  mills, of grind slowly, 747.
  moves in a mysterious way, 632.
  my Father and my Friend, my, 394.
  nature's, looks through nature up to, 808.
  nearer my, to thee, 373.
  never made work for man to mend, 671.
  noblest work of, an honest man's the, 780.
  of storms, 620.
  only, may be had for the asking, 424.
  or devil, every man was, 909.
  save the king, 603.
  sees in clouds, 306.
  send thee good ale enough, belly, 946.
  sendeth and giveth both mouth and the meat, 394.
  servant of, well done, 395.
  served my, with half the zeal, 322.
  strong son of, immortal Love, 393.
  sunflower turns to her, when she sets, 174.
  takes a text and preaches Pa-ti-ence, 364.
  the Father God the Son, 394.
  the jolly, in triumph comes, 771.
  to scan presume not, 792.
  trust in, and keep your powder dry, 602.
  vapory, court the, 816.
  varied, these are but the, 417.
  vengeance to, alone belongs to, 899.
  voice of, Duty stern Daughter of, 797.
  ways of, to man, vindicate the, 807.
  ways of, to men, justify the, 395.
  who is our home, we come from, 758.
  will be our King this day, 602.
  with, he passed the days, 399.
God's dear power, loving, 807.
  first temples, the groves were, 452.
  providence seeming estranged, 335.
Goddess, night, sable, 491.
  thrifty, like a, 707.
Godfathers of heaven's lights, 804.
Godlike reason, capability and, 808.
Godliness, cheerful, 907.
Gods, blest as the immortal, 184.
  dish fit for the, carve him as a, 900.
  kings it makes, 800.
  makes men look like, 723.
  on murderers fix revengeful eyes, 900.
  take the good the, provide, 725.
  temples of his, 567.
  whom the, love die young, 107.
Goeth a sorrowing, who goeth a borrowing, 347.
Gold bright and yellow hard and cold, 802.
  covetous for, I am not, 811.
  fringing the road with harmless, 495.
  gild refined, 726.
  illumed with fluid, 719.
  in phisik is a cordial, 809.
  litel, in cofre, 696.
  narrowing lust of, 752.
  patines of bright, 775.
  to airy thinness beat, 248.
Golden clime, poet born in a, 807.
  exhalations of the dawn, 490.
  lads and girls all must come to dust, 301.
  mean, holds fast the, 815.
  numbers, add to, 550.
  opinions, 810.
  progress in the east, 816.
  sorrow, wear a, 347.
Gone before, not dead but, 311.
  he is, and forever, 283.
Good and evil, much they argued of, 808.
  and ill together, 792.
  apprehension of the, 346.
  better made by ill, the, 348.
  by proud world I'm going home, 794.
  captive, attending captain ill, 398.
  crowning, repressing ill, 599.
  deed in a naughty world, 797.
  die first, the, 309.
  do, by stealth, 797.
  educing, from seeming evil, 418.
  evil be thou my, 395.
  finds his own in all men's, 541.
  gray head which all men knew, 65, 942.
  great man, 739.
  hold thou the, 397.
  impious in a, man to be sad, 348.
  in everything, 489.
  is oft interréd with their bones, 875.
  lose the, we oft might win, 800.
  loves the, he does, 395.
  luxury of doing, learn the, 398.
  man's sin, 395.
  man's smile, share the, 688.

Good name, filches from me my, 811.
  name in man or woman, 811.
  nature and good sense must ever join, 798.
  near to, is what is fair, 711.
  night, a fair, to each to all, 816.
  night, my native land, 238.
  night, say not, 304.
  night till it be to-morrow, say, 241.
  noble to be, 't is only, 268.
  nothing either, or bad, 808.
  obscurely, content to be, 601.
  old cause, homely beauty of, 814.
  or bad for human kind, issues, 539.
  Parent of, 363.
  present, or ill the joy or curse, 800.
  scrupulous, man, 724.
  sense, only is the gift of heaven, 798.
  some fleeting, that mocks me, 396.
  sword rust, his, 539.
  the gods provide, 772.
  the, he scorned, 396.
  the more communicated, 398.
  universal, 489.
  will be the final goal of ill, 392.
Goodliest man of men, Adam the, 712.
Goodly outside falsehood hath, what a, 797.
Goodness and greatness not means but ends, 739.
  felt how awful, is, 398.
  if, lead him not, 395.
  soul of, in things evil, 802.
Goon on pilgrimages, 695.
Goose, pampered, 405.
  sing by day when every, is cackling, 495.
Gordian knot of it he will unloose, 723.
Gorgons and hydras and chimæra dire, 868.
Gory locks, never shake thy, at me, 868.
Gospell bookes, lineaments of, 904.
Gospel-light first from Bullen's eyes, 396.
Goths, arise ye, and glut your ire, 681.
Govern thou my song, Urania, 807.
Governess, whipping virtue's, 108.
Government, a land of settled, 603.
  forms of, fools contest for, 397.
Gown, honors of the, 108.
  plucked his, 688.
Grace, essential form of, 940.
  free nature's, you cannot rob me of, 489.
  living, 807.
  melancholy, 206.
  my cause in speaking for myself, little shall I, 145.
  native, sat fair-proportioned, 795.
  power of, the magic of a name, 810.
  proclaims by many a, 793.
  purity of, 133.
  rule of courtly, 721.
  simplicity a, 713.
  swears with so much, 204.
  sweet attractive softness and, 711.
  sweet attractive kinde of, 904.
  tender, of a day that is dead, 315.
  thy more than beauty, thy, 796.
  was in all her steps, heaven in her eye, 209.
  what a, was seated on this brow, 721.
  which love makes for thee, 495.
Graceless zealots fight, let, 397.
Graces, shot forth peculiar, 203.
Grain, reaps the bearded, at a breath, 276.
Grampian hills, feeds his flocks on the, 650.
Grand old name of gentleman, 797.
Grandeur, old Scotia's, 386.
Grandsire, gay, skilled in gestic lore, 232.
Grant an honest fame or none, 811.
  me still a friend, 120.
Grapple them to thy soul, 121.
Grasp it like a man of mettle, 800.
  the ocean with my span, 808.
Grass, an El Dorado in the, 495.
Grateful evening mild, 206.
Gratulation, earth gave sign of, 209.
Grave, an obscure, a little little grave, 346.
  an untimely, 309.
  dark and silent, 745.
  dread thing, 310.
  Druid lies in yonder, 940.
  earliest at his, last at his cross, 795.
  funeral marches to the, 770.
  glory or the, rush to, 513.
  hungry as the, 310.
  is not its goal, 760.
  low laid in my, 348.
  my large kingdom for a little, 346.
  night of the, when shall day dawn on the, 737.
  or mellow, humors, 724.
  paths of glory lead but to the, 306.
  poet's sylvan, 940.
  rush to glory or the, 513.
  shall bear the chiefest prize away, 725.
  strewed thy, 311.
  sun shine sweetly on my, 493.
  to gay from lively to severe, 911.

Grave, where is thy victory, O, 365.
  without a, unknelled uncoffined, 607.
Graves, green, of your sires, 582.
  of memory where sleep the joys, 410.
  such, as his are pilgrim-shrines, 917.
  worms and epitaphs, let 's talk of, 310.
Gray, amice, morning came forth in, 490.
  't is gone and all is, 490.
  mantled o'er with sober, 490.
Gray-hooded even like a sad votarist, 830.
Great and small, all things both, 860.
  First Cause, 370.
  lord of all things a prey to all, 792.
  men all remind us, lives of, 770.
  none think the, unhappy but the great, 347.
  of old, silent worship of the, 681.
  Original, pronaunt their, 376.
  princes have, playthings, 541.
  taskmaster's eye, as ever in my, 395.
  though fallen, 581.
  wits are sure to madness near allied, 909.
Greatness, a long farewell to all my, 321.
  goodness and, not means but ends, 739.
  highest point of all my, 346.
  is a ripening, 321.
Grecian chisel, ne'er did, trace, 721.
Greece, Athens the eye of, 719.
  but living Greece no more, 303.
  fulmined over, 804.
  her knee in suppliance bent, 582.
  in early, she sung, 773.
  isles of, where burning Sappho loved and sung, 580.
  might still be free, 580.
  sad relic of departed worth, 581.
Greek, small Latin and less, 905.
Greeks joined Greeks, when, 541.
Green and yellow melancholy, 251.
  be the turf above thee, 937.
  dances on the, in hamlets, 202.
  grassy turf, 493.
  in youth, now withering on the ground, 792.
  keep his memory, 921.
  making the, one red, 883.
  thy leaf has perished in the, 309.
Green-eyed monster, 207.
Greenland's icy mountains, 395.
Green-robed senators of mighty woods, 494.
Greet, it gars me, 847.
Greetings where no kindness is, 404.
Greets the dappled morn, 671.
Greyhounds in the slips, stand like, 503.
Grief and pain, naught but, 468.
  bravery of his, 725.
  fills the room up of my absent child, 107.
  gave, but when he died, 120.
  glistering, perked up in a, 347.
  master a, every one can, 345.
  no greater, than to remember joy, 346.
  patch, with proverbs, 312.
  silent manliness of, 690.
  smiling at, sat like patience on a monument, 251.
  that does not speak, 312.
  treads upon heels of pleasure, 214.
  what, I should forget, 899.
  worm the canker and the, are mine alone, 250.
Griefs that harass the distrest, 345.
  what private, they have I know not, 876.
Grieve for an hour, mourn for a year, 312.
  his heart, show his eyes and, 868.
Grieves, if aught inanimate e'er, 512.
Griffith, such an honest chronicler as, 811.
Grim death in opposition sits, 310.
  repose, hushed in, 108.
Grimace, life's, 310.
Grimes, old, is dead that good old man, 976.
Grim-visaged war, 541.
Grin, devil did, for his darling sin, 396.
  every, so merry, 798.
  owned with a, that his favorite sin, 949.
  sit and, a sin for me to, 323.
  to see nobler nature vanquished, 558.
Grind exceeding small, 747.
  the poor, laws, 809.
Gripe, put a barren sceptre in my, 345.
Groan, bubbling, sinks with, 607.
  nature gave a second, 899.
  the knell the pall the bier, 583.
Groaned and died, so, 794.
Groans of the dying, 510.
  scorn is bought with, 204.
Grooves of change, ringing, 258.
Ground, classic, seem to tread on, 807.
  holy, ay call it, 587.
  lets us sit upon the, 310.
  purple all the, with flowers, 494.
  solid, of nature, 489.
  tract of inland, 631.
  what 's hallowed, 788.
Grove of Academe, olive, 720.
  thick and lofty, 867.

Grove, tufted, cast a gleam over this, 491.
Groves, pathless, 316.
  were God's first temples, 452.
Grown by what it fed on, appetite, 205.
Grows in paradise our store, 120.
Growth, children of a larger, men are but, 107.
  give it vital, again, 900.
  which some deem sleep, 807.
Grudge, I will feed fat the ancient, I bear him, 899.
Grudges, here grow no damnèd, 311.
Grunt and sweat under a weary life, 297.
Guardian angel o'er his life presiding, 212.
  angels sung the strain, 576.
Gudeman 's awa, when the, 246.
Guerdon, fair, 812.
Guest, speed the parting, 121.
  welcome, though unexpected here, 92.
Guests praise it, not the cooks, 805.
Guide path motive, original and end, 394.
  philosopher and friend, 911.
  Providence their, 321.
Guid-willie waught, tak a right, 119.
Guilt 's in that heart, I know not if, 185.
  only art her, can cover, 336.
  or fear disturb man's rest, 310.
Guilty creatures sitting at a play, 804.
  thing, started like a, 868.
  thing surprised, tremble like a, 759.
Guinea, jingling of the, helps the hurt, 256.
Guinea's stamp, rank is but the, 341.
Gum, their medicinal, 725.
Guns, vile, a soldier but for these, 506.

Habit, costly thy, as thy purse can buy, 722.
Habitation, a local, and a name, 867.
Habits, ill, gather by unseen degrees, 493.
Hackney sonneteer, starved, 812.
Hail Columbia happy land, 603.
  holy light, 407.
  to the Chief who in triumph advances, 519.
Hails my Tom or Jack, man that, 121.
Hair, amber-dropping, 869.
  beauty draws us with a single, 203.
  distinguish and divide a, 945.
  each particular, to stand on end, 725.
  every, a soul doth bind, 203.
  gems entangled in her, 721.
  my fell of, 900.
  tangles of Neæra's, 203.
Hair-breadth 'scapes i' the imminent deadly breach, 145.
Hale green tree, 454.
Half a league onward, 517.
  broken-hearted, 241.
  his foe, overcome but, 815.
  man is but, without woman, 232.
  made up, scarce, 938.
  part of a blessèd man, 232.
Hallo my fancy, 788.
Hallowed ground, what 's, 788.
Halls of death, silent, 307.
  Tara's, harp that once through, 577.
Hame, whaur his, what his name or, 187.
Hamlet, close of the day when the, is still, 737.
  rude forefathers of the, 305.
  smith stand with his, 276.
Hammer, no sound of, or of saw, 493.
Hammers, busy, closing rivets up, 540.
Hampden, some village, 306.
Hand, death lays his icy, on kings, 301.
  her 'prentice, she tried on man, 191.
  her rash, in evil hour, 899.
  I see a, you cannot see, 311.
  in thy right, carry gentle peace, 322.
  laid my, upon thy mane, 607.
  licks the, raised to shed his blood, 496.
  may no rude, deface it, 311.
  mortality's strong, 309.
  nature's own sweet and cunning, 122.
  of Douglas is his own, 648.
  of war, infection and the, 603.
  open as day for melting charity, 724.
  that gives the blow, adore the, 312.
  that made us is divine, 376.
  that rounded Peter's dome, 736.
  the kindlier, 752.
  Time's deformed, 799.
  touch of a vanished, 315.
  unlineal, wrenched with an, 345.
  rosy, unbarred the gates with, 490.
  upon the ocean's mane, laid his, 919.
  very mould and frame of, 107.
  waved her lily, adieu she cried and, 235.
  with my heart in 't, here 's my, 205.
  wizard, lies cold, 940.
Hands, by fairy, their knell is rung, 563.
  idle, Satan finds mischief for, 108.
  little, were never made to tear, 108.
  promiscuously applied, 814.
  shake, with a king upon his throne, 603.